THE TEN-FOOT INTEGRATING SPHERE AT THE NATIONAL PHYSICAL
LABORATORY.

PHOTOMETRY

BY

JOHN W. T. WALSH

O.B.E., M.A. (Oxon.), D.Sc. (Lond.), M.I.E.E.

President of the International Commission on Illumination ;
Past President and Hon. Member of the Illuminating Engineering Society

DOVER PUBLICATIONS, INC.
NEW YORK

Published simultaneously in Canada by General Publishing Co., Ltd., 222 Adelaide St. W., Toronto, Ontario.

Published in the United Kingdom by Constable and Company, Ltd., 10 Orange Street, London W. C. 2.

This Dover edition, first published in 1965, is an unabridged and unaltered republication of the third edition, published by Constable and Company in 1958.

This edition is published by special arrangement with Constable and Company, Ltd.

Library of Congress Catalog Card Number: 65-12452

Manufactured in the United States of America

Dover Publications, Inc.
180 Varick Street
New York, N. Y. 10014

PREFACE TO THE THIRD EDITION

THERE have been few developments of outstanding importance in photometry since the publication of the second edition of this book. In preparing the present edition the opportunity has been taken to correct errors and, in certain sections, to improve the treatment of the subject and to bring it up to date. A few further changes in nomenclature have been made in order to conform to the latest international agreements.

References to most papers of importance published during the last six years have been included.

The author would like to express his thanks to those who have been good enough to draw his attention to errors in previous editions and to acknowledge once again the valuable assistance received from his former colleagues at the National Physical Laboratory.

JOHN W. T. WALSH

TEDDINGTON
April, 1958

FROM THE PREFACE TO THE FIRST EDITION

THE author has endeavoured to describe, in such detail as the limitations of space permit, those instruments and methods which he has used at the National Physical Laboratory, those which he has seen used elsewhere, or those which his personal experience has led him to regard as of value in photometric work. The description of obsolete or obsolescent apparatus has been reduced to a few lines, and in many cases it has been omitted altogether, only mention by name and a reference to the original description having been inserted for the sake of completeness.

It has been found necessary strictly to limit the scope of this book to a description of those matters, both theoretical and practical, which affect the measurement of light flux, candle-power, illumination, etc., and to exclude any treatment of the use to which such measurements may be put after they have been made. Thus, for example, in the sections dealing with illumination, only the methods of measuring that quantity have been described and no attempt has been made to outline the principles which should be followed in designing an installation to produce a given degree of illumination under certain specified conditions. Similarly, the effect of different factors (e.g. voltage, gas pressure, etc.) on the candle-power of light sources has been dealt with only to the small extent necessary to ensure that measurements of the candle-power of such sources may be free from errors due to lack of proper control of such factors. Again, no general discussion has been given of the effect of shades and reflectors on the distribution of light from a source. On the other hand, a description will be found in Chapter VII * of the methods of photometric measurement by means of which the effect of such appliances may be quantitatively determined in any given case.

* Now Chapter VIII.

TO

MY FATHER AND MOTHER
THIS BOOK IS DEDICATED

PORTIA. How far that little candle throws his beams!
So shines a good deed in a naughty world.
NERISSA. When the moon shone, we did not see the candle.
PORTIA. So doth the greater glory dim the less : . . .
(*Merchant of Venice*, Act V., sc. 1.)

CONTENTS

CONTENTS

APPENDIXES

ILLUSTRATIONS

LIST OF ABBREVIATIONS

THE following is a list of the abbreviations employed in this book to designate those books and periodicals which occur most frequently. The periodicals are, in general, those which contain most of the papers on the subject of photometry and certain cognate matters. Those marked with an asterisk are specially rich in photometric literature. Those marked with an obelisk have ceased publication.

BOOKS

Abbreviation	Full Title
Colour Vision	J. H. Parsons. *Introduction to the Study of Colour Vision.* (Camb. Univ. Press, 1924.)
Dict. Appl. Phys.	R. T. Glazebrook (editor). *Dictionary of Applied Physics.* (Macmillan, 1923–24.)
Illumination, etc.	A. P. Trotter, *Illumination, Its Distribution and Measurement.* (Macmillan, 1911.)
Photométrie	A. Palaz. *Photométrie Industrielle.* (Carré, Paris, 1892.) (Refs. to pages in English trans. given in brackets.)
Physiol. Optik	H. von Helmholtz. *Handbuch der Physiologischen Optik* (3rd edition). (Voss, Hamburg, 1909–11.) (Refs. to English trans. in brackets.)
Prakt. Phot.	E. Liebenthal. *Praktische Photometrie.* (Vieweg, Brunswick, 1907.)
Researches, etc.	W. D. Wright. *Researches on Normal and Defective Colour Vision.* (Kimpton, 1946.)

PERIODICALS

Abbreviation	Full Title
Am. Acad., Proc.	*Proceedings of the American Academy of Arts and Sciences.* Boston, U.S.A.
Am. Chem. Soc., J.	*Journal of the American Chemical Society.* Easton, Pa., U.S.A.
Am. Gas Light J.	*American Gas Light Journal.* New York.
Am. I.E.E., J. (Trans., Proc.).	*Journal (Transactions, Proceedings) of the American Institute of Electrical Engineers.* New York.
Am. J. Sci.	*American Journal of Science (Silliman's Journal).* New Haven, Conn., U.S.A.
Am. Phil. Soc., Proc.	*Proceedings of the American Philosophical Society.* Philadelphia, U.S.A.
Amsterdam Acad., Proc.	*Proceedings of the Royal Academy of Amsterdam* (Eng. trans. of the *Verslagen, Koninklijke Akademie van Wetenschappen te Amsterdam*). Amsterdam.
Ann. Chim. Phys.	*Annales de Chimie et de Physique.* Paris. (Continued from 1914 as *Ann. de Phys.* and *Ann. de Chim.*)
Ann. d. Chem.	*Annalen der Chemie und Pharmacie.* (See *Liebig's Ann.*)
Ann. de Chim.	*Annales de Chimie.* Paris.
Ann. de Phys.	*Annales de Physique.* Paris.
Ann. d. Phys.	*Annalen der Physik.* Leipzig. (Series before 1900 also known as Gilbert's (1799–1824), Poggendorff's (1824–77) or Wiedemann's (1877–99) *Annalen.*)
Arch. des Sci.	*Archives des Sciences Physiques et Naturelles.* (*Bibliothèque Universelle.*) Geneva.
Assn. Franç., C.r.	*Association Française pour l'avancement des Sciences, Comptes rendus.* Paris.
Assn. Suisse Elect., Bull.	*Bulletin de l'Association Suisse des Electriciens.* Zurich. (Also known as *Schweizerischer Elektrotechnischer Verein, Bull.*)
Astron. Nachr.	*Astronomische Nachrichten.* Kiel.

Astrophys. J.	Astrophysical Journal. Chicago.
B. A. Report.	Report of the British Association for the Advancement of Science. London.
Berlin Ber. (Abh.)	Sitzungsberichte (Abhandlungen) der Preussischen Akademie der Wissenschaften zu Berlin (Phys.-Math. Klasse). Berlin.
Bibl. Univ.	Bibliothèque Universelle. (See Arch. des Sci.)
Bureau of Standards, Bull., Sci. Papers, J. of Research (Circ., Technol. Paper, Misc. Publ.)	Bulletin, from Vol. 15 Scientific Papers, from 1928 Journal of Research (Circular, Technologic Paper, Miscellaneous Publication) of the Bureau of Standards, Washington, D.C.
Central-Ztg. f. Opt. u. Mech.	Central-Zeitung für Optik und Mechanik, Elektrotechnik u. verwandte Berufszweige. Berlin.
† Centralbl. f. Elektrot.	Centralblatt für Elektrotechnik. Munich. (Continuation of Zeits f. angewandte Elektricitätslehre : now included in E.T.Z.)
Chem. Soc. J. (Trans.)	Journal (Transactions) of the Chemical Society. London.
Chem. Ztg.	Chemiker-Zeitung. Cöthen.
* C.I.E., Proc.	Recueil des Travaux de la Commission Internationale de l'Eclairage (before 1913 the Comm. Int. de Photométrie).
C.R.	Comptes Rendus Hebdomadaires des Séances de l'Académie des Sciences. Paris.
† Deut. Phys. Gesell., Verh.	Verhandlungen der Deutschen Physikalischen Gesellschaft (now Z.f.Phys.). Brunswick.
*† Ecl. El.	L'Eclairage Electrique. Paris. (Now merged in Rev. Gén. de l'El. See also Lum. El.)
Electrician	Electrician. London.
Elettrot.	L'Elettrotecnica. Milan.
El. Rev.	Electrical Review. London.
† El. Rev. (N.Y.)	Electrical Review. New York. (Continued in El. Rev. and W. Elect.)
† El. Rev. and W. Elect.	Electrical Review and Western Electrician. Chicago. (Included El. Rev. (N.Y.) from 1908.)
El. World	Electrical World. New York.
E.u.M.	Elektrotechnik und Maschinenbau. Vienna. (Continuation of Z. f. Elektrot.) Papers in the supplement Lichttechnik are referred to by page numbers following Lichttech.
E.T.Z.	Elektrotechnische Zeitschrift. Berlin.
Frank. Inst., J.	Journal of the Franklin Institute. Philadelphia.
Gas J.	Gas Journal. London. (Formerly J. of Gas Lighting.)
G.E.C. Journ.	G.E.C. Journal. London.
Gen. El. Rev.	General Electric Review. Schenectady, N.Y.
Harvard Coll. Obs., Ann. (Bull. or Circ.)	Annals (Bulletin or Circular) of the Harvard College Observatory. Cambridge, Mass., U.S.A.
Helv. Phys. (Chim.) Acta	Helvetica Physica (Chimica) Acta. Basle.
* Illum. Eng.	Illuminating Engineer. London. (Continued from 1936 as Light and Lighting.)
*† Illum. Eng. (N.Y.)	Illuminating Engineer. New York. (Continued (1912) as Good Lighting which ceased in 1913.)
* Illum. Engng.	Illuminating Engineering. New York. (Continuation from 1940 of Illum. Eng. Soc. N.Y., Trans.)
* Illum. Eng. Soc. Lond., Trans.	Transactions of the Illuminating Engineering Society. London.
* Illum. Eng. Soc. N.Y., Trans.	Transactions of the Illuminating Engineering Society. New York. (Continued from 1940 as Illuminating Engineering.)
Inst. Civ. Eng., Proc.	Proceedings of the Institution of Civil Engineers. London.
Inst. El. Eng., J.	Journal of the Institution of Electrical Engineers. London.
Inst. Gas Eng., Trans.	Transactions of the Institution of Gas Engineers. London.
Inst. Mech. Eng., J.	Journal of the Institution of Mechanical Engineers. London.

J. de Phys.	*ournal de Physique.* Paris. (Now... *de Physique et le Radium.*)
J.G.W.	*Journal für Gasbeleuchtung und verwandte Beleuchtungsarten, sowie für Wasserversorgung.* Munich and Berlin. (Later, *Das Gas- u. Wasserfach.*)
J. of Gas Lighting	*Journal of Gas Lighting.* London. (Now the *Gas Journal.*)
J. Sci. Inst.	*Journal of Scientific Instruments.* London.
Leipzig Ber. (*Abh.*)	*Berichte über die Verhandlungen (Abhandlungen) der (Königlichen) Sächsischen Akademie (Gesellschaft) der Wissenschaften* (*Math.-Phys. Klasse*). Leipzig.
*† Licht	*Das Licht.* Berlin.
* Lichttechnik	*Lichttechnik.* Berlin.
* Licht u. Lampe	*Licht und Lampe.* Berlin.
Liebig's Ann.	*Liebig's Annalen der Chemie.* Leipzig. (Continuation of *Ann. d. Chem. u. Pharmacie.*)
* Light and Ltg.	*Light and Lighting.* London. (Continuation from 1936 of *Illum. Eng.*)
*† Lum. El.	*La Lumiere Electrique.* Paris. (In the same series with *Ecl. El.*)
† Mélanges phys. chim.	*Mélanges physiques et chimiques tirés du Bulletin de l'Acad. Imp. des Sci. de St. Pétersbourg.*
Munich Ber. (*Abh.*)	*Sitzungsberichte (Abhandlungen) der (Königlichen) Bayerischen Akademie der Wissenschaften* (*Math.-Phys. Klasse*). Munich.
Nat. Acad. Sci., Proc. (*Mem.*)	*Proceedings (Memoirs) of the National Academy of Sciences.* Washington.
N. Cimento	*Il Nuovo Cimento.* Bologna.
Nela Bull.	*Abstract-Bulletin of Nela Research Laboratory.* Cleveland, Ohio.
N.P.L., Coll. Res.	*Collected Researches of the National Physical Laboratory.* Teddington.
* Opt. Soc. Am., J.	*Journal of the Optical Society of America.* New York.
† Opt. Soc., Trans.	*Transactions of the Optical Society.* London. (Ceased in 1932.)
Phil. Mag.	*The London, Edinburgh and Dublin Philosophical Magazine and Journal of Science.* London.
Phil. Trans.	*Philosophical Transactions of the Royal Society.* London. (Series A is intended except where otherwise stated.)
Photog. J.	*Photographic Journal.* London.
Phys. Rev.	*Physical Review.* New York.
Phys. Soc., Proc.	*Proceedings of the Physical Society of London.*
Phys. Z.	*Physikalische Zeitschrift.* Leipzig.
* Rev. d'Opt.	*Revue d'Optique.* Paris.
* Rev. Gén. de l'El.	*Revue Génerale de l'Electricité.* Paris.
Rev. Sci. Insts.	*Review of Scientific Instruments.* Lancaster, Pa. and New York.
Roy. Astron. Soc., M.N.	*Monthly Notices of the Royal Astronomical Society.* London.
Roy. Soc. Edinburgh, Proc. (*Trans.*)	*Proceedings (Transactions) of the Royal Society of Edinburgh.*
Roy. Soc., Proc.	*Proceedings of the Royal Society.* London. (Series A is intended unless otherwise stated.)
Schweiz. Elektrot. Ver., Bull.	See *Assn. Suisse Elect., Bull.*
Soc. Belge Elect., Bull.	*Bulletin de la Société Belge d'Electriciens.* Brussels.
Soc. Chem. Ind., J.	*Journal of the Society of Chemical Industry.* London.
Soc. Franç. Elect., Bull.	*Bulletin de la Société Française des Electriciens.* Paris.
Soc. Int. Elect., Bull.	*Bulletin de la Société Internationale des Electriciens.* Paris.
Washington Acad. Sci., J.	*Journal of the Washington Academy of Sciences.*
Wien Ber.	*Sitzungsberichte* (*Math.-Naturwiss. Klasse*) *der (Kaiserlichen) Akademie der Wissenschaften in Wien.* Vienna.
Zentralblatt.	See *Centralblatt.*
† Z. f. angewandte Elektrizitätslehre.	Continued as *Centralbl. f. Elektrot.* and amalgamated (1890) with *E.T.Z.*

*† *Z. f. Bel.*	*Zeitschrift für Beleuchtungs-Wesen, Heiz- und Lüftungs-Technik.* Berlin.
Z. f. Elektrot.	*Zeitschrift für Elektrotechnik.* Vienna. (Continued as *E.u.M.*)
Z. f. I.	*Zietschrift für Instrumentenkunde.* Berlin.
Z. f. Phys.	*Zeitschrift für Physik.* Brunswick. (Continuation from 1920 of *Deut. Phys. Gesell., Verh.*)
Z. f. techn. Phys.	*Zeitschrift für technische Physik.* Leipzig.
Z. phys. Chem.	*Zeitschrift für physikalische Chemie.* Leipzig.
Z. wiss. Photog.	*Zeitschrift für wissenschaftliche Photographie, Photophysik und Photochemie.* Leipzig.

The following abbreviations have been used in referring to the titles of periodicals not included in the above list :

Abh.	Abhandlungen
Acad., Accad., Akad.	Academy, Académie, Accademia, Akademie
Am.	America(n)
Ann.	Annals, Annales, Annalen
Assn.	Association, Associazione
Ber.	Berichte
Brit.	Britain, British
Bull.	Bulletin
Chem.	Chemical, Chemistry, Chemie
Chim.	Chimie
Com.	Committee, Commission
C. r.	Comptes rendus
Deut.	Deutsche
Ecl.	Eclairage
El.	Electric(al), Electro-, etc., Electrique
Elektrot.	Elektrotechnische, Elektrotechnik
Eng., Engrs.	Engineering, Engineer(s)
Exp.	Experimental
Franç.	Français(e)
ges.	gesammte
Illum.	Illumination, Illuminating
Ind.	Industry, Industrial, Industrie
Ing.	Ingenieur, Ingegnere
Inst., Ist.	Institution, Institute, Istituto
Int.	International(e)
J.	Journal, Jornal, Jurnal
Mem.	Memoirs, Mémoires, Memorie
Obs.	Observatory, Observatoire
Opt.	Optics, Optical, Optique, Optik
Phil.	Philosophical
Photog.	Photography(ic), Photographie(ique), Photographische
Phys.	Physics, Physica, Physique, Physik, Physical, etc.
Physiol.	Physiology, Physiological, etc.
Proc.	Proceedings
Psychol.	Psychology, Psychological, etc.
R.	Reale
Rend.	Rendiconti
Rep.	Repertorium
Rev.	Review, Revue
Roy.	Royal(e)
Sci.	Science(s), Scientific, Scienza(e), Ciencia(s)
Soc.	Society, Société, Società
Trans.	Transactions
Verh.	Verhandlungen
Wiss.	Wissenschaft(liche)
Z.	Zeitschrift
Ztg.	Zeitung

PHOTOMETRY

CHAPTER I

HISTORICAL NOTE

The First Photometers—A little over two centuries ago, in 1729, Pierre Bouguer (1698-1758), Professor of Hydrography at Havre, laid the foundation of the practice of photometry by his description, in an *Essai d'optique sur la gradation de la lumière* [1], of the earliest known form of apparatus designed for the comparison of the luminous intensities of two sources of light. The instrument he described is shown in Fig. 1, which is taken from the fuller description contained in Bouguer's

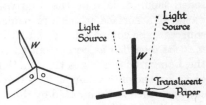

FIG. 1. Bouguer's Photometer.

Traité d'optique sur la gradation de la lumière, published posthumously by the astronomer, the Abbé de la Caille, at Paris in 1760.

In the same year, 1760, there appeared at Augsburg the work of the versatile scientist and mathematician, Johann Heinrich Lambert (1728-1777), *Photometria, sive de mensura et gradibus luminis colorum, et umbrae* [2], which contained the enunciation of the fundamental laws of photometry, viz. the law of addition of illuminations, the inverse square law (already employed by Bouguer), the cosine law of illumination, the cosine law of emission, etc. Lambert also described a form of shadow photometer [3] which was identical in principle with that later used and perfected by Count Rumford, the great American *savant*, philanthropist and statesman, Sir Benjamin Thompson, who in 1792 and 1793 wrote to Sir Joseph Banks letters in which he described "A Method of Measuring the comparative Intensities of the Light emitted by Luminous Bodies". These papers were communicated to the Royal Society [4] and contained a very detailed account of the photometer shown in Fig. 2. It has been well

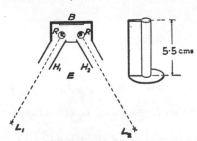

FIG. 2. Rumford's Photometer.

pointed out by A. P. Trotter [5] that the ordinary textbook description
of the Rumford photometer is most misleading.   Instead of one circular rod, as generally shown, Rumford employed two, R, R, of the form
shown on the right in Fig. 2.   These were turned about their vertical
axes until the shadows cast by the two lamps L_1 and L_2 were just in
contact at the centre of the opaque paper screen B.   This was viewed
by an observer, E, situated between the tables carrying the lamps,
and equality of brightness was obtained by moving the lamps by
means of cords operated by handles at H_1, H_2 [6].

The marked distinction which is generally drawn between the
photometer of Bouguer and that of Lambert or Rumford seems to
lack justification.   Both photometers, like those which have superseded them, depend on the comparison of the brightness of the two
parts of a surface which are respectively illuminated by the two
sources to be compared.   The dividing wall, W, of the Bouguer form
may be regarded as equivalent to the shadow-forming object, R, of
the Lambert form, since the function of both is to prevent the light
given by one of the sources from reaching that part of the comparison
surface which is illuminated by the other source.   The chief difference
lies in the use of transmitted or reflected light.   Thus the Foucault
photometer [7], which was used by Dumas and Regnault in their
study of the lighting of Paris, has sometimes been referred to as a
modification of the Lambert-Rumford form, whereas it would be
described more correctly as a Bouguer instrument (Liebenthal
" Prakt. Phot. ", p. 161 ; Trotter, " Illumination, etc. ", p. 80, etc.).
It is remarkable that the instrument officially adopted in this country
for gas testing until a few years ago was a simple modification of the
original Bouguer photometer [8].   Its general construction will be

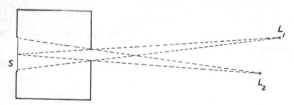

FIG. 3. The Gas Referees' Photometer.

clear from Fig. 3. S is a translucent surface and L_1, L_2 the lamps to
be compared.

From Rumford's time until the invention of the Ritchie wedge
but little progress was made in the methods of photometric measurement.   W. A. Lampadius in 1814 used an instrument in which the
criterion of intensity was the number of sheets of a semi-transparent
material, such as horn, which had to be placed before the eye to

cause the source to disappear [9]. Such an instrument, which may be called an " extinction photometer ", had already been employed before Bouguer's time by François Marie [10]. Although possessing little real claim to the title of photometer, it has repeatedly been revived in various forms [11], and was made use of in the " wedge " type of photometer at one time used for the comparison of stellar magnitudes (see p. 476).

The Ritchie Wedge—A distinct advance in photometry was made by William Ritchie, who, after many attempts to adapt the differential thermometer to the comparison of light sources, devised the form of photometer head which is generally known by his name [12]. In its first form, shown in Fig. 4, this photometer was a modification of Bouguer's. Two pieces of mirror, CF, FD, reflected the light from the sources to the translucent paper EG. Ritchie, however, also used the same form of head

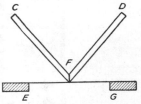

FIG. 4. Ritchie's Photometer.

without the translucent paper, pasting opaque matt white paper over the mirrors, and comparing the brightness of these two surfaces directly. The prism, CFD, which is generally known as the Ritchie " wedge ", has formed the basis of many instruments, each designed, generally, with the object of producing as sharp and fine a division as possible between the surfaces, for this was early recognised as being an important feature in accurate photometry [13]. The forms of Ritchie wedge devised by Sir J. Conroy [14], S. P. Thompson and C. C. Starling [15], L. Weber [16], A. P. Trotter [17], and Q. Majorana [18] are shown in Fig. 5, from which the particular features of each will be seen immediately. In Yvon's form [19] the sources are arranged so that the light is incident normally at both surfaces of the wedge.

Polarisation Photometers—The work of Malus and Arago in the first years of the nineteenth century on the laws governing the intensity of polarised light made possible a new form of photometer which was independent of the inverse square law. The first polarisation photometer was that of D. F. J. Arago [20], in which he made use of double refraction prisms for both polariser and analyser. Later instruments of the same type were those of A. Beer [21], F. de la Provostaye and P. Desains [22], F. Bernard [23], H. W. Dove [24], E. Becquerel [25], D. Salomons [26] and the modern instrument of F. F. Martens (see p. 219). Reflection from glass (see p. 157) was used as the means of polarising the light from one or both sources by J. Jamin [27], J. Babinet [28], J. C. F. Zöllner [29], W. Crookes [30], and H. Wild [31]. The use of polarisation as a means for varying the intensity is very common in spectrophotometry, owing to the optical

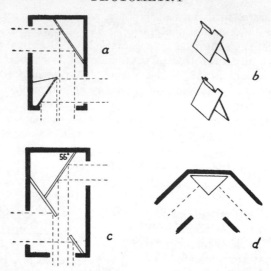

FIG. 5. Different Forms of Photometer based on the Ritchie Wedge. (a) Conroy. (b) Thompson-Starling. (c) Trotter and Weber (Dachphotometer). (d) Yvon.

difficulties introduced by altering the distance between the photometer head and the source of light.

The Bunsen Photometer—In the design of instruments depending on the inverse square law, little progress was made after the work of Ritchie until 1843, when R. Bunsen first described the famous photometer head known by his name. This photometer was originally designed for use in an exhaustive investigation on the chemical action of light which Bunsen was then carrying out in collaboration with Sir H. E. Roscoe [32]. The Bunsen photometer, which is still frequently employed and which is, in fact, capable of exceedingly accurate work when carefully constructed and properly used, is fully described in Chapter VII of this book. The chief modification of it, the Lummer-Brodhun cube, is also described in detail in the same chapter. This was first used by W. Swan [33] and described by him some thirty years before its introduction by Lummer and Brodhun. These workers, however, were undoubtedly responsible for the use of the contrast principle which has enabled still greater accuracy to be obtained in modern photometry.

The Joly Block Photometer—This photometer head consisted of two equal thin blocks of some translucent material, preferably opal glass, separated by a thin sheet of silver foil or other opaque material, as shown in Fig. 6 [34]. The light reaching the outer surfaces of the blocks was diffused internally, and gave the sides of the blocks seen by the eye a certain brightness. The photometric setting was made by obtaining equality of brightness on both sides of the dividing line. Disadvantages of this photometer were (a) the absorption of light in the blocks, which made it unsuitable for comparing sources of low intensity, and (b) the uncertain position of the surface from which the lamp distance was to be measured.

Standards of Light: The Candle—The gradual improvement in the instruments available for photometric measurement naturally resulted in a growing dissatisfaction with the hitherto accepted standard of luminous intensity, the candle, for it was soon found that this standard was not reproducible to the accuracy of measurement even when the composition, form and rate of burning were carefully specified [35]. Although once officially adopted in several countries and by various testing bodies [36], candles were in due course superseded by one or other of the various flame standards which had been designed to give greater constancy and reproducibility. Chief among

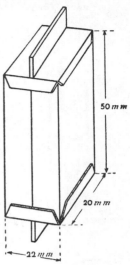

FIG. 6. The Joly Block Photometer.

them were the Carcel lamp, the Vernon Harcourt pentane lamp in its different forms and the Hefner lamp.

The Carcel Lamp—The first standard to supersede the candle was the Carcel lamp, a modification of the Argand [37], in which a clockwork pump was used to supply the wick with colza oil at a given rate (see Fig. 7). The standard luminous intensity was that given when the rate of oil consumption was 42 gm. per hour. Small departures from this standard rate were allowed for by a simple proportional rule, the actual consumption being conveniently measured by using the lamp on a form of balance and noting the time in which it lost 10 gm. in weight. This lamp, devised by Carcel in 1800 [38], was used by Dumas and Regnault in their photometric work [39] but the difficulties attending its use were very great, and different observers were unable to obtain results either consistent among themselves [40] or in agreement with one another to the same degree of accuracy as that attainable with other flame standards. The luminous intensity under the standard conditions was variously estimated at from 9·4 to 10 candles [41].

Kerosene lamps in various forms were proposed as standards or as sub-standards at different times [42], but were found not to be satisfactory.

A coal-gas flame of given dimensions was proposed by H. Giroud [43], but this was inferior as regards constancy to the light given

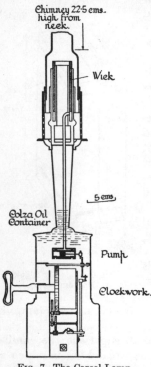

Chimney 22·5 cms. high from neck.

Wick

5 cms

Colza Oil Container

Pump

Clockwork.

FIG. 7. The Carcel Lamp.

by a specified area of the brightest part of a gas flame. This form of standard, originally proposed by W. W. Fiddes [44] and later by S. Elster [45], was developed by Methven, who found that the brightness was constant when the flame was burning under specified conditions in an Argand burner [46]. After much experiment this standard also was found to be unsatisfactory [47] and subsequent modifications did not improve it sufficiently to make it suitable for use as a standard of light [48].

The Pentane Lamp [49]—The only practical flame standards were those in which a volatile hydrocarbon of definitely known chemical composition was burnt in a lamp of carefully specified dimensions. The first lamp of this kind was made in 1877 by A. G. Vernon Harcourt [50]. It burnt a mixture of pentane vapour (C_5H_{12}) and air from a wickless burner, and had a luminous intensity of one candle. After undergoing several modifications [51], including forms in which a wick was used to convey liquid pentane into the burner tube, although the wick did not enter the flame or even approach the top of the tube [52], the lamp was completely redesigned in a larger form so as to have a luminous intensity of ten candles [53], and this was adopted in place of the candle as the official standard of the Metropolitan Gas Referees in their " Notification " for 1898. Lamps burning pentane were devised also by W. J. Dibdin (ten candles) [54] and by J. Simmance (two candles) [55]. The Vernon Harcourt pentane lamp, in its final form, is shown diagrammatically in Fig. 8. The saturator A held the fuel, liquid pentane, a highly inflammable and very volatile hydro-carbon distilled from petroleum, and was filled to about two-thirds of its capacity before the lamp was lighted. The saturator was connected, by means of a wide india-rubber tube, with the burner B, which consisted of a steatite ring pierced with thirty holes, and at which the issuing mixture of air and pentane vapour was ignited. The rate of flow of the mixed vapour, and therefore the height of the flame, could be adjusted by means of the stop-cocks S_1 and S_2 on the saturator. The chimney tube CC was furnished near its base with a mica window, across which was placed a horizontal bar 38 mm. above

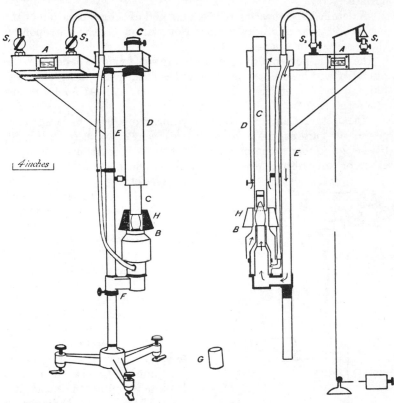

FIG. 8. The Pentane Lamp.

the bottom of the chimney. The chimney was set, by means of a cylindrical wooden gauge G, so that its lower end was exactly 47 mm. above the steatite ring burner. Surrounding the chimney CC was a concentric tube D, up which a current of air was drawn by the heating of the chimney, and this heated air passed into the hollow supporting pillar E, and so down through F to the centre of the steatite ring, where it was used in the combustion of the pentane. H was a conical shade for protecting the flame from draught. When the lamp was in use the stop-cocks S_1 and S_2 were adjusted to give a flame of specified height.

In making photometric measurements all distances were reckoned from the centre of the flame, i.e. the geometric centre of the steatite ring, but since this was not the position of the " equivalent light centre " of the flame (see p. 149), it was specified that the lamp should be used at a fixed distance (1 metre) from the photometer surface.

A detailed specification of the lamp and of the preparation of the pentane [56], was published in the " Notification " of the Metropolitan Gas Referees for the year 1916.

The candle-power of the pentane lamp was found to depend on the humidity and barometric pressure of the atmosphere in which it was burning and the effect of these variables was allowed for by means of a formula [57].

The Hefner Lamp [49]—Other hydrocarbons used in lamps suggested at various times as standards were : (i) ethyl ether [58], (ii) benzol, either alone or mixed in definite proportions with ethyl ether or with ethyl alcohol [59], (iii) acetylene [60], and (iv) amyl

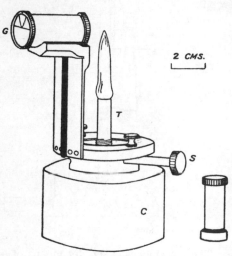

acetate $(C_7H_{14}O_2)$. The last-named fuel was used in the lamp first devised in 1884 by F. von Hefner Alteneck [61] and until 1940 the official standard of candle-power in Germany and some other European countries, having, in 1893 superseded [62] the Vereins-kerze set up in 1868 by the Deutsche Verein von Gas- und Wasserfachmän-nern [63]. It was also adopted as the custodian of the bougie décimale by the International Electro-technical Congress at Geneva in 1896 [64]. This lamp

FIG. 9. The Hefner Lamp.

is shown in Fig. 9. It consisted of a container C made of brass, 70 mm. in diameter and 38 mm. high. It held about 115 c.c. of amyl acetate, a specially pure grade of this compound being required for photometric purposes [65]. A thin German silver tube T, constructed very accurately to the dimensions of 25 mm. in height, 8 mm. internal diameter, and 0·15 mm. in thickness of metal held a wick of fifteen to twenty strands of untwisted cotton, which could be adjusted in height by means of the screw S. G was a gauge consisting of a lens and ground glass screen with a horizontal cross-line [66]. The lens formed an inverted image of the flame on the screen, and by this means the tip of the flame could be adjusted very accurately to the correct height of 40 mm. above the level of the tube. The luminous intensity of the flame depended appreciably on its height, and one of the chief disadvantages of this standard was the fact that the flame was very lambent and sensitive to draught, so that in the absence of any chimney its use was attended with great difficulty for practical work [67]. With the Hefner, as with the pentane lamp, allowance had to be made for barometric pressure and for humidity [68].

Incandescence Standards—In spite of very careful specifications of constructional details and of numerous elaborate determinations of the correction factors to be applied on account of atmospheric conditions, none of the flame standards proved really adequate to the needs of accurate photometry and suggestions were made from time to time to construct some form of standard depending on the radiation given by a specified area of some surface at a given temperature [69]. Of the proposals in this class the most important was the melting platinum standard, first given a practical form by J. Violle and therefore generally known as the " Violle standard " [70]. It was the light given by one sq. cm. of a surface of molten platinum at the temperature of solidification. The Violle standard, on account of its obvious theoretical advantages, was regarded as a promising advance on the existing flame standards, and unsuccessful attempts were made at various times to place it on a satisfactory basis [71]. Very careful work on this standard was carried out by J. E. Petavel [72] who found that the effect of slight contamination of the platinum with either silica or carbon was very marked. He concluded that the probable variation in the light emitted by molten platinum under standard conditions was within 1 per cent. This standard was adopted by the International Electrical Congress in 1889, and its one-twentieth part was given the name " bougie décimale " [73].

In order to avoid the possible variations in the temperature of fusion or of solidification of the platinum, O. Lummer and F. Kurlbaum proposed to use the metal at a temperature below the melting point, and to define the temperature as that at which a layer of water 2 cm. in thickness transmitted 10 per cent of the total resultant radiation [74], this ratio being determined by means of a bolometer. Petavel found that the bolometer method of temperature adjustment was not sufficiently fundamental to enable this apparatus to fulfil the conditions of a primary standard.

The use of a filament lamp as a standard was proposed from time to time but was found to be impracticable as it was not possible even to specify, still less to manufacture such a lamp to the extreme accuracy required for a standard of light [75]. A lamp of this kind can, however, be used as the custodian of a *unit* of light since, by special construction, very good constancy can be obtained. Special types of electric lamps are, in fact, used at the national standardising laboratories for this purpose. This matter is dealt with more fully in Chapter VI where a description of the form of standard now adopted by international agreement will be found.

A standard which cannot well be classed with any of the others that have been proposed is that furnished by a definite area of a discharge tube containing either helium or sodium [76].

Other Problems—Side by side with the development of accurate means for measuring the luminous intensity of a source and the search for a convenient standard reproducible to an accuracy at least comparable with that of photometric measurement, other cognate problems have had to be studied as they arose. The comparison of sources giving lights of different colours was, from the first, found to be an operation of special difficulty, and the means which have been adopted for overcoming this difficulty are described in Chapters IX and XI of this book.

The development of physical methods of photometry and of the *instrumentum thermometro analogus* of Lambert is described in Chapter IV so that it need not be further mentioned here. The measurement of illumination, as distinct from the measurement of luminous intensity is now an important branch of photometry. The first illumination photometer was constructed by Sir Wm. Preece in 1883 [77] and since that time numerous instruments have been produced for this special class of measurement. Here especially, physical photometry shows every sign of superseding the use of visual methods.

The study of illumination and the development of means for redistributing the light given by a source, have led to a radical change in the rating of illuminants. It is the total light output, rather than the luminous intensity in a single direction or group of directions, which is chiefly of interest to the lighting engineer, and the result has been a rapid development of methods of measuring luminous flux. The use of integrating photometers, generally of the Ulbricht sphere type, is now the rule rather than the exception in photometric laboratories, and Chapter VIII is therefore devoted to this branch of photometry.

The Future—Progress in the future lies mainly in two directions : (i) the production of instruments and standards of greater precision for use in the laboratory where accurate measurement is called for, and (ii) the simplification of photometric apparatus, particularly the portable photometer, without too much sacrifice of accuracy, so that the measurement of illumination may become as simple and as common an operation as the measurement of temperature or length, and require as little special training or technical experience. Considerable progress has been made in the latter direction, and the principal remaining problem is the production of some more mechanically robust means for measuring the small photocurrents available, or some convenient method by which these can be increased.

In precision photometry, unless some visual criterion still more sensitive than that of the contrast field can be discovered, progress must necessarily lie in the use of physical methods. There is no definite limit which can be set to the accuracy so obtainable, but it has to be remembered that the precision of the other measurements involved must be correspondingly increased. Thus, for example, in order to attain a certainty of 1 part in 10,000 in measuring the luminous intensity of a filament lamp by means of a photometer based on the inverse square law, the voltage must be measurable to 1 part in 40,000, and the effective position of the light source must be known within 0·1 mm. if the lamp is at a distance of 2 metres from the photometer. It is probable, therefore, that progress in the direction of increased precision in photometric measurement will be slow. The accuracy at present attainable is ample for commercial purposes, but barely sufficient for scientific research. Experience in other branches of measurement (e.g. that of power, whether electrical or thermal) shows, however, that what is sufficient to-day may lag seriously behind even commercial requirements in ten or twenty years' time. Progress, therefore, is essential. Increased precision must be attained so that, in all that concerns the production and utilisation of light, progress may not be hindered nor development retarded [78].

BIBLIOGRAPHY

The history of photometry is dealt with in greater or less detail in several of the books listed in Appendix I (p. 511), particularly those of Palaz and Liebenthal, and in a series of articles in *Engineering*, Vol. 35, 1883. There is also an extensive bibliography in the first edition of this book (pp. 8–15).

REFERENCES

1. Paris, *1729*. [Reprinted, Paris, *1921*, in *Les Maîtres de la Pensée Scientifique*.] The first use of the photometer was, however, made four years earlier, on November 23rd, *1725*. This date must therefore be regarded as the true birthday of the science of photometry. See Histoire de l'Acad. Royale des Sci., Paris, *1726*, p. 11. See also D. Colladon, Soc. des Amateurs des Sci., Lille, Recueil des Travaux, *1825*, p. 20.

2. A translation into German by E. Anding is published in Nos. 31–33 of Ostwald's *Klassiker d. exakten Wissenschaften* (Engelmann, Leipzig, *1892*). This contains (No. 33, pp. 51 *et seq.*) a good account of Lambert's life. He is chiefly notable for having introduced the use of hyperbolic functions into trigonometry.

3. Although many writers have attributed to Lambert the invention of the Rumford photometer, A. P. Trotter (Illum. Eng., 12, *1919*, p. 315), says : " The question remains : did he or did he not invent a photometer? I am inclined to think, in spite of the title of his great work, that he did not, and that Bouguer was the first man to measure light." He apparently bases this opinion largely on a passage in *Photometria* (p. 8), where Lambert says : " Oculus ergo caret instrumentis et thermometro et organo analogis, sibi soli relictus judicium ferre debet." This remark, however, might well refer only to the absence of a photometer *analagous to a thermometer*, i.e. one capable of measuring light directly (as distinct from a measurement by comparison).

4. Phil. Trans., 84, *1794*, p. 67 ; Rumford's *Collected Works* (Boston, *1875*), vol. 4, p. 1.

5. *Illumination, Its Distribution and Measurement*, p. 77. For an example see R. Hiecke, E. u. M., 44, *1926*, Lichttechn., p. 49.

6. It has been stated (see E. Karrer, Illum. Eng. Soc. N. Y., Trans., 12, *1917*, p. 99) that Rumford was the first to employ a unit of illumination. His " degree of light " was, however, a unit of luminous intensity, being, in fact, equal to one hundredth of the luminous intensity of a wax candle burning at the rate of 108 grains per hour. (" On the Management of Light in Illumination," Rumford's *Collected Works*, vol. 4, p. 187.)

7. L. Foucault. *Recueil des Travaux Scientifiques* (Paris, *1878*), p. 100.

8. See the *Notification of the Gas Referees, 1916*, p. 22 ; F. Clowes, Gas Inst., Trans., *1901*, p. 69 ; J. of Gas Lighting, 77, *1901*, p. 1648.

9. J. f. Chem. u. Phys., 11, *1814*, p. 361 ; Annals of Philosophy, 7, *1816*, p. 3.

10. *Nouvelles découvertes sur la lumière* (Paris, *1700* ; Italian trans. by D. Cecchi, Padova, *1707*) ; P. Bouguer, *Traité d'Optique*, p. 46.

11. See refs. in note (11) on p. 10 of *Photometry* (*1926*) ; also D. R. Barber, Phil. Mag., 14, *1932*, p. 404 ; E. Brumberg and S. I. Wawilow, Acad. Sci. U.R.S.S., C.r. (Doklady), 3, *1934*, p. 409.

12. Roy. Soc. Edin., Trans., 10, *1826*, p. 443.

13. P. Bouguer. *Traité d'Optique*, p. 14.
Rumford. Phil. Trans., 84, *1794*, p. 73.

14. Phys. Soc., Proc., 5, *1882*, p. 253.

15. Phys. Soc., Proc., 12, *1893*, p. 361.

16. Naturwiss. Verein f. Schleswig-Holstein (Kiel), Schriften, 10. *1893*, p. 116 ; Illum. Eng. (N.Y.), 1, *1906*, p. 901.

17. Phys. Soc., Proc., 12, *1893*, p. 354.

18. Reale Accad. dei Lincei, Rendic., 9 (II), *1900*, p. 87 ; Phil. Mag., 1, *1901*, p. 555.

19. P. Yvon. C.R., 75, *1872*, p. 1102 ; J. of Gas Lighting, 22, *1873*, p. 60.

20. *Œuvres Complètes* (Paris, *1858*), vol. 10, p. 198.

21. Ann. d. Phys., 84, *1851*, p. 37 and 86, *1852*, p. 78.

22. C.R., 38, *1854*, p. 977.

23. Ann. Chim. Phys., 35, *1852*, p. 385 ; C.R., 36, *1853*, p. 728.

24. Ann. d. Phys., 114, *1861*, p. 145.

25. *La Lumière, ses causes et ses effets*, vol 1 (Paris, *1867*), p. 74 ; Ann. Chim. Phys., 62, *1861*, p. 5.

26. Inst. El. Eng., J., 22, *1893*, p. 197.

27. Ann. Chim. Phys., 19, *1847*, p. 296.

28. C.R., 37, *1853*, p. 774 ; B. A. Report, *1854*, p. 2.

29. Ann. d. Phys., 100, *1857*, p. 381 and 109, *1860*, p. 244.

30. Roy. Soc., Proc., 17, *1868*, p. 358.

31. Ann. d. Phys., 99, *1856*, p. 235 and 118, *1863*, p. 193 ; Z. f. I., 9, *1889*, p. 180.

32. R. Bunsen and H. E. Roscoe. Phil. Trans., 149, *1859*, p. 891.

33. Roy. Soc. Edin., Trans., 22, *1859*, p. 33.
C. G. Knott. Phil. Mag., 49, *1900*, p. 118.
O. Lummer and E. Brodhun. *Ibid.*, p. 541.

34. J. Joly. Roy. Dublin Soc., Proc., 4, *1884*, p. 345.
See also the other references in notes (41) and (42) on p. 189 of *Photometry (1926)*.

35. See, e.g., B. A. Report, *1888*, p. 39 and A. Palaz, *loc. cit. infra*.

36. For the different specifications of the standard candles, see, for example, A. Palaz, *Photométrie*, p. 105 (Eng. trans., p. 121) ; W. J. Dibdin, *Practical Photometry*, p. 87 ; E. Liebenthal, *Prakt. Phot.*, p. 105.

37. See Observations sur la Physique, etc., 24, *1784*, p. 159.

38. B. G. Carcel and Careau. Ann. des Arts et Manufactures, 6, *1802*, p. 269 ; Nicholson's J., 2, *1802*, p. 108.

39. P. Audouin and P. Bérard. Ann. Chim. Phys., 65, *1862*, p. 423 ; J. of Gas Lighting, 12, *1863*, p. 15.

40. See, e.g., E. Durand, Le Gaz, 3, *1859*, p. 193 ; J. of Gas Lighting, 8, *1859*, p. 611 ; A. Broca, Ecl. El., 6, *1896*, p. 148.

41. F. W. Hartley. Brit. Assn. of Gas Managers, Proc., *1880*, p. 146.
W. J. Dibdin. J. of Gas Lighting, 45, *1885*, p. 626.
C. C. Paterson. Inst. El. Eng., J., 38, *1907*, p. 271.
For a detailed description of the Carcel lamp and of the method of using it, see A. Palaz, *Photométrie*, p. 101 (Eng. trans., p. 114).

42. W. B. Rogers. B. A. Report, *1864* (2), p. 39.
T. W. Keates. J. of Gas Lighting, 18, *1869*, p. 181.
H. H. Edgerton. Engineering and Mining J., 25, *1878*, p. 94.
B.O.T. Committee's Report. J. of Gas Lighting, 38, *1881*, p. 719.
W. J. Dibdin. J. of Gas Lighting, 45, *1885*, p. 626.
A. Lecomte. *Ibid.*, 90, *1905*, p. 963.
A. H. Elliott. *Ibid.*, 93, *1906*, p. 97 and 94, *1906*, p. 578 and 96, *1906*, p. 98.

43. Soc. technique de l'Industrie du Gaz, C. r., 5, *1878*, p. 260 and 7, *1880*, p. 76 and 9, *1882*, p. 235.
H. Krüss. Central-Ztg. f. Opt. u. Mech., 4, *1883*, pp. 161 and 169.
A. Palaz. *Photométrie*, p. 127 (Eng. trans., p. 143).
F. Uppenborn. Central-Ztg f. Opt. u. Mech., 9, *1888*, pp. 121 and 135.

44. J. of Gas Lighting, 15, *1866*, p. 509.

45. J.G.W., 11, *1868*, p. 306.

46. J. Methven. Brit. Assn. of Gas Managers, Proc., *1878*, p. 54.

47. Report of the B.O.T. Committee on Photometric Standards. J. of Gas Lighting, 38, *1881*, p. 719.

48. J. Methven. Gas Institute, Trans., *1882*, p. 155 ; J. of Gas Lighting, 40. *1882*, p. 42.
W. J. Dibdin. J. of Gas Lighting, 45, *1885*, p. 718 and 50, *1887*, p. 290.
W. S. Rawson. *Ibid.*, 48, *1886*, p. 612.
R. Norris. Am. Gas Light J., 71, *1899*, p. 730 and 73, *1900*, p. 762 ; J. of Gas Lighting, 74, *1899*, p. 1373 and 76, *1900*, p. 1338.

49. For a fuller account of the pentane lamp and of the Hefner lamp see Chapter V of *Photometry (1926)*.

50. B.A. Report, *1877*, p. 51 ; J. of Gas Lighting, 30, *1877*, p. 337.

51. Report of the B.O.T. Committee on Photometric Standards. J. of Gas Lighting, 38, *1881*, p. 720.
A. G. Vernon Harcourt. B.A. Report, *1883*, p. 426 and *1885*, p. 916 ; J. of Gas Lighting, 41, *1883*, p. 1143.
W. J. Dibdin. J. of Gas Lighting, 45, *1885*, p. 673 and 50, *1887*, p. 290 and 52, *1888*, p. 1108.
W. Sugg. Gas Institute, Trans., *1892*, p. 133.

52. A. G. Vernon Harcourt. B.A. Report, *1887*, p. 617 ; El. Rev., 20, *1887*, p. 421 ; see also J. of Gas Lighting, 51, *1888*, p. 371.
A. G. Vernon Harcourt. B.A. Report, *1894*, p. 582. (This was a 10 candle lamp.)

53. B.A. Report, *1898*, p. 845 ; J. of Gas Lighting, 70, *1897*, p. 1050 and 71, *1898*, pp. 1252 and 1551.

54. J. of Gas Lighting, 50, *1887*, p. 290 and 65, *1895*, p. 1021 and 67, *1896*, p. 222.
Report of B.O.T. Committee. Nature, 52, *1895*, p. 356 ; J. of Gas Lighting, 66, *1895*, p. 175.

55. E. L. Pryce. Inst. Gas Eng., Trans., 8, *1898*, p. 112.

56. On the effect of the purity of the pentane see E. Liebenthal, J.G.W., 49, *1069*, p. 559 ; *Prakt. Phot.*, p. 129.

57. W. J. A. Butterfield, J. S. Haldane and A. P. Trotter. Illum. Eng., 4, *1911*, p. 509.

C. C. Paterson and B. P. Dudding. Phys. Soc., Proc., 27, *1915*, p. 263.
K. Takatsu and M. Tanaka. Illum. Eng., 11, *1918*, p. 214.

58. V. Wartha. Deut. Chem. Gesell., Ber., 7, *1874*, p. 103.

59. W. Crookes. Chem. News, 18, *1868*, p. 25.
F. Eitner. J.G.W., 24, *1881*, p. 722 and 28, *1885*, p. 799.
F. v. Hefner-Alteneck. E.T.Z., 4, *1883*, p. 445 ; Lum. El., 10, *1883*, p. 501.
Report of Netherlands Photometric Commission (Leiden, 1894). See also J. of Gas Lighting, 64, *1894*, pp. 1161 and 1209.
A. Blondel. Assn. Franç., C.r., *1898* (2), p. 223 ; Ecl. El., 16, *1898*, p. 317 ; El. World, 33, *1899*, p. 350.
Benzine has frequently been used for secondary standards or comparison lamps. See, e.g., L. Weber, note (54), p. 239; H. Krüss, J.G.W., 45, *1902*, p. 738 and 47, *1904*, p. 917.

60. J. Violle. Soc. Franç. de Phys., Séances, *1895*, p. 165 and *1896*, p. 39.
E. L. Nichols. Int. El. Congress, St. Louis, *1904*, Proc., Vol. II, p. 811 ; Electrician, 54, *1904*, p. 101.
C. Féry. J. de Phys., 3, *1904*, p. 838.
J. Baillaud. Ann. de Phys., 7, *1917*, p. 300 ; Congrès Int. de l'Acetylène, 10, *1930*, p. 164.
See also Chapter VI, p. 185.

61. E.T.Z., 5, *1884*, p. 20 ; Electrician, 12, *1884*, p. 511.

62. Centralblatt f. d. Deutsche Reich, 20, *1893*, p. 124.

63. J.G.W., 12, *1869*, p. 363 and 15, *1872*, p. 377.

64. Soc. Int. des Elect., Bull, 13, *1896*, p. 365.
It was also recommended for adoption by a committee of the Am. I.E.E., see Trans., 14, *1897*, p. 90.
Amyl acetate lamps have frequently been employed as comparison lamps. See e.g., J. of Gas Lighting, 73, *1899*, p. 80 ; 80, *1902*, p. 1541 and 93, *1906*, p. 649.

65. See the P.T.R. Specification for amyl acetate, Z.f.I., 13, *1893*, p. 257.

66. H. Krüss. J.G.W., 30, *1887*, p. 817.
F. F. Martens. Deut. Phys. Gesell., Verh., 2, *1900*, p. 108.
See also H. Strache, C.I.E., Proc., 3, *1911*, p. 105.

67. E. Gehrcke, M. Goebert and C. Müller. Phys. Z., 37, *1936*, p. 881.

68. See the refs. in note (57) *supra* and E. B. Rosa, E. C. Crittenden and A. H. Taylor, Illum. Eng. Soc. N.Y., Trans., 10, *1915*, p. 843.

69. Suggested standards of this kind were (a) the brightness of an iron vessel containing boiling zinc (A. Crova, Ann. Chim. Phys., 19, *1880*, p. 498), (b) a coil of platinum wire heated to the temperature of a hydrogen flame (J. C. Draper, Frank Inst., J., 62, *1871*, p. 368), (c) the light given by burning magnesium (T. T. P. Bruce-Warren, Electrician, 13, *1884*, p. 104).

70. J. W. Draper. Phil. Mag., 30, *1847*, p. 345 and 9, *1880*, p. 76.
J. Violle. Congrès Int. des Electriciens, Paris, *1881*, C.r., p. 352 ; C.R., 98, *1884*, p. 1032 ; Phil. Mag., 17, *1884*, p. 563.

71. W. v. Siemens. Berlin Ber., *1884*, p. 601.
C. R. Cross. Am. Acad. Arts and Sci., Proc., 22, *1886*, p. 220 ; El. Rev., 19, *1886*, p. 426.
B.A. Report, *1888*, p. 47.
O. Lummer. Z.f.I., 14, *1894*, p. 267.

72. Roy. Soc., Proc., 65, *1899*, p. 469.

73. Congrès Int. des Electriciens, Paris, *1889*, C.r., p. 109 ; Lum. El., 33, *1889*, p. 477. See also the French decree of 1919 making the *bougie décimale* (b.d.) the legal unit of luminous intensity in France (J. Officiel, 101, *1919*, p. 3474 ; Rev. Gén. de l'El., 5, *1919*, p. 616).

74. Z. f. I., 13, *1893*, p. 121 and 14, *1894*, p. 266 ; Electrician, 34, *1894*, p. 37.
J. E. Petavel. Roy. Soc., Proc., 65, *1899*, p. 469. See also W. A. Harwood and J. E. Petavel, Roy. Soc., Proc., 86, *1912*, p. 409.

75. L. Schwendler. Phil. Mag., 8, *1879*, p. 392.
  J. Trowbridge. Am. Acad. Arts and Sci., Proc., 20, *1885*, p. 494.
  B.A. Report, *1885*, p. 61.
  W. J. Dibdin. J. of Gas Lighting, 50, *1887*, p. 290.

76. P. G. Nutting. Bureau of Standards, Bull., 4, *1908*, p. 511 and 8, *1912*, p. 487.
  L. Ornstein and H. C. Burger. Z. f. Phys., 76, *1932*, p. 777.
  H. Schmellenmeier. *Ibid.*, 93, *1935*, p. 705.

77. Roy. Soc., Proc., 36, *1884*, p. 270.

78. " All the natural sciences aim, then, at becoming exact sciences and become exact through the making, correlation and reduction of measurements. Any branch of natural science without measurements is not above the qualitative stage. The number and degree of precision of the measurements in a branch of science is a gage of the extent to which that branch has become exact." (A. E. Kennelly. Illum. Eng. Soc. N.Y., Trans., 6, *1911*, p. 580.)

CHAPTER II

RADIATION

The Nature of Light—Light, like radiant heat, Röntgen rays (X-rays) and the electromagnetic radiation used in radio communication, is a form of radiant energy ; that is to say it is that form of energy which is transmitted through space in straight lines and without the intervention of matter at a constant velocity of about $2 \cdot 997925 \times 10^{10}$ cm. per sec. [1]. This velocity, one of those invariable fundamental quantities which have been termed " constants of nature," will be referred to throughout this chapter as c.

For many years it was thought that a complete explanation of the phenomena of radiation was to be found in the wave theory of light. Towards the end of the last century, however, it was realised that this theory could not satisfactorily account for all the facts ; in particular it could not be made to give a correct formula for the spectral distribution of pure temperature radiation (*vide infra*). The quantum theory was proposed by Planck to overcome this difficulty, but although this theory was brilliantly successful in explaining some of the phenomena associated with radiation it seemed to be quite irreconcilable with others which were satisfactorily explained on the wave theory and so, for a time, the two theories existed side by side in apparent contradiction.

In due course it was shown that the contradiction arose from the fact that both theories were used to explain the phenomena of radiation in terms of apparently analogous phenomena already familiar in other branches of physics, whereas what was needed was an entirely new mechanics applicable to the behaviour of particles of sub-atomic size. This need was supplied by the theory of wave-mechanics which, in a sense, embraced both the older theories and has been found to explain all the known phenomena with perfect consistency.

Such a theory is, of necessity, somewhat abstruse and for the present purpose it is convenient to make use of the conceptions and language of the two older theories in their original form, using each of them in considering those phenomena for the discussion of which it is peculiarly suited.

The Wave Theory of Light—About the year 1678 the Dutch philosopher Huyghens first propounded a theory of light in which it was supposed that a luminous body acted as a source of disturbance in a hypothetical all-pervading medium called the (luminiferous) ether. This disturbance was imagined to travel through the ether in the form of waves, which, on reaching the eye, produced the sensation of vision. On this theory light waves travel in space with the velocity c and carry energy from the body which produces them to that by which they are absorbed [2].

The essential characteristic of a wave motion is that, by means of a periodic disturbance transmitted continuously from one portion of a medium to the next portion in the line of propagation, energy is carried from one place to another without any motion of translation on the part of the medium or of any portion of it. The familiar example of a sheet of water, one end of which is agitated by a regular up-and-down movement of a piece of wood, will serve to illustrate these fundamental characteristics of a wave system. Ripples will be formed by the wood and will travel across the water with a certain velocity of propagation which is almost independent of the size of the ripples. That the actual particles of water have no motion, other than that of a simple vertical oscillation, is shown by the fact that a floating cork merely bobs up and down and is not carried along with the ripples. That energy is transmitted through the water by means of the ripples is shown by the fact that a piece of wood floating at the far end of the water will be caused to oscillate in synchronism with the movement of the wood causing the disturbance.

Effect of Frequency and Amplitude of Waves—In the last paragraph the general characteristics of a wave motion were described. It now remains to consider in what ways different kinds of waves may be distinguished one from another, and at once there are two prominent characteristics which claim attention. These are (a) the amplitude, or extent of the oscillation ; and (b) the frequency, or number of oscillations executed per second. With regard to the first, it is at once apparent that the energy conveyed by any given wave depends on the amplitude of that wave, and it may be said at once that in the case of the ether waves the energy transmitted is proportional to the square of some vector which, in the absence of any definite picture of the method of propagation of energy waves in the ether, may be termed for convenience the amplitude of vibration. For, the simplest example of oscillation, the case of a particle executing free vibrations in simple harmonic motion, $x = a \sin \omega (t - \theta)$ where x is the displacement, $2\pi/\omega$ the period (periodic time), and a the amplitude. Hence the total energy, which is equal to the kinetic energy ($\frac{1}{2}m\dot{x}^2$) when $x = 0$, is $\frac{1}{2}m\omega^2 a^2$.

With regard to the second characteristic, in the case of ether waves the frequency determines the kind of effect which they will have on our senses. In fact, the different kinds of radiant energy mentioned above are carried by ether waves which differ only in frequency. If ν is the number of vibrations per second [3], then, when ν is below about 10^{12} per second the waves are quite incapable of affecting our senses at all. These are the waves used in wireless telegraphy. When ν lies between about 10^{12} and 4×10^{14} the waves are capable of producing on our bodies the sensation of heat, but they cannot affect our eyes in such a way as to produce the sensation we call vision. To waves for which ν is above the limit of $4 \cdot 0 \times 10^{14}$ and does not exceed about $7 \cdot 5 \times 10^{14}$ the human eye is variously sensitive, and the effect produced on it differs both in kind and degree according to the value of ν.

The variation in *degree* will be more fully considered in the next chapter, which deals with the behaviour of the eye as a receptor of luminous radiation. It is sufficient for our present purpose to say that the eye is not equally sensitive to light waves of all frequencies ; in fact, its response to a given rate of reception of radiant energy, even when this is conveyed by waves within the limits of frequency stated above, depends on the absolute frequency of the radiation or, what is the same thing, on the colour of the light. For the variation in the *kind* of effect produced on the eye by waves of different frequencies gives rise to the sensation which we term " colour." Waves for which $\nu = 5 \times 10^{14}$ give the sensation of red, those of rather higher frequency form what appears to us as yellow light, and so on through green and blue to violet, which is the sensation produced by light waves of the highest frequencies which the eye is capable of appreciating at all [4]. Waves of still higher frequency (the ultra-violet) cannot affect the eye in such a way as to give the sensation of light though they may affect it profoundly in other ways. These waves are, however, capable of producing chemical changes in a photographic emulsion and are termed " actinic." Waves of still higher frequency, from 3×10^{17} to 2×10^{19}, are produced by special means, and are the Röntgen or X-rays which, on account of their power of penetrating the less dense forms of matter, are used for photographing, on plates specially sensitive to waves of this frequency, the forms of denser objects concealed within a medium which, although less dense, is nevertheless opaque to luminous radiation.

Wave-Length and Wave Number—It has long been customary to express the periodicity of radiation in terms of " wave-length " (λ) rather than " frequency " (ν). The former quantity is the distance (in the line of propagation of the radiation) which separates consecutive points undergoing the same " displacement " [5]. For example, in the case of ripples on water it is the distance between consecutive points having the same absolute displacement and the same direction of motion, such as A and B (Fig. 10). From this definition it follows that for light *in vacuo* $\lambda \nu = c$. Since, as will be seen later, the velocity of light varies according to the medium through which it is propa-

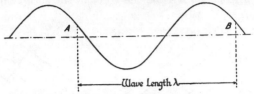

Fig. 10. Diagram of Wave-motion.

gated, and since the frequency of vibration cannot alter, λ must depend on the medium.

It will be clear that the frequency is more fundamentally characteristic of a particular kind of radiation than is its wave-length but only the latter can be measured directly so that the frequency must be deduced from the relation $\nu = c/\lambda$. The accuracy of wave-length measurement[6] far surpasses that with which the velocity of light is known (about 1 part in 500,000) and it is therefore sometimes convenient to use, in place of the frequency, the simple reciprocal of the wave-length. This reciprocal is called the wave-number $(1/\lambda)$.

Applications of the Wave Theory: The Inverse Square Law and Cosine Law—From the outline of the theory given above its agreement with the principal observed facts concerning radiation is readily demonstrated. For instance, the two fundamental laws of photometry, the inverse square law and the cosine law, follow at once if a luminous point is considered as the source of a system of spherical waves diverging from it as centre. For the area of any such wave as it travels outwards from the source must increase as the square of its radius, and since its energy must be regarded as uniformly distributed over its surface, the surface density of this energy must vary inversely as the square of the radius of the wave, that is, of the distance from the source. Similarly, since the direction of motion is always perpendicular to the

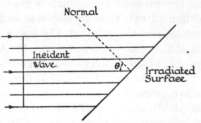

Fig. 11. The Cosine Law of Irradiation
or Illumination.

wave front, it follows that an elementary area can only receive energy in proportion to its area projected in that direction (Fig. 11) ; that is, the surface density of the energy received by any such area is proportional to cos θ where θ is the angle between the normal to the surface and the direction of propagation of the incident wave.

Reflection and Refraction on the Wave Theory—The well-known laws of reflection and refraction are also in agreement with the wave theory. In Fig. 12 let AA' be the trace of the surface of separation

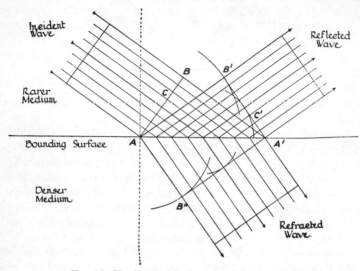

Fig. 12. The Laws of Reflection and Refraction.

of two media, and AB the trace of a plane wave surface incident at it. (This may, for convenience, be regarded as a portion of a spherical wave emanating from a very distant source.) Let it be supposed that the plane of the paper is perpendicular to both these surfaces. Then each successive portion of the separation surface AA', as soon as the incident wave surface reaches it, is assumed to become the origin of two new waves, one in the upper medium (the reflected wave) and the other in the lower medium (the refracted wave) [7]. If BA' is drawn perpendicular to AB, BA' is the direction of propagation of the incident wave, and if AB' and $A'B'$ are drawn equal respectively to $A'B$ and AB, then it is clear that when the reflected wave originating at A has just reached B' along the path AB', the original wave from B will just have reached A'. Similarly, the time taken from any point C on AB to a corresponding point C' on $A'B'$ will be found to be the same. Hence $A'B'$ must be the trace of the reflected wave surface at the instant the original wave reaches the point A'.

This new wave surface is the plane envelope of spheres having their centres at A, A' and all intermediate points, and their radii equal to the distances of these points from the line $A'B'$. It will, therefore, be perpendicular to the plane of the paper. Hence it follows that the incident and reflected rays (perpendiculars to the wave fronts) are in the same plane with each other and with the normal to the surface of separation, and further, that they make equal angles with this normal on opposite sides of it.

Now let a point B'' be taken below AA', such that (i) $AB'' = BA'/n$, and (ii) $A'B''$ is perpendicular to AB''. Then, if it is supposed that the velocity of propagation of the wave in the lower medium is $1/n$ times that in the upper medium, it follows, as in the last paragraph, that $A'B''$ is the trace of the refracted wave surface at the instant the wave reaches A'. Again it follows that the incident and refracted rays are in the same plane with each other and with the normal to the surface, and that in this case the sines of the angles made with this normal are in the ratio of n to 1 or, if i and r be the angles of incidence and refraction, $\sin i/\sin r = n$.

An important case arises when light passes from an optically denser to a rarer medium so that $n < 1$. If, in this case, i is greater than $\sin^{-1} n$ the equation of refraction gives r an impossible value. The light, in fact, does not emerge at all, but is reflected at the bounding surface according to the ordinary law of reflection. This phenomenon is known as " total reflection " and is much used in optical instruments. For instance, in the constant deviation prism shown in Fig. 17 (p. 25) the light at B is totally reflected at the glass-air surface because $i = 45°$, whereas n for glass to air is about 0·67, so that $\sin^{-1} n = 42°$.

It will be noticed that a new property has now been ascribed to the mechanism of wave propagation, viz. that the velocity of propagation is inversely proportional to the refractive index of the medium, as measured by the deviation suffered by a ray of light on entering that medium. This assumption has been fully verified by direct experiment [8] and so forms one of the great triumphs of the wave theory of radiation.

Lenses and Prisms—The deviation suffered by light on passing from one medium to another is one of the most important of optical phenomena forming, as it does, the basis of the action of all lenses and prisms. Let ABC (Fig. 13) represent a right section through a triangular glass prism, and let MN represent the front of a plane wave perpendicular to the paper and travelling in the direction NO. By the previous paragraph the position of the wave front inside the glass will be parallel to PO where $NO = n\ MP$. On emergence into air again the reverse action takes place and the final wave front is parallel to $M'N'$ where $O'N' = n\ P'M'$. The angle through which the wave front has been turned by the action of the prism, i.e. the " deviation," is δ. It is clearly equal to $i + i' - A$, where A is the " refracting " angle of the prism, and i, i' represent respectively

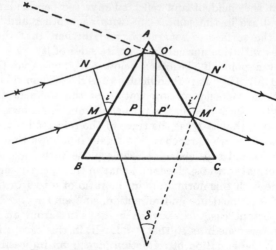

FIG. 13. The Passage of Light through a Prism.

NMO and $N'M'O'$ the angles of incidence and emergence of the light.
Since $\sin i = n \sin POM$, and $\sin i' = n \sin P'O'M'$, while

$$POM + P'O'M' = A,$$

i.e.
$$\sin^{-1}\left(\frac{\sin i}{n}\right) + \sin^{-1}\left(\frac{\sin i'}{n}\right) = A,$$

it follows that δ can be found when either i or i' is known. For the
special case $i = i'$, δ is a minimum, and is equal to $2i - A$, where
$2\sin^{-1}\left(\dfrac{\sin i}{n}\right) = A$, i.e. $\sin i = n \sin \dfrac{A}{2}$, so that

$$\delta = 2\sin^{-1}\left(n \sin \frac{A}{2}\right) - A.$$

It will be clear that an object seen through a prism will appear
to be shifted from its real position
and will seem to lie on the backward
continuation of the emergent ray.
It follows that if an object is seen
through a prism of the type shown in
Fig. 14 it will appear to be doubled,
for to an eye at E it will seem as
if the object lies on the backward
continuation of each of the lines,
EM, EM'. This form of prism, known
as a Fresnel biprism is used in
some photometers (see, for example,
p. 204).

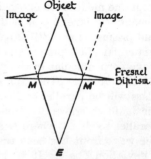

FIG. 14. The Action of a Fresnel
Biprism.

The effect of a lens can most easily be explained by reference to Fig. 15. Suppose AMB to be the spherical surface, radius r_1, of a

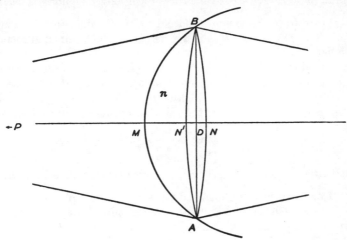

FIG. 15. Refraction at a Spherical Surface.

refracting medium of index n. Then, if a wave diverges from a point P, at the instant it reaches A it will have the form $AN'B$, instead of the form ANB which it would have had if unrefracted, MN being equal to nMN'. If $PN = u$, the new radius of curvature of the wave s is given by the equations $r_1 DM = uDN = sDN' = \frac{1}{2}AD^2$ if AD be assumed small with respect to u and r_1 [9]. On eliminating DM and DN by the aid of the relationship $MN = nMN'$, it is found that

$$(1/u) - (n/s) = (1 - n)/r_1 \qquad \text{......................(i)}$$

since, on the usual convention, s and r_1 are negative.

If now the light emerges again through a surface of radius r_2 in the opposite direction, the radius of curvature v of the emergent wave is similarly given by

$$(n/s) - (1/v) = (n - 1)/r_2 \qquad \text{......................(ii)}$$

since s and v are both negative and r_2 positive.

Hence $$\frac{1}{u} - \frac{1}{v} = (n - 1)\left(\frac{1}{r_2} - \frac{1}{r_1}\right). \qquad \text{......................(iii)}$$

This equation shows at once that light radiated from a point at distance u from a double convex lens having surfaces of radii r_1 and r_2 and refractive index n, is brought to a point again at a distance v on the opposite side of the lens. Thus, for various values of u the image can be kept stationary either by moving the lens (change of v) or altering its curvature (change of r_1 or r_2) or both. For a fixed lens, such as those used in optical apparatus, the reciprocal of the constant $(n-1)\left(\dfrac{1}{r_1}-\dfrac{1}{r_2}\right)$ is called the focal length f and it is clearly the distance from the lens of the image of a distant point for which $u=\infty$. The position of this image is called the "principal focus" of the lens.

A special case of some importance in photometry is the apparent shift in the position of an object seen through a plate of glass or other refractive medium of thickness d. In this case $r_1=r_2=\infty$, and the equations for finding the relation between u and v become

$$\frac{1}{u}-\frac{n}{s}=0 \quad \text{and} \quad \frac{n}{s+d}-\frac{1}{v+d}=0,$$

so that $u-v=d\left(1-\dfrac{1}{n}\right)$. Thus the effective distance of a light source from a surface is shortened by the insertion of a plane sheet of refractive medium, the amount of shortening being equal to the thickness of the sheet multiplied by $(n-1)/n$ (see Fig. 16).

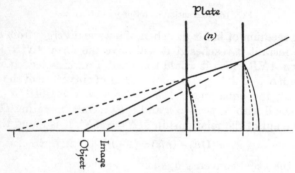

FIG. 16. Apparent Shift of an Object seen through a Plate.

Unless the requirement mentioned above, that the "aperture" $(AB$, Fig. 15) should be small compared with u and v, is adequately met, the rays from one point do not converge accurately to a single second point, but intersect one another somewhere along a short portion of the line forming the axis of the system $(PMN$ is the axis in Fig. 15). This departure of the rays from the stigmatic condition is termed "spherical aberration," and is a serious defect when a clearly-defined image is required. It can only be corrected by the use of non-spherical refracting surfaces, or by using a combination of lenses [10].

It should be noticed that a paraxial ray of light (i.e. a ray whose inclination to the axis of the optical system is small) passes undeviated through the *centre* of a thin lens, since to a first approximation the portions of the lens surfaces at which the light enters and leaves may be regarded as parallel, and therefore the deviation at entrance is compensated by the equal and opposite deviation at emergence.

It follows from this fact that the linear dimensions of an object and its image formed by a lens are in the ratio $u : v$, so that the areas are in the ratio $u^2 : v^2$.

Reflection at a spherical mirror may clearly be treated like refraction at a single spherical surface, putting $s = v$ and $n = -1$.

Dispersion—In the last three paragraphs it was tacitly assumed that the light was *homogeneous*, that is, that it consisted entirely of waves of a single frequency. Most light ordinarily met with, however, is composite, and may be regarded as a mixture, in varying proportions, of waves of all frequencies to which the eye is capable of responding [11].

It can readily be demonstrated by experiment that the ratio $\sin i/\sin r$, or n, generally termed the index of refraction of the second medium with reference to the first, is not the same for light of all wave-lengths. In passing from air to glass, for instance, n increases as the wave-length decreases, so that it follows that the velocity in glass must be less for violet light than for red light, for in space (and, very nearly, in air) the speed of propagation is independent of wave-length ; otherwise a new star, or an occulted star, would gradually change colour after its first appearance [12].

An important application of this variation of velocity in glass is to the resolution of a composite light into its various components by means of a glass prism. A convenient form of prism used for this purpose in the spectrometer is that shown in section in Fig. 17, where the composite light entering at A is spread out by reason of the change of refractive index of the glass with change of wave-length. After total reflection at B and refraction at C, the light emerges in the form of a coloured band, known as a "spectrum," which extends from red to violet if all colours are present in the original beam.

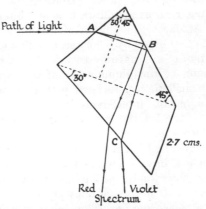

FIG. 17. The Constant Deviation Prism.

This variation of refractive index with wave-length is frequently made use of in optical and photometric (especially spectrophotometric) apparatus, but allowance for it has also to be made occasionally when analysis of the light is not desired. Clearly, no spreading can take place when the light is incident normally to the surface, for then $i = r = 0$.

From the presence of the quantity n in formula (iii) of p. 23, it will be clear that the position of the image formed by a lens depends on the wave-length of the light, and in the case of composite light the image of a point source is spread out into a line of images ranging in colour from violet (nearest the lens) to red. This spreading is termed " chromatic aberration," and can only be corrected by the use of a combination of lenses.

Interference—Another phenomenon which can be accounted for satisfactorily on the wave theory of light is interference. This phenomenon may, in brief, be looked upon as the effect of the superposition of two or more waves so as to produce a resultant of different amplitude. It is clear that, referring again to the illustration of the ripples on water, if two sets of ripples of the same amplitude and wave-length are arranged to meet, so that at any instant the crests of either set alone would occupy exactly the same positions as the troughs of the other set alone, the result of the superposition of the two sets will be complete extinction, and if two sets of ripples cross, regions of undisturbed water will be seen at the positions where such extinction takes place [13]. In other positions, however, where crest coincides with crest, and trough with trough, the ripples will be very much increased in amplitude. By suitable means, one of which will be described below, similar effects can be detected in the case of light waves. Both extinction and reinforcement must be regarded as manifestations of " interference," and perhaps the most satisfactory definition of this term for the purpose of this chapter is that given by Schuster, as follows [14] : " If the observed illumination of a surface by two or more pencils of light is not equal to the sum of the illumination of the separate pencils, we say that the pencils have interfered with each other and class the phenomenon as one of ' interference.' "

The Interference Grating—One of the most frequently employed pieces of apparatus involving interference is that known as a " grating." This consists, in its ordinary form, of a glass plate on which have been ruled with a fine diamond point a large number of exceedingly fine lines at regular close intervals (Rowland's gratings have about 14,400 lines per inch). The principle of its action will be clear from Fig. 18, which represents a section through the grating, it being understood that the whole effect depends on exact *similarity* between the individual lines or corrugations. Let A_1, A_2, A_3 ... be the trace of the incident wave front at the instant it reaches the similar points A_1, A_2, A_3 ... of the grating. Then A_1, A_2, A_3 ...

become the centres of new waves, and, on account of the similarity at these points, all these waves will be equal in amplitude at equal distances from their centres. Considering the direction A_1B_1, it is

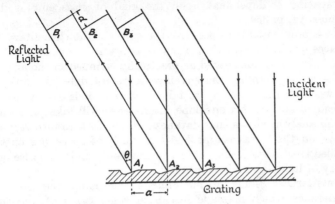

FIG. 18. The Diffraction Grating.

clear that, when the wave from A_1 has travelled as far as B_1, that from A_2 will have reached B_2, and so on. The waves thus follow in regular succession at a distance of separation equal to the projection of B_1B_2 on B_1A_1, that is, d. The value of d depends on the distance between the lines on the grating, and the direction of the reflected waves considered. It is clearly equal to $a \sin \theta$, where a is the separation of the lines and θ the angle which the reflected light makes with the normal. If it so happens that the distance d is half the length of a wave (or an odd number of half wave-lengths), destructive interference will take place between each pair of waves, and at a considerable distance from the grating darkness will result. If, however, in the direction of the reflected waves considered, d is equal to one or any whole number of wave-lengths, then all the sets of waves will reinforce one another and brightness will result in that direction, for every other set of similar points of the grating will behave like the set $A_1, A_2, A_3 \dots$.

This provides a direct method for measuring the wave-length of light, for clearly $\lambda = a \sin \theta$, where θ is the smallest angle of maximum intensity for light of wave-length λ. It also provides a means for analysing a composite light, for since λ is proportional to $\sin \theta$, it is clear that the reflected light will be analysed in such a way that the maximum intensity for light of a smaller wave-length (violet) will appear nearest to the direction of the incident light, while that for the longer waves (red) will appear nearly twice as far from this direction. Thus a grating may be used to produce a spectrum in which the different colours of a composite light are arranged in the order of their wave-lengths according to a known law of spacing (equiangular, since $\sin \theta \backsimeq \theta$ when θ is small). In this respect its spectrum, often referred to as a "normal spectrum," is superior to that of a prism in which the spacing is dependent upon the kind of glass employed (see Chapter XI, p. 354).

It is now possible to see why the effect of the elementary wave surfaces originating at all the points between A and A' in Fig. 12 of p. 20 could be considered as practically confined in the aggregate to the region forming the envelope represented by the line $A'B'$, for, when all these waves are taken together, it is easy to see that at regions not on this envelope interference will take place, and a careful analysis shows that darkness will, in fact, result everywhere except on the "wave-front" $A'B'$. Lack of space prevents any detailed treatment of the subject in this book, and a treatise on the theory of light should be consulted [15].

Interference Bands in Thin Films—There is one phenomenon of interference which is made use of in some types of photometer (see p. 232), viz. the alternate light and dark bands produced when light passes through, or is reflected from, a thin layer of air between two glass prisms. Let ABC (Fig. 19) be a ray incident at such an

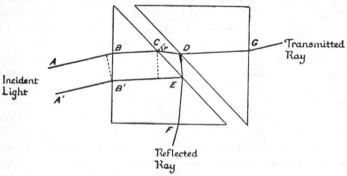

Fig. 19. Herschel's Fringes.

angle that BC is close to the direction of total reflection, then this ray is partly reflected and partly refracted at C, the refracted ray CD making with the interfaces of the prisms an angle r which is very nearly 90°. The ray CD is partly transmitted along DG, and partly reflected along the path DEF. Now there is a ray $A'B'$, parallel to AB, which is refracted along the path $B'E$, and is partly reflected at E. If the path difference between the rays reflected at D and at E is an odd multiple of a half wave-length, i.e. if it equals $(m + \frac{1}{2})\lambda$, where m is an integer, then destructive interference will take place and the total intensity in the direction EF

will be diminished. It is clear that for another pair of rays very slightly inclined to AB and $A'B'$ the path difference will be m or $(m+1)$ wave-lengths, so that the reflected parts of these rays will reinforce each other. Thus a featureless surface seen by reflection in such a double prism will appear to be covered with alternate bright and dark bands. Like reasoning will show that an exactly similar process takes place in those portions of the light which are transmitted along DG, etc. [16].

Double Refraction—In what has been written so far it has been assumed that the medium in which the waves of light are propagated is isotropic, that is, that it behaves in exactly the same way whatever be the path which these waves pursue within it. In some crystals, notably a form of calcite termed Iceland spar, this is not the case, except for waves in which the light vector, which has so far been termed a vibration without any statement as to its physical nature, is in a certain direction ; for it is found that in these crystals the incident light gives rise to two elementary waves at every point of the bounding surface. One of these waves is spherical, and obeys the ordinary laws of refraction, being propagated with the same velocity in all directions. The other is, however, propagated with a velocity which depends on its direction in the crystal. It is consequently not spherical, but ellipsoidal, and its minor axis is (for Iceland spar) of the same magnitude as the radius of the spherical wave, and is in the direction of a line of symmetry called the optic axis of the crystal [17]. The two waves are shown in Fig. 20, where

AB is the trace of the wave front in air, the circle CD that of the elementary "ordinary" spherical wave originating from A, and the ellipse $C'D$ that of the "extraordinary" ellipsoidal wave originating from the same point ;

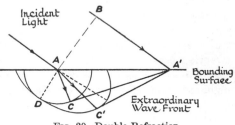

FIG. 20. Double Refraction.

AD, the optic axis of the crystal, is here taken as in the plane of the paper. $A'C$ is now the ordinary wave front, and $A'C'$ the extraordinary wave front, in the crystal. Naturally, these two sets of waves give rise to two images, and the familiar double appearance of an object seen through a crystal of Iceland spar results.

It thus appears that a crystal of Iceland spar possesses the property of resolving a light wave into two components quite independently of frequency (since both images are practically uncoloured). In one of these components the waves follow the ordinary laws of refraction and are propagated with the same velocity in all directions. In the other component, the velocity of the wave is found to depend upon the direction of propagation. This phenomenon can be at once explained on the wave theory of light by assuming that the light vector or " vibration " is transverse, that is, perpendicular to the direction of propagation ; for if this " vibration " is longitudinal there can be no possible asymmetry of the wave about the direction of propagation, but with a spherical transverse wave it is at once apparent that asymmetry exists, and that the vector at any point of the wave can be resolved into two components respectively in and perpendicular to any given plane containing the line of propagation. If this plane is supposed to be that containing the optic axis of the crystal at the centre of the wave (the plane of the paper in Fig. 20), then it may well be that when the vector is perpendicular to the paper the velocity of propagation is the same, whatever be the angle between the optic axis and the direction of propagation (angle DAC), while when the vector is in this plane the velocity of propagation varies with this angle (angle DAC'). This supposition provides an adequate explanation of double refraction if the law of variation is assumed to be

$$c^{-2} = c_o{}^{-2} \cos^2 \theta + c_e{}^{-2} \sin^2 \theta,$$

where θ is the angle DAC', c_e the maximum velocity of the extraordinary wave, and c_o the velocity of the ordinary wave. c/c_e is known as the extraordinary index of refraction of the crystal, n_e.

Polarised Light: The Nicol Prism—In ordinary light, as would naturally be expected, the light vectors are oriented without any regularity, and in the waves set up by any source they are distributed in all directions in the plane of the wave surface. Inside a doubly refracting crystal, however, matters are different, and each of the two wave surfaces contains only waves in which the vectors are in a single direction. Such waves are said to be " plane-polarised," and as light of this nature is much used in some branches of photometry it is desirable to consider its properties in further detail.

Unless special means are adopted to isolate one of these sets of waves the two will naturally be mixed on emerging once more into the air, and the property of polarisation will be lost. The simplest method of isolation is that used in the Nicol prism, which consists of a rhomb of Iceland spar of the form shown in Fig. 21a, where AB' is about three times AD. This is cut in half by a plane passing through AA' and parallel to BD, and the two pieces are then cemented together by Canada balsam. Now the refractive index of the balsam is greater than n_e and less than n_o, so that if the light is incident sufficiently obliquely on the balsam surface the ordinary ray will be

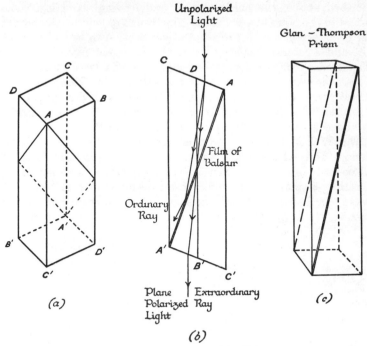

FIG. 21. The Nicol Polarising Prism.

stopped by total reflection (see p. 21), while the extraordinary ray will be transmitted (Fig. 21b). It results that light passing through the Nicol prism will be plane polarised.

If this light is transmitted through a second Nicol, its intensity will depend on the relative directions in space of the optic axes of the two prisms, for, clearly, if the second Nicol can only transmit light for which the vector is in the direction OA (Fig. 22), and if the light falling upon it is plane polarised so that the vector is in the direction OB and of amplitude a, then this light will be divided into two components, of which one will be stopped and the other transmitted. The latter portion will have its vector in the direction OA and, by the law of resolution of vectors, will have amplitude $a \cos \theta$, so that the intensity of the light passing through both prisms varies as $\cos^2 \theta$, where θ is the angle between the optic axes.

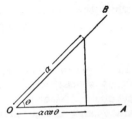

FIG. 22. The Law of Resolution of a Vector.

It is to be noticed that in the ordinary form of Nicol prism described above, the light entering and leaving the prism is not normal to the bounding surfaces. The results of this are the production of a certain amount of elliptic polarisation in the transmitted light and a lateral displacement of the emergent ray. The latter difficulty may be avoided by trimming the end faces of the prism so that they are perpendicular to the sides. This form of Nicol is generally used in photometric instruments in which the prism has to be rotated [18]. One form of prism in which the elliptic polarisation is avoided is the Glan-Thompson form shown in Fig. 21c.

The Wollaston Prism—Another device used for separating the ordinary and extraordinary waves is known as Wollaston's prism, and consists of two prisms of calcspar, or quartz (another doubly refracting crystal, which differs from Iceland spar in that c_e is always less than c_o), cut with the same angle and cemented together as shown in Fig. 23. The optic axis of the left-hand prism is parallel

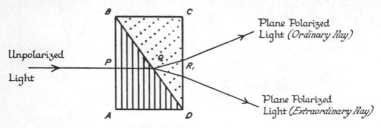

FIG. 23. The Wollaston Prism.

to AB, while in the right-hand prism it is perpendicular to the paper. It results that if light is incident normally on the face AB, no separation of the waves takes place ; the ordinary wave traverses the path PQ with velocity c_o, while the extraordinary wave traverses it with velocity c_e. On arrival at Q separation takes place and the ordinary wave traverses the second prism as an extraordinary wave, while the extraordinary becomes an ordinary wave. If α denotes the angle of the prism and δ the deviation of the extraordinary wave at Q, $\sin(\alpha+\delta)/\sin\alpha = c_e/c_o$, and if r_1 is the angle of emergence at R_1, $\sin\delta/\sin r_1 = c_e/c$, so that, since δ is small, $\sin r_1 = (n_o - n_e)\tan\alpha$. The angle between the two wave envelopes is, therefore, $2r_1$.

It is clear that if the two waves thus separated are caused to pass through a Nicol prism, the intensity of one on emergence will be $\sin^2\theta$, and of the other $\cos^2\theta$, since they are polarised in mutually perpendicular planes. It results that the ratio of the intensities will vary as $\tan^2\theta$.

It is to be noted that, since the waves suffer deviation in passing through a Wollaston prism, a certain amount of colour analysis takes place.

In Rochon's prism this effect is avoided by having the prism *ABD* cut so that the optic axis is parallel to *AD* (see Fig. 23). The ordinary ray then passes through *BCD* without deviation (and therefore without dispersion), the extraordinary ray being deviated as in the Wollaston prism.

Polarisation by Reflection—The light reflected from the surface of a glass plate is polarised to an extent depending on the angle of incidence (see Chapter V, p. 157). The polarisation should theoretically be complete when $i = \tan^{-1} n$, where n is the refractive index of the glass [19]. Reflection at the polarising angle i has been used for polarising a beam of light in some of the older forms of polarisation photometers (see p. 3).

The Electromagnetic Theory of Light—In what has gone before, the adequacy of the wave theory of light to explain the results of experiment has been demonstrated, but so far no hypothesis has been suggested as to the nature of the vector involved in the propagation of the waves other than that this vector is perpendicular to the direction of propagation.

In 1864 Maxwell proposed the electromagnetic theory, in which the light waves are assumed to be of the same nature as the electromagnetic waves set up by a rapidly oscillating electric current, such as that obtained in the spark discharge. The identical velocity of the two sets of waves was experimentally established, and the theory is now universally accepted, as it not only is in agreement with the known phenomena, particularly as regards polarisation, but it connects the waves of heat and light with those produced by electrical means, and it has enabled phenomena in the realm of electricity to be related to other phenomena, before apparently quite independent, in the realm of optics.

Maxwell's hypothesis rests on his conception that, just as stress in an elastic solid produces a strain, that is, a displacement of matter, so in dielectrics the application of electric force produces a displacement of some unknown character, and this is identical in all its effects with an electric current. The observed laws connecting an electric current and a magnetic field are then sufficient to enable him to deduce the three following equations connecting the components of current u, v, w with those of magnetic force α, β, γ :

$$4\pi u = dy/dy - d\beta/dz, \text{ etc.} \quad \ldots\ldots\ldots\ldots\ldots\ldots(\text{i})$$

and three of the following form, where μ is the magnetic permeability and P, Q, R are the components of electric force :

$$-\mu\dot{\alpha} = dR/dy - dQ/dz, \text{ etc.} \quad \ldots\ldots\ldots\ldots\ldots\ldots(\text{ii})$$

But for a non-conductor whose specific inductive capacity is K

$$u = (K/4\pi) \, dP/dt, \text{ etc.}$$

Hence (i) and (ii) may be combined to give the following three equations :

$$K\dot{P} = d\gamma/dy - d\beta/dz, \text{ etc. } \quad \ldots\ldots\ldots\ldots\ldots\ldots(iii)$$

Further, differentiating the three equations of (ii) with respect to x, y and z respectively, and adding

$$\frac{d}{dt}\left(\frac{d\alpha}{dx} + \frac{d\beta}{dy} + \frac{d\gamma}{dz}\right) = 0,$$

so that $\dfrac{d\alpha}{dx} + \dfrac{d\beta}{dy} + \dfrac{d\gamma}{dz}$ is a constant with respect to time, and this constant is zero, since that is its value for the undisturbed medium.

Differentiating (ii) with respect to time, and eliminating P, Q and R by means of (iii), the following equations therefore result :

$$K\mu\ddot{\alpha} = \nabla^2\alpha, \text{ etc. } [20].$$

Similarly, the following equations may be obtained :

$$K\mu\ddot{P} = \nabla^2 P, \text{ etc.}$$

These two sets of equations show that both the magnetic and electric forces are propagated with a velocity $1/\sqrt{K\mu}$. For *vacuo* and (very nearly) for all dielectrics $\mu = 1$. K *in vacuo* is equal to 1 on the electrostatic system of units, but $1/m^2$ in the electromagnetic system if m is the number of electrostatic units of quantity of electricity in one electromagnetic unit. Hence the velocity of propagation is equal to this ratio m, which experiment shows to be approximately 3×10^{10} c.g.s. units. This is the same as the velocity of light within experimental error, and the remarkable verification of this theoretical deduction from Maxwell's hypothesis is one of the triumphs of the electromagnetic theory of light. It is to be noted that Maxwell's theory does not afford any explanation of the nature of light. " It only expresses one unknown quantity (light) in terms of other unknown quantities (magnetic and electric disturbances), but magnetic and electric stresses are capable of experimental investigation, while the elastic properties of the medium through which, according to the older theory, light was propagated could only be surmised from the supposed analogy with the elastic properties of material media. Hence it is not surprising that the electromagnetic equations more correctly represent the actual phenomena. Whatever changes be introduced in future in our ideas of the nature of light, the one great achievement of Maxwell, the proof of the identity of luminous and electromagnetic disturbances, will never be overthrown " [21].

The application of the theory to the phenomena of reflection, refraction, polarisation, etc., cannot be dealt with here. It will be found in any modern book on the theory of optics [22].

Theory of the Light Radiating Mechanism—For light waves, the origin of the " disturbance " or " oscillation " referred to above lies within the atom of the light-giving body and the atomic structure which it is convenient to picture when considering the radiation of energy from an atom will be discussed more fully in a later section of this chapter. Meanwhile the various different kinds of light emission may be conveniently classified by the way in which the atoms are kept supplied with energy to replace that which they radiate.

When the source of this energy is chemical action, as in the case of the oxidation of phosphorus, or the chemical action which is probably the cause of the glow emitted by light-giving animals such as the firefly, the emission is called *chemi-luminescence* or, in the latter case, sometimes *bio-luminescence*. When the energy is supplied by light or ultra-violet radiation which has been absorbed by a substance, the re-emission of this absorbed energy may be called *photo-luminescence* : if the emission is immediate and ceases directly the source of energy is removed it is termed *fluorescence* ; if it dies away gradually after the removal of the exciting radiation, it is called *phosphorescence*. When electrical energy is converted directly into light, as in a luminous discharge in a gas, the phenomenon may be called *electro-luminescence*, although this term is most generally used in a restricted sense to denote the emission of light when certain substances are subjected to an alternating electric field. Finally, if a body emits light solely because it is at a high temperature, the emission is called *temperature radiation* or *thermo-luminescence*.

Pure Temperature Radiation—It is first necessary to define what is generally known in the study of radiation as a " black body " or " full radiator " (or sometimes a " total " or " complete " radiator or, for a reason which will appear later, a " Planckian radiator "). Every body in nature reflects some of the radiation which is incident upon it and most bodies are selective in the extent to which they reflect radiation of different frequencies. A truly black body is one that totally absorbs light of all frequencies and reflects none of the radiation that falls upon it. Such a body must, from thermo-dynamical considerations which will now be described briefly, emit radiation in which the energy contained in any frequency range is connected with that frequency and with the temperature of the radiator according to a law which can be deduced from theoretical considerations. No such body exists in nature, but the desired condition is fulfilled to a very close approximation for a small opening in a hollow body with absorbing walls. For this reason a full radiator is sometimes known as a "cavity radiator". The practical form of full radiator used as a standard of light will be described in Chapter VI.

Kirchhoff's Law—To Balfour Stewart and G. Kirchhoff is due the principle that the ratio of the radiation emitted to that absorbed by any body in thermal equilibrium depends only on the temperature of the body and that this ratio is equal to the emission of a black body (for which the absorption is perfect) at the same temperature. This is a consequence of the experimental fact that a number of bodies within an impervious enclosure which contains no source of heat will ultimately acquire the same temperature ; but the law enunciated above goes further in that it applies to radiation for any given frequency and not merely to the total radiation ; for it is possible to imagine a hollow enclosure of uniform temperature in which a portion of the wall is composed of a body whose absorption factor (ratio of energy absorbed to that received) for radiation of wave-length λ is α_λ and whose emission at the temperature of the enclosure is η_λ while the remainder of the wall is perfectly black, and therefore has absorption unity and emission E_λ. The absorption and emission of all parts of the wall must balance, or the temperature equilibrium will be disturbed. Hence, if A_λ is the energy of wave-length λ received by all parts of the wall, for the non-black portion $\alpha_\lambda A_\lambda = \eta_\lambda$, and for the black portion $A_\lambda = E_\lambda$. Hence $\alpha_\lambda E_\lambda = \eta_\lambda$ [(23)].

Three deductions follow at once from this result. (i) If α_λ is determined for any body, and the relation between E_λ and temperature is known, η_λ is found. (ii) Since α_λ cannot be greater than unity, no body can radiate more at any frequency than can a black body at the same temperature. Thus a more suitable name for a black body is that of " full radiator." (iii) In a hollow enclosure of uniform temperature, the radiation proceeding by reflection and emission from any part of the inner surface is the same as that emitted by a black body at the same temperature ; for suppose it receives A_λ then it absorbs $\alpha_\lambda A_\lambda$, and since it emits η_λ and when the temperature is constant, emission and absorption must be equal, it follows that $\eta_\lambda = \alpha_\lambda A_\lambda$. Thus $A_\lambda = E_\lambda$, and, again, since it must return, by reflection and emission, as much as it receives, it follows that the emission is E_λ. Thus, as already mentioned, since no surface behaves exactly as a black body at all temperatures, the best approach to a full radiator is a very small opening in a uniformly heated enclosure.

Other consequences of this law are (i) good reflectors are bad absorbers, and consequently bad radiators ; (ii) transparent bodies, being bad absorbers, are also bad radiators. This is well shown by the bright appearance of a spot of opaque material on a piece of heated glass.

The Pressure of Radiation—It is now easy to show on thermo-dynamic principles that the pressure exerted by a succession of plane waves incident normally at a perfectly black surface is equal to the energy contained per unit volume of the space in which these waves are travelling; for, considering a cylinder of unit cross-section whose axis is normal to the oncoming waves, if this cylinder is closed at one end by a black surface, the energy of the waves will be completely absorbed, and the amount so absorbed in time t will be Ect, where E is the energy contained per unit volume of the cylinder. If now the black surface is displaced a distance δx along the axis of the cylinder, then the work done by the movement of the surface is equal to the energy contained in the increased volume δx of the cylinder, i.e. to $E\,\delta x$, so that if p is the pressure upon the surface, $p\,\delta x = E\,\delta x$, or $p = E$.

As an example of the magnitude of p, it may be said that since the energy flow from the sun at the earth's surface (the solar constant) is $1\cdot3 \times 10^6$ ergs/sec. per sq. cm. [24], this energy is contained in 3×10^{10} c.c. Hence the value of E in this case is 4×10^{-5} ergs per c.c., i.e. $p = 4 \times 10^{-5}$ dynes per sq. cm., or 4×10^{-8} gm. weight (approx.).

The Stefan-Boltzmann Law—From Kirchhoff's law and the result obtained above it is possible to deduce the law connecting the radiation from a black body and the absolute temperature T of the body; for, considering a closed cylinder of length x and unit cross-section, the walls of which are totally black and impervious to radiation, if the energy per unit volume is E, the pressure on the end wall will be $\frac{1}{3}E$, since the contained energy must be due to waves travelling in *all* directions, and the average resolved component in one of three mutually perpendicular directions will, therefore, be $\frac{1}{3}E$. Now suppose the end of the cylinder to move inwards by a distance δx, and the energy density to be changed by an amount δE in consequence, then (a) the work done by the movement will be $\frac{1}{3}E\,\delta x$, and (b) the change in the amount of energy contained within the cylinder will be $Ex - (E - \delta E)(x - \delta x)$. Thus, by the principle of the conservation of energy,

$$\tfrac{1}{3}E\,\delta x + Ex - (E - \delta E)(x - \delta x) = 0,$$

or $\frac{4}{3}E\,\delta x + x\delta E = 0$, or E varies as $x^{-\frac{4}{3}}$. Further, if the change of temperature produced by the adiabatic volume change δx is equal to δT, then by Carnot's principle

$$\tfrac{1}{3}E\,\delta x/Ex = -\delta T/T,$$

so that T varies as $x^{-\frac{1}{3}}$, i.e. E varies as T^4 [25].

Since a black body absorbs all the radiation that it receives, it follows from Kirchhoff's law that the radiation in equilibrium with it is proportional to that which it emits from unit area in unit time. Hence the energy of the radiation emitted by a black body at a temperature T is equal to σT^4, where σ is a constant known as the

Stefan-Boltzmann constant, after the names of the discoverers of the law, the first by experimental work, the second from theoretical principles. The value of σ is $5 \cdot 670 \times 10^{-5}$ erg cm.$^{-2}$ deg.$^{-4}$ sec.$^{-1}$ [26].

Wien's Displacement Law [27]—In the Stefan-Boltzmann law the energy is treated as a whole, and its partition among waves of different frequencies is not considered. It now becomes necessary to find out in what manner this partition is affected by a change in T. It can readily be proved that the effect of the compression δx above considered is to increase the frequencies of the radiation enclosed in the cylinder; for if a series of plane waves of length λ and frequency ν strike a surface moving with opposing velocity u, $\nu\lambda = c$ initially, and after reflection $\nu' = \nu + 2u/\lambda$ [28]. Hence

$$\delta\nu = 2u/\lambda = 2u\nu/c.$$

Now $u = -\dot{x}$, and the number of reflections per second in the cylinder is $\tfrac{1}{3}c/2x$, for again, since the waves within the cylinder are travelling in all directions, the average resolved component in one direction is $\tfrac{1}{3}c$. Hence the rate of increase of frequency is the increase per reflection multiplied by the number of reflections per second, i.e.

$$\dot{\nu} = (2\nu u/c)(c/6x) = -(\nu/3x)\,\dot{x} \; ;$$

$$\therefore \quad d\nu/dx = -\nu/3x \quad \text{or} \quad \nu \text{ varies as } x^{-\frac{1}{3}}.$$

Now let the energy per unit volume of the radiation in the range of frequency from ν to $(\nu + \delta\nu)$ be denoted by $E_\nu\,\delta\nu$, where E_ν may be called the energy density per unit range at frequency ν. When the contraction δx takes place, $E_\nu\,\delta\nu$ varies as $x^{-\frac{4}{3}}$ (see above). But ν, and therefore $\delta\nu$, varies as $x^{-\frac{1}{3}}$, so that E_ν varies as x^{-1}, i.e. as T^3.

This shows that, comparing E_ν in two full radiations at different temperatures, and taking *corresponding* frequencies given by $T/\nu = \text{constant}$, E_ν is proportional to the cube of the temperature. This relation may then be written

$$E_\nu = T^3\phi(T/\nu), \quad \text{or} \quad E_\nu = \nu^3\psi(T/\nu).$$

This is known as Wien's displacement law, and it leads readily to an expression for $\nu_{\max}$, the frequency of maximum energy at any temperature, for, at any given temperature, when E_ν is a maximum E_ν/T^3 is a maximum, so that $\phi(T/\nu_{\max})$, and therefore $(T/\nu_{\max})$, is a constant independent of temperature.

These expressions in ν may be readily transformed to the corresponding expressions in λ by using the transformation $\nu = c/\lambda$, so that $\delta\nu = -(c/\lambda^2)\,\delta\lambda$. Since $E_\lambda\,\delta\lambda = E_\nu\,\delta\nu$, the expression for E_λ becomes $E_\nu(c/\lambda^2) = (c^4/\lambda^5)\psi(T\lambda/c)$, which may be written

$$E_\lambda = \lambda^{-5}F(\lambda T).$$

Here E_λ is the energy per unit range at wave-length λ. The constant

$\lambda_{max}T$, often written A_λ, may be shown to have the value 0·2898 cm. deg. [29].

The Quantum Theory—In the above expression for the energy at any frequency the form of the function written as $F(\lambda T)$ is left quite undetermined. The further consideration of the form of this function depends fundamentally on the manner in which energy can be exchanged. In the classical mechanics it was assumed that energy could be exchanged between molecules, etc., in any amount, and not necessarily in definite multiples of an indivisible unit or " quantum ". On this assumption it can be shown [30] that the probability that any one molecule, regarded as a " seat of energy," will have energy lying between the values E and $E + \delta E$ (the probability being defined as the fraction of the total time for which its energy lies between these limits) is $(1/kT) e^{-E/kT} \delta E$, where k if the atomic gas constant, i.e. the ordinary gas constant R divided by the number of molecules in the gramme-molecule [31]. It follows that the *average* energy in such a seat is $\int_0^\infty (E/kT) e^{-E/kT} dE$, or simply kT. This is the theorem known as the " equipartition of energy," and the result just quoted can readily be shown to lead to the value $8\pi R\lambda T$ for $F(\lambda T)$ in Wien's displacement law which thus becomes $E_\lambda = 8\pi RT\lambda^{-4}$. This is known as the Rayleigh-Jeans form.

It will be at once apparent that if λ is very small, E_λ will be very large and in consequence it must be concluded that the energy density in the ether becomes infinitely great for waves of infinite frequency, a conclusion which is quite untenable. To overcome this difficulty, Planck in 1901 [32] proposed a new hypothesis in which he assumed that energy could only be radiated in multiples of some indivisible amount ϵ which varied directly as the frequency of the radiation. If this hypothesis be granted, a seat of energy can only gain or lose by multiples of this quantity, and it can then be shown that the probability of such a seat having energy $p\epsilon$ is $e^{-p\epsilon/kT}/(1 - e^{-\epsilon/kT})$, and that therefore the average energy is $\epsilon/(e^{\epsilon k/T} - 1)$. This is the partition formula resulting from Planck's theory and it will be recognised at once that, since when the frequency is very large $p\epsilon$ is also very large, the average energy at very high frequencies is very small, a result to be expected *a priori*, since the probability of an exchange of energy taking place at all is small if it can only be carried out by the transfer of a large quantity of energy. The factor of proportionality between ϵ and ν is h, so that $\epsilon = h\nu$ and thus the average energy of a system of seats of energy will be, not kT, but $h\nu(e^{h\nu/kT} - 1)$. The constant h is called Planck's elementary quantum and has the value $6·625 \times 10^{-27}$ erg sec. [33].

Wien's displacement law now becomes $E = 8\pi hc\lambda^{-5}/(e^{hc/k\lambda T} - 1)$

and this expression gives the energy per cubic cm. inside a radiating enclosure. The energy radiated in a given time from an aperture in the enclosure is, per sq. cm., one quarter of the energy passing through one cubic cm. of the enclosure in the same time. Thus the energy radiated from an aperture one sq. cm. in area is equal to the above expression multiplied by $c/4$ [34]. In other words the energy radiated per second per unit range of wave-length at wave-length λ from one sq. cm. of a full radiator is equal to $2\pi hc^2\lambda^{-5}/(e^{hc/k\lambda T} - 1)$ which may also be written $c_1\lambda^{-5}/(e^{c_2/\lambda T} - 1)$ where c_1 and c_2 are constants respectively equal to $2\pi hc^2$ and hc/k [35]. The present accepted values for these constants are, respectively, $3 \cdot 74 \times 10^{-5}$ erg cm.² sec.⁻¹ and $1 \cdot 4380$ cm. degrees [36].

The curve calculated by this formula for the energy distribution in the spectrum of a full radiator is in remarkable agreement with that found by experiment. This agreement is exhibited by the curve of Fig. 24, which shows the energy emitted within unit wave-length interval by a full radiator at a temperature of 1596° K. The line

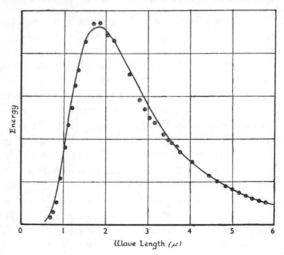

FIG. 24. Planck's Formula. Circles indicate observations ; full line represents the computed curve. (See *Bureau of Standards, Bull.*, 13, 1916, p. 476.)

gives the distribution calculated according to Planck's formula, using the value of c_2 quoted above, while the circles indicate observed points [37]. The scale of ordinates is arbitrary.

A formula similar to Planck's was derived some years earlier by W. Wien [38]. Wien's radiation formula is $c_1\lambda^{-5}e^{-c_2/\lambda T}$ and is sometimes used instead of Planck's formula as it is much more convenient for calculation and the difference between the two is comparatively small except for large values of λT, e.g. it is less than one per cent so long as λT does not exceed about 3000 μ deg. (see Appendix V) [39].

Non-Selective and Selective Radiation : Emissivity—The full radiator is used as a basis for measuring the energy at different regions of the spectrum given by other incandescent bodies. It has been said already that no surface is perfectly black and it follows that the radiation from such a body as, for example, a tungsten filament may follow a different law. It has already been pointed out that no body can emit more temperature radiation than a full radiator at the same temperature. The ratio of the energy at any wave-length emitted by a body to that emitted by an equal area of a full radiator at the same temperature is known as the " emissivity " of the body for that wave-length, e_λ. It will be seen that by Kirchhoff's law (p. 36) e_λ is equal to the absorption factor of the body, α_λ. If e_λ is the same for all wave-lengths the radiation from the body clearly has the same spectral distribution as that of a full radiator at the same temperature. Such a body is known as a " non-selective radiator," or sometimes a " grey body " by analogy with the term black body. Any radiator for which e_λ is not the same at all wave-lengths is said to be " selective " and all known bodies radiating in the open are selective to a greater or less extent. The nearest approach to a black body is carbon.

The sun, as viewed from the earth's surface, may be regarded as an approximation to a full radiator at a temperature of about 5400° K., though the composition of sunlight differs somewhat from that of the light given by a full radiator, owing to unequal absorptions at different frequencies during its passage through our atmosphere (see Appendix IX).

For slightly selective bodies, such as platinum, iron or copper oxide, tungsten, carbon, etc., it has been found that the emission is very approximately given by the generalised formulae $E = \sigma' T^n$ and $E_\lambda = c_1' \lambda^{-(n+1)} e^{-c_2'/\lambda T}$ where σ', n, c_1' and c_2' are constants of the selective body [40]. Generally, however, it is necessary to use tables giving the emissivity of the body at different temperatures for two or more wave-lengths [41].

In the case of some selective radiators the energy distribution in the visible region of the spectrum approximates closely to that of a full radiator, i.e. these bodies are non-selective as regards their visible radiation. An important example is tungsten for which the emissivity is not quite constant but decreases slightly with increase of wave-length. This decrease is regular and, as a result, the energy distribution in the visible spectrum is nearly the same as that of a full radiator at a slightly higher temperature [42]. When the energy distribution of the radiation in the visible spectrum from an incandescent body is similar to that of a full radiator at some temperature T_c, this temperature is known as the " colour temperature " of the body. T_c is generally somewhat different from the true temperature of the body. It will be considered further in Chapters X and XI.

Full Radiation and Selective Radiation—The above description of the principal characteristics of temperature radiation may be sum- marised briefly as follows :

(1) For a full radiator the *emission at any frequency* increases continually with the temperature, but the higher frequencies increase most rapidly, so that the frequency of *maximum emission* shifts continually towards the blue as the temperature rises. The area of the curve within the limits of the visible spectrum is but a small portion of the whole, so that the energy radiated as light is only a small portion of the total energy emission. This proportion increases, however, as the temperature rises, until it reaches a maximum of about 44 per cent at a temperature of slightly over 6,700° K [43].

(2) For a selective radiator the *emission at every frequency* is less than that of a full radiator at the same temperature, but the *dis- tribution* is different, so that the proportion of the total emission which is within the limits of the visible spectrum may be higher than for a full radiator at the same temperature. For some selective radiators the energy distribution in the *visible* part of the spectrum is approximately the same as that in the spectrum of a full radiator.

Radiation produced Electrically—It will have been observed that all that has been said above applies only to temperature radiation, but, as already mentioned, there are types of radiators which do not depend upon temperature to supply the energy which they emit and to which, therefore, the above conclusions do not apply. One of the most important of these types of radiator is that in which the source of the energy is electrical, and as this type of radiator is of considerable importance in light production, it will be considered briefly here.

It has long been known that when an electric discharge is passed through certain gases contained in a tube at low pressure they glow with a light which is characteristic of the gas and of the conditions under which the discharge takes place. The well-known Geissler tubes are examples of this, and modern gas discharge lamps are applications of the same principle to practical lighting. For these sources the energy distribution departs very markedly from that of a full radiator, and, in fact, it is found that the radiation is concen- trated, to a greater or less extent according to circumstances, in the neighbourhood of certain definite frequencies, which are well-marked characteristics of the nature of the gas, insomuch that the gases present in a tube can generally be named at once from inspection of the energy distribution curve under electric discharge. The striking fact of the invariability of these frequencies is the basis of spectrum analysis.

The Structure of the Atom—The phenomena which have just been described depend upon the behaviour of the system of particles of which the atom is composed. This behaviour can only be completely expressed in mathematical language, using the theory of wave-mechanics, but a mental picture which can serve as a useful basis for discussing all the simpler phenomena of light production is provided by the Rutherford-Bohr atom model. In this model the atom is pictured as consisting of a central positively charged nucleus with a surrounding planetary system of electrons (elementary negative charges) rotating in certain orbits. Such a system is unstable unless Planck's quantum hypothesis is adopted, for otherwise the energy of rotation of the electrons would gradually be radiated and the orbit would, in consequence, become smaller and smaller so that the electron would finally be merged in the nucleus. Further, the alteration of orbit would cause a gradual change of frequency in the emitted radiation, and this is certainly contrary to observation. It is therefore assumed that an electron can only gain or lose energy in amounts equal to an integral number of quanta and that unless this happens it continues to move in a fixed orbit and no energy is radiated. Further, it is supposed that only certain orbits are possible, each corresponding to a fixed amount of energy. It follows that passage from one orbit to another results in the emission or absorption of radiation of a certain definite frequency ν such that $h\nu$ is equal to the difference between the respective amounts of energy in the two orbits. The energy is frequently expressed, not in ergs but in terms of the work done in moving an electron through a potential difference of one volt in an electric field. Since the electronic charge is $4 \cdot 803 \times 10^{-10}$ electrostatic units and one volt is $1/299 \cdot 8$ e.s.u. of potential, the work done is $1 \cdot 602 \times 10^{-12}$ ergs. This unit is known as the electron-volt.

Line Spectra—When an electric discharge takes place in a gas or vapour, some of the atoms lose an electron and are said to be " ionised ". These, and the freed electrons, move under the influence of the electric field and collide with other atoms which may in consequence be ionised in their turn or may, on the other hand, merely suffer a disturbance of the electronic system. In the latter case one or more of the electrons are moved out of their normal orbits and the atom is said to be " excited." The return of such an electron to normality is accompanied by the emission of energy and, on the theory outlined above, this can only take place at one or more frequencies dictated by the values of energy possible for the electron. Thus the radiation from the atoms of a given substance is confined to a limited number of frequencies and if this radiation is analysed by means of a prism or grating (see p. 27) the spectrum is found to consist of a number of lines. Such a line spectrum is characteristic of the nature of the radiating atom and so, as mentioned earlier, it provides a sure and very sensitive method of identification.

The form of diagram shown in Fig. 25 is often used to represent graphically the various levels of energy possible for the different electrons in an atom and the frequencies corresponding to transitions from one level to another. The horizontal lines show the energy levels on the left-hand vertical scale of electron-volts, while on the right of the diagram is a scale of wave-numbers. It will be seen that the difference of wave-number between any two levels, when multiplied by hc, is equal to the difference between the energies (in ergs) at the two levels (1 el. volt corresponds to a wave-number of 8066 cm.$^{-1}$ or a wave-length of 1239·8$m\mu$ [36]) and thus the wavelength corresponding to a transition between any two energy levels is equal to the reciprocal of the difference of wave-number between those two levels. Fig. 25 shows a simplified energy-level diagram for

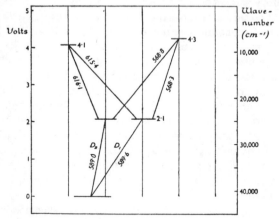

Fig. 25. Simplified Energy-Level Diagram for Sodium.

sodium. The two lines marked D_1 and D_2 represent the familiar pair having wave-lengths of 589·6 $m\mu$ and 589·0 $m\mu$ respectively. The upper limit of the diagram, corresponding to 5·1 electron-volts, represents the energy which is just sufficient to remove an electron from the atom altogether; in other words, it is the " ionisation potential " in volts.

Band Spectra—In addition to the line spectra described in the previous paragraphs there are also band spectra due to molecules containing more than one atom. Such a spectrum, when resolved by a dispersion system of sufficiently high power, is seen to consist of one or more groups of fine lines very close together, the intervals between the lines in a group becoming smaller and smaller as one end is approached. The end line, which may be at either the long or the short wave extremity of the group, is termed the "head of the band".

Spectra which show no marked discontinuities are known as "continuous" spectra; the spectrum of a full radiator is a particular case. Such a spectrum contains radiation of all frequencies.

Photo-Luminescence—The third class of light emission is that which takes place when radiation within a suitable range of frequencies is absorbed by a body, most frequently a solid, of special composition. The body then emits light in a continuous spectrum which often covers a wide range of frequencies. Substances which cease to emit immediately the exciting radiation is cut off are called "fluorescent"; others in which the emission dies away gradually, sometimes over a period of several hours, are called "phosphorescent." Many luminescent substances show both effects.

The mechanism of photo-luminescence is complicated and is still not well understood though attempts have been made to explain it on the energy-band theory of solid insulators, a theory which postulates a system somewhat analogous to the system of energy levels in the theory of atomic structure [44]. There are, however, certain general principles which may be regarded as well established.

Any one luminescent material responds only to radiation of frequencies lying between certain well-defined limits and the effect

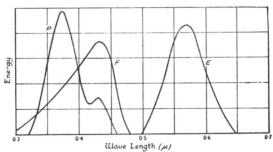

FIG. 26. Excitation and Emission Curves.
P—Excitation Curve for Phosphorescence.
F—Excitation Curve for Fluorescence.
E—Emission Curve.

produced by a given amount of energy depends on the frequency in a manner which can be shown in the form of an "excitation curve" like those in Fig. 26. For a given frequency the effect is proportional to the energy absorbed. When the same substance shows both fluorescence and phosphorescence there are separate excitation curves for the two classes of luminescence as shown in Fig. 26. The spectral distribution of the emitted radiation is independent of the frequency of the exciting radiation. The excitation curve always lies on the higher frequency side of the emission curve (though there is occasionally a slight overlap) and this fact is expressed in Stokes' law which states that, in photo-luminescence, the frequency of the emitted radiation is always less than that of the incident radiation [45].

Although some substances exhibit photo-luminescence when in the pure state, most of the more important ones consist of an inorganic salt (generally crystalline) into which quite a small quantity of some other substance has been introduced in solid solution. This substance is called an " activator " and its nature and concentration in the " matrix " of the principal salt, as well as the process by which it is introduced, determine the intensity and spectral distribution of the emitted radiation [46].

Receptors of Radiation—The foregoing sections of this chapter have dealt mainly with the phenomena of the propagation and emission of radiation and of the theories put forward to explain these phenomena. This section will deal with the reception of radiation. For the spectral region which is of primary interest in photometry, viz. the visible range, the most important receptor is the eye. Its behaviour will therefore be described in some detail in the next chapter. A quite different kind of receptor, which is now very widely used in photometric measurements of all kinds, is the photocell and this will be described in Chapter IV.

For total energy measurements and for certain classes of spectral energy determinations, the most useful form of receptor is one in which the energy is converted into heat so that the receptor is completely non-selective in its response [47]. The thermopile is the instru-

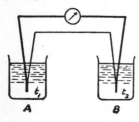

FIG. 27. The Thermo-electric Circuit.

ment of this kind which is most generally employed. It depends on the fact that when a circuit is composed of two dissimilar metals, a difference of temperature between the two junctions of these metals in the circuit results in a flow of electricity round the circuit. For example, if junction A (Fig. 27) is at the temperature t_1, while junction B is at temperature t_2, an electromotive force of $\alpha(t_1 - t_2)$ volts is generated in the circuit, so that if a galvanometer is included, and the total resistance of the circuit (including the galvanometer) is R ohms, a current of $\alpha(t_1 - t_2)/R$ ampères will flow round the circuit. The value of α, the thermo-electric power, depends on the two metals forming the junction.

In Boys' radiomicrometer, shown in Fig. 28 [48], the thermo-junction T is connected to the small loop of wire which forms the

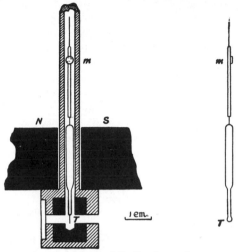

FIG. 28. Boys' Radiomicrometer.

circuit and is suspended by means of a fine quartz fibre between the poles of a magnet N, S, so that when radiation is absorbed by T the difference in temperature produced causes a current in the loop, and therefore a deflection due to the magnet. This deflection is measured by means of the small mirror m, which reflects a beam of light as in the case of an ordinary galvanometer.

In the thermopile the thermo-electric voltage is increased by employing a number of thermo-junctions in series. A form of thermopile used for spectral distribution measurements in shown in Fig. 29. It is linear and consists of a row of metal squares to

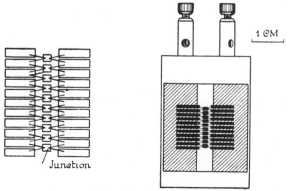

FIG. 29. The Linear Thermopile.

each of which is soldered a pair of thermo-junctions, frequently of bismuth and silver for which the thermo-electric power is about 7×10^{-5} volt/deg. The breadth of the exposed surface is reduced as much as possible in order that it may occupy only a narrow strip of the spectrum when used in the eyepiece of a spectrometer. It is generally enclosed in a cell of the form shown on the right of the figure. The front surface of the thermopile is covered with a matt black coating of soot or platinum black to obtain as complete an absorption as possible of the incident radiation, and the heat capacity is a minimum, so that a given amount of energy produces the greatest possible rise of temperature [49]. A considerable increase in sensitivity (up to as much as 80 microvolts per microwatt of incident energy) can be obtained by mounting a linear thermopile in a high vacuum [50].

Another non-selective receptor is the bolometer which depends on the fact that when radiation is absorbed by a long and very thin strip of blackened platinum (see Fig. 30) its electrical resistance is

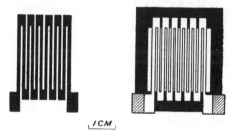

$\lfloor$ 1 CM $\rfloor$

FIG. 30. The Bolometer.

altered owing to the rise in temperature which takes place [51]. If, therefore, four bolometers are arranged in a Wheatstone bridge, as shown in Fig. 31, a very sensitive means for measuring the difference in the radiation reaching the two sides of the apparatus is obtained.

Bolometers

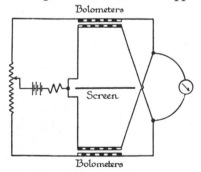

Bolometers

FIG. 31. The Measurement of Radiation by the Bolometer.

SELECTED BIBLIOGRAPHY

(A) WAVE THEORY AND GENERAL OPTICS

P. Drude. *Lehrbuch der Optik.* (Hirzel, Leipzig, *1912.*) (Eng. trans. by C. H. Mann and R. A. Millikan. Longmans, *1902.*)

T. Preston. *Theory of Light.* (Macmillan, *1928.*)

R. A. Houstoun. *Treatise on Light.* (Longmans, *1938.*)

Glazebrook's *Dictionary of Applied Physics.* (Macmillan, *1923.*) Vol. IV

A. Schuster and J. W. Nicholson. *Introduction to the Theory of Optics.* (Arnold, *1924.*)

(B) RADIATION THEORY

P. Drude. (See above.)

T. Preston. (See above.)

J. H. Poynting and J. J. Thomson. *Text-book of Physics : Heat.* (Griffin, *1952.*)

C. G. Darwin. Article " Radiation Theory " in *Dict. Appl. Phys.*, Vol. IV.

W. W. Coblentz. Article " Radiation " in *Dict. Appl. Phys.*, Vol. IV.

(C) QUANTUM THEORY

M. Planck. *Theorie der Wärmestrahlung.* (Barth, Leipzig, *1913.*) (Eng. trans. by M. Masius, Blakiston, Philadelphia, *1914.*)

J. H. Jeans. *Dynamical Theory of Gases.* (Cambridge University Press, *1925.*)

C. G. Darwin. Article " Quantum Theory " in *Dict. Appl. Phys.*, Vol. IV.

G. Birtwistle. *The Quantum Theory of the Atom.* (Cambridge University Press, *1926.*)

O. Lodge. Deama C., 10, 1000, pp. 10, 00, 110 and 011.

(D) WAVE MECHANICS

A. Haas. *Wave Mechanics and the New Quantum Theory.* (Eng. trans. by L. W. Codd. Constable, *1928.*)

R. W. Gurney. *Elementary Quantum Mechanics.* (Cambridge Univ. Press, *1934.*)

W. Heitler. *Elementary Wave Mechanics.* (Clarendon Press, *1945.*)

(E) ATOMIC SPECTRA AND ELECTRO-LUMINESCENCE

H. Cotton. *Electric Discharge Lamps.* (Chapman & Hall, *1946.*)

G. Herzberg. *Atomic Spectra and Atomic Structure.* (Dover, New York, *1944.*)

H. E. White. *Introduction to Atomic Spectra.* (McGraw-Hill, *1934.*)

(F) FLUORESCENCE

E. Hirschlaff. *Fluorescence and Phosphorescence.* (Methuen, *1938.*)

P. Pringsheim and M. Vogel. *Luminescence of Liquids and Solids.* (Interscience, New York, *1946.*)

E. J. Bowen. *Chemical Aspects of Light.* (Clarendon Press, *1946.*)

GENERAL

G. Castelfranchi. *Recent Advances in Atomic Physics.* (Eng. trans. by W. S. Stiles and J. W. T. Walsh. Churchill, *1932.*)

REFERENCES

1. Kaye and Laby's *Tables of Physical and Chemical Constants* (12th ed.). See also L. Essen, Nature, 165, *1950*, p. 582 ; E. Bergstrand, Arkiv för Fysik, 2, *1950*, p. 119. For a summary, see R. Dupeyrat, J. de Phys., 19, *1958*, p. 557.

2. For an excellent historical account of the wave theory, see H. Buckley, *A Short History of Physics* (Methuen, *1927*) and T. Preston, *Theory of Light*, Chapter I et al. See also C. Huyghens, *Traité de la Lumière* (Leyden, *1690*, reprinted, Paris, *1920* ; Eng. trans. by S. P. Thompson, Macmillan, *1912.*), Chap. I.
For a condensed general treatment of the theory, see Rayleigh, Article on " Wave Theory of Light," in Encyc. Brit. (9th edit.), vol. 24, or *Collected Works*, vol. 3, p. 47.

3. A frequency of 10^{12} vibrations per second is sometimes termed a frequency of 1 fresnel.

4. On the relation between colour names and frequency see, e.g. H. P. J. Verbeek and M. L. Bazen, Physica, 2, *1935*, p. 380.

5. This term is here used generally to indicate the degree of departure from normal conditions which is brought about by the propagation of an " ether wave " through a point.

6. The wave-length of a certain homogeneous light (*Cd* red) in air at 15° C. and 760 mm. pressure with $g = 980 \cdot 67$ is $6438 \cdot 4696 \times 10^{-10}$ metres. (Int. Solar Union, Trans., 2, *1907*, p. 20 ; J. E. Sears and H. Barrell, Phil. Trans., 233, *1934*, p. 143.) (The radiation is assumed to be emitted in a gravitational field of the value stated.)

7. Huyghens' construction. See T. Preston, *Theory of Light*, § 66 ; A. Schuster and J. W. Nicholson, *Theory of Optics*, § 18 ; A. Fresnel, *Oeuvres* (Paris, *1866*), vol. I, p. 28 and vol. II, p. 80.

8. H. Fizeau and L. Breguet. C.R., 30, *1850*, pp. 562 and 771.
L. Foucault. Ann. de Chim., 41, *1854*, p. 129.
A. A. Michelson. Astronomical Papers for the American Ephemeris and Nautical Almanac, 2, *1885*, p. 237 ; B. A. Report, *1884*, p. 654 ; Am. J. Sci., 31, *1886*, p. 62.
See also Rayleigh, Nature, 24, *1881*, p. 382 and 25, *1881*, p. 52 ; A. Schuster, *ibid.*, 33, *1886*, p. 439.

9. For the sake of clearness this requirement has not been met in the figure.

10. See, e.g., A. E. Conrady, Article on " Optics of the Microscope " in *Dict. Appl. Phys.*, vol. IV, p. 202 and R. A. Sampson, " The Telescope," *ibid.*, p. 842.

11. On the real character of the vibration in a composite light see, e.g., R. W. Wood, *Physical Optics* (Macmillan Co., *1919*), Chapter XXIII ; also A. Schuster, Phil. Mag., 37, *1894*, p. 509 and 7, *1904*, p. 1 ; J. S. Ames, Astrophys. J., 22, *1905*, p. 76 ; Rayleigh, Phil. Mag., 10, *1905*, p. 401 ; J. Larmor, *ibid.*, p. 574.

12. In this way it has been shown that the velocities *in vacuo* of blue and yellow lights do not differ by as much as 1 part in 10^{10}. See various authors, C.R., 146, *1908*, pp. 266, 383, 570 and 1254 ; 147, *1908*, p. 170 ; H. Shapley, Nat. Acad. Sci., Proc., 9, *1923*, p. 386.

13. See, e.g. G. A. Hoadley, Illum. Eng. Soc. N.Y., Trans., 7, *1912*, p. 288 ; R. A. Houstoun, *Light and Colour* (Longmans, Green, *1923*), p. 22.

14. A. Schuster and J. W. Nicholson. *Theory of Optics*, § 29.

15. See, e.g. P. Drude, *Lehrbuch d. Optik*, Part II, Chapter III ; A. Schuster and J. W. Nicholson, *Theory of Optics*, § 47.

16. See T. Preston, *Theory of Light*, Chapter VIII. Fig. 19 is distorted for the sake of clearness.

17. See, e.g. C. Huyghens, *Traité de la Lumière*, Chapter V or T. Preston, *Theory of Light*, § 178.

18. On the modifications of the Nicol prism, see K. Feussner, Z.f.I., 4, *1884*, p. 41 ; S. P. Thompson, Opt. Convention, *1905*, p. 216 ; A. B. Dale, article " Polarized Light, etc.," in *Dict. Appl. Phys.*, Vol. IV, p. 490. See also F. E. Wright, Opt. Soc. Am., J., 2, *1919*, p. 93 ; W. Grosse, Central-Ztg. f. Opt. u. Mech., 8, *1887*, p. 157 ; *Die gebräuchlichen Polarizationprismen* (Clausthal, *1887*).

19. See T. Preston, *Theory of Light*, §§ 166 and 171.

20. ∇^2 is written for the operator $-\left(\dfrac{d^2}{dx^2} + \dfrac{d^2}{dy^2} + \dfrac{d^2}{dz^2} \right)$.

21. A. Schuster and J. W. Nicholson. *Theory of Optics*, § 141 *et seq.*

22. See Bibliography.

23. A similar line of argument shows that E_λ cannot depend on the nature of the black body, for so long as $\alpha_\lambda = 1$, $\eta_\lambda = E_\lambda$.

24. C. G. Abbot *et al.* Smithsonian Misc. Coll., 77, No. 3, *1925.*

25. T is here expressed on the absolute (thermodynamic) scale.

26. See note (36) and F. E. Hoare, Phil. Mag., 14, *1932*, p. 445.

27. For a simple discussion of this law see E. Buckingham, Bureau of Standards, Bull., 8, *1912*, p. 545 ; Phil. Mag., 23, *1912*, p. 920.

28. For the number of waves reaching the moving surface in unit time is increased by u/λ owing to the advance of the surface, and since the reflected waves arise from a surface advancing with velocity u, the number reaching a stationary point per unit time is again increased in the ratio $c/(c - u)$, i.e. $\nu/(\nu - u/\lambda)$.

29. See note (36).

30. J. H. Jeans. *Dynamical Theory of Gases* (Camb. Univ. Press, *1925*), § 485.

31. The value of k is $1\cdot3805 \times 10^{-16}$ erg deg.$^{-1}$.

32. M. Planck, Deut. Phys. Gesell., Verh., 2, *1900*, pp. 202 and 237 ; Ann. d. Phys., 4, *1901*, p. 553.

33. See note (36).

34. This may be proved most clearly by making use of the conceptions of luminous flux and luminous intensity described in Chapter V. The flux is the rate of passage of the energy, i.e. it is $E_\lambda \times c$ and since it is uniformly distributed as regards direction the intensity is $E_\lambda c/4\pi$. This is therefore the luminous intensity of unit area of the aperture in the direction of its normal, so that the flux it emits in all directions is equal to $\pi(E_\lambda c/4\pi)$, i.e. $E_\lambda \times (c/4)$.

35. For a fuller account of the derivation of this expression, see the works quoted in the bibliography at the end of this chapter.

36. The values adopted for the constants mentioned in this chapter are those given in Kaye and Laby's *Tables of Physical and Chemical Constants* (12th ed.). (See also F. Benford, Gen. El. Rev., 46, *1943*, pp. 377 and 433.) The value of c_2 is that adopted internationally in 1948 (Comité Int. des Poids et Mesures, Procès-verbaux, 21, *1948*, p. 135) ; the value of hc/k is, however, $1\cdot4388$ cm. deg.

It should be noted that the constants c_1 and c_2 are connected with the constant of Stefan's law and the constant $A_\lambda (= T\lambda_{max})$ by the following relationships :

(i) $\sigma T^4 = \displaystyle\int_0^\infty c_1\lambda^{-5} (e^{c_2/\lambda T} - 1)^{-1} d\lambda$.

The expression under the integral sign may be expanded by the binomial theorem and when integrated term by term it gives :

$$\sigma T^4 = 6(c_1 T^4/c_2^4) \sum_1^\infty n^{-4} \quad \text{or} \quad \sigma = \pi^4 c_1/15 c_2^4.$$

(ii) Since the equation $dE_\lambda/d\lambda = 0$ gives the value of λ_{max} it follows that if β be put for c_2/A_λ then $5(e^{-\beta} - 1) + \beta = 0$, which gives $\beta = 4\cdot965114$.

37. W. W. Coblentz. Bureau of Standards, Bull., 13, *1916-17*, p. 476. See also O. Lummer and E. Pringsheim, Deut. Phys. Gesell., Verh., 1, *1899*, p. 215

38. Ann. d. Phys., 58, *1896*, p. 662.

39. R. S. Estey. Opt. Soc. Am., J., 28, *1938*, p. 293.
E. Q. Adams. *Ibid.*, 37, *1947*, p. 695.
See also P. Moon and D. E. Spencer, J. Appl. Phys., 17, *1946*, p. 506.

40. See, e.g. F. Paschen, Ann. d. Phys., 58, *1896*, p. 455 and 60, *1897*, p. 662 ; O. Lummer and E. Pringsheim, Deut. Phys. Gesell., Verh., 1, *1899*, p. 215 ; W. W. Coblentz, Bureau of Standards, Bull., 5, *1909*, p. 339 ; E. P. Hyde, Astrophys. J., 36, *1912*, p. 89.
The values of n are, for carbon 4 to $4\cdot1$, for tungsten 6 and for platinum 5 to $5\cdot4$.

41. See, e.g. W. W. Coblentz, Int. Critical Tables, Vol. 5, p. 242 ; L. S. Ornstein, Physica, 3, *1936*, p. 561 (tungsten) ; R. E. Stephens, Opt. Soc. Am., J., 29, *1939*, p. 158 (platinum).

42. W. E. Forsythe. Opt. Soc. Am., J., 7, *1923*, p. 1115.
W. E. Forsythe and A. G. Worthing. Astrophys. J., 61, *1925*, p. 146.

43. W. E. Forsythe. Opt. Soc. Am., J., 16, *1928*, p. 307.

44. See, e.g. J. T. Randall, Roy. Soc. Arts, J., 85, *1937*, p. 354 ; R. P. Johnson, Opt. Soc. Am., J., 29, *1939*, p. 387 ; Various authors, Faraday Soc., Trans., 35, *1939*, esp. pp. 69, 74 and 101 ; J. T. Randall and M. H. F. Wilkins, Roy. Soc., Proc., 184, *1945*, pp. 365 and 390.

See also the books listed in section (*F*) of the bibliography at the end of this chapter.

45. G. G. Stokes. Phil. Trans., 142, *1852*, p. 463.

46. See, e.g. P. Lenard, " Phosphoreszenz u. Fluoreszenz," Vol. 23 of *Handbuch d. Experimentalphysik* (Leipzig, *1928*) ; H. Rupp, *Die Leuchtmassen u. ihre Verwendung* (Borntraeger, Berlin, *1937*) ; J. W. Ryde, Illum. Eng. Soc. Lond., Trans., 3, *1938*, p. 114.

47. T. Preston. *Theory of Heat*, Chapter VI, Sect. IV.

J. H. Poynting and J. J. Thomson. *Heat*, p. 221.

W. W. Coblentz. Bureau of Standards, Bull., 4, *1907-8*, p. 391 ; 9, *1913*, p. 7 ; 11, *1914-15*, p. 131 ; 12, *1915-16*, p. 503 ; 17, *1922*, pp. 187 and 725.

48. C. V. Boys. Article " Radio-Micrometer " in *Dict. Appl. Phys.*, Vol. III, p. 720.

49. W. W. Coblentz. *Loc. cit.*, note (47).

P. A. and W. G. Leighton. J. Phys. Chem., 36, *1932*, p. 1882.

50. W. J. H. Moll and H. C. Burger. Phil. Mag., 50, *1925*, p. 618.

H. C. Burger and P. H. van Cittert. Z. f. Phys., 66, *1930*, p. 210.

See also E. Picker and G. Rudinger, Z. f. techn. Phys., 16, *1935*, p. 265 ; H. Theissing, Phys. Z., 38, *1937*, p. 557.

51. S. P. Langley. Am. Acad. Arts and Sci., Proc., 16, *1881*, p. 342.

T. Preston. *Theory of Heat*, § 272.

O. Lummer and F. Kurlbaum. Ann. d. Phys., 46, *1892*, p. 204 ; Electrician, 34, *1894*, pp. 168 and 192.

E. A. Griffiths. Article, " Radiant Heat, etc." in *Dict. Appl. Phys.*, Vol. III, p. 706.

CHAPTER III

THE EYE AND VISION

In spite of the now extensive use of physical methods of photometry, visual methods are still employed in many of the less routine types of photometric measurement. Even in physical photometry the aim is to obtain an instrument which will give results in accord with those which would be obtained visually, so that it may be said that the eye remains, and must remain, the ultimate judge of light, both qualitatively and quantitatively. Certainly the spectroscope makes it possible to distinguish between light waves of neighbouring frequencies which are quite indistinguishable by visual means, and similarly a sensitive photocell can detect differences of intensity which the eye cannot perceive ; but for all ordinary photometric purposes the eye is the final arbiter, and it is, therefore, necessary in any treatment of the subject of photometry to give some description of the construction and mode of working of this organ of special sense [1].

The Structure of the Eye—The eye is an ellipsoidal, nearly globular organ about 23 mm. in diameter. It will be seen from the section given in Fig. 32 that it is enclosed in a tough outer skin (S) termed

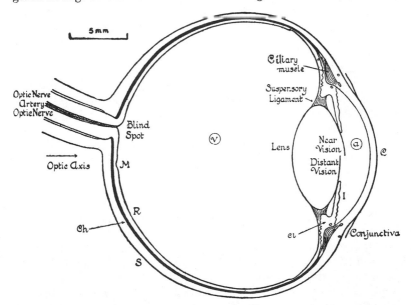

Fig. 32. Human Right Eye divided nearly Horizontally through the Middle.

the *sclera*, which is opaque to light. This is replaced at the front of the eye, however, by a transparent cartilaginous lamina termed the *cornea* (C), which is more convex than the sclera. Under the sclera is a second coat, termed the *choroid* (Ch), which is much more delicate and consists almost entirely of blood vessels and nerves. It is black, being covered with a layer of black pigment which prevents interference with vision due to stray light reflected from its surface. In front of the eye this coat is replaced by the *iris* (I), which forms an adjustable shutter capable of considerable alteration of aperture (from about 2 to 8 mm. diameter) according to the brightness of the field of view. The innermost coating of the eye, the *retina* (R), is an extremely delicate film, consisting chiefly of nerve cells and nerve fibres which spread out from the *optic nerve* over the whole of the anterior surface of the choroid.

The interior of the eye contains three transparent media. The first, which fills the space between the cornea and the crystalline lens, is nearly pure water, and is termed the *aqueous humour* (a). This has a refractive index of 1·336. Just behind the iris is a lens formed of a substance resembling very thick jelly or soft gristle, and having a refractive index of 1·45 at the centre, changing to 1·41 at the edge, so that the effective index is 1·437 [2]. This lens is double convex, with the posterior surface of greater curvature than the anterior. It is suspended in its place by a set of little bands proceeding from the choroid coat, and known as the *ciliary processes* (ci). The whole of the space enclosed between the crystalline lens and the retina is filled with a thin jelly termed the *vitreous humour* (v), which has a refractive index of 1·338.

Pupillary Aperture—The action of the iris in stopping down the lens under the influence of a bright light is very rapid and completely automatic. While it undoubtedly reduces the discomfort experienced when the retina is suddenly exposed to excessive radiation, there is some evidence that the purpose of the contraction is, at any rate in part, for the improvement of the retinal image by reducing the aberrations of the lens system and increasing the depth of focus [3]. Naturally a limit is set to the improvement possible in this direction because the apparent brightness of the image is reduced as the pupil is made smaller and it is therefore only when the field brightness is moderately high that the iris is able, by stopping down, to improve the retinal image without decreasing its apparent brightness below that required for easy vision. In support of this suggestion it may be mentioned that the iris also contracts when the eye is looking at very close objects (within about 30 cm.), a condition for which the greater depth of focus given by a lens of small aperture is most advantageous. The variation of pupillary diameter with brightness of the field of view is shown in Fig. 33 which represents the behaviour of the average eye [4]. This variation has been made the basis of a suggested method of absolute photometry [5].

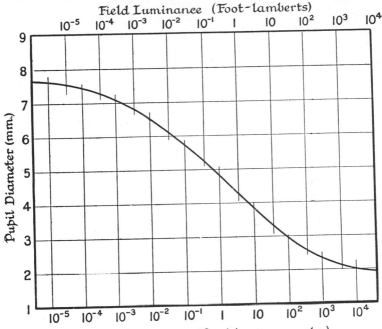

FIG. 33. The Relation between Pupillary Diameter and Field Luminance. *

Accommodation—When an object is looked at, light from the various parts of it enters the eye at the cornea and is refracted by the various media so that an image of the object is formed on the surface of the retina. Now the position of an image produced by any optical device depends upon the relative positions of the object and of the refracting elements of the device (see p. 23). Hence, in order to produce a sharρ image on the retina for objects at different distances, the refracting elements of the eye must be adjusted to suit the position of the particular object viewed at any given instant. This adjustment, termed *accommodation*, is achieved almost involuntarily by means of the ciliary muscles, which produce a slight change in both the position and the curvature of the crystalline lens. The effect of these changes was described in the last chapter (p. 23).

When light enters the eye at the cornea, it undergoes refraction at the surface, according to equation (i), p. 23, with r_1 put equal

* The term *luminance* is used in preference to *brightness* when referring to the physical stimulus rather than the sensation (see p. 75).

to 7·8 mm. It undergoes further similar changes due to refraction at the surfaces separating the various media within the eye, and finally an image is formed on the retina if the crystalline lens is properly adjusted in position and curvature.

When the eye is at rest it is focused for distant objects [6], and the retina is at the position of the principal focus of the refracting system, viz. 15·9 mm. behind the posterior surface of the lens, while the radii of curvature of the front and back surfaces of the lens are respectively 10 mm. and 6 mm. When the eye is accommodated for seeing near objects, these radii are changed to 6 and 5·5 mm. respectively, while the front surface of the lens is shifted outward by about 0·4 mm. The limit of accommodation is generally for objects about 25 cm. from the eye for comfortable vision, although nearer objects may be accommodated with a certain amount of strain. The power of accommodation generally decreases with age.

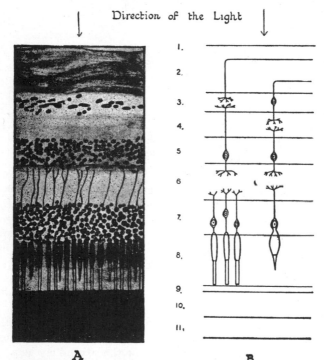

Direction of the Light

A   B

Fig. 34. Section through the Retina. (A) Semi-diagrammatic. (B) Schematic only.

1. Inner limiting membrane.
2. Nerve layer.
3. Layer of ganglion cells.
4. Inner reticular (molecular) layer.
5. Inner nuclear layer.

6. Outer reticular layer.
7. Outer nuclear layer.
8. Layer of rods and cones.
9. Pigment epithelium.
10. Choroid.   11. Sclera.

The Mechanism of Vision—So far a description has been given of the optical method by which objects seen form an image on the retina [7]. The mechanism by which this image is conveyed to the brain so as to produce the impression of sight is still obscure. The retina consists of a large number of elements (of the order of 120 millions in all) of two kinds, termed respectively the *rods* and the *cones*. These are shown diagrammatically in Fig. 34, where a magnified section through a portion of the retinal layer is also given.

The rods contain a peculiar photochemically sensitive substance which when unilluminated is of a deep reddish-purple colour, but which is rapidly bleached on exposure to light. This fluid is called the visual purple, and there seems to be no doubt that it is in some way connected with the phenomenon of vision [8]. It has been found, for instance, that its absorption and its bleaching rate for radiation of different frequencies are proportional to the sensitivity of the dark-adapted human eye to light of those frequencies (see p. 81).

The rods and cones are not equally distributed over the surface of the retina. There is at a point slightly below and inwards of the optical centre of the eye an area, some 2 to 2·5 mm. in diameter, over which there are very few rods at all, while the cones are very fine in structure and very closely packed (see Fig. 35). It is significant that it is at this region of the retina (termed the *macula lutea*, M in Fig. 32) that vision is most clear, and the muscles control-

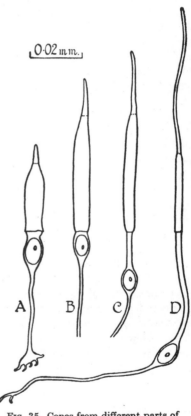

Fig. 35. Cones from different parts of the Retina.

A. Equatorial Region.
B. Periphery of Macula.
C. Margin of Fovea.
D. Centre of Fovea.

ling the eyeballs always move these so that the image of an object, or part of an object, to which attention is being directed at any instant is formed in each eye on the very centre of the macula, where vision is at its sharpest. This centre, termed the *fovea centralis*, is about 0·5 sq. mm. in area, and consists almost entirely of cones of extremely fine structure, rods being completely absent over an area about 0·5 mm. in diameter in the very centre of the macula. Over the other parts of the retina the proportion of rods to cones steadily increases with distance from the macula, and in the eye as a whole they preponderate in a ratio of about 20 to 1[9]. The diameter of the cones varies from 0·001 to 0·003 mm. at the fovea. This is approximately the same as the image size of the smallest detail of an object which the optical system of the eye is capable of resolving, for on account of interference of the light waves, two points cannot be distinguished if their angular separation at the eye is less than about $1·2\lambda/D$, where D is the diameter of the pupil [10]. Since the refractive index of the vitreous humour is 1·34 the corresponding angular separation within the eye is $1·2\lambda/1·34D$ and the distance of the retina from the second nodal point of the lens system being about 17 mm. this formula gives $17(1·2/1·34D)$ as the distance apart on the retina of the images of two just resolvable points. For $D = 4$ mm. and $\lambda = 0·55\mu$ this distance is approximately 0·002 mm. It is probable that two points cannot be resolved unless their images on the retina are separated by at least one less stimulated cone [11].

The rods and the cones are very different in their behaviour to light. There is no colour sensation associated with the rods, but on the other hand the threshold of their response to light is very much below that of the cones which cease to respond when the luminance (see p. 75) of the object, seen through the natural pupil, is less than about 10^{-3} to 3×10^{-4} candelas per sq. metre (see p. 136) [12].

Under ordinary conditions of brightness, cone vision is predominant and the fineness of the cone structure in the fovea gives the wealth of detail normally associated with vision at the centre of the field of view when the brightness is adequate. The main function of the peripheral portions of the retina under these conditions is to give a more or less vague impression of the field surrounding the object looked at and so to act as a " finder " for the macula which, by means of very slight and rapid movements of the eyeball, is made to explore the whole of the image, just as the finger may be made to feel over a surface in order to obtain an accurate knowledge of its details. The full-line curve in Fig. 36 shows how the visual acuity varies across the retina on a line passing through the fovea [13]. At low values of brightness, for which vision is by means of the rods alone, and therefore colourless, the visual acuity becomes more or less the same all over the retina (except at the fovea where it is less than elsewhere) as shown by the broken line in Fig. 36.

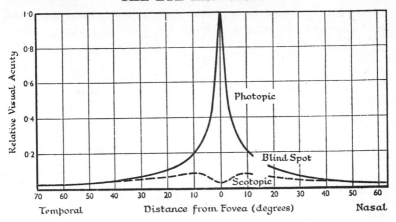

FIG. 36. Variation of Visual Acuity across the Retina.

There is one important respect in which the optical system of the eye does not behave like an ordinary lens system. When an image is formed by a lens, the illumination of the image is proportional to the area of the lens exposed to light from the object (see p. 151). In the case of the eye, however, it has been found that when the pupil is expanded the outer parts of the lens are much less efficient than the more central parts as far as the apparent brightness of the retinal image at or near the fovea is concerned. In fact the contribution to the apparent brightness which is made by the light passing through one square millimetre of the lens at a distance of 3 mm. from the centre is less than half as great as that made by one square milli- metre at or near the centre. This phenomenon is known as the Stiles-Crawford effect [14] and it has to be allowed for whenever the brightness of a foveal retinal image is significant ; results obtained with an expanded natural pupil cannot be reduced to those which would be obtained with an artificial pupil one sq. mm. in area by simply dividing by the pupillary area in sq. mm. The table below shows the relative apparent brightness of the retinal image for differ- ent pupillary diameters, the value for a pupil (natural or artificial) of 2 mm. diameter being taken as unity [15]. The magnitude of the effect is nearly independent of the colour of the light [16].

It should be noted that the Stiles-Crawford effect only occurs in cone vision [17]. For parafoveal vision at low values of brightness, when only the rods are operative, as well as in all cases where the pupil, natural or artificial, is less than about 2 to 2·5 mm. in diameter, the apparent brightness of the retinal image is proportional to its illumination. This is sometimes expressed in terms of a unit known as the troland, which is the retinal illumination produced by a surface having a luminance of one candela per sq. metre when the pupil area is one sq. millimetre [18].

THE STILES-CRAWFORD EFFECT

Pupil Diam. (mm.)	Relative Area	Relative Apparent Brightness
2	1	1·00
3	2·25	2·14
4	4	3·53
5	6·25	4·99
6	9	6·34
7	12·25	7·46
8	16	8·26

The eye is called upon to perform tasks of many different kinds of which the most important, as far as photometric measurement is concerned, are (a) the perception of small differences in the brightness of adjacent surfaces of either the same or different colours, (b) the perception of small differences of colour between equally bright adjacent surfaces and (c) the perception of flicker due to rapid alternations of surfaces which are slightly different in brightness and which may be of the same or of different colours. The visual sensitivities which do not involve colour differences will be discussed first and of these sensitivity to small differences of brightness is the most important in photometry.

Sensitivity to Brightness Difference—The general law of sensation enunciated by E. H. Weber in 1834 [19] and known as Weber's law is that the increase of stimulus which is necessary to produce a just perceptible increment of sensation bears a constant ratio to the whole stimulus. The application of this law to vision was studied by G. T. Fechner [20] who, on the hypothesis that the least perceptible increase of stimulus always gave rise to the same increment of sensation, deduced [21] that the change of sensation produced by a change of stimulus from B_1 to B_2 was proportional to $\log B_2 - \log B_1$; in other words, the sensation increased in arithmetical progression as the stimulus increased in geometrical progression. This is known as Fechner's law, or sometimes the Weber-Fechner law, but as there is no scale for the measurement of sensation, Fechner's hypothesis cannot be verified and to that extent the law rests on an insecure foundation [22]. On the other hand, this extension of Weber's law to supra-liminal increments gives the valuable rule that, to the eye, increases or decreases of luminance which are in the same ratio appear as approximately equal steps [23]. For this and other reasons curves showing visual sensitivities as functions of luminance are often conveniently plotted to a logarithmic scale of this quantity.

It has been suggested that, on account of the Weber-Fechner law, when photometric observations are averaged, the mean should be the geometric (antilog of mean log) instead of the arithmetic [24]. The difference is generally too small, however, to be appreciable.

The ratio of the least perceptible increase of luminance, δB, to the luminance B is often known as *Fechner's fraction*. Although constant, to a close approximation, over the range of brightness commonly met with under ordinary conditions of lighting, it increases progressively as B is reduced from about 10 candelas per sq. metre downwards (for monocular vision) and is greatly affected by the conditions of observation. There have been several careful determinations of it over a wide range of values of B [25]. The quantity δB has been referred to as the brightness difference theshold (B.D.T.) or the liminal brightness increment, more strictly called the liminal increment of luminance.

Fig. 37 shows the general form of the curve connecting δB and B. The abscissae are values of field luminance in candelas per sq. metre or in foot-lamberts on a logarithmic scale, while the ordinates are values of Fechner's fraction, i.e. the liminal increment of luminance expressed as a fraction of the field luminance. The upper curve shows the results found by König and Brodhun [26] for monocular vision through an artificial pupil, with the values of B recomputed so that they refer to luminance viewed through the natural pupil instead of to luminance viewed through an artificial pupil 1 sq. mm. in area. No allowance has been made for the Stiles-Crawford effect since it is inappreciable at any value of luminance above 10 cd/m^2 (when the natural pupil is small) or below about $10^{-3}cd/m^2$ (when rod vision predominates). The lower curve refers to binocular vision with an extended field of view [27]. Both these curves refer to white light but the values obtained for other colours are very much the same as long as B represents the *equivalent luminance* (see p. 74).

The curves shown in Fig. 37 can only be regarded as typical, owing to differences between individual eyes and, what is even more important, the effect of the viewing conditions. In particular, it has been found that the liminal increment of luminance is increased, especially at low values of field brightness, by reduction in the angular size of the field of view [28]. Conversely, when the test field is small the liminal increment is reduced, and therefore the precision of a brightness match increased, by using an extended surround of a brightness which is approximately equal to, or a little less than that of the test field [29]. This is clearly of importance in the design of a photometer head in which, for one reason or another, a small field of

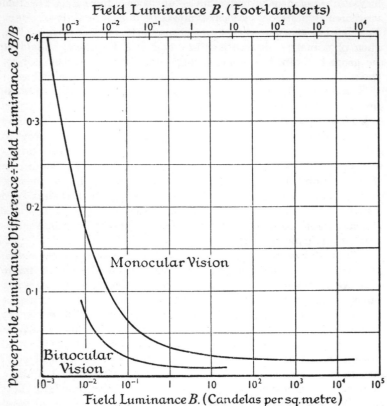

FIG. 37. The Variation of Fechner's Fraction with Field Luminance.

view has to be used. When there is no such restriction, the most important fact is that as the value of B falls below about 3 candelas per sq. metre, $\delta B/B$ becomes rapidly greater. It follows that in any photometer which depends on a visual judgement of equality of brightness, the value of B (after allowing for losses in the optical system if one is used) should be kept well above this critical value; it has been found, in fact, that the precision of setting increases with increase of the field luminance to a value at least ten times as great as that just stated [30]. Further, these values are for a field of view seen through the natural pupil which, under these conditions, is about 4 mm. in diameter. If a smaller artificial pupil is used, the field luminance should be increased accordingly, in order to retain the necessary apparent brightness for the retinal image. If, for any reason, a considerably lower field luminance is unavoidable, the sensitivity of the photometer is correspondingly diminished.

Contrast or Spatial Induction—The term " contrast " has been used in many different ways to express dissimilarity, either of brightness or of colour, between different parts of a field of view. Frequently attempts have been made to define it as some particular function of δB and B. This practice is very likely to lead to confusion and should be avoided ; when any particular function is intended, that function should be explicitly stated [31] and the word contrast should only be used quite generally. This is the more desirable since the same word has also been used as a name for the effect which may be noticed when contiguous parts of the retina are very differently stimulated as, for example, when viewing a grey patch on a uniform background of very different brightness. Such a patch appears darker when viewed on a white background than it does when viewed on a black background. There is a corresponding colour effect and a bright red patch, for instance, on a darker colourless background appears to be surrounded with a faint halo of a colour which is not far removed from its complementary green [32]. A better term for this phenomenon is *spatial induction* [33]. It has formed the basis of suggested methods of heterochromatic photometry [34] and the colour effect probably helps to increase the sensitivity of a colour match between adjacent parts of a field of view [35].

Visual Acuity—The ability to distinguish fineness of detail is very closely connected with the brightness of the object viewed and the contrast which the details present to the eye.

Individuals, as might be expected, show wide variations and the form of the test object has a considerable influence on the results obtained [36]. The object now generally adopted is the Landolt broken circle shown in Fig. 38. The width of the gap is equal to the breadth of the black line and visual acuity is defined as the reciprocal of the angle, in minutes of arc, subtended at the eye by this gap when it just ceases to be detectable. For

Fig. 38. The Landolt Test Object for Visual Acuity.

example, if the gap in a Landolt circle with a 1 mm. line just ceases to be distinguishable at a distance of d millimetres from the eye the visual acuity is $\pi d/10800 = 0 \cdot 00029d$.

Fig. 39 shows how the visual acuity increases with the field luminance for white light when the natural pupil is used [37]. Visual acuity is higher with binocular than with monocular vision [38]. The effect of colour of the light has not been studied very systematically but there is some evidence that acuity is higher with a monochromatic than with a composite light [39]. The matter is complicated by the increase of acuity brought about by pupillary contraction. As in the case of sensitivity to brightness difference, it has been found that visual acuity is at its best when the general brightness of the surroundings is approximately the same as, or slightly less than that of the test field. It falls off rapidly as the surrounds

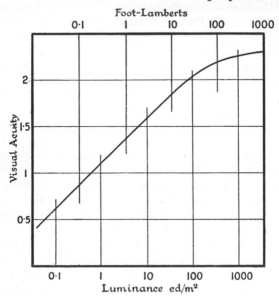

FIG. 39. The Variation of Visual Acuity with Luminance.

become brighter and much more slowly as they become darker than this [40].

Forms of photometer for the rough measurement of illumination have been based on the relation between field brightness and the ability to distinguish fine detail (see p. 291 and note (15), p. 413).

Adaptation—The enormous range of sensitivity possessed by the eye can readily be appreciated from the fact that the ratio of the luminance of objects seen by direct sunlight to that of the same objects seen by starlight on a clear moonless night is at least 10 million to 1. So perfect is the adaptation over a very extensive part of this range that alterations of luminance in a ratio of as much as 10 to 1 or even 100 to 1 are often scarcely noticed if the change is not too sudden, for a book may be read quite as comfortably in a room which is well lighted by artificial means as under the open sky at noon on a fine day in winter when the luminance of the pages is at least 100 times as great. This power of adapting itself to different conditions of lighting makes the eye useless for the direct measurement of luminous energy and in all practical visual photometry the eye is relied upon solely for the determination of the *equality* of two adjacent fields as regards either brightness or contrast [41].

The process of adaptation, although so thorough, takes some little time for its completion, and the inability to see detail when the eye is brought suddenly from bright to dark surroundings, or vice versa, is evidence of this. In some way the retina alters its sensitivity to suit the order of brightness of the images formed on it. The mechanism by which this is accomplished is not yet understood [42], but it is a phenomenon of great importance in photometry, especially when surfaces of exceptionally low brightness are being compared [43], because, as adaptation proceeds, the liminal increment of luminance falls, at first rapidly and then more slowly, to the value appropriate to the new conditions [44].

The course of adaptation to complete darkness after gazing at a bright field of view follows a curve of the type shown in Fig. 40 [45], in which each ordinate shows the minimum luminance just perceptible after the eye has been in complete darkness for the time indicated by the corresponding abscissa. The first part of the curve represents the combined recovery of both rods and cones, while the part following the discontinuity shows the slower rod adaptation.

The curve in Fig. 40 represents the mean of a number of observers originally adapted to a luminance of about 700 ft.-lamberts

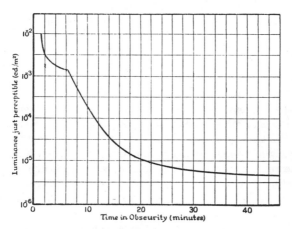

FIG. 40. The Course of Dark Adaptation.

(2400 cd/m^2). Reduction of the luminance to which the eye is originally exposed somewhat alters the shape of the adaptation curve and causes a general shift to the left and downwards, as would be expected, but the final value reached after long continued adaptation is not affected. The speed and extent of adaptation tend to become less with advancing age [46].

The minimum perceptible luminance after adaptation is complete, often referred to as the threshold of vision, will be considered in a later section of this chapter (see p. 77).

The opposite process of adaptation from conditions of darkness to a field of view of high brightness is very much more rapid and its course is correspondingly more difficult to determine [47]. It is however, of comparatively little importance in photometry.

The condition of light-adaptation is generally referred to as " photopic " and, similarly, adaptation to very low values of brightness is known as the " scotopic " condition of the eye [48].

Glare—The term glare is used to denote the various effects produced on the eye by the presence in the field of view of some object which is either very bright compared with the general level of brightness to which the eye is adapted, or much brighter than the object upon which attention has to be concentrated. These effects may be such as to impair visual performance, for instance by reducing the sensitivity of the eye to small differences of brightness, but without causing any sense of discomfort. On the other hand there may be a sense of unease or distraction without, for a time at least, any lowering of the standard of visual performance. More frequently, however, the two types of effect, sometimes known as *disability glare* and *discomfort glare* respectively [49], are experienced together.

The reduction of visual performance produced by any condition of disability glare can be measured and it has been found [50] that the effect of a bright object in the field of view, as far as sensitivity to brightness difference is concerned, is to raise the adaptation level of the eye by an amount which is proportional to E/θ^n, where E is the illumination produced by the glaring source at the observer's eye and θ is the angular distance of the source from the object of attention ; the value of n is approximately 2. If θ is in degrees, the factor of proportionality is about 30 when E is in lumens per sq. foot and the adaptation luminance in foot-lamberts, or 10 when E is in lumens per sq. metre and the adaptation luminance in candelas per sq. metre.

According to this result, if the luminance of the general field of view to which the eye is adapted is B ft.-lamberts, the liminal increment of luminance in the absence of any glare is that corresponding to luminance B in Fig. 37. If, however, a source of glare is present, the eye is adapted to a higher value of luminance, $B + 30E/\theta^2 = B'$, say, and the higher liminal increment under these conditions is that corresponding to the luminance B' in Fig. 37. B' is sometimes called the *equivalent background luminance* [51].

The change in the liminal increment of luminance is a measure of the disability glare [52]. If B and B' are both in the region where the liminal increment is proportional to the luminance, it will be seen that the effect of the glare is to reduce the sensitivity of the eye to luminance difference in the ratio of B to B'. The effects of a number of sources of glare on the liminal increment are additive, i.e. the value of luminance to which the eye is adapted is given by $B + K\Sigma(E_n/\theta_n{}^2)$, where K has the same value as for a single source [53]. The effect of glare on visual acuity is much less than its effect on the liminal increment of luminance [54].

Another cause of interference with vision, generally known as *veiling glare*, is the interposition, between the eye and the object looked at, of a " veil " of luminous material such, for example, as a sheet of slightly diffusing material or an illuminated haze. The reduction of sensitivity in this case is due partly to a reduction of contrast and partly to the effect of the diffusing material in raising the level of adaptation of the eye and so increasing the liminal increment of luminance. This effect is of great importance in the measurement of visibility in meteorology (see p. 165).

The lack of a close correlation between discomfort and disability in glare makes it impossible to arrive at any other than a most rough and general measure of the former. However, attempts have been made to express it by means of a " glare constant " which is a function of ω, the angular area of the source of glare (in steradians, measured at the eye), B_S its luminance and B_F the general luminance in the field of view. One simple formula, which has been found to hold over a useful range of conditions [55] is $B_S{}^{2n}\omega^n/B_F$ where $n = 0.8$. With values of B in foot-lamberts, if the glare constant exceeds 150, conditions are found to be " uncomfortable ".

It is to be noted that the image of a bright object in a highly polished surface is just as effective in causing glare as a self-luminous object similar to the image in size and brightness.

In photometry it is clearly essential to avoid even the slightest degree of disability glare and, further, it is well known that anything which tends to the discomfort, not only of the eye but of any organ of the body, induces fatigue and a consequent impairment of the capacity of the eye for accurate work. Both on this account and to prevent possible distraction of the attention, any condition which can be described as glaring, even to the slightest extent, must be avoided if the highest degree of photometric precision is to be achieved. This matter will be dealt with further in a later chapter, when what may be called the psychology of photometric measurement is under consideration (see p. 233).

Talbot's Law—So far it has been assumed that the illumination of the object looked at, and therefore of the retinal image, has remained steady, but the effect of rapid variations of illumination is of very great importance in photometric work, as will be seen when considering (a) the sector disc, in which the effective brightness of a surface is reduced by a rapid periodic extinction of the light and (b) the flicker photometer, in which the illumination of the field under observation is rapidly alternated from one intensity, or one colour, to another.

The sector disc is very widely used, and the principle on which it is founded was first proposed by Fox Talbot in 1834, and may be thus stated : " If a point of the retina is excited by a light which undergoes regular and periodic variations, and which has the duration of its period sufficiently short, it produces a continuous impression equal to that produced if the light emitted during each period were distributed uniformly throughout the duration of the period " [56]. It follows that the apparent intensity of an intermittent light bears to the actual intensity the ratio of the time of exposure to the total time, provided the speed of alternation exceeds that at which flicker ceases to be perceptible. In this form it is known as Talbot's law [57] (or sometimes the Talbot-Plateau law), and it has been found to hold at all flicker speeds above the necessary lower limit [58], and down to a ratio of at least 3 per cent for light of all colours, with an accuracy of at least 0·3 per cent [59].

This law might well be expected to hold if the eye responded instantaneously to changes of illumination, or if the rates of change of response were identical for both increasing and decreasing illuminations. The first alternative cannot be true, or flicker would never disappear, and the well-known phenomenon of persistence of vision would be absent [60]. Like all physiological actions, the response of the eye to light, though rapid, is far from instantaneous [61]. It has been found, in fact, that when the retina is suddenly illuminated, the sensation does not at once assume its final value but, rising rapidly from zero, it often overshoots to a maximum from which it then falls away more slowly until the steady state is reached [62]. The extent of the overshoot increases, and the time taken to settle down to the final value decreases with increasing intensity of the retinal illumination, as illustrated in Fig. 41 [63] which refers to white light. The effect is similar in general character for all colours, though the rate of rise and the extent of the overshoot are greater for blue than for other colours [64].

The decay of the sensation after the illumination has ceased is at first very rapid. It is followed by an after-image which may be " positive," i.e. one in which the sensation preserves its original pattern but at a lower level, or " negative," i.e. one in which the lighter and darker parts of the original are interchanged. If the original is coloured, the positive after-image is similar to it but the negative after-image appears in more or less complementary colours. The intensity and duration of the original stimulation determine the

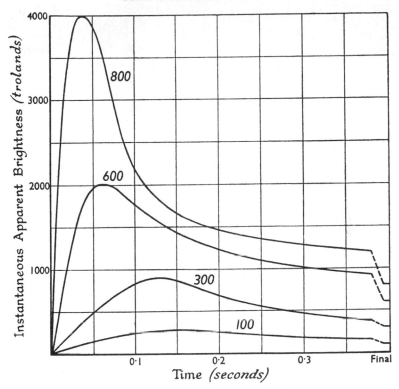

Fig. 41. The Initiation of Visual Sensation.

vividness and persistence of the after-image and whether this is positive or negative. Sometimes the image may change after a while from positive to negative or vice versa and more than one such change is not unusual. Stimulation with coloured light may give rise to a series of after-images of different colours [65].

A different type of after-image is that seen when exposure to a stimulation of fairly high intensity is followed, not by complete absence of stimulation as in the cases considered above, but by stimulation of a much lower intensity. This occurs, for instance, when the eye, after gazing fixedly at a bright pattern, is turned quickly towards an extended featureless surface of lower brightness. The after-image seen is then a negative one, the intensity and persistence of which depend on the duration of the original stimulation and its brightness relative to that of the final field of view.

Another phenomenon which may be mentioned here is that often noticed when a very small bright object, such as an illuminated pinhole surrounded by a dark field, is gazed at steadily for some time.

The brightness appears gradually to diminish with lapse of time, and in the case of an object near the limit of visibility, it frequently appears to wax and wane if the gaze is directed to it continuously.

Flicker Sensitivity: Persistence of Vision—In the statement of Talbot's law given above, the condition was laid down that the frequency of the variation in the brightness stimulation should be sufficiently high to avoid any sensation of flicker. The lowest frequency at which flicker just ceases to be noticeable depends on the mean value of the brightness and on the amplitude and wave-form of the variation [66]. It also depends on the colour if the brightness is low.

The simplest case is that in which periods of stimulation by a constant brightness alternate with equal periods of complete darkness, the wave-form being as nearly as possible rectangular. A close

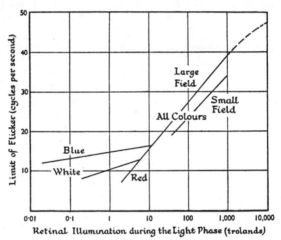

FIG. 42. Critical Frequency of Flicker.

approximation to these conditions can be obtained by using a sector disc with two 90° or three 60° openings, if these are large compared with the field of view. The lowest frequency at which no flicker is seen is known as the critical frequency. It has been measured for light of different colours over a wide range of values of luminance [67] and the general form of the relationship is shown in Fig. 42. The abscissae are retinal illuminations during the light phase, in trolands to a logarithmic scale, while the ordinates show the number of cycles (i.e. half the number of alternations) per second at the limit of the flicker sensation.

It will be seen that when the retinal illumination alternated with darkness exceeds about 12 trolands, the critical frequency is independent of colour. At lower values of brightness, however, the effect of colour becomes gradually more marked. The fact that the relation is a linear one over a wide range of values of brightness is often referred to as the Ferry-Porter law. The critical frequency is higher for the outer parts of the retina, and flicker is therefore sometimes noticeable by indirect vision when it is absent by direct vision [68], although some of this additional sensitivity is quickly lost [69]. Critical frequency has been used as an absolute measure of brightness but the accuracy attainable is very low [70].

In practical photometry a more important condition than that of alternation of light with complete darkness is the alternation of two lights of slightly differing intensities. Since one method of photometry depends on the disappearance of flicker when the alternating brightnesses are equal, it is naturally of the utmost importance to determine for variously coloured lights, and at various speeds of alternation, the difference of brightness which just produces the flicker sensation. This has been studied extensively by Dow [71], who has found that the percentage difference of luminance detectable as flicker depends on both the brightness and frequency of alternation, the minimum for white light being about $1\frac{1}{2}$ per cent when a lumin-

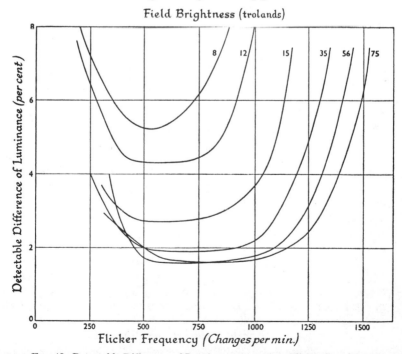

FIG. 43. Detectable Difference of Luminance at various Flicker Speeds.

ance of about $3cd/m^2$ or over is viewed through the natural pupil and
the alternation frequency is 10 to 15 per sec. The results for white
light are shown by the curves of Fig. 43.

Colour Sensitivity: The Luminous Efficiency of Radiation—As
already stated, (p. 18) the sensitivity of the eye to radiant energy
depends upon the wave-length ; equal rates of reception of energy
from the blue and yellow parts of the spectrum, for example, do not
produce the same degree of visual sensation. In fact, since radiations
of different wave-lengths produce effects on the eye which differ in
kind (colour) as well as in degree (intensity), it follows that no real
equality can ever be attained. On the other hand, if the difference
of colour is not too pronounced it is a matter of common experience
in photometry (where, in fact, exact identity of colour is the exception rather than the rule) that the eye can give an equality judgement which can not only be repeated within a reasonable tolerance
by the same individual, but which will also agree with similar
measurements made by other eyes so long as these do not possess any
marked peculiarity as regards colour vision.

The reciprocal of the rate of incidence of energy of each wave-
length which will produce a certain degree of visual sensation is
termed the relative luminous efficiency of radiation of that wave-
length (V_λ). The scale is such that $V_\lambda = 1$ for the wave-length for
which the relative luminous efficiency is greatest. It is found that
the curve connecting V_λ with λ, really the sensitivity curve of the eye,
is not independent of the conditions of observation, especially as
regards the brightness and extent of the field of view. However,
provided the brightness exceeds about 100 trolands and the size of the
field is not far from 2° to 3° in diameter, the variations are small
compared with the differences between normal sighted individuals,
for it must be emphasized that even normal eyes have not all the
same curve of response to energy of different wave-lengths, i.e.
they do not all give exactly the same curve for V_λ [72]. It is therefore necessary for practical purposes to adopt a conventional
mean curve which represents fairly the behaviour of the average eye ;
only in this way is it possible to arrive at an unambiguous and
consistent photometric scale for light of any colour, as will be
explained in Chapter IX.

The curve for V_λ now adopted internationally is shown in
Fig. 44 where the line marked " photopic " gives, for each wave-
length λ, the corresponding value of V_λ. The ordinates have been
plotted on a logarithmic scale so as to give a uniform accuracy of
reading over the very wide range of values involved. The values of
V_λ, which was formerly called the relative luminosity (or visibility)
factor, will be found tabulated in Appendix IV [73].

The V_λ curve has been determined by a number of workers using different methods and various conditions of observation [74]. The international values are based mainly upon five careful investigations, three by the flicker method [75] and two by the direct comparison of light from adjacent sections of the spectrum, the so-called

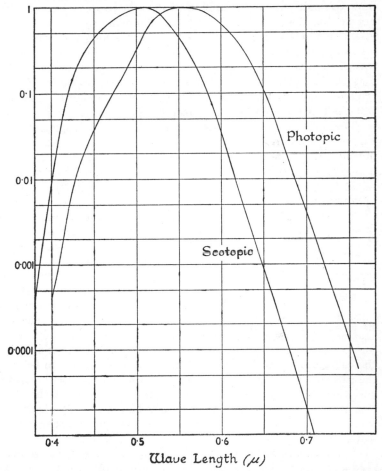

FIG. 44. The Relative Luminous Efficiency of Radiation.

" step-by-step " method [76]. The two methods give results which are in satisfactory agreement so long as only the central portion of the retina is used and the brightness of the field of view is not less than about 8 candelas per sq. mm. viewed through the natural pupil [77].

The Purkinje Effect—It has already been mentioned (see p. 58)

that at ordinary values of brightness, vision, at any rate over the central part of the retina where it is most distinct, takes place by means of the cones, whereas at very low brightnesses the cones cease to respond and vision is due entirely to the rods.

It is not surprising, therefore, to find that the curve of relative luminous efficiency which applies to cone (or photopic) vision, does not hold at low values of brightness. Since the rods are relatively insensitive to red, it might be expected that the long-wave end of the curve applicable to rod (or scotopic) vision would be at a shorter wave-length than the corresponding end of the photopic curve. In fact it is found that the two curves are very similar in shape and that the scotopic lies more or less bodily some 40 to 60 $m\mu$ to the short-wave side of the photopic, as shown in Fig. 44 [78].

The difference between the scotopic and the photopic curves of Fig. 44 explains the curious fact that the relative apparent brightness of coloured objects may change as the light by which they are illuminated is reduced in intensity. For example, if a red surface and a

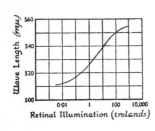

FIG. 45. The Wave-length of Maximum Luminous Efficiency at different Values of Brightness.

blue surface appear equally bright at ordinary values of illumination, a reduction of the illumination to a small fraction of its original value, so that the brightness lies in the scotopic region, causes the red surface to appear much darker than the blue. This is known as the Purkinje effect [79]. It is necessarily absent at the central, or rod-free part of the fovea [80], but for a large field with a brightness between those for which vision is definitely photopic or scotopic, the curve of relative luminous efficiency may lie anywhere between the two shown in Fig. 44 [81]. The way in which the position of the curve changes with brightness is shown in Fig. 45 in which the wave-length of maximum luminous efficiency has been plotted, for the range of brightness which lies between the scotopic and the photopic states [82]. This is sometimes called the Purkinje range [83].

Equivalent Luminance—The Purkinje effect brings into prominence a matter which is of great importance in photometry but one which can be easily overlooked so long as measurements are confined to the photopic region. This is the fact that visual photometry depends on the comparison of sensations, whereas photometric measurements, if they are to be of value, must be related to the magnitudes of the physical stimuli causing those sensations. As long as equal stimuli, measured physically, produce equal sensations, at least to the required degree of accuracy, no difficulty arises, but the distinction between the two sets of phenomena is present nevertheless. It is unfortunate that the term " brightness " has been used indiscriminately to describe both of them and outside the photopic region this has led to much confusion and misunderstanding. It is therefore desirable to employ two distinct terms and the word *luminance* is now used to denote the physical stimulus, i.e. radiant power weighted in accordance with the factor V_λ, some other term such as *subjective brightness* or *luminosity* being used when reference to the sensation is intended.

The relation between the subjective brightness and the luminance for lights of different spectral distributions is invariable throughout the photopic region and is determined by the table of values of V_λ. Outside this region, however, the subjective brightness corresponding to a given value of luminance varies with the spectral distribution in a different way and, within the Purkinje range, in a way which depends on the value of the luminance. It is therefore impossible to relate subjective brightness to luminance in a unique manner except in the photopic region. It is, however, necessary to have some scale on which subjective brightness may be expressed without ambiguity and the most convenient system is one in which it is agreed (*a*) to relate subjective brightness to luminance on the photopic scale for *all* values of luminance in the case of a specified spectral distribution and (*b*) to express the subjective brightness of light of any spectral distribution whatever in terms of that of light of the specified spectral distribution. The value so obtained is termed the *equivalent luminance*. It will be seen that, for light of any spectral distribution whatever within the photopic region, and for light of the specified spectral distribution at all values of luminance, the equivalent luminance is the same as the luminance, whereas in all other cases the two cease to be identical [84].

The argument set out in the immediately preceding paragraphs can be illustrated in a general way by means of Fig. 46. The short

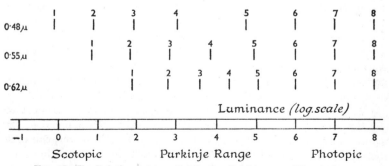

FIG. 46. The Relation between Subjective Brightness and Luminance.

vertical lines in the top row indicate a series of subjective brightnesses with light of wave-length 0.48μ and, by their positions over the logarithmic scale of luminance at the bottom of the diagram, show the values of luminance which correspond to each of these subjective brightnesses. The lines in the second and third rows refer to the same series of subjective brightnesses with light of wave-lengths 0.55μ and 0.62μ respectively.

The numbers attached to the lines are to be regarded at this stage as for identification purposes only, since no scale of magnitudes can be set up for subjective brightness (or for any other sensation), but all the lines marked with the same number refer to the same subjective brightness.

It will be seen that, outside the photopic region, the lines referring to the same subjective brightness are displaced relatively to each other to a greater or less extent, i.e. the corresponding values of luminance are not the same. Clearly the positions of the vertical lines and the numbers attached to them can be made identical with the luminance scale for any one selected wave-length or, by extension, for any selected spectral distribution, and when this has been done, the scale for any other wave-length or spectral distribution is fixed and can be determined experimentally.

It has been agreed to adopt as the specified spectral distribution that of the light given by a full radiator at the temperature of solidification of platinum, viz. $2042°$ K (see p. 314) and the equivalent luminance of any surface, if outside the photopic region, is found by matching it with a surface giving light of this spectral distribution and then determining the luminance of this comparison surface by the ordinary photometric procedure to be described in Chapter XII (see esp. p. 401) [85]. The scales in Fig. 46 have been drawn so that the scale for full radiation at $2042°$ K is identical with the luminance scale.

Sensitivity to Colour Difference—Corresponding to the sensitivity of the eye to small differences of brightness, there is the sensitivity to small differences of colour which is of importance in photometry and, to an even greater extent, in colorimetry. Two types of differences are principally encountered, viz. (a) differences of *hue*, such as those which are noticed between neighbouring portions of the spectrum, and (b) differences of *saturation*, in which one colour differs from the other only by the addition of a small amount of white light, i.e. the colours differ slightly in " dilution " with white.

The smallest difference of wave-length which can just be detected by the normal eye varies somewhat irregularly from one end of the spectrum to the other, as shown in Fig. 47 which, however, can only be regarded as typical since the differences between individuals are fairly large [86].

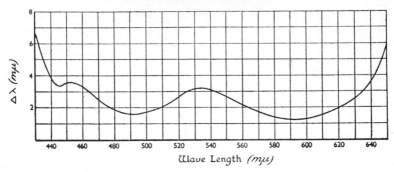

FIG. 47. The Sensitivity of the Eye to Hue Difference.

The sensitivity to saturation can be expressed either by the number of just perceptibly different mixtures of white with light of any given wave-length, or by the smallest amount of light of a given wave-length which, when added to pure white, gives the mixture a just perceptible hue [87]. In both cases it is found that, as might perhaps be expected, the sensitivity to saturation is least (i.e. the number of steps between white and the pure spectral radiation is least, or the just perceptible addition to white is greatest) for wavelengths in the yellow part of the spectrum, viz. about 0.57μ, and that it rises fairly rapidly on either side of this minimum. This is illustrated in Fig. 48 which shows, for each wave-length the number of just perceptible steps between pure white and homogeneous radiation of that wave-length [88]. The least amount of pure spectral radiation which, in a mixture with white light gives it a just perceptible hue is about 5 to 10 per cent for yellow light of wave-length 0.57μ and falls to about 1 to 2 per cent for red and to less than 1 per cent for blue [89].

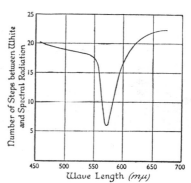

FIG. 48. The Sensitivity of the Eye to Change of Saturation.

Threshold of Vision—Although it is the sensitivity of the eye to small differences of brightness or colour which is of primary importance in photometry, nevertheless the absolute thresholds of sensation are not without interest. The use of the threshold of the sensation of brightness for plotting the course of dark adaptation has already been mentioned (see p. 65). For the fully dark-adapted eye this threshold usually lies between 10^{-4} and 10^{-3} troland in the case of an extended field [90], though it varies considerably, being much higher for certain individuals who are generally described as " night-blind ". This threshold is naturally independent of the spectral distribution of the light if it is expressed on the equivalent luminance scale explained above, but not if it is expressed on the photopic scale of luminance.

Except at the long-wave end of the spectrum, the threshold for the sensation of colour is considerably higher than that for the sensation of light, so that there is a range over which the light appears colourless whatever its spectral distribution. This range, often known as the *photochromatic interval*, is most conveniently expressed by the ratio of the radiant energy flux required for colour perception to that required for the perception of light at the threshold of brightness. This *photochromatic ratio* rises fairly rapidly from about 2 for red light to between 100 and 150 for all wave-lengths from 0.55μ to the extreme blue [91]. The threshold for colour is no doubt closely connected with the threshold for light by cone vision which is about 0.01 to 0.1 troland [92]. This is similar to the brightness threshold for a small field viewed foveally [93].

When the size of the luminous surface looked at is very small indeed, as, for example, in the case of a signal light viewed from a considerable distance, it has been found that both the limit at which the light ceases to be visible and the apparent intensity of a source which is above that limit, depend on the total amount of light entering the eye, i.e. for a given pupillary aperture it is not the brightness alone but the product of the brightness and the solid angular size of the source that matters. This is known as Riccò's law [94]. It holds for foveal and near foveal vision so long as the diameter of the surface does not exceed a few minutes of arc [95] and it implies that the effect of light on the retina is cumulative and independent of the area over which it is distributed up to this limit. As the surface is increased in size the effect of accumulation gradually diminishes but it is not negligible, i.e. the threshold brightness of a surface is not independent of the angle it subtends at the eye unless this is quite large, certainly over $15°$ in diameter in the case of a disc [96].

Sources of very small angular dimensions are often referred to as " point sources " and the limits at which they just cease to be visible or at which recognition of their colour ceases have been the subject of a great deal of study [97]. Since the light entering the eye is equal to the product of the pupillary aperture and the illumination at the iris, it is usual to express the effect produced by a point source of light in terms of this illumination, a constant pupillary aperture being tacitly assumed. This quantity is termed the *point brilliance* of the source [98]. It may be expressed in ordinary illumination units, but as it is usually very small it is more convenient to employ a sub-multiple such as the microlumen per sq. metre or microlux (μlx). The mile-candle (the illumination produced by a source of one candela at a distance of one mile) has also been used. It is equal to 0·385 μlx.

The limit of perception of a point source of white light is about 0·1 to 0·2 μlx for foveal vision and of the order of 0·004 μlx when the source is viewed extra-foveally [99]. For coloured sources the limit for foveal vision is similar to that for white sources but for parafoveal vision it varies considerably according to the colour. For blue light, the threshold of perception of light (not of colour) is of the order of 0·0004 μlx while for red it is about the same as for foveal vision. For green and orange, the values are intermediate, viz. of the order of 0·002 and 0·02 μlx respectively [100]. It will be clear that in the case of a light of any colour for which the threshold by parafoveal vision is considerably less than the threshold for foveal vision, i.e. for white, green and, most of all, for blue, the light may be invisible when looked at directly but may " flash up " when the attention is directed to a point at a small angular distance (of the order of 5° to 10°) away from it [101]. There is little difference between binocular vision and vision with one eye only [102].

All the above values refer to a source seen against a perfectly dark background, but values have also been obtained for the case of a source seen against a background of which the luminance is not zero [103].

Intermittent Light—So far it has been assumed that the light to be observed is either continuous and steady or that the frequency of any change is above the critical frequency of flicker. In photometry this is generally the case, but an exception occurs in the measurement of a flashing light which is either non-periodic or for which the frequency is comparatively low, e.g. less than 10 to 15 per second. In such a case it has been found that if t is the duration of the flash in seconds, and E the illumination at the eye during the flash, the apparent intensity is equal to that of a steady light giving an illumination E_0 where $E_0/E = t/(a+t)$. This is known as the Blondel-Rey law [104] and it has been found that with $a = 0·2$ sec. it gives a good approximation to the observed values when E_0 is near the threshold of visibility for white light. For coloured light, the value of a is different, except in the case of a red light viewed foveally [105].

It will be seen that when t is very small the Blondel-Rey formula approximates to $E_0 = k\,Et$; in other words the threshold of visibility for very brief flashes of light is determined by the product of the illumination at the eye and the duration of the flash [106].

When E_0 is above the threshold, the value of a in the Blondel-Rey formula is smaller [107] and, to a first approximation, it varies inversely as E_0, so that the formula becomes $E - E_0 = b/t$, the value of b being about 0·05 when E is measured in mile-candles and t in seconds [108]. It will be clear that such a formula cannot hold for very small values of t but it represents the observed results to a fair approximation for values of E_0 from the threshold to 4 mile-candles (1·5 μlx), so long as t is greater than about 0·05 sec.

The very high sensitivity of the eye as a detector of radiation can be better appreciated if the figures given above for the threshold of visibility of point sources of light are converted to energy units, using the known relationship between rate of energy reception and illumination (see p. 138). An illumination of 0·004 μlx in monochromatic light of the wave-length for which the luminous efficiency is a maximum equals a rate of energy reception of about $6·2 \times 10^{-5}$ erg per sec. per square metre, i.e. about 28×10^{-10} erg per sec. over the area of the fully dilated pupil, taken as about 45 sq. mm. [109]. This equals about 750 quanta per sec. The least amount of energy which, as a flash of light, will just excite the sensation of vision has been determined experimentally and has been found to be of the order of 100 quanta for radiation of wave-length 0·51μ [110].

Theories of the Visual Mechanism—The mechanism of vision is still very imperfectly understood. Although many theories have been proposed to explain the observed phenomena, none of them is entirely satisfactory. Nevertheless it is possible, by combining some of the features of the more successful of these theories, to arrive at a mental picture which can serve the purpose of co-ordinating the array of factual data of which some account has been given in the preceding sections [111].

The sensitive elements in the retina are the rods and cones. The former, in conjunction with the visual purple, are concerned with the perception of light and of movement, while the latter are responsible for the appreciation of form and of colour. This theory of the dual nature of the visual mechanism is usually known as the " duplicity theory " of von Kries [112].

There are generally no rods at the fovea, the normal fixation area, but over the remainder of the retina both rods and cones are present in varying ratios (see p. 57). The rods have a much lower threshold of sensitivity to light than the cones, but at light intensities above the cone threshold the response of these latter elements predominates [113]. Over a range of intensities, the sensation produced is partly dependent on the relative numbers of rods and cones present in the portion of the retina stimulated.

The rods give no sensation of colour. The curve representing their response to radiation of different wave-lengths is the sensitivity curve of the dark-adapted eye, i.e. the scotopic curve of relative luminous efficiency (see Fig. 44, p. 73).

In the retina the rods contain the visual purple (rhodopsin) which absorbs light and, in so doing, undergoes a chemical change which results in bleaching. The relation between the rate of bleaching and the wave-length of the light is very similar to the scotopic curve of luminous efficiency [114]. On removal of the light, the visual purple is regenerated at a rate which is largely dependent on the extent of the previous bleaching. This regenerative action is associated with the progressive dark-adaptation of the eye.

For vision at all ordinary light intensities the cones are by far the more important elements. Their sensitivity to radiant energy of different wave-lengths is that found for the light-adapted eye, i.e. it is given by the photopic curve in Fig. 44.

The cones give the sensation of colour as well as that of light and having regard to the experimentally established facts of colour mixture (see Chapter X, p. 320) it seems natural to postulate the existence of three different kinds of receptors, or three photochemical substances, which give rise to the sensations of red, green and blue respectively when they are stimulated by light. This is the trichromatic theory of colour vision originated by Thomas Young [115] and elaborated by von Helmholtz [116].

Although no histological evidence has so far been found for any triple mechanism such as that required in the Young-Helmholtz theory, nevertheless that theory provides a satisfactory framework for the study of colour vision. In particular it provides a mental picture which is very useful in any discussion of the phenomenological science of colour measurement which will be outlined in Chapter X.

In conclusion it must be emphasized that all that it has been possible to give in this chapter is a somewhat disjointed and very cursory description of some of the phenomena of vision, most attention having necessarily been devoted to the particular aspects of the subject which are of greatest importance in everyday photometry. A lack of appreciation of the peculiarities of the visual process has led repeatedly to the publication of results which are totally lacking in value, either because they refer to a condition of the eye which is different from that prevailing in ordinary circumstances or because insufficient details are given to enable the results to be correlated with other data obtained, probably, under quite different visual conditions. The influence of field size and brightness on the results obtained by means of a flicker photometer may be cited as a particular example. It is more than likely that in many of the branches of practical photometry there are unrecognised sources of uncertainty which may, later on, be traced to some at present unsuspected phenomenon of vision.

BIBLIOGRAPHY

Construction of the Eye and Optical Characteristics

W. S. Duke-Elder. *Text-Book of Ophthalmology*, Vol. I. (Kimpton, *1932*.)

H. von Helmholtz. *Handbuch d. Physiologischen Optik*. (3rd edit., Voss, Hamburg and Leipzig, *1909–11*.) English trans. by J. P. C. Southall *et al.*, Optical Soc. America, *1924–5*. In the references, page numbers in this translation are given in square brackets.

Sensitivities of the Eye

Y. Le Grand. *Optique Physiologique, Vol II*. (Rev. d'Optique Press, 1948). English trans., *Light, Colour and Vision* (Chapman and Hall, 1957).

R. J. Lythgoe. *Illumination and Visual Capacities*. Medical Research Council, Special Report No. 104. (H.M. Stationery Office, *1926*.)

L. T. Troland. Illum. Eng. Soc. N.Y., Trans., 26, *1931*, p. 107. (Mainly bibliography.)

W. D. Wright. *The Perception of Light*. (Blackie, *1938*.) *Photometry and the Eye*, (Hatton Press, *1949*.)

Colour Vision

J. H. Parsons. *Introduction to the Study of Colour Vision*. (2nd edit., Camb. Univ. Press, *1924*.)

W. D. Wright. *Researches on Normal and Defective Colour Vision*. (Kimpton, *1946*.)

REFERENCES

1. " Bei der Beurteilung von Licht in der Beleuchtungstechnik hat man zu beachten, dass Licht nicht eine rein physikalische Erscheinung ist, sondern auch in seinen physiologischen Wirkungen betrachtet werden muss. Bei Lichtmessungen kann man daher in letzter Linie die Mitwirkung des menschlichen Auges nicht entbehren." (F. Uppenborn, *Lehrbuch d. Phot.*, p. 1.)

2. These figures are only approximate. For a full description of the structure of the eye, see W. S. Duke-Elder, *Text-Book of Ophthalmology*.

3. See, e.g. P. W. Cobb, Am. J. of Physiol., 36, *1915*, p. 335 and other work reported in R. J. Lythgoe, *Illn. and Visual Capacities*, p. 24.

4. This curve is based on the results of several workers, especially P. Reeves, Opt. Soc. Am. J., 4, *1920*, p. 35 and B. H. Crawford, Roy. Soc., Proc. (B), 121, *1936*, p. 376. Refs. to other work will be found in note (21) on p. 77 of *Photometry (1926)* and in P. Moon and D. E. Spencer, Opt. Soc. Am., J., 34, *1944*, p. 319.

See also R. Faillie, R. Jonnard and H. Vial de Sachy, C. R., 199, *1934*, p. 89 ; M. Luckiesh and F. K. Moss, Opt. Soc. Am., J., 24, *1934*, p. 130 ; M. Nagel and A. Klughardt, Z. f. Phys., 101, *1936*, p. 372 ; F. Flamant, Rev. d'Opt., 27, *1948*, p. 751.

On methods of pupillometry, see, e.g. W. S. Duke-Elder, *Text-Book of Ophthalmology*, p. 539 ; A. Broca, Rev. d'Opt., 3, *1924*, p. 493 ; F. K. Moss, Opt. Soc. Am., J., 22, *1932*, p. 735 ; R. C. Jones, *ibid.*, 29, *1939*, p. 531.

5. See, e.g. J. Gorham, Roy. Soc., Proc., 37, *1884*, p. 425 or A. Lipowitz, Ann. d. Phys., 61, *1844*, p. 140.

6. W. S. Duke-Elder. *Text-Book of Ophthalmology*, p. 750.
Under conditions of dark adaptation the eye is usually slightly myopic (see, e.g
G. Wald and D. R. Griffin, Opt. Soc. Am., J., 37, *1947*, p. 321).

7. For a description of the dioptrics of the eye as regards spherical aberration, axial chromatic aberration and oblique astigmatism, see A. Ames and C. A. Proctor, Opt. Soc. Am., J., 5, *1921*, p. 22. On the chromatic aberration of the eye, see C. Sheard, Opt. Soc. Am., J., 12, *1926*, p. 79 and H. Hartridge, J. of Physiology, 52, *1918*, p. 175 and " Discussion on Vision " (Phys. and Opt. Socs., *1932*), p. 309.

8. There is a vast literature on the properties of the visual purple and its rôle in vision. See, e.g. W. S. Duke-Elder, *Text-Book of Ophthalmology*, pp. 830 et seqq., W. D. Wright, *Researches, etc.*, p. 12 and the papers cited in note (114).

9. A full description of the retinal structure will be found in S. L. Polyak, *The Retina* (Univ. of Chicago Press, *1941*). Photomicrographs showing the distribution of rods and cones at different parts of the retina are given by E. F. Fincham, Opt. Soc., Trans., 26, *1925*, pp. 198 and 239 and Photog., J., 76, *1936*, p. 268. See also S. R. Detwiler, Opt. Soc. Am. J., 30, *1940*, p. 42.

10. See, e.g. A. Schuster and J. W. Nicholson, *Theory of Optics*, Chap. VII, §§ 74⁻5 ; L. C. Martin, Opt. Convention, *1926*, Pt. I, p. 166.

11. R. S. Creed. " Discussion on Vision " (Phys. and Opt. Socs., *1932*), p. 288.
See also H. Hartridge, J. of Physiol., 57, *1923*, p. 52 and Phil. Mag., 46, *1923*, p. 49 ; S. Hecht and E. U. Mintz, J. of Gen. Physiol., 22, *1939*, p. 593 ; Y. Le Grand, C.R., 200, *1935*, p. 490 and 202, *1936*, p. 592 ; H. Schober and H. Jung, Z. f. techn. Phys., 17, *1936*, p. 84 ; G. L. Walls, Opt. Soc. Am., J., 33, *1943*, p. 487.

12. W. D. Wright. *Perception of Light*, p. 3.
See also p. 78 and note (92).

13. This fig. is based on data quoted by H. Piéron, Rev. Gén. des Sci., 32, *1921*, p. 390.

14. W. S. Stiles and B. H. Crawford. Roy. Soc., Proc. (B), 112, *1933*, p. 428.
W. Dziobek. Licht, 4, *1934*, p. 150.
W. D. Wright and J. H. Nelson. Phys. Soc., Proc., 48, *1936*, p. 401.
W. S. Stiles. Science Progress. 33, *1939*, p. 676.
See also R. Teucher, Z. f. Ophthalmol. Optik, 30, *1942*, p. 161 and F. Flamant, Rev. d'Opt., 28, *1949*, p. 44.

15. P. Moon and D. E. Spencer. Opt. Soc. Am., J., 34, *1944*, p. 319.

16. W. S. Stiles. Roy. Soc., Proc. (B), 123, *1937*, p. 90.

17. B. H. Crawford. Roy. Soc., Proc. (B), 124, *1937*, p. 81.
F. Flamant and W. S. Stiles. J. of Physiol., 107, *1948*, p. 187.

18. Originally termed the *photon* (L. T. Troland, Illum. Eng. Soc. N.Y., Trans 11, *1916*, p. 947). To avoid confusion with the quantum of radiation the names *luxon* and *troland* were proposed (C.I.E., Proc., 11, *1948*, p. 155). The latter is now generally used. H. E. Ives used a similar " illumination unit " (I.U.) but his external surface was of magnesium oxide at an illumination of one lux (Phil. Mag., 24, *1912*, p. 149).

19. E. H. Weber. *De pulsu resorptione auditu et tactu* (Leipzig, *1834*). See especially p. 172.

20. G. T. Fechner. Leipzig Abh., 4, *1859*, p. 455.
See also P. Bouguer, *Traité d'Optique.*, p. 52.

21. G. T. Fechner. *Elemente der Psychophysik*, (Leipzig, *1860*), Vol. II.

22. J. Guild. " Discussion on Vision " (Phys. and Opt. Socs., *1932*), p. 1 ; B. A. Report, *1938*, p. 296.
J. H. Parsons. " Discussion on Vision " (Phys. and Opt. Socs., *1932*), p. 272. (See, however, L. F. Richardson, *ibid.*, p. 112.)
P. W. Cobb. Psychol. Rev., 39, *1932*, p. 533.
See also A. Kühl, Phys. Z., 37, *1936*, p. 865 ; W. D. Wright, Illum. Eng. Soc. Lond., Trans., 4, *1939*, p. 1.

23. This rule, although not explicitly formulated, was the basis of the scale of stellar magnitudes used from the time of Ptolemy (see p. 475).
The term " brig " is sometimes used to indicate a tenfold change in any quantity so that two numbers N_1 and N_2 differ by n brigs or $10n$ decibrigs when $n = \log_{10}(N_1/N_2)$ (A. H. Davis, Phys. Soc., Proc., 46, *1934*, p. 631). The name log-unit is also used.

24. H. Seeliger. Astron. Nachr., 132, *1893*, col. 209.
See also J. Hrdlička, Int. Illum. Congress, *1931*, Proc., Vol. I, p. 146.

25. The classical measurements are those of A. König and E. Brodhun (see first ref. in note 26 below). Their unit of retinal illumination was that due to a magnesium oxide surface illuminated by 10 sq. mm. of freezing platinum (about 2·2 candelas) at a distance of one metre, the pupillary aperture being one sq. mm. It was therefore equal to about 0·7 troland. (See also H. Schroeder, Z. f. Sinnesphysiologie, 57, *1926*, p. 195.)

For early work on this subject see the refs. in note (7) on p. 75 of *Photometry (1926)* and the literature cited by L. T. Troland in Illum. Eng. Soc. N.Y., Trans., 26, *1931*, p. 107. See also J. Blanchard, Phys. Rev., 11, *1918*, p. 81 and the summary given by R. J. Lythgoe in *Illumination and Visual Capacities*, p. 17.

The following are more recent papers on the subject :

R. A. Houstoun and J. F. Shearer. Phil. Mag., 10, *1930*, p. 433.

R. A. Houstoun. Phil. Mag., 8, *1929*, p. 520 and 12, *1931*, p. 538 ; " Discussion on Vision " (Phys. and Opt. Socs., *1932*), p. 167.

E. M. Lowry. Opt. Soc. Am., J., 21, *1931*, p. 132.

W. S. Stiles and B. H. Crawford. Roy. Soc., Proc. (B), 113, *1933*, p. 496 and 116, *1934*, p. 55.

S. Hecht. Nat. Acad. Sci., Proc., 20, *1934*, p. 644.

A. H. Holway. Opt. Soc. Am., J., 27, *1937*, p. 120.

S. Hecht, J. C. Peskin and M. Patt. J. Gen. Physiol., 22, *1938*, p. 7.

See also S. Hecht, J. Gen. Physiol., 7, *1924*, p. 235 and 18, *1935*, p. 767 ; C. H. Graham and E. H. Kemp, J. Gen. Physiol., 21, *1938*, p. 635 (these workers studied the effect of time of exposure) ; W. J. Crozier and A. H. Holway, J. Gen. Physiol., 22, *1939*, p. 341 ; K. J. W. Craik, J. of Physiol., 92, *1938*, p. 406 ; A. Kühl, Z. f. I., 63, *1943*, p. 405.

König and Brodhun (see note 26) and Hecht, Peskin and Patt (*loc. cit. supra*) give results for lights of different wave-lengths as well as for white light.

26. Berlin Ber., *1888*, p. 917 and *1889*, p. 641.

P. G. Nutting. Bureau of Standards, Bull., 3, *1907*, p. 59.

See also I. G. Priest, Opt. Soc. Am., J., 15, *1927*, p. 82 ; A. van Krefeld and J. A. M. van Liempt, Physica, 5, *1938*, p. 345.

27. W. S. Stiles. " The Effect of Glare on the Brightness Difference Threshold." Illum. Research Technical Paper No. 8. (H.M. Stationery Office, *1929*.)

See also E. M. Lowry, Opt. Soc. Am., J., 18, *1929*, p. 29.

28. P. Lasareff. Arch. f. d. ges. Physiol., 142, *1911*, p. 235.

P. Reeves. Opt. Soc. Am., J., 1, *1917*, p. 148.

E. Karrer and E. P. T. Tyndall. Bureau of Standards, Bull., 15, *1920*, p. 679.

J. Steinhardt. J. Gen. Physiol., 20, *1936*, p. 185.

See also I. Runge, Phys. Z., 30, *1929*, p. 76 ; W. J. Crozier and A. H. Holway, J. Gen. Physiol., 23, *1939*, p. 101 ; C. H. Graham and N. R. Bartlett, J. Exp. Psychol., 27, *1940*, p. 149 ; H. R. Blackwell, Opt. Soc. Am., J., 36, *1946*, p. 624.

29. P. W. Cobb and L. R. Geissler. Psychol. Rev. (N.Y.), 20, *1913*, p. 425.

P. W. Cobb. Psychol. Rev. (N.Y.), 21, *1914*, p. 23 ; Illum. Eng. Soc. N.Y., Trans., 8, *1913*, p. 292 and 11, *1916*, p. 372 ; J. Exp. Psychol., 1, *1916*, pp. 419 and 540.

L. C. Martin. Roy. Soc., Proc. (A), 104, *1924*, p. 302.

W. D. Wright. J. of Physiol., 83, *1935*, p. 466.

K. J. W. Craik. J. of Physiol., 92, *1938*, p. 406.

See also J. F. Shearer, Phil. Mag., 13, *1932*, p. 975 ; R. O. Schumacher, Licht, 11, *1941*, p. 134; W. Dziobek, Sci. et Indust. Photog., 20, p. *1949*, 167.

30. J. Dauber. Z. f. I., 35, *1915*, p. 308.

E. M. Lowry. Opt. Soc. Am., J., 21, *1931*, p. 132.

31. R. G. Hopkinson, W. R. Stevens and J. M. Waldram. Illum. Eng. Soc. Lond., Trans., 6, *1941*, p. 37.

32. The induced colour is not the exact complementary unless the eye is dark adapted. See J. H. Parsons, *Colour Vision*, pp. 141-2.

33. J. H. Parsons. *Colour Vision*, p. 138.

34. G. Révész. Kongress f. exp. Psychol., Ber., 4, *1911*, p. 217.

C. E. Ferree and G. Rand. J. Exp. Psychol., 1, *1916*, p. 1.

35. H. Hartridge. J. of Physiol., 50, *1915*, p. 101 ; Cambridge Phil. Soc., Proc., 19, *1919*, p. 271.

36. See the literature cited in notes (15) and (16) on p. 76 of *Photometry (1926)*.

For the effect of age of the observer see, e.g., C. E. Ferree, G. Rand and E. F. Lewis, Illum. Eng. Soc. N.Y., Trans., 29, *1934*, p. 296.

For the effect of contrast in the test object, see, e.g. P. W. Cobb and F. K. Moss, J. Exp. Psychol., 10, *1927*, p. 350; J. P. Conner and R. E. Ganoung, Opt. Soc. Am., J., 25, *1935*, p. 287; H. Siedentopf, E. J. Meyer and J. Wempe, Z. f. I., 61, *1941*, p. 372. For the effect of colour of the test object, see D. L. MacAdam, Rev. d'Opt., 28, *1949*, p. 161.

37. R. J. Lythgoe. "The Measurement of Visual Acuity." Medical Research Council Special Report No. 173 (H.M. Stationery Office, *1932*). Extensive bibliographies of the subject will be found in this report and in Illum. Eng. Soc. N.Y., Trans., 26, *1931*, p. 107.
See also S. Shlaer, J. Gen. Physiol., 21, *1937*, p. 65.
An increase of visual acuity with distance of the object from the eye has been found by E. Freeman (Opt. Soc. Am., J., 22, *1932*, pp. 285 and 729) and by M. Luckiesh and F. K. Moss (*ibid.*, 23, *1933*, p. 25 and 31, *1941*, p. 594).

38. C. E. Ferree, G. Rand and E. F. Lewis. Illum. Eng. Soc. N.Y., Trans., 29, *1934*, p. 296.

39. See, e.g. L. Bell, El. World, 57, *1911*, p. 1163; M. Luckiesh, *ibid.*, 58, *1911*, pp. 450 and 1252 and 62, *1913*, p. 1160; M. Luckiesh and F. K. Moss, Opt. Soc. Am., J., 10, *1925*, p. 275; M. Luckiesh, Frank. Inst., J., 215, *1933*, p. 401; W. Arndt, Licht, 3, *1933*, p. 213; W. Arndt and A. Dresler, *ibid.*, p. 231; P. J. Bouma, De Ingenieur, 49, *1934*, pp. A31 and A243; Philips Techn. Rev., 1, *1936*, p. 215; H. Schober and K. Wittmann, Licht, 8, *1938*, p. 199.
See also S. Schlaer, *et al.* J. Gen. Physiol., 25, *1942*, p. 553.

40. P. W. Cobb and L. R. Geissler. Psychol. Rev. (N.Y.), 20, *1913*, p. 425.
P. W. Cobb. Psychol. Rev. (N.Y.), 21, *1914*, p. 23; Illum. Eng. Soc. N.Y., Trans., 8, *1913*, p. 292 and 11, *1916*, p. 372.
R. J. Lythgoe. Loc. cit., note 37, p. 31; Illum. Eng. Soc. Lond., Trans., 1, *1936*, p. 3.
K. J. W. Craik. Brit. J. Psychol., 29, *1938*, p. 252.

41. "Nous croyons que cette règle indispensable de ramener dans cette rencontre tout au rapport d'égalité, ne peut être remplacée par aucune autre ; car ce rapport est le seul sur lequel on soit sûr de ne se pas tromper tout à fait grossièrement" (P. Bouguer, *Traité d'Optique*, p. 43). See also *Essai d'Optique*, pp. 5 *et seqq.*
"... non tamen inter gradus claritatis aliam dignoscere valet rationem praeter rationem aequalitatis." (J. H. Lambert, *Photometria*, p. 16.)

42. R. J. Lythgoe. Brit. J. Ophthalmol., 24, *1940*, p. 21.

43. L. Bell. Illum. Eng. Soc. N.Y., Trans., 6, *1911*, p. 671.

44. B. H. Crawford. Roy. Soc., Proc. (B), 123, *1937*, p. 69.

45. E. W. Godding. Roy. Soc. Medicine, Proc., 38, *1945*, p. 155; Illum. Eng. Soc. Lond., Trans., 10, *1945*, p. 27.
See also J. Blanchard, Phys. Rev., 11, *1918*, p. 81; A. Brückner, "Discussion on Vision" (Phys. and Opt. Socs., *1932*), p. 161; S. Hecht, C. Haig, and G. Wald, J. Gen. Physiol., 19, *1935*, p. 321; C. P. Winsor and A. B. Clark, Nat. Acad. Sci., Proc., 22, *1936*, p. 400; S. Hecht, C. Haig and A. M. Chase, J. Gen. Physiol., 20, *1937*, p. 831; H. Lossagk, Licht, 6, *1936*, p. 126; S. Hecht and S. Shlaer, Opt, Soc. Am., J., 28, *1938*, p. 269; K. J. W. Craik and M. D. Vernon, Brit. J. Psychol., 32, *1941-2*, pp. 62 and 206; M. Luckiesh and A. H. Taylor, Illum. Eng. Soc., N.Y.. Trans., 38, *1943*, p. 189; C. Sheard, Opt. Soc. Am., J., 34, *1944*, p. 464; W. D. Wright, *Researches*, etc., pp. 209 *et seqq.*
On the effect of binocular vision see R. J. Lythgoe and L. R. Phillips, J. of Physiol., 91, *1938*, p. 427.

46. H. Piper. Z. f. Psychol. u. Physiol. d. Sinnesorgane, 31, *1903*, p. 161.
W. Walker. Z. f. Psychol., 103, *1927*, p. 323.

47. W. Lohmann. Z. f. Sinnesphysiologie, 41, *1906*, p. 290.
See also H. Eguchi, Int. Illum. Congress, *1931*, Vol. I, p. 28; W. D. Wright, Illum. Eng. Soc. Lond., Trans., 4, *1939*, p. 1.

48. J. H. Parsons. *Colour Vision*, p. 20.

49. W. S. Stiles. Illum. Eng., 22, *1929*, p. 304.
A bibliography to 1925 will be found in Illum. Eng. Soc., N.Y., Trans., 26, *1931*, p. 107.

50. M. Luckiesh and L. L. Holladay. Illum. Eng. Soc., N.Y., Trans., 20, *1925*, p. 221.
L. L. Holladay. Opt. Soc. Am., J., 12, *1926*, p. 271 and 14, *1927*, p. 1.
W. S. Stiles. Roy. Soc., Proc. (B), 104, *1929*, p. 322; C. I. E., Proc., 7,

1928, p. 220 ; " The Effect of Glare on the Brightness Difference Threshold," Illum. Research Tech. Paper No. 8 (H.M. Stationery Office, *1929*).

    W. S. Stiles and B. H. Crawford. Roy. Soc., Proc. (B), 122, *1937*, p. 255. (See also " Discussion on Vision ", Phys. and Opt. Socs., *1932*, p. 194.)

    See also R. G. Weigel, Licht u. Lampe, 18, *1929*, pp. 995 and 1051 ; J. F. Schouten, Amsterdam Acad., Proc., 37, *1934*, p. 506 ; G. A. W. Rutgers, Rev. d'Opt., 28, *1949*, p. 33.

    51. See also P. Moon and D. E. Spencer, Opt. Soc. Am., J., 33, *1943*, p. 444.

    52. See, e.g. M. Luckiesh, Illum. Eng. Soc. N.Y., Trans., 22, *1927*, p. 542 ; U. Bordoni, C.I.E., Proc., 6, *1924*, p. 349 ; Elettrot., 11, *1924*, p. 585 and 15, *1928*, p. 260 ; J. Dourgnon and P. Waguet, C.I.E., Proc., 8, *1931*, p. 367 ; Y. Le Grand, C.R., 198, *1934*, p. 1075.

    A description of an instrument for measuring disability glare has been given by W. S. Stiles and B. H. Crawford (Illum. Eng., 23, *1930*, p. 279 ; J. Sci. Insts., 12, *1935*, p. 177).

    53. B. H. Crawford. Phys. Soc., Proc., 48, *1936*, p. 35.

    54. R. J. Lythgoe. " The Measurement of Visual Acuity." Medical Research Council Special Report No. 173 (H.M. Stationery Office, *1932*), p. 33.

    55. P. Petherbridge and R. G. Hopkinson. Illum. Eng. Soc. Lond., Trans., 15, *1950*, p. 39.

    See also L. L. Holladay, Opt. Soc. Am., J., 12, *1926*, p. 271 ; W. Harrison, Illum. Engng., 40 *1945*, p. 525 and (with P. Meaker) 42, *1947*, p. 153 ; M. Luckiesh and S. K. Guth, *ibid.*, 41, *1946*, p. 485 and 44, *1949*, p. 650.

    56. H. von Helmholtz. *Handbuch d. Physiologischen Optik* (3 Aufl.), Vol. 2, p. 174 [207].

    57. W. H. Fox Talbot. Roy. Soc., Abs. 3, *1834*, p. 298; Phil. Mag., 5, *1834*, p. 327. J. Plateau. Acad. Roy. des Sci., Brussels, Bull., 2, *1835*, pp. 52 and 89.

    58. G. N. Stewart. Roy. Soc. Edin., Proc., 15, *1887–8*, p. 441.

    59. E. P. Hyde. Bureau of Standards, Bull., 2, *1906*, p. 1.

    H. Köllner. Licht, 7, *1937*, pp. 55 and 75.

    C. S. Sherrington (Roy. Soc., Proc., 71, *1902*, p. 71) found a departure from Talbot's law in the case of binocular vision. See also E. Haschek, Wien Ber. (IIa), 138, *1929*, p. 17.

    The validity of the law for very short flashes of white light has been verified by T. E. Gilmer (Opt. Soc. Am., J., 27, *1937*, p. 386).

    60. An interesting application of persistence of vision to photometry is to be found in the instrument generally known as Wheatstone's photometer. See J. F. Daniell's *Introduction to the Study of Chemical Philosophy*, 2nd edit., *1843*, p. 172, or Engineering, 35, *1883*, p. 75. See also the refs. in note (47) on p. 78 of *Photometry* (1926).

    61. See Francis Bacon, *Novum Organum*, Lib. II, Aph. XLVI ; " At in visu (cujus actio est pernicissima) liquet etiam requiri ad eum actuandum momenta certa temporis . . . Videmus etiam species visibiles a visu citius excipi quam dimitti."

    62. A. Broca and D. Sulzer. C.R., 134, *1902*, p. 831 ; J. de Physiol. et de Path. Gén., 4, *1902*, p. 632.

    63. It is to be noted that the ordinates in Fig. 41 show the values of brightness of a continuously exposed field which appears to match another with the brightness stated as the " final " value, when this is exposed for the times shown by the abscissae.

    64. A. Broca and D. Sulzer. C.R., 137, *1903*, pp. 944, 977 and 1046 ; J. de Physiol. et de Path. Gén., 6, *1904*, p. 55.

    N. Kleitman and H. Piéron. C.R., 180, *1925*, p. 393.

    W. H. Stainton. Opt. Soc. Am., J., 16, *1928*, p. 26.

    Differences in the rate of rise for different colours would explain the appearance of Benham's top (C. E. Benham and others, Nature, 51, *1895*, pp. 113, 167, 200, 292, 321 and 510). See W. S. Duke-Elder, *Text-book of Ophthalmology*, p. 933.

    The similar effect in the case of point sources was investigated by C. Gallissot (C.R., 155, *1912*, p. 1590).

    65. See, e.g. J. H. Parsons, *Colour Vision*, pp. 113 *et seqq.* or W. S. Duke-Elder, *Text-book of Ophthalmology*, pp. 954 *et seqq.* The after-image known as Bidwell's ghost (or the Purkinje after-image) is there described.

    66. M. Luckiesh. Phys. Rev., 4, *1914*, p. 1.

    H. E. Ives and E. F. Kingsbury. Phys. Rev., 7, *1916*, p. 149.

    H. E. Ives. Opt. Soc. Am., J., 6, *1922*, p. 254.

67. E. L. Nichols. Am. J. Sci., 28, *1884*, p. 243.

E. S. Ferry. Am. J. Sci., 44, *1892*, p. 192.

T. C. Porter. Roy. Soc., Proc., 63, *1898*, p. 347 ; 70, *1902*, p. 313 ; 86, *1911-12*, p. 495.

F. Allen. Phil. Mag., 38, *1919*, p. 81 ; Opt. Soc., Am., J., 13, *1926*, p. 383.

R. J. Lythgoe and K. Tansley. " The Adaptation of the Eye ; its Relation to the Critical Frequency of Flicker." Medical Research Council Special Report No. 134 (H.M. Stationery Office, *1929*). This paper contains an extensive bibliography.

R. J. Lythgoe and K. Tansley. Roy. Soc. Proc. (B), 105, *1929*, p. 60.

S. Hecht *et al.* J. Gen. Physiol., 17, *1933*, p. 237 and 19, *1936*, p. 965 ; Nat. Acad. Sci., Proc., 19, *1933*, p. 522. (Note : In the 1933 papers the values of retinal illumination should be multiplied by 40.)

See also P. W. Cobb, Opt. Soc. Am., J., 24, *1934*, pp. 91 and 107.

68. See, e.g. P. Woog, C.R., 168, *1919*, p. 1222 ; S. Hecht and others, loc. cit. note 67 supra ; R. S. Creed and T. C. Ruch, J. of Physiol., 74, *1932*, p. 407.

69. Y. Le Grand and E. Geblewicz, C.R., 205, *1937*, p. 297.

70. H. E. Ives. Phil. Mag., 24, *1912*, p. 352.

71. J. S. Dow. Electrician, 59, *1907*, p. 255.

See also A. E. Kennelly and S. E. Whiting, El. World, 49, *1907*, p. 1208.

72. See, e.g. E. C. Crittenden, Illum. Eng. Soc. N.Y., Trans., 19, *1924*, p. 194 and the individual data given by Gibson and Tyndall, loc. cit., note (76).

73. C.I.E., Proc., 6, *1924*, p. 67.

Comité Int. des Poids et Mesures, Proc. Verb., 15, *1933*, pp. 202 and 65.

74. See the papers referred to in notes (2) to (9) and (12) to (15) on p. 311 of *Photometry (1926)*. See also R. Weigel, Licht, 5, *1935*, pp. 15, 43 and 71 (also pp. 259 and 275) and H. Lüthy, Helv. Phys. Acta, 15, *1942*, p. 343 and J. Schiess, Lichttechnik, 3, *1951*, pp. 57 and 85. For values of V_λ from 0·70 to 0·90μ see C. F. Goodeve, Roy. Soc., Proc. (A), 155, *1936*, p. 664.

75. H. E. Ives. Phil. Mag., 24, *1912*, p. 853.

P. G. Nutting. Illum. Eng. Soc. N.Y., Trans., 9, *1914*, p. 633.

W. Coblentz and W. B. Emerson. Bureau of Standards, Bull., 14, *1918*, p. 167.

76. E. P. Hyde, W. E. Forsythe and F. E. Cady. Astrophys., J., 48, *1918*, p. 65.

K. S. Gibson and E. P. T. Tyndall. Bureau of Standards, Bull., 19, *1923*, p. 131 ; Illum. Eng. Soc. N.Y., Trans., 19, *1924*, p. 176.

For an outline of a method not involving heterochromatic comparison see P. Fleury, C.R., 214, *1942*, p. 706.

77. K. S. Gibson. C.I.E., Proc., 6, *1924*, p. 232.

See also H. E. Ives, Phil. Mag., 24, *1912*, p. 853.

Certain workers (W. Arndt, Licht, 6, *1936*, p. 75 ; A. Dresler, *ibid.*, 7, *1937*; pp. 81 and 107 ; N. T. Fedorov and V. I. Fedorova, Acad. Sci. U.R.S.S., C.r. (Doklady), 11, *1936*, p. 377 ; A. Dresler, Z. f. techn. Phys., 19, *1938*, pp. 206 and 369 ; P. Jainski, Licht u. Lampe, 27, *1938*, p. 689 ; J. S. Preston, Phys. Soc., Proc., 50, *1938*, p. 398 and 51, *1939*, p. 757 ; M. Jaggi, Helv. Phys. Acta, 12, *1939*, p. 77 ; A. Dresler, Naturwiss., 29, *1941*, p. 225 ; E. Buchwald, Phys. Z., 42, *1941*, p. 378 ; N. T. Fedorov *et al.*, J. of Phys. U.S.S.R., 3, *1940*, p. 5) have found minor departures from the international values, especially on the short-wave side of the maximum, but the differences are not sufficient to invalidate these values as sufficiently representative of the average eye for the purposes of photometry (C.I.E., Proc., 10, *1939*, Vol. I, p. 44 and Vol. III, p. 2 ; H. König, Assn. Suisse Elect., Bull., 30, *1939*, p. 729 ; K. S. Gibson, Opt. Soc. Am., J., 30, *1940*, p. 51 ; J. S. Preston, Illum. Eng. Soc. Lond., Trans., 5, *1940*, p. 109).

78. W. S. Stiles and T. Smith. Phys. Soc., Proc., 56, *1944*, p. 251.

B. H. Crawford. Roy. Soc., Proc. (B), 62, *1949*, p. 321.

See also K. S. Weaver, Opt. Soc. Am., J., 27, *1937*, p. 36 ; N. I. Pinegin, Acad. Sci. U.R.S.S., C.r. (Doklady) 30, *1941*, p. 3 ; R. G. Weigel and O. H. Knoll, Licht, 12, *1942*, p. 160 ; A. H. Taylor, Illum. Eng. Soc. N.Y., Trans., 38, *1943*, p. 89 ; G. Wald, Science, 101, *1945*, p. 653 ; W. S. Stiles, Nederlandsch Tijdschrift Natuurkunde, 15, *1949*, p. 125.

The curve shown in Fig. 44 is drawn from the table of values adopted internationally by the C.I.E. in 1951.

79. J. Purkinje. Magazin f. d. ges. Heilkunde, etc. (Berlin), 20, *1825*, p. 199.

Note : The form of the name used in this book is that customary in the literature.

It is the transliteration which appears in the periodical quoted above ; the pronunciation should therefore be as in German. The transliteration used in the International Catalogue of Scientific Literature is Purkyně.

80. See, e.g. L. T. Troland, Frank. Inst., J., 182, *1916*, p. 111.

81. H. V. Walters and W. D. Wright. Roy. Soc., Proc. (B), 131, *1943*, p. 340.
R. G. Weigel and O. H. Knoll. Licht, 12, *1942*, p. 192.
W. S. Stiles. Phys. Soc., Proc., 56, *1944*, p. 329.

82. A. König. *Gesammelte Abhandlungen zur Physiologischen Optik* (Barth, Leipzig, *1903*), p. 144. On the magnitude of König's unit of retinal illumination see note 25.

K. S. Weaver. Opt. Soc. Am., J., 27, *1937*, p. 36.

83. W. D. Wright. *Researches, etc.*, p. 75.

84. O. Reeb and M. Richter. Licht, 4, *1934*, p. 59.
P. J. Bouma. Physica, 8, *1941*, p. 413 ; Philips, Tech. Rev., 1, *1936*, p. 142 and 6, *1941*, p. 161.
J. Wetzel. Soc. Franç. des Elect., Bull., 10, *1950*, p. 199.
See also H. Bertling, Licht u. Lampe, 23, *1934*, pp. 82, 130, 207 and 227 ; Licht, 4, *1934*, p. 98 ; Licht u. Lampe, 24, *1935*, p. 77 ; L. Schneider, *ibid.*, p. 159.

85. C.I.E., Proc., 11, *1948*, pp. 2 and 46.
Several other spectral distributions have been proposed ; see, e.g. A. Dresler. Licht, 10, *1940*, pp. 118 and 145 ; J. W. T. Walsh, Illum. Eng. Soc. Lond., Trans., 6, *1941*, p. 117 ; P. J. Bouma, Licht u. Lampe, 24, *1935*, p. 217 and Physica, 8, *1941*, p. 413 ; A. H. Taylor, Illum. Engng., 38, *1943*, p. 89 ; British Standard. for Fluorescent and Phosphorescent Materials, No. 1316, *1946* ; C.I.E., Proc., 11. *1948*, p. 156.

86. D. B. Judd. Opt. Soc. Am., J., 22, *1932*, p. 72.
W. D. Wright and F. H. G. Pitt. Phys. Soc., Proc., 46, *1934*, p. 459.
G. Haase. Ann. d. Phys., 20, *1934*, p. 75.
W. D. Wright. J. of Physiol., 88, *1936*, p. 167.
See also E. P. T. Tyndall, Opt. Soc. Am., J., 23, *1933*, p. 15 ; W. R. J. Brown and D. L. MacAdam, *ibid.*, 39, *1949*, p. 808.

87. L. C. Martin, F. L. Warburton and W. J. Morgan. " Determination of the Sensitiveness of the Eye to Differences in the Saturation of Colours." Medical Research Council Special Report No. 188 (H. M. Stationery Office, *1933*).
W. D. Wright. *Researches, etc.*, pp. 161 *et seqq.*

88. L. C. Martin *et al.* *Loc. cit. supra* and " Discussion on Vision " (Phys. and Opt. Socs., *1932*), p. 92.
L. A. Jones and E. M. Lowry. Opt. Soc. Am., J., 13, *1926*, p. 25.

89. I. G. Priest and F. G. Brickwedde. Bureau of Standards, J. of Research, 20, *1938*, p. 673.
D. McL. Purdy. Brit. J. of Psychol., 21, *1931*, p. 283.
W. D. Wright and F. H. G. Pitt. Phys. Soc., Proc., 49, *1937*, p. 329.
J. H. Nelson. Phys. Soc., Proc., 49, *1937*, p. 332.
See also W. D. Wright and F. H. G. Pitt, Phys. Soc., Proc., 47, *1935*, p. 205 ; J. G. Brennan and S. M. Newhall, Opt. Soc. Am., J., 38, *1948*, p. 696 ; Y. Le Grand, Rev. d'Opt., 29, *1950*, p. 79.

90. See, e.g. K. J. W. Craik and M. D. Vernon. Brit. J. of Psychol., 32, *1942*, p. 206 ; E. W. Godding, Roy. Soc. Medicine, Proc., 38, *1945*, p. 155.

91. W. de W. Abney and E. R. Festing. Phil. Trans., 183, *1892*, p. 531.
W. de W. Abney. Roy. Soc., Proc., 83, *1910*, p. 290. See also Phil. Trans., 190, *1897*, p. 155 and *Researches in Colour Vision* (Longmans, *1913*).
See also D. McL. Purdy, Brit. J. of Psychol., 21, *1931*, p. 283.

92. See, e.g. K. J. W. Craik and M. D. Vernon, Brit. J. of Psychol., 32, *1942*, p. 206.

93. W. S. Stiles and B. H. Crawford. Roy. Soc. Proc. (B), 113, *1933*, p. 496., W. S. Stiles. Roy. Soc., Proc. (B), 127, *1939*, p. 64.

94. A. Riccò. Regia Accad. di Sci., Modena, Mem., 17, *1877*, p. 47.

95. F. Löhle. Z. f. Phys., 54, *1929*, p. 137.
See also I, Langmuir and W. F. Westendorp, Physics, 1, *1931*, p. 273 ; Y. Le Grand and E. Geblewicz, C.R., 208, *1939*, p. 1845 ; R. G. Weigel and O. H. Knoll, Licht, 10, *1940*, p. 179.

96. F. Löhle, Z. f. Phys., 54, *1929*, p. 137
H. Borchardt. Z. f. Sinnesphysiologie, 48, *1914*, p. 176.
P. Reeves. Astrophys. J., 47, *1918*, p. 141.

G. Wald. J. Gen. Physiol., 21, *1938*, p. 269.

C. H. Graham *et al.* J. Exp. Psychol., 24, *1939*, pp. 555 and 574.

P. J. Bouma. Philips Tech. Rev., 3, *1939*, p. 15.

97. W. S. Stiles, M. G. Bennett and H. N. Green. " Visibility of Light Signals." Aeronautical Research Committee, Reports and Memoranda, No. 1793 (H.M. Stationery Office, *1937*).

See also C. Gallissot, *La photométrie du point lumineux, etc.* (Thèse, Faculté des Sci. de Lyon, *1921*.)

98. C.I.E., Proc., 9, *1935*, p. 164 and 10, *1939*, Vol. III, p. 1. (See also 8, *1931*, p. 316.)

A. Blondel. C.R., 192, *1931*, p. 782 ; Rev. Gén. de l'El., 32, *1932*, p. 3.

99. *Loc. cit.*, note 97, pp. 30 *et seqq.* (esp. p. 37).

See also J. M. Otero, L. Plaza and F. Salaverri, Opt. Soc. Am., J., 39, *1949*, p. 167.

100. *Loc. cit.*, note 97, p. 39.

See also G. A. W. Rutgers, Physica, 8, *1941*, p. 875 and P. J. Bouma, *ibid.*, p. 890.

101. *Loc. cit.*, note 97, p. 14.

102. B. H. Crawford. Roy. Soc., Proc. (B), 128, *1940*, p. 552.

103. I. Langmuir and W. F. Westendorp. Physics, 1, *1931*, p. 273.

B. Schönwald. Licht, 9, *1939*, pp. 197 and 245 ; 11, *1941*, p. 15.

P. J. Bouma. Physica, 8, *1941*, p. 398.

J. D. Lash and G. F. Prideaux. Illum. Eng. Soc. N.Y., Trans., 38, *1943*, p. 481.

H. A. Knoll, R. Tousey and E. O. Hulburt. Opt. Soc. Am., J., 36, *1946*, p. 480 (see also 37, *1947*, p. 59).

See also N. E. G. Hill, Phys. Soc., Proc., 59, *1947*, p. 574.

104. A. Blondel and J. Rey. J. de Phys., 1, *1911*, p. 530.

Loc. cit., note 97, p. 23.

On periodic lights see A. E. Schuil, Illum. Eng. Soc. Lond., Trans., 5, *1940*, p. 117.

105. See, e.g., H. Piéron, C.R., 170, *1920*, p. 1203.

106. A. M. Bloch. Soc. de Biologie, C.r., 37, *1885*, p. 493. (This rule is sometimes known as Bloch's law.)

A. Blondel and J. Rey. C.R., 178, *1924*, pp. 276 and 1245.

107. A. K. Toulmin-Smith and H. N. Green. Illum. Eng., 26, *1933*, p. 304.

108. A more elaborate formula is given by W. M. Hampton (Illum. Eng., 27, *1934*, p. 46).

See also G. K. Neeland, M. K. Laufer and W. R. Schaub, Opt. Soc. Am., J., 28, *1938*, p. 280.

109. For experimental determinations of the minimum steady radiation visually perceptible, see various authors in Astrophys. J., 44, *1916*, p. 124 ; 45, *1917*, p. 60 ; 46, *1917*, pp. 167 and 296 ; 47, *1918*, p. 141 and R. Hiecke, E.u.M., 50, *1932*, Licht-technik, p. 1.

110. S. Hecht, S. Shlaer and M. H. Pirenne. Science, 93, *1941*, p. 585 ; J. Gen. Physiol., 25, *1942*, p. 819.

M. H. Pirenne. *Vision and the Eye.* (Pilot Press, *1948*.)

See also J. von Kries, Z. f. Sinnesphysiologie, 41, *1906*, p. 373 ; H. de Vries, Physica, 10, *1943*, p. 553 ; H. A. van der Velden, Physica, 11, *1944*, p. 179 ; M. A. Bouman and H. A. van der Velden, Opt. Soc. Am., J., 37, *1947*, p. 908 and 38, *1948*, pp. 231 and 570.

111. See, e.g., L. H. Hardy, Illum. Engng., 36, *1941*, p. 295.

112. Z. f. Psychol. u. Physiol. d. Sinnesorgane, 9, *1896*, p. 81.

113. For a general discussion of night vision see, e.g. G. L. Walls, Illum. Engng., 39, *1944*, p. 93.

114. R. J. Lythgoe. Phys. Soc., Proc., 50, *1938*, p. 321. This paper contains an extensive bibliography.

See also E. E. Schneider, C. F. Goodeve and R. J. Lythgoe, Roy. Soc., Proc. (A), 170, *1939*, p. 102 ; S. Hecht, J. Applied Physics, 9, *1938*, p. 156.

115. Phil. Trans., 92, *1802*, p. 12.

116. See H. von Helmholtz, *Handbuch d. Physiol. Optik* (3 Aufl.), Vol. 2, pp. 120 *et seqq.* [143 *et seqq.*].

For an account of the principal theories of colour vision see J. H. Parsons, *Colour Vision.*

CHAPTER IV

PHOTO-ELECTRIC CELLS

THERE are two types of light-sensitive devices used in photometry which depend for their action on the release of electrons by light. They are both known as photo-electric cells or, more briefly, photocells, but as not only the construction, but also the action of the light and the method of use are different in the two types it is convenient to consider them separately.

Photo-electric Emission—One type of photocell, frequently particularised as a photo-emissive cell, depends upon the fact that for many metals, the incidence of radiation on the surface causes the emission of electrons from that surface. A metal can be pictured as containing a large number of ionised atoms, and a corresponding number of electrons moving more or less freely among the ions and the unionised atoms. Within the body of the metal there is no resultant force on such an electron but near the surface there is a resultant which is exerted inwards and tends to prevent the electron from leaving the metal. The energy that an electron must have in order that it may just escape from the surface is known as the work-function ϕ and this depends on the nature of the metal surface. ϕ is usually expressed in electron-volts (see p. 43).

When the radiation reaching a metal surface is such as to give some of the electrons close to the surface an energy greater than ϕ, these electrons may escape from the metal, so that it is left positively charged. If an electric field is then established with the metal as cathode, the emission of electrons becomes a continuous process as long as the radiation and the field persist. This is what takes place in the photo-emissive cell.

The Photo-electric Threshold—There are two laws governing the photo-electric emission of electrons, viz. (i) the rate of emission of electrons is proportional to the intensity of the radiation, so long as this is of constant spectral distribution ; (ii) the frequency of the radiation must be greater than a certain threshold value characteristic of the metal surface, and the maximum energy which any released electron can have is proportional to the difference between the frequency of the radiation and this threshold frequency [1].

The second of these laws is a direct consequence of the theory of photo-electric emission explained above, for if radiation of frequency ν falls on a metal surface, an electron can receive energy equal to the quantum energy $h\nu$ and if this exceeds the work-function ϕ the electron may leave the surface ; for radiation of any frequency less than ν_0, where $h\nu_0 = \phi$ no emission of electrons can take place. The following table shows the work-function of certain metals [2] and the corresponding values of λ_0, the longest wave-length giving photo-emission, known as the photo-electric threshold of the metal. It will be seen from the equation connecting ν_0 and ϕ that $\lambda_0 = 1239 \cdot 8/\phi$ if λ_0 is expressed in $m\mu$ and ϕ in volts (see p. 44).

TABLE I

Metal	Work-function	Photo-electric Threshold
Platinum -	6·30 volts	197 mμ
Tungsten -	4·54	273
Sodium - -	2·46	504
Potassium -	2·24	554
Rubidium -	2·18	568
Caesium - -	1·9	650

Spectral Selectivity—It will be noticed that so far nothing has been stated with regard to the relative effectiveness of radiation of different frequencies in producing emission. It would naturally be expected that the effectiveness would increase continuously with the frequency and this is true for most metals. Those for which the threshold lies in the visible spectrum or in the infra-red, particularly the alkali metals, are, however, remarkable in showing a greatly enhanced sensitivity over a limited range of frequencies, and since this range includes some or all of the visible spectrum it is these metals which are used in the construction of light-sensitive cells [3]. The maximum ordinates of the spectral sensitivity curves occur at longer wave-lengths and become progressively smaller in passing from sodium through potassium and rubidium to caesium [4].

It must be emphasised that photo-electric emission is a surface and not a bulk effect and is therefore greatly affected by the condition of the metal surface. The properties of many different kinds of surfaces have been studied [5] and it has been found that, by special treatment of an alkali metal or by the use of a thin film (of atomic dimensions) of such a metal deposited on some other metal, itself often specially treated, not only can the sensitivity be greatly increased but the form of the spectral sensitivity curve can be profoundly changed and the value of ϕ may be made much lower than that given in the above table [6].

The Photo-emissive Cell—A simple form of cell which depends for its action on the effect just described is shown in Fig. 49. It consists of an evacuated glass bulb into the centre of which projects a wire loop or a grid of platinum, nickel, or other suitable metal, to form the anode of the cell. The cathode consists of the sensitive surface,

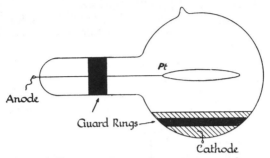

FIG. 49. A Simple Photo-emissive Cell.

formed on a backing layer of metal deposited on the wall of the bulb. Earthed metal guard rings on both the internal and the external surfaces of the glass are frequently provided to prevent conduction leakage over the surface of the glass between the anode and the cathode.

An alternative method of construction is that shown in Fig. 50. The anode in this case consists of an open wire mesh which covers the

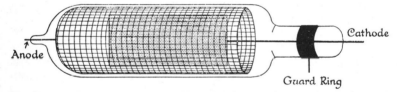

FIG. 50. A Photo-emissive Cell with Wire-mesh Anode.

internal surface of the bulb. The light passes through this mesh to the sensitive surface deposited on one side of the rectangular metal plate which forms the cathode of the cell.

Cells have been made with many different kinds of sensitive surface [7] but those most commonly employed in photometric work can be grouped in two classes. In the first, the surface consists of a very thin film of an alkali metal, usually potassium, rubidium or caesium, deposited on silver the surface of which has been oxidised [8]. In the case of the caesium cells the sensitive surface may consist of very thin films of caesium, caesium oxide, silver oxide and silver in various arrangements designed to give maximum sensitivity at different parts of the spectrum [9].

In cells of the second class the alkali metal, generally caesium, is deposited on a layer of a metal such as antimony or bismuth [10] or on a composite layer of bismuth, oxygen and silver [11]. The advantage of cells of this class is their high sensitivity over at least the greater part of the visible spectrum [12].

The Gas-Filled Cell—In the cells just described the bulb is exhausted to a high vacuum (10^{-6} mm. of mercury or less) after the process of forming the sensitive surface has been completed. There is, however, a different type of photo-emissive cell in which the bulb contains an inert gas or mixture of gases, frequently argon, at a pressure of less than one mm. of mercury [13]. The effect of the gas-filling is to enable a higher current to be obtained from a cell by increasing the voltage between the electrodes [14]. In the ordinary vacuum cell the photo-current approaches saturation at about 20 volts [15] as shown by the curve of Fig. 51. If the cell contains gas at

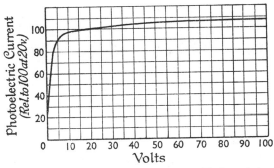

FIG. 51. A Voltage-current Curve for a Vacuum Photo-emissive Cell.

low pressure, however, the current at the higher voltages is greatly increased because these voltages impart a high velocity to the electrons emitted from the cathode and these ionise atoms of the gas by collision (cf. p. 43). The ions thus formed travel towards the electrodes and so the current passing through the cell is multiplied up to nine times. The voltage applied must be below that at which a glow discharge passes through the cell as this, if allowed to persist for even a short time, ruins the sensitive surface of the cell [16].

Secondary Emission and Photo-multiplier Cells—A method of increasing the sensitivity of a photocell without the disadvantages attendant on gas-filling is to cause the electrons emitted from the cathode to impinge on a second (or " target ") electrode with a sensitive surface, which may or may not be similar to that of the cathode [17]. This target electrode is maintained at a potential between that of the anode and that of the cathode so that, while acting as an anode to the latter, it acts as a cathode as far as the real anode is concerned. An electron emitted from the true cathode when it strikes the sensitive surface of the target electrode, causes it to emit several electrons which then travel to the anode and thus the photocurrent is increased, it may be fivefold or even more. The circuit is as shown in Fig. 52 ; the total voltage across the cell may in this case be about 400, with 100 volts between the target electrode and the anode.

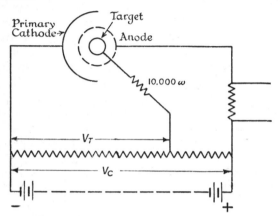

FIG. 52. Simple Circuit of Secondary Emission Photo-cell.

It will be clear that there is no reason why the process just described should not be applied to the electrons emitted from the target electrode and, in fact, the multiplication of the primary emission could, in theory, be repeated an indefinite number of times. This is the principle of the photo-multiplier cell, one form of which is shown diagrammatically in Fig. 53 [18]. K is the true cathode and M_1, M_2, etc., a series of fine mesh sensitised grids which act as intermediate electrodes, often called dynodes. P is a plate with a sensitive surface which acts as the final electrode before the grid anode A is reached. S is a metal shield which is at the same potential as K. The great advantage of the photo-multiplier cell is the extreme rapidity of its response to a transient or fluctuating illumination. In this respect it is greatly superior to a system consisting of an ordinary photo-emissive cell and an amplifier. It should be used under a constant illumination only when this is small ; otherwise the final current is likely to be sufficiently large to damage the electrodes by overheating them [19].

Characteristics of Photo-emissive Cells—For photometry, vacuum photocells are almost always preferable to gas-filled cells. The sensitivity of the latter is much affected by small changes in the gas pressure and by variations in the applied voltage, whereas with the vacuum cell the photocurrent for a given illumination is nearly

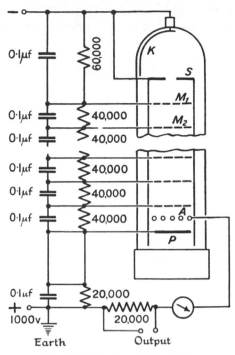

FIG. 53. A Photo-multiplier Cell.

independent of the applied voltage, provided this is higher than the saturation voltage at which practically all the electrons emitted at the cathode are collected at the anode. The working voltage for most vacuum cells is therefore between 20 and 30 volts (see Fig. 51).

A well-made vacuum cell of the thin-film alkali metal type is generally very stable over considerable periods of time, so long as care is taken not to overload it by taking too high a photocurrent [20].

The Relation between Photocurrent and Illumination: Linearity— For many purposes in photometry it is very desirable that the photocurrent should be strictly proportional to the illumination of the cell over as wide a range as possible [21]. In order to secure this the design and construction must be such that the electric field within the cell, when it is in use, is as uniform as possible. This implies, among other things, that the cathode should be a good conductor and electrically continuous. If this is not the case, semi-isolated parts of the cathode may reach relatively high potentials and, as a result of the field distortion so produced, the cathode may behave as if its effective area diminishes as the current it supplies decreases. The current-illumination characteristic of the cell then ceases to be linear. Discontinuity of the cathode is also a contributory factor in causing a " fatigue " effect, or gradual diminution of the photocurrent with sustained illumination of the cell [22].

The conditions mentioned above as desirable are generally more easily satisfied in a cell of the design shown in Fig. 50. Such a cell, when correctly constructed, usually exhibits only negligible fatigue and a departure from linearity of response of only a few parts in ten thousand over a range of 10 to 1 in illumination [23].

A form of cell designed specially with the object of securing the highest possible degree of linearity [24] is shown in Fig. 54. In this

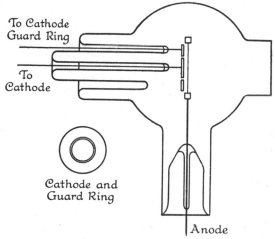

FIG. 54. A Photocell with Linear Response.

cell the cathode is in the form of a flat disc and is surrounded with a guard ring coplanar with it and of a breadth approximately equal to the radius of the disc. The cathode and guard ring leads are separated and the bulb is so designed that the leakage paths over the walls between these leads and the anode lead are quite long. The anode consists of a grid of parallel vertical tungsten wires 18μ in diameter and at a distance apart of the order of 0·25 to 1 mm. This anode is mounted 2 mm. in front of the cathode. The cathode and the guard ring both have the same sensitive surface and, in use, both are kept at the same potential with the result that every electron emitted from the cathode reaches some part of the anode. The saturation voltage is very low, usually less than 4 volts. This avoids the ionisation of any gas still present in the cell and minimises the possibility that positive ions may be emitted from the anode under bombardment by the photo-electrons. In a cell of this type the departures from linearity are too small to be measured with certainty.

Uniformity of the Sensitive Surface—It cannot be assumed in the case of any photocell that the sensitivity is uniform over the whole area of the cathode and in many photo-emissive cells it may vary greatly from one part of the sensitive surface to another [25]. This is an important consideration if the illumination of the cathode is at all uneven for any reason, e.g. if the cross-section of the beam of light to be measured is smaller than the sensitive surface [26] (see, e.g., p. 364).

The Effect of Temperature—Most cells have a perceptible temperature coefficient, the sensitivity decreasing with rise of temperature at a rate which may be in the neighbourhood of 0·2 per cent per degree centigrade [27]. Other components in the circuit in which a cell is used, particularly a resistance (Fig. 57) or a condenser (Fig.

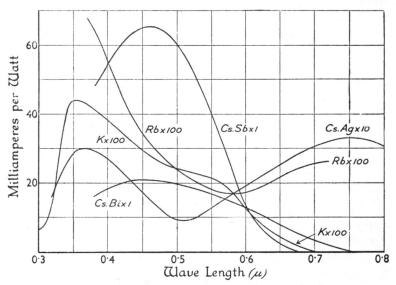

Fig. 55. Spectral Sensitivity Curves of Photo-emissive Cells.

56), may also show a temperature effect, although in the case of a condenser it is usually small enough to be neglected. If a colour filter is used for correcting the spectral sensitivity of the cell (see p. 112), this, too, will have a temperature coefficient.

Dark current—There is one characteristic of all photo-emissive cells which is of importance in photometry. This is the current which passes through the cell when no light is falling on the cathode [28]. This " dark current " is mainly due to thermionic emission from the cathode and so is related to the work-function of the sensitive surface. In general, therefore, it becomes more serious the longer the threshold wave-length, i.e. the more red-sensitive the cell. In any given cell it increases with temperature. For most potassium and rubidium cells, the dark current at room temperatures is too small to cause any difficulty, at any rate when they are used by the direct-reading method and the two readings required can be made quickly one after the other (see p. 99), but in a caesium cell which is sensitive in the infra-red (curve $Cs.Ag$ in Fig. 55), the thermionic current may be as much as 0·005 microamp. per sq. inch of cathode at 20° C. and double this at 30° C. In a caesium cell having a sensitivity curve similar to $Cs.Bi$ in Fig. 55, the dark current is very much smaller [29].

Intermittent Illumination—It has been found that in an emission photocell of the vacuum type the mean photocurrent for a certain average illumination is the same, no matter whether the illumination is steady or whether it is intermittent or fluctuating, at any rate within the limits of frequency normally met with in photometry as, for example, when using a sector disc. In other words, the cell obeys Talbot's law (see p. 67) and this irrespective of the degree of proportionality between illumination and photo-current for the particular cell used [30]. At the same time, when the illumination is fluctuating or intermittent, care must be taken to ensure that the characteristics of the electrical circuit in which the photocell is used are not such as to introduce errors. Gas-filled cells do not obey Talbot's law [31].

Spectral Sensitivity of Photo-emissive Cells—As would probably be expected, the curve of relative sensitivity of a photo-emissive cell for light of different wave-lengths is quite unlike the sensitivity curve of the average eye (see p. 72). In fact one cell differs noticeably from another in this respect, even when they are of the same type and of similar construction [32] and it is not possible, therefore, to do more than indicate the general form of the sensitivity curve for the types most commonly used in photometric work.

Fig. 55 shows typical curves for a thin film potassium cathode on silver oxide (K) and for three different types of caesium cells, viz. caesium on silver oxide ($Cs.Ag$), caesium on antimony and oxygen ($Cs.Sb$) and caesium on bismuth and oxygen ($Cs.Bi$). The sensitivity is expressed in terms of the photocurrent, in milliamperes, per watt of incident radiation. It will be noticed that the scale is different for the different curves, the caesium cells being much more sensitive than the potassium or rubidium. The ordinates must be divided by the figure shown against each curve, as this indicates the multiplier which has been used in drawing that curve.

There is some evidence that the spectral sensitivity curve of a photo-emissive cell is not independent of temperature changes [33].

Measurement of the Current from Photo-emissive Cells—There are several ways in which the small current given by a photo-emissive cell can be measured, but it is generally necessary to use an amplifier to increase the sensitivity. Direct reading methods have been employed [34] but these depend on a knowledge of the characteristics of the amplification system and some indirect method is usually preferable for accurate work. One such method depends on determining the rate at which the photocurrent charges a constant capacitor [35]. The amplifier is then used solely to facilitate the determination of the instant at which the capacitor reaches a certain voltage and no knowledge of the amplification factor is needed. In another method the photocurrent is exactly balanced by a current which can itself be accurately measured, the amplifier being used solely as a sensitive detector of the condition of balance.

The former of these two indirect methods can be explained by reference to Fig. 56. If the light falling on the photocell C is constant, the resulting photocurrent charges the condenser F at a steady rate and the increasing potential difference, applied to the grid of the electrometer triode V, causes a steady increase in the reading of the microammeter M. Thus the time taken for the needle of M to travel from one chosen reading to another is inversely proportional to the rate of charge of F and this rate is itself proportional to the sum of (a) the photocurrent through C, (b) any dark current and insulation leakages and (c) the grid current in V. Unless

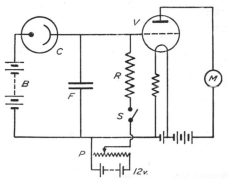

FIG. 56. The Measurement of Photo-current with a Capacitor.

(b) and (c) are together negligible compared with (a) it is necessary to take two timings, one (T_D) with the cell in the dark and the other (T) with it illuminated. The photocurrent is then proportional to $(1/T - 1/T_D)$. In practice, T_D should be at least equal to $10T$, or the inaccuracy introduced by uncertainty in the measurement of T_D is likely to be serious. It follows that if small photocurrents are to be measured, the cell should be one in which the dark current is small and the valve employed should be of a type such as the electrometer triode which has a small grid current [36].

The apparatus is set by bringing the grid of V to a suitable negative potential with respect to the filament so that a convenient indication is obtained on M. This is done by closing the switch S and thus connecting the grid through a high resistance R (of the order of 1000 megohms) to a potentiometer P. Alternatively, the apparatus may be set by reversing B and illuminating C, for every photocell, if sufficiently illuminated, gives enough emission in the reverse direction to bring the reading of M rapidly back to just below the desired starting point. B is then connected in the original sense and the apparatus is in readiness for another reading.

It will be seen that this apparatus can be used, not only to measure a steady illumination of constant value, but also to give the integral with respect to time of a fluctuating or transient illumination (see pp. 237 and 396) [37].

The Current-Balance Method of Measuring Photocurrent—A typical circuit often used when the current-balance method is

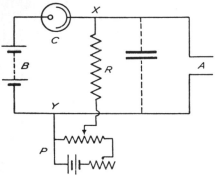

Fig. 57. The Current-Balance Method of measuring Photocurrent.

adopted is shown in Fig. 57 where C is the photocell, in series with the battery B, the high resistance R and the potentiometer P. A is a d.c. valve amplifier, the function of which is simply that of a very sensitive detector of small potential differences ; in other words, it acts as a super-sensitive galvanometer to indicate when the difference of potential between X and Y has been brought to zero or to a definite (though unknown) small value. The resistance of P must be negligible compared with that of R.

In order to measure the light reaching C it is necessary first to take a reading of A with C in the dark and P set at zero. Then, when C is illuminated, P is adjusted until the reading of A is the same as before. This indicates that the voltage drop due to the photocurrent flowing through R is exactly balanced by the opposing voltage injected at P. Thus, if R is constant, the reading of P is proportional to the photocurrent. Since the voltage supplied by P should, for a reason to be explained presently, be between 1 and 2 volts, it is convenient to have the value of R, in megohms, about the same as the reciprocal of the photocurrent to be measured, in microamperes. If R is too small the voltage injected at P is correspondingly small and therefore the sensitivity of the system is reduced, since this is limited by the smallest *difference* of potential that A can detect. It follows that means should, if possible, be

provided for changing the value of R to suit the magnitude of the
photocurrent to be measured [38]. The sensitivity of the circuit is
checked from time to time by finding the indication on A which
corresponds to a fixed out-of-balance setting on P.

The Amplifier[39]—It will be noticed that the chief requirement
of A is that it should be sensitive and have a stable zero. For this
reason use is frequently
made of a valve bridge [40]
to reduce the effect of drift
in the voltages of the supply
batteries, and Fig. 58 shows
a typical circuit in which
such a bridge is used [41].
R is the high coupling resistance and P the potentiometer of Fig. 57. V_1 and
V_2 are triodes (preferably
of the electrometer type
having a very high grid
insulation and low anode
voltage), R_1 and R_2 are high

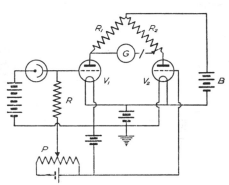

Fig. 58. A Valve-bridge Amplifier for
Measuring Photocurrents.

resistances (of the order of 10,000 ohms each, for electrometer triodes),
G is a galvanometer, not of especially high sensitivity, and B a
battery giving a voltage suitable for the valves used. The bridge is
first balanced by adjusting R_2 so that there is no deflection of G
when the input from the photocell circuit is zero. Any subsequent
lack of balance in this circuit, due to illumination of the photocell,
unbalances the bridge and causes G to deflect. The bridge balance
is then restored by adjusting P as explained above.

A still more sensitive arrangement [42] is that shown in Fig. 59.

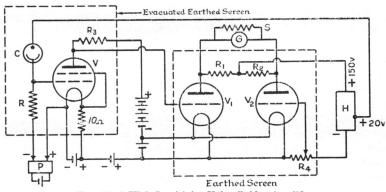

Fig. 59. A High Sensitivity Valve-Bridge Amplifier.

Here V is an electrometer tetrode coupled, through the very high resistance R_3 (of the order of 250,000 ohms), to a bridge system which is similar to that just described. This bridge is balanced independently of the first stage by adjustment of the grid bias of one valve (V_2) by means of a 500 ohm wirewound grid potentiometer R_4.

With this circuit a voltage change of one millivolt at the input stage gives a current of the order of 2 microamperes through the galvanometer and if R is, say, 10,000 megohms, this corresponds to a photocurrent of 10^{-13} amps., so that the amplification is over 10 million to one. Thus, if the cell gives 10^{-9} amps. for an illumination of 1 lumen per sq. metre, a galvanometer current of 1 microampere corresponds to an illumination of 10^{-4} lumens per sq. metre.

An alternative form of bridge in which only one valve is used [43] is shown in Fig. 60. R_1 is of the order of 5000 ohms and R_2 about

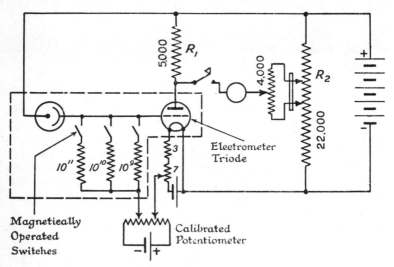

FIG. 60. Circuit of " Universal " Photo-electric Photometer.

20,000 ohms. Three alternative values of R are provided, viz., 10^9, 10^{10} and 10^{11} ohms respectively. Fig. 61 shows the complete instrument in which this circuit is used.

Of the circuits illustrated in Figs. 56 to 60, and others which have been described by various workers, each has its peculiar advantages and disadvantages [44]; that adopted for any particular photometric measurements must depend on the conditions under which those measurements are to be made.

A very slight elaboration of the circuit shown in Fig. 57, viz. the insertion of a variable resistor in the potentiometer circuit so that

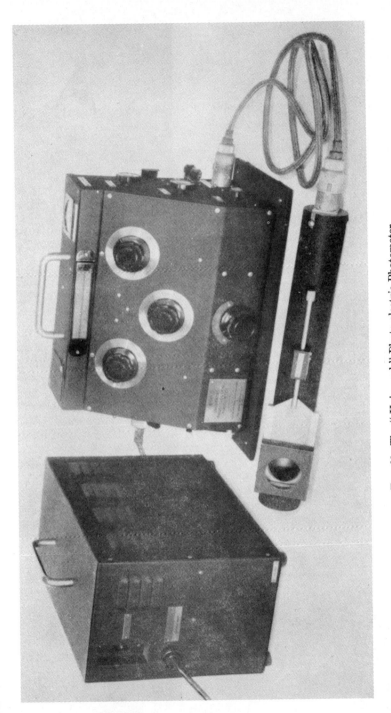

Fig. 61. The " Universal " Photo-electric Photometer.

(Photograph by courtesy of the Research Laboratories of The General Electric Co., Ltd., Wembley, England)

the current through P can be varied at will, is of great practical convenience in the routine measurement of lamps (see p. 274).

When the illumination of the cell is fluctuating or intermittent, e.g. when a sector disc is employed, or when a source with rapid periodic fluctuations of light output is being measured, the time constant of the circuit must be great enough to ensure that no ripple is imposed on the input circuit of A, for this, if large enough, might cause an error in the null indication, due to non-linear characteristics of the amplifier. The time constant may be increased by inserting a condenser, as shown by the broken lines in Fig. 57 so as to increase the inherent capacity of the grid circuit of the amplifier [45].

Leakage Prevention and Screening—There are certain precautions which have to be taken in the construction of apparatus of the very high sensitivity necessary for accurate measurement of the minute currents usual in photo-electric photometry. Leakages due to damp can be very troublesome and it is generally desirable to house the photocell, the high resistance R and the input valve V in an air-tight case containing a dessicant such as silica gel. Where very high values of R are used, e.g. 10^{10} ohms or more, these components are often placed in an evacuated vessel [46].

Electrostatic screening is generally necessary to reduce the effect of extraneous electrical disturbances. The components mentioned in the previous paragraph should always be screened, e.g. by enclosure within an earthed metal box provided with a glass window for admitting light to the cathode of the photocell. In cases where high sensitivity is aimed at, enclosure of the whole apparatus is desirable, separate sections being connected by means of screened cable.

The Photo-voltaic Cell—This type of photocell is entirely different, both in principle and in method of use, from the emission cell. Its outstanding feature is that it requires no battery, the current being generated by direct conversion of the energy of the incident light. The cell bears a similarity, both in construction and in mode of action, to the form of a.c. rectifier which consists of a metal plate coated with a layer of some semi-conducting material [47]. Such a device, of which the most familiar form is a copper plate coated on one face with a very thin film of cuprous oxide, can be used to obtain direct current from an alternating current supply because the resistance when the metal is negative with respect to the semi-conductor is very much less than when the polarity is reversed [48]. The effect occurs at the inter-face between the metal and the semi-conductor, as if there were a barrier layer there, opposing the flow of electrons from the semi-conductor to the metal. If a rectifier of this type is constructed with selenium as the semi-conductor, the metal being in the form of a film so thin as to be semi-transparent, it is found that when the film is illuminated, so that light passing through it reaches the barrier layer, a difference of potential is set up at this layer and the selenium takes up a positive potential with respect to the metal [49].

The form of construction usually adopted is shown in Fig. 62. The semi-conducting layer is of the grey (crystalline) variety of selenium [50], attached to a base-plate, usually of iron or aluminium. This layer is coated on its upper surface, generally by cathodic sputtering, with a very thin film of some non-corrodible metal, such as gold or platinum, with or without an intermediate film of some other semi-conductor or an insulator [51].

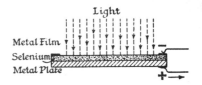

Fig. 62. The Photo-voltaic Cell.

Although the metal film should transmit as much light as possible to the interface or the barrier layer, it must be thick enough to ensure electrical continuity, i.e. all parts of it must be in good metallic connection with the collecting electrode, usually a strip of fusible metal at the periphery. This electrode is the negative pole of the cell, the positive being the metal base-plate in contact with the selenium.

This form of cell is sometimes known as a " barrier-layer cell " or, alternatively, a " rectifier cell " [52] as although the action of the light at the interface or barrier layer is not well understood, it seems certain that its connection with the rectifying properties of a similar system of metal and semi-conductor is not entirely fortuitous [53].

Photo-voltaic cells of good construction are reasonably robust and if carefully treated preserve their properties unchanged for a long time. The metal film is usually protected with a lacquer coating but in spite of this, care should be taken not to expose a cell to damp. High temperatures, too, may cause damage and the cell should preferably not be exposed to a high illumination while connected in a low-resistance circuit [54] or the current generated may be sufficient to cause damage to the thin metal film. Exposure to light under conditions in which the current through the cell is limited to the safe carrying capacity of the film causes no damage.

Characteristics of Photo-voltaic Cells—The current given by a photo-voltaic cell is never strictly proportional to the illumination of the cell over more than a limited range and the departure from this condition increases with the resistance in the circuit (including that of the cell itself) and with the current output, i.e. with the illumination [55]. An approximate figure for the sensitivity of a good cell is 300 to 500 microamperes per lumen, corresponding to about 0·5 to 0·8 microamps for an illumination of one lumen per square metre on

a circular cell 45 mm. in diameter.   Fig. 63*a* shows a typical series
of current-illumination curves for a cell in a circuit with different

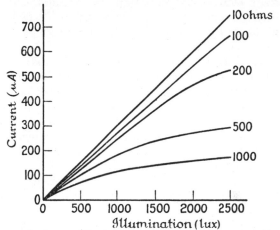

FIG. 63*a*. Current-Illumination Curves for a Photo-voltaic Cell.

values of external resistance.   The voltage-illumination curve is of
the kind shown in Fig. 63*b* [56] ; for a very high illumination the vol-

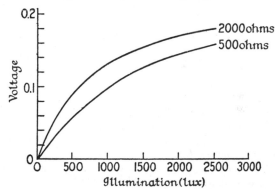

FIG. 63*b*. Voltage-Illumination Curves for a Photo-voltaic Cell.

tage approaches a limiting value which depends on the type of cell
but is usually less than 0·6 volt.   The voltage of a cell on open circuit
is subject to much greater uncertainties than the current under
fixed circuit conditions, so that for photometric work photo-voltaic
cells should never be used either on open circuit or in voltage opposition to one another.

All photo-voltaic cells show a " fatigue " or " drift " effect to a
greater or less extent, i.e. on exposure to a steady illumination
(unless this is very small) the current shows a slow drift, usually

downwards, which may persist for some considerable time, although the greater part of the effect occurs within the first few minutes [57]. The difference between the initial and final values, which may be several per cent, increases with the illumination. It depends on the wave-length of the light, being generally greater for the extreme red (about 0.65μ upwards) than for the other parts of the spectrum [58].

Uniformity of the Sensitive Surface—As in the case of the photo-emissive cell, it cannot be assumed that the sensitivity of a photo-voltaic cell is uniform over the whole of the surface (see p. 97) [59], and therefore the photocurrent produced by a given amount of flux incident on the cell may not be independent of the area over which the flux is distributed [60]. The illumination of one region does not, however, affect the response from other regions [61].

The Effect of Obliquity of the Incident Light—The sensitivity of a photo-voltaic cell depends on the angle at which the light is incident. For a given value of illumination the output of the cell falls off as the angle of incidence increases, though the effect is not consider-able at angles of less than about 50–60°. Fig. 64 shows the marked errors which occur when the light is incident very obliquely [62]. The effect is due, at any rate in great part, not to any change in the behaviour of the cell itself, but to increasing reflection of the incident light from the glossy lacquer or the glass plate covering the surface of the cell. The use of a matt lacquer or finish gives some improvement in this respect [63] but has certain disadvantages. A number of other devices have

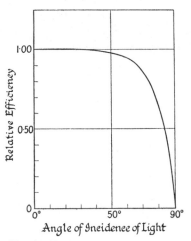

FIG. 64. Reduction of Sensitivity of a Photo-voltaic Cell with increasing Obliquity of the Incident Light.

been proposed for automatic correction of this obliquity error [64] but none has come into general use and in most cases the use of the cells under conditions which are likely to lead to considerable errors on this account can be avoided.

The Effect of Temperature—All photo-voltaic cells have a temperature coefficient which may be either positive or negative, depending on the construction of the cell, the external resistance in the circuit and the illumination of the cell [65]. In nearly all cases it is within ± 1.5 per cent per degree centigrade and for many cells it is considerably less, viz. in the neighbourhood of -0.3 per cent per degree. Some cells show a " hysteresis " effect, i.e. the current-illumination relationship at a given temperature depends to a certain extent on the previous history of the cell as regards temperature [66].

Intermittent Illumination—When the illumination of a photo-voltaic cell is fluctuating or intermittent, it cannot be assumed that the photocurrent is exactly that corresponding to the mean value of the illumination, i.e. that the cell obeys Talbot's law (see p. 67). The extent of the difference is not the same for all cells and it depends on the frequency of the interruption or fluctuation of the light [67]. As the frequency is increased the current approximates more and more closely to the value corresponding to the mean value of the illumination. The frequency necessary to ensure a given degree of approximation is higher the higher the circuit resistance.

Spectral Sensitivity—Photo-voltaic cells of the normal construc-

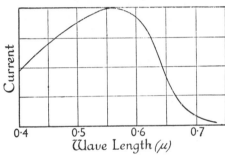

FIG. 65. Spectral Sensitivity Curve of a Photo-voltaic Cell.

tion described above are much more uniform than emission cells as regards their spectral sensitivity[68]. For most commercial cells the curve is of the general form shown in Fig. 65.

Circuits for Photo-voltaic Cells—The simplest form of circuit used with a photo-voltaic cell consists of a galvanometer or microammeter in series with the cell [69]. The effect of the external resistance (including that of the measuring instrument) on the proportionality between current and illumination has already been mentioned (see Fig. 63a). A simple circuit of this kind is used in many illumination photometers and the instrument is provided with a series of shunts as a convenient means of changing the range of the apparatus.

The effect of external resistance may be entirely eliminated by the use of the circuit shown in Fig. 66, gener-ally known as the Camp-bell-Freeth circuit [70]. C, the photocell, is connec-ted in series with a fixed

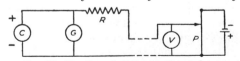

FIG. 66. The Campbell-Freeth Circuit for a Photo-voltaic Cell.

resistance R and a device for providing an adjustable potential difference P operating in the same sense as the photocell, not in opposition to it. G is a sensitive galvanometer and the potential, measured at V, is adjusted until G shows no deflection. Under these conditions the current passing through R is the same as that passing through C, i.e. it is the photocurrent i and therefore $Ri = P$. Thus if the value of R in megohms is roughly equal to the reciprocal of the photocurrent in microamperes, P will be in the neighbourhood of one volt. Further, since G shows no deflection at the instant when the value of P is observed, the potential difference across the cell terminals must be zero and so the cell is operating as though it were connected to a circuit of zero resistance.

It will be seen that with this circuit it is possible to obtain a very high sensitivity, since G is used solely as a balance indicator and is not in circuit with the photocell, so that it may have a high resistance without disadvantage.

The Application of Photocells to Photometry—The use of photocells for making photometric measurements of various kinds will be mentioned in later chapters where those measurements are dealt with in detail. Photo-electric methods have several advantages compared with visual methods, but at the same time they are subject to certain definite limitations [71]. Among the advantages are high speed of operation, a very much better precision, or degree of repetition, and freedom from the uncertainties which arise from the visual characteristics of individual observers. Accuracy is a different matter and will be discussed presently.

The photo-cell possesses one great advantage over the eye in that it is free from anything like the Purkinje effect : its relative response to light of different colours is unaffected by the value of the illumination at the sensitive surface so that all measurements are necessarily made on the same scale. It is therefore very valuable for certain types of photometric measurement in which it is difficult, if not impossible, to avoid reducing the luminance of the comparison surfaces in a visual photometer to values well within the Purkinje range of the eye (see p. 74). One important case is the determination of the light distribution curve of a lamp or fitting of large mechanical dimensions but not of correspondingly high intensity, at any rate in certain directions. A lower limit is set to the distance between the lamp and the photometer if the errors due to the size of the source are not to exceed a certain acceptable percentage (see p. 250), but the illumination at this distance is sometimes so low that visual photometry is likely to be subject to large errors unless there is a good match of spectral energy distribution in the photometer head. Again, when the total luminous flux output from a source of this kind is measured in a photometric integrator, as described in Chapter VIII, it is necessary to use a sphere, or other integrator, which is large in comparison with the source (see p. 282), but in some cases this reduces the luminance of the sphere window to such an extent that, again, visual photometry is both difficult and subject to error on account of the Purkinje effect.

The measurement of low values of illumination, such as are commonly met with in street lighting, is another field in which the photocell is much superior to the eye, especially in view of the wide range of spectral distributions given by the sources in common use for this class of lighting. It will be clear, however, that the very invariability of its spectral sensitivity, which makes the photocell so valuable in cases of the kind just mentioned, makes it quite useless for the measurement of equivalent luminance (see p. 74) ; this, by its very nature, is a measurement which can only be made visually.

Another outstanding advantage of the photocell is the facility with which it can be used to obtain a continuous record of fluctuations in the light to which it is exposed. It is also able to give a time integration of a variable or transient light, such as is required, for example, in the case of the sources of light of brief duration used in photography. It is, however, doubtful whether this can properly be regarded as a photometric measurement since the result has no meaning as far as the eye is concerned ; one light-sensitive device is here being used to obtain a measurement applicable to another such device.

The two types of photocell have their different characteristics which give them, to a great extent, different fields of usefulness [72]. The photo-emissive cell is by far the better for all purposes for which a very high sensitivity is required, or where stability, precision and proportionality of photocurrent to illumination are more important than portability or simplicity of the apparatus [73]. This cell is therefore extensively employed in laboratory work. It is also suitable for routine measurements with a permanently installed photometer [74]. The great advantages of the photo-voltaic cell are its robustness and the simplicity and portability of the apparatus used with it [75]. Further, since the sensitive surface of the cell is flat and unobstructed it lends itself readily to the measurement of illumination in any location or position. It is also used in certain laboratory work where high precision is not needed and where portability is necessary. Conversely, photo-emissive cells are sometimes used in portable apparatus designed for use outside the laboratory, particularly where high sensitivity is indispensable. This may appear surprising since, while the sensitivity of the photo-voltaic cell may, as already mentioned, be as high as 500 μA/lumen that of a photo-emissive cell is usually not greater than 10μA/lumen. The explanation is that valve amplification can be used to raise the sensitivity of a photo-emissive cell to as much as 20 amps./lumen without serious loss of stability, whereas in the case of a photo-voltaic cell the current can only be amplified by using some form of magnetic amplifier [76], although the use of a galvanometer amplifier is sometimes a convenient alternative [77].

The Balance Method of Photometry with Photocells—It has already been mentioned (see p. 64) that the only judgement which the eye can make with any precision is one of equality. Practically all visual photometry, therefore, depends on securing equality by altering, according to a known law, one or both of two illuminations. A photocell, however, is not subject to this limitation and can measure the ratio between two unequal illuminations, within the limits over which linearity or a known relation between illumination and photocurrent can be secured. The principle of adjustment to equality is, however, sometimes used in photo-electric photometry.

In the case of the photo-emissive cell the two sources in turn illuminate a single cell and the illuminations are adjusted, either by alteration of distance or otherwise, until the same photo-current is obtained in both cases (see p. 234). This adjustment is sometimes controlled by balancing each photo-current in turn against that given by a second cell the illumination of which is maintained at a constant value [78]. The arrangement is then exactly similar to that used for a visual measurement. Another method is to cause the light from the two sources to alternate rapidly on the cell and to use an amplifier and galvanometer, in conjunction either with a commutator synchronised with the alternating device, or with a valve rectifier, to detect inequality of the photocurrents [79].

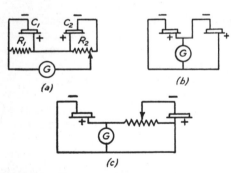

(a)

(b)

(c)

Fig. 67. The Balance Method of Photometry with Photo-voltaic Cells.

In the case of the photo-voltaic cell, two similar cells or a single symmetrically divided cell [80] may be used. A suitable circuit is shown in Fig. 67a. C_1, C_2 are the two cells or the two halves of a single cell, while R_1 and R_2 are two similar low resistances. G is a sensitive galvanometer and its point of connection to R_2 is adjusted until zero deflection is obtained when C_1 and C_2 are equally illuminated. The apparatus can then be used to indicate equality of illumination with a sensitivity depending upon the instrument used at G.

A circuit for which two separate cells are needed is shown in Fig. 67b. Here the cells are operated under short-circuit conditions and zero reading at G indicates equality of the photo-currents. This, however, does not correspond exactly to equality of the illuminations and so the apparatus indicates, not equality but a fixed ratio, usually not far from unity, of one illumination to another. Another circuit [81] of a similar kind is shown in Fig. 67c.

The method of alternating the two lights on a single cell, described above in connection with photo-emissive cells, has also been used with photo-voltaic cells [82].

The Accuracy of Measurement with Photocells—The accuracy of a photo-electric photometer, as distinct from its sensitivity [83], is greatly affected by two things, viz. (i) the proportionality of photo-current and illumination, often referred to as the " linearity " of the photocell and (ii) the degree to which the spectral sensitivity curve is identical with that of the eye (see p. 72).

It has already been mentioned that strict linearity can be secured by the use of a photo-emissive cell of suitable design (see p. 96), but that it is never obtained over any considerable range with a photo-voltaic cell even under the most favourable conditions (see p. 105). In the case of photo-voltaic cells it is advisable to use a cell which is no larger than is required to give a photo-current sufficient for accurate measurements to be made at illuminations within the range under consideration. It follows that the larger sizes of cell should be used only in the measurement of very low values of illumination. When the area which can be illuminated is limited, the cell used should preferably have a sensitive surface which is no larger than this, so that the uncertain shunting effect of the unilluminated cell surface is avoided [84].

Sometimes, especially with photo-voltaic cells, lack of linearity of the cell is allowed for, either in the calibration of the instrument in which it is used, or by the use of an experimentally determined photo-current—illumination curve. Such a curve can be conveniently found for any particular photocell by exposing it to the light from a number of lamps mounted side by side, either in a whitened enclosure [85] or behind a screen with a number of independent shutters [86]. The lamps are lit (in the first case) or exposed (in the second case), both individually and then in convenient combinations, and from the results obtained the response curve is plotted for the range of illumination from that given by a single lamp to that given by all the lamps together. It should be noted that even when cells are used, as in the circuit shown in Fig. 67a, to adjust two illuminations to equality, errors may be introduced unless both cells have the same response curve.

The Correction of Spectral Sensitivity by Colour Filters—Since light is defined by reference to the response which it evokes in the average eye (see p. 120), it is clear that, except in cases where the difference of spectral distribution between the lights being compared is absent or negligible, some means must be found to correct every cell used in photometry so as to bring its spectral sensitivity curve as close as possible to the photopic curve in Fig. 44 (p. 73).

The obvious way in which this can be attempted is to use with each cell a colour filter which, in general terms, has a high transmission at those wave-lengths for which the relative sensitivity of the cell is lower than that of the eye and a low transmission for light to which the sensitivity of the cell is too great [87]. The whole subject of colour filters will be dealt with in Chapter IX, and the way in which the spectral sensitivity curve of a cell may be determined will be described in Chapter XI (see page 364). Here it is sufficient to say that it is usually possible to prepare, from a limited number of stable inorganic salts in solution, a liquid filter which will correct the sensitivity curve of any photocell to that of the eye with a degree of approximation adequate for many fields of photometric measurement [88], although the advent of the discharge tube form of light source in its many different varieties has raised acutely certain problems which occur both in visual and in photo-electric photometry alike (see p. 312).

Correction Factors for Coloured Light—It is, of course, possible to avoid the use of a correcting filter by applying to the readings given by a photocell a multiplying factor calculated from the spectral sensitivity curve of the cell and the spectral energy distribution curve of the light being measured. This procedure is extensively used in illumination photometry (see p. 394) and is generally satisfactory where no great accuracy is required [89]. It may be mentioned here that if a photo-voltaic cell is used without a correcting filter for measuring the light from tungsten filament lamps at various efficiencies, ranging from that of the vacuum lamp to that of the projector type of gas-filled lamp, the error is not likely to exceed about 3 to 5 per cent if the cell has been calibrated to read correctly for a general service gas-filled lamp running at normal efficiency.

As will be seen later, there are certain photometric measurements in which no colour difference is involved and for which, therefore, the spectral sensitivity of the photocell is unimportant [90]. One example is the determination of curves of light distribution (see Chapter VIII) in which all the measurements save one are purely relative. The principal requirement in this case is strict linearity of response of the cell over a fairly wide range of illumination. Other examples are (i) the measurement of the transmission factors of neutral media (see p. 435) and (ii) the automatic recording of a variable illumination (see p. 395). In spectrophotometry (see page 362) the photo-emissive cell is unrivalled because the light used is practically mono-chromatic so that no question of spectral sensitivity correction arises and full advantage can be taken of the high precision available.

Other Sources of Error—Errors in photo-electric photometry are often caused by temperature changes which may affect not only the photocell itself but the auxiliary apparatus, particularly the colour filter if one is used for correcting the spectral sensitivity curve of the cell.

Mention should also be made of the effect of polarisation of the light incident on a photocell. If the light is incident normally on the surface there can be no effect, but in the case of obliquely incident light, the photo-current depends on the relation between the plane of polarisation and the plane of incidence. This is true both for photo-emissive [91] and for photo-voltaic cells [92] but the effect is very different in the two cases. It is very unusual in photometric work to illuminate a photo-emissive cell with other than normally incident light, though if the cathode is not plane some parts of its surface are illuminated obliquely. Photo-voltaic cells are frequently used for illumination measurements with obliquely incident light and if, as in the case of daylight, the light is partially polarised the measurements may be in error to a greater or less extent on this account.

From all that has been stated above it will be clear that both visual and photo-electric photometry have their respective fields of usefulness, though these are by no means mutually exclusive. There is much overlapping and the choice of the most appropriate method in any particular case calls for a thorough knowledge of both and for judgement based to a great extent on practical experience.

BIBLIOGRAPHY

PHOTO-ELECTRICITY

H. S. Allen. *Photo-electricity.* (Longmans, *1925.*)

B. Gudden. *Lichtelektrische Erscheinungen.* (Springer, Berlin, *1928.*)

A. Ll. Hughes and L. A. DuBridge. *Photo-electric Phenomena.* (McGraw-Hill, *1932.*)

PHOTO-ELECTRIC CELLS

V. K. Zworykin and E. G. Ramberg. *Photo-electricity and Its Application.* (Wiley, N.Y., *1949.*)

R. Fleischer and H. Teichmann. *Die Lichtelektrische Zelle.* (Steinkopff, Dresden, *1932.*)

G. Déjardin. Rev. Gén. de l'El., 33, *1933*, pp. 3 and 36 ; 34, *1933*, pp. 515, 555, 591 and 629.

N. R. Campbell and D. Ritchie. *Photo-electric Cells.* (Pitman, *1934.*)

R. C. Walker and T. M. C. Lance. *Photo-electric Cell Applications.* (Pitman, *1938.*)

A. Sommer. *Photo-electric Tubes.* (Methuen, *1951.*)

J. D. McGee. Inst. El. Eng., Proc., 104, *1957*, Part B, p. 467.

F. A. Benson. Illum. Eng. Soc., Lond., Trans. 23, *1958*, p. 127.

PHOTO-ELECTRIC PHOTOMETRY

H. Simon and R. Suhrmann. *Lichtelektrische Zellen und ihre Anwendung.* (Springer, Berlin, *1932.*)

R. Sewig. *Objektive Photometrie.* (Springer, Berlin, *1935.*)

B. Lange. *Photoelemente und ihre Anwendung.* (Barth, Leipzig, *1940.*) Eng. trans. of 1st. edit. by A. St. John. (Reinhold, N.Y., *1938.*)

J. S. Preston. Illum. Eng. Soc., Lond., Trans., 8, *1943*, p. 121.

J. Terrien. Mesures (Paris), 13, *1948*, pp. 77, 111, 149, 187 and 231.

G. T. Winch. Inst. El. Eng., J., 96, *1949*, Part II, p. 452.

REFERENCES

1. A. Einstein. Ann. d. Phys., 17, *1905*, p. 132.
R. A. Millikan. Phys. Rev., 7, *1916*, p. 355.

2. A. L. Reimann. *Thermionic Emission* (Chapman and Hall, *1934*), p. 99.

3. The pioneers in the development of the alkali metal photocell were J. Elster and H. Geitel (see Ann. d. Phys., 38, *1889*, p. 497 ; 41, *1890*, p. 161 ; 42, *1891*, p. 564 ; 43, *1891*, p. 225 ; 46, *1892*, p. 281 and 48, *1893*, p. 625). For this reason this type of cell was at one time known as the Elster-Geitel cell.

4. See A. L. Hughes and L. A. DuBridge, *Photo-electric Phenomena*, pp. 160-163 ; E. F. Seiler, Astrophys. J., 52, *1920*, p. 129.

5. See, e.g. H. E. Ives, Astrophys. J., 60, *1924*, p. 209 and 62, *1925*, p. 309 , H. E. Ives and A. L. Johnsrud, Opt. Soc. Am., J., 15, *1927*, p. 374 ; N. R. Campbell, Phil. Mag., 6, *1928*, p. 633 ; H. E. Ives and H. B. Briggs, Phys. Rev., 38, *1931*, p. 1477 ; A. L. Hughes and L. A. DuBridge, *Photo-electric Phenomena*, Chap. XII.

6. The first to use sensitized surfaces of the alkali metals were J. Elster and H. Geitel (see Phys. Z., 11, *1910*, pp. 257 and 1082 ; 12, *1911*, p. 609 and 13, *1912*, p. 468). There is now a vast literature on this subject and for further details the books cited in the Bibliography should be consulted, especially those by Hughes and DuBridge, by Zworykin and Ramberg and by Campbell and Ritchie.

7. J. Elster and H. Geitel, *loc. cit.* notes (3) and (6).
R. Lindemann. Ann. d. Phys., 19, *1906*, p. 807.
A. L. Hughes. Phil. Mag., 25, *1913*, p. 679.
J. Kunz and J. Stebbins. Phys. Rev., 7, *1916*, p. 62.
R. C. Burt. Phil. Mag., 49, *1925*, p. 1168.
L. Márton and E. Rostás. Z. f. techn. Phys., 10, *1929*, p. 52.
V. K. Zworykin and E. D. Wilson. Opt. Soc. Am., J., 19, *1929*, p. 81.
P. Selényi. " Photo-electric Cells and their Applications." Phys. and Opt. Socs., *1930*, p. 25.
T. W. Case. *Ibid.*, p. 49. (See also Phys. Rev., 17, *1921*, p. 398.)
J. Kunz. *Ibid.*, p. 61.
A. R. Olpin. Phys. Rev., 36, *1930*, p. 251.
G. Déjardin. Rev. d'Opt., 9, *1930*, p. 337.
W. Kluge. Z. f. Phys., 67, *1931*, p. 497.
V. K. Zworykin. Frank. Inst., J., 212, *1931*, p. 1.
R. Jouaust. Soc. Franç. des Elect., Bull., 2, *1932*, p. 1024.

8. S. Asao. Physics, 2, *1932*, p. 12.
W. Kluge. Phys. Z., 34, *1933*, p. 115. .

9. L. R. Koller. Opt. Soc. Am., J., 19, *1929*, p. 135 ; Phys. Rev., 36, *1930*, p. 1639.
R. Suhrmann. Z. wiss. Photog., 29, *1930*, p. 156.
J. H. de Boer and M. C. Teves. Z. f. Phys., 65, *1930*, p. 489 and 74, *1932*, p. 604.
L. J. Davies and H. R. Ruff. " Photo-electric Cells and their Applications," Phys. and Opt. Socs., *1930*, p. 43.
N R. Campbell. *Ibid.*, p. 10 ; Phil. Mag., 12, *1931*, p. 173.

S. Asao and M. Suzuki. Inst. Radio Eng., Proc., 19, *1931*, p. 655.
M. C. Teves. Z. f. techn. Phys., 12, *1931*, p. 556.
R. Sewig. Z. f. Phys., 76, *1932*, p. 91.
C. H. Prescott and M. J. Kelly. Bell System Techn. J., 11, *1932*, p. 334 ;
Am. Electrochem. Soc., Trans., 62, *1932*, p. 297.
P. Görlich. Z. f. Phys., 116, *1940*, p. 704.
W. Hartmann. Z. f. techn. Phys., 24, *1943*, p. 111 (with bibliography).
T. M. C. Lance. Electronic Engng., 15, *1943*, p. 501.

10. P. Görlich. Z. f. Phys., 101, *1936*, p. 335 ; Z. f. techn. Phys., 18, *1937*, p. 460 ;
Z. f. Phys., 109, *1938*, p. 374 ; Phil. Mag., 25, *1938*, p. 256.
P. Görlich et al. Z. f. I., 56, *1936*, p. 423 and 57, *1937*, p. 249.
Various authors in Jurnal technicheskoi Fisiki, U.S.S.R., 7,*1937*, p. 1900 ; 8,
1938, p. 2103 and 9, *1939*, pp. 376 and 661. (In Russian.)
P. Görlich. Opt. Soc. Am., J., 31, *1941*, p. 504.
A. Sommer. Phys. Soc., Proc., 55, *1943*, p. 145.

11. British Patents Nos. 532,259 and 540,739 (1939-40).

12. A. Sommer. Television Soc., J., 4, *1944*, p. 51 ; *Photo-electric Tubes*, pp. 36
and 47.
See also J. S. Preston, Rev. d'Opt., 27, *1948*, p. 513.

13. See, e.g. J. G. Kemp, Phys. Rev., 1, *1913*, p. 274 ; L. R. Koller, Opt. Soc. Am.,
J., 19, *1929*, p. 135 ; K. H. Kingdon and H. E. Thomson, Physics, 1, *1931*, p. 343.

14. See, e.g. N. R. Campbell, Phil. Mag., 3, *1927*, p. 945 ; G. A. Boutry, J. de
Phys., 3, *1932*, p. 520.

15. A. Sommer. *Photo-electric Tubes*, p. 62.
See also H. E. Ives and T. C. Fry, Astrophys. J., 56, *1922*, p. 1.

16. H. Rosenberg. Z. f. Phys., 7, *1921*, p. 18.

17. H. Iams and B. Salzberg. Inst. Radio Eng., Proc., 23, *1935*, p. 55.
R. Kollath. Phys. Z., 38, *1937*, p. 202.
General Electric Coy., Ltd. J. Sci. Inst., 14, *1937*, p. 250.
V. K. Zworykin, J. E. Ruedy and E. W. Pike. J. Applied Phys., 12, *1941*,
p. 696.
F. Trey. Phys. Z., 44, *1943*, p. 38.

18. H. Simon and R. Suhrmann. *Lichtelektrische Zellen*, p. 99.
P. Görlich. Z. f. Phys., 96, *1935*, p. 588.
G. Weiss. Z. f. techn. Phys., 17, *1936*, p. 623.
R. C. Winans and J. R. Pierce. Rev. Sci. Inst., 12, *1941*, p. 269.
For descriptions of other forms of photo-multiplier cells see, e.g., V. K. Zworykin,
G. A. Morton and L. Malter, Inst. Radio Eng., Proc., 24, *1936*, p. 351 ; V. K. Zwory-
kin and J. A. Rajchman, *ibid.*, 27, *1939*, p. 558 ; W. Kluge, O. Beyer and H. Steyskal,
Z. f. techn. Phys., 18, *1937*, p. 219 ; W. H. Rann, J. Sci. Inst., 16, *1939*, p. 241 ;
C. C. Larson and H. Salinger, Rev. Sci. Inst., 11, *1940*, p. 226 ; R. B. Janes and A. M.
Glover, R.C.A. Rev., 6, *1941*, p. 43 ; J. A. Rajchman and R. L. Snyder, Electronics,
13, *1940*, Dec., p. 20 ; M. C. Teves, Philips Techn. Rev., 5, *1940*, p. 253.
On the characteristics of photo-multiplier cells see R. W. Engstrom, Opt. Soc. Am.,
J., 37, *1947*, p. 420 ; S. Rodda, J. Sci. Inst., 26, *1949*, p. 65 ; also S. F. Rodionov,
Jurnal technicheskoi Fisiki, U.S.S.R., 9, *1939*, p. 1180 (In Russian).

19. A. Sommer. Electronic Engng., 17, *1944*, p. 164.

20. See, e.g. H. H. Poole and W. R. G. Atkins, Phil. Trans. (A), 235, *1936*, p. 1 ;
W. Kluge, E.T.Z., 57, *1936*, p. 145 ; J. S. Preston, Illum. Eng. Soc. Lond., Trans., 8,
1943, p. 121 ; A. Sommer, Electronic Engng., 17, *1945*, p. 504.

21. F. K. Richtmyer. Phys. Rev., 29, *1909*, pp. 71 and 404.
J. Elster and H. Geitel. Phys. Z., 14, *1913*, p. 741, 15, *1914*, p. 610 and 17,
1916, p. 268.
H. E. Ives. Astrophys. J., 39, *1914*, p. 428.
H. E. Ives, S. Dushman and E. Karrer. *Ibid.*, 43, *1916*, p. 9.
J. Kunz. *Ibid.*, 45, *1917*, p. 69.
H. Geitel. Ann. d. Phys., 67, *1922*, p. 420.
H. v. Halban and L. Ebert. Z. f. Phys., 14, *1923*, p. 182.
N. R. Campbell and E. G. New. J. Sci. Inst., 3, *1925*, pp. 2, 38 and 77.
G. Kortüm. Phys. Z., 32, *1931*, p. 417.

22. This " fatigue " effect is generally much more pronounced in gas-filled than in
vacuum cells (A. Sommer, *Photo-electric Tubes*, p. 77).

23. J. S. Preston and L. H. McDermott. Phys. Soc., Proc., 46, *1934*, p. 256.

24. G. A. Boutry. C.R., 204, *1937*, p. 120.

G. A. Boutry and P. Gillod. C.R., 206, *1938*, p. 1807 ; Phil. Mag., 28, *1939*, p. 163.

25. J. Terrien, C. Anglade and G. Touvay. C.R., 225, *1947*, p. 1142.

N. Laycock and G. T. Winch. *Ibid.*, 226, *1948*, p. 1445.

J. Terrien. Mesures, 13, *1948*, p. 149.

26. T. H. Harrison. "Photo-electric Cells and their Applications," Phys. and Opt. Socs., *1930*, p. 118.

P. Fleury. Rev. d'Opt., 11, *1932*, p. 385.

27. J. S. Preston. Illum. Eng. Soc. Lond., Trans., 8, *1943*, p. 121.

J. C. Peters and E. B. Woodford. Physics, 3, *1932*, p. 172.

28. A. Sommer. *Photo-electric Tubes*, p. 95.

29. J. S. Preston. *Loc. cit.* note (27).

30. E. Marx and K. Lichtenecker. Ann. d. Phys., 41, *1913*, p. 124.

C. Müller and R. Frisch. Z. f. techn. Phys., 9, *1928*, p. 445.

G. H. Carruthers and T. H. Harrison. Phil. Mag., 7, *1929*, p. 792.

W. S. Stiles. *Ibid.*, p. 812.

See, however, G. A. Boutry, C.R., 202, *1936*, p. 1580.

31. See, e.g. N. R. Campbell *et al.*, "Photo-electric Cells and their Applications," Phys. and Opt. Socs., *1930*, p. 64 ; Phil. Mag., 14, *1932*, p. 465 ; Phys. Soc., Proc., 48, *1936*, p. 589 ; G. Kortüm, Phys. Z., 32, *1931*, p. 417 ; W. Leo and C. Müller, Phys. Z., 36, *1935*, p. 113.

32. See, e.g. H. E. Ives, Astrophys. J., 40, *1914*, p. 182 and 46, *1917*, p. 241 ; H. E. Ives and E. F. Kingsbury, Opt. Soc. Am., J., 21, *1931*, p. 541 ; H. Bertling, Licht, 1, *1931*, pp. 359 and 385 ; S. Asao, Physics, 2, *1932*, p. 12.

33. G. T. Winch. Illum. Eng. Soc. Lond., Trans., 11, *1946*, p. 107.

34. See, e.g. J. Kunz, Phys. Rev., 10, *1917*, p. 205 ; W. E. Story, Illum. Eng. Soc. N.Y., Trans., 15, *1920*, p. 827 ; R. Jouaust, Soc. Franç. des Elect., Bull., 6, *1926*, p. 1167 ; G. Ferrié, L'Onde El., 4, *1925*, p. 97 ; R. P. Lejay, *ibid.*, 10, *1931*, p. 363 ; G. H. St. John, Illum. Eng. Soc. N.Y., Trans., 23, *1928*, p. 439 ; Q. S. Heidelberg and W. A. Rense, Rev. Sci. Inst., 11, *1940*, p. 386.

35. See, e.g. G. Rougier, Rev. d'Opt., 2, *1923*, p. 133 ; E. B. Moss, "Photo-electric Cells and their Applications," Phys. and Opt. Socs., *1930*, p. 71.

See also S. Strauss, E. u. M., 50, *1932*, Lichttech., p. 17.

36. G. F. Metcalf and B. J. Thompson. Phys. Rev., 36, *1930*, p. 1489.

G. W. Warren. G.E.C. Journ., 6, *1935*, p. 118.

G. H. Gabus and M. L. Pool. Rev. Sci. Inst., 8, *1937*, p. 196.

H. van Suchtelen. Philips Techn. Rev., 5, *1940*, p. 54.

37. R. H. Müller and G. E. Shriver. Rev. Sci. Inst., 6, *1935*, p. 16.

38. G. T. Winch and C. T. Harper. G.E.C. Journ., 3, *1932*, p. 149.

39. The amplification of photocurrents is dealt with from the practical point of view by A. E. Whitford in J. Strong's *Modern Physical Laboratory Practice* (Blackie, 1938).

40. C. E. Wynn-Williams. Camb. Phil. Soc., Proc., 23, *1927*, p. 811 ; Phil. Mag., 6, *1928*, p. 324.

J. Razek and P. J. Mulder. Opt. Soc. Am., J., 19, *1929*, p. 390.

L. A. DuBridge. Phys. Rev., 37, *1931*, p. 392.

W. Soller. Rev. Sci. Inst., 3, *1932*, p. 416.

A. H. Taylor and G. P. Kerr. *Ibid.*, 4, *1933*, p. 28.

L. A. Turner and C. O. Siegelin. *Ibid.*, 4, *1933*, p. 429.

L. A. DuBridge and H. Brown. *Ibid.*, 4, *1933*, p. 532.

P. Donzelot and J. Divoux. J. de Phys., 5, *1934*, p. 357.

D. B. Penick. Rev. Sci. Inst., 6, *1935*, p. 115.

41. See, e.g. G. T. Winch, Inst. El. Eng., J., 68, *1930*, p. 533 ; G. T. Winch and C. T. Harper, G.E.C. Journ., 3, *1932*, p. 149.

42. J. S. Preston. Illum. Eng. Soc. Lond., Trans., 8, *1943*, p. 121.

43. G. T. Winch. Illum. Eng. Soc. Lond., Trans., 11, *1946*, p. 107.

See also J. Terrien and F. Desvignes, Mesures, 13, *1948*, p. 411.

44. See, e.g. J. Dubois, C.R., 220, *1945*, p. 768, for a circuit designed for use with a cell having a low internal resistance or high dark current.

45. J. S. Preston. J. Sci. Inst., 18, *1941*, p. 57.

46. J. F. H. Custers. Z. techn. Phys., 14, *1933*, p. 154.
G. T. Winch and C. F. Machin. G.E.C. Journ., 6, *1935*, p. 205.
R. C. Walker and T. M. C. Lance. *Photo-electric Cell Applications*, p. 50.

47. B. Lange. Phys. Z., 31, *1930*, pp. 139 and 964.
L. Bloch. Licht u. Lampe, 20, *1931*, p. 179.
A. Dresler. *Ibid.*, 21, *1932*, pp. 35 and 211.
A. Goldmann and M. Lukasiewitsch. Phys. Z., 34, *1933*, p. 66.
L. O. Grondahl. Rev. of Modern Physics, 5, *1933*, p. 141 (with bibliography).

48. *Admiralty Handbook of Wireless Telegraphy* (H.M. Stationery Office, *1939*), Vol. II, Section H 10.

49. L. Bergmann. Phys. Z., 32, *1931*, p. 286.

50. Cu_2O was at first used as the semi-conductor in photocells. See, e.g. R. Sewig, *Objective Photometrie*, p. 29 or H. Simon and R. Suhrmann, *Lichtelektrische Zellen und ihre Anwendung*, p. 115.
Combinations of selenium with other substances have been used. See, e.g. C. G. Fink and D. K. Alpern, Am. Electrochem. Soc., Trans., 62, *1932*, p. 369 and G. P. Barnard, Phys. Soc., Proc., 47, *1935*, p. 477 and 48, *1936*, p. 153.

51. W. C. van Geel and J. H. de Boer. Physica, 2, *1935*, p. 892.
P. Görlich *et al.* Z. f. techn. Phys., 16, *1935*, p. 268 ; Z. phys. Chem. (B), 41, *1938*, p. 23 ; Z. f. Phys., 112, *1939*, p. 490.
F. Eckart and A. Schmidt. Z. f. Phys., 118, *1941*, p. 199.
See also J. S. Preston, Rev. d'Opt., 27, *1948*, p. 513 ; Roy. Soc., Proc., 202, *1950*, p. 449 ; W. Berger, Lichttechnik, 8, *1956*, p. 16.

52. Occasionally the name " selenium cell " is used, but this term should be reserved for the form of light-sensitive cell (not now used in photometry) which depends on the change of resistance of selenium when illuminated (see G. P. Barnard, *The Selenium Cell*, Constable, *1930*). See also N. R. Campbell, J. Sci. Inst., 9, *1932*, p. 369 and C. H. Sharp, Opt. Soc. Am., J., 25, *1935*, p. 165.

53. See, e.g. N. F. Mott, Roy. Soc., Proc. (A), 171, *1939*, pp. 27 and 281 ; A. E. Sandström. Phil. Mag., 37, *1946*, p. 347.

54. R. Higgonet. Rev. Gén. de l'El., 35, *1934*, p. 125.
H. H. Poole and W. R. G. Atkins. Phil. Trans. (A), 235, *1936*, p. 1.
L. Bergmann and R. Pelz. Z. f. techn. Phys., 18, *1937*, p. 177.
R. H. Mighell. Gen. El. Rev., 40, *1937*, p. 372.
W. Behrendt. Z. f. techn. Phys., 19, *1938*, p. 92.
W. Finkelnburg and H. Schulze. *Ibid.*, 24, *1943*, p. 72.
J. S. Preston. Rev. d'Opt., 27, *1948*, p. 513.

55. L. Bergmann. Phys. Z., 33, *1932*, p. 513.
A. Dresler, M. Goldmann and O. Reeb. Licht, 3, *1933*, p. 228. (See also *ibid.*, 4, *1934*, p. 40.)
L. A. Wood. Rev. Sci. Inst., 6, *1935*, p. 196.
E. Elvegård. Phys. Z., 37, *1936*, p. 129.
J. T. MacGregor-Morris and R. M. Billington. Inst. El. Eng., J., 79, *1936*, p. 435.
J. R. Atkinson, N. R. Campbell, E. H. Palmer and G. T. Winch. Phys. Soc., Proc., 50, *1938*, p. 934.
H. H. Poole and W. R. G. Atkins. Roy. Dublin Soc., Proc., 22, *1941*, p. 393.
Y. Björnståhl. Z. f. I., 62, *1942*, p. 181.

56. A. Goldmann. Phys. Z., 34, *1933*, p. 74.
H. T. Wrobel. Gen. El. Rev., 45, *1942*, p. 585.
W. C. van Geel. Philips Techn. Rev., 8, *1946*, p. 65.

57. W. Grundmann and L. Kassner. Phys. Z., 35, *1934*, p. 16.
L. Bergmann. *Ibid.*, p. 450.
H. C. Hamaker and W. F. Beezhold. Physica, 1, *1934*, p. 119.
G. Marchal and L. Marton. Rev. d'Opt., 15, *1936*, p. 1.
J. S. Preston. Inst. El. Eng., J., 79, *1936*, p. 424.
E. Elvegård, S. Lindroth and E. Larsson. Opt. Soc. Am., J., 28, *1938*, p. 33.
R. A. Houstoun. Phil. Mag., 31, *1941*, p. 498.
T. Land. Iron and Steel Inst., J., 149, *1944*, p. 481 P.

58. E. Ferencz and J. Urbanek. Rev. d'Opt., 14, *1935*, p. 317.
J. A. Hall. Iron and Steel Inst., J., 149, *1944*, p. 547 P J. Sci. Inst., 23, *1946*, p. 59.

J. S. Preston. Nature, 153, *1944*, p. 680 ; Rev. d'Opt., 27, *1948*, p. 513.
See also W. Gurski, Licht, 12, *1942*, pp. 176 and 217.

59. E. Ferencz and J. Urbanek. Rev. d'Opt., 14, *1935*, p. 317.
G. P. Barnard. Phys. Soc., Proc., 48, *1936*, p. 153.
J. S. Preston. Inst. El. Eng., J., 79, *1936*, p. 424.
I. Mrozowska. Acad. Sci. Techn. Warsaw, Ann., 5, *1938*, pp. 151 and 164.

60. L. Bergmann and R. Pelz. Z. f. techn. Phys., 18, *1937*, p. 177.

61. J. Terrien and C. Anglade. C.R., 225, *1947*, p. 729.

62. J. S. Preston. Inst. El. Eng., J., 79, *1936*, p. 424.
See also B. Lange, Z. f. I., 53, *1933*, p. 344.

63. S. English. Illum. Eng., 28, *1935*, p. 94.

64. W. N. Goodwin. Illum. Eng. Soc. N.Y., Trans., 27, *1932*, p. 828.
O. Höpcke. Licht, 4, *1934*, p. 41.
R. Sewig and W. Vaillant. *Ibid.*, p. 57.
G. P. Barnard. Phys. Soc., Proc., 48, *1936*, p. 153.
O. H. Knoll and R. G. Weigel. Licht, 8, *1938*, pp. 39 and 65.
G. Pleijel and J. Longmore. J. Sci. Inst., 29, *1952*, p. 137.

65. B. Lange. Phys. Z., 32, *1931*, p. 850 ; Z. f. I., 53, *1933*, p. 344.
C. Roy-Pochon. Soc. Franç. des Elect., Bull., 4, *1934*, p. 1199.
J. K. Putzeiko. Jurnal technicheskoi Fisiki, U.S.S.R., 7, *1937*, p. 10 (In Russian).
L. Bergmann and R. Pelz. Z. f. techn. Phys., 18, *1937*, p. 177.
J. R. Atkinson *et al.* Phys. Soc., Proc., 50, *1938*, p. 934.
H. T. Wrobel and H. H. Chamberlain. Gen. El. Rev., 49, *1946*, Apr., p. 25.

66. J. S. Preston. Inst. El. Eng., J., 79, *1936*, p. 424.
See also A. Mittmann, Z. f. Phys., 88, *1934*, p. 366.

67. P. Görlich. Z. f. techn. Phys., 14, *1933*, p. 144.
P. R. Gleason. Phys. Rev., 45, *1934*, p. 745.
J. S. Preston. Inst. El. Eng., J., 79, *1936*, p. 424.
F. W. Gundlach. Archiv. f. Elektrot., 30, *1936*, p. 625.
See also J. T. MacGregor-Morris and R. M. Billington, Inst. El. Eng., J., 79, *1936*, p. 435.

68. B. Lange. Naturwiss., 19, *1931*, p. 525.
O. H. Knoll. Licht, 5, *1935*, p. 167.
G. P. Barnard. Phys. Soc., Proc., 47, *1935*, p. 477 and 51, *1939*, p. 222.
E. Puceiko. Jurnal technicheskoi Fisiki, U.S.S.R., 8, *1938*, p. 645 (In Russian).
P. Görlich. Z. f. Phys., 112, *1939*, p. 490.
J. S. Preston. J. Sci. Inst., 27, *1950*, p 135.
On a change of spectral sensitivity with the value of the illumination on the cell, see A. Dresler, Licht, 11, *1941*, p. 139.

69. For a description of a ballistic method see H. König, Helv. Phys. Acta, 8, *1935*, p. 505 and 9, *1936*, p. 602.

70. N. R. Campbell and M. K. Freeth. J. Sci. Inst., 11, *1934*, p. 125.
See also L. A. Wood, Rev. Sci. Inst., 7, *1936*, p. 157 ; H. H. Poole and W. R. G. Atkins, Roy. Dublin Soc., Proc., 21, *1934*, p. 133 ; T. H. Projector, M. K. Laufer and C. A. Douglas, Rev. Sci. Inst., 15, *1944*, p. 107.

71. See, e.g. E. Gambetta, Rev. d'Opt., 10, *1931*, p. 297 ; H. Singer, E.u.M., 50, *1932*, Lichttech., p. 29 ; B. Lange, Z.f.I., 53, *1933*, pp. 344 and 379 ; H. Schober, E.u.M., 51, *1933*, Lichttech., p. 33 ; J. S. Preston and L. H. McDermott, Illum. Eng., 27, *1934*, p. 245 ; P. Fleury and G. A. Boutry, Rev. Gen. de l'El., 38, *1935*, p. 323 ; R. Tucker, Light and Ltg., 40, *1947*, p. 9.

72. See, e.g. Licht, 7, *1937*, p. 229.

73. J. Terrien and H. Moreau. Rev. d'Opt., 27, *1948*, p. 295.

74. G. T. Winch and C. T. Harper. G.E.C. Journ., 3, *1932*, p. 149.
W. E. Forsythe. Illum. Eng. Soc. N.Y., Trans., 31, *1936*, p. 181.

75. See, e.g. L. Bloch, Licht u. Lampe, 20, *1931*, p. 179.

76. S. E. Tweedy. Electronic Engng., 20, *1948*, pp. 38 and 84.

77. See, e.g. J. S. Preston, J. Sci. Inst., 23, *1946*, p. 173.

78. T. H. Harrison. Opt. Convention, Proc., *1926*, p. 245 ; Opt. Soc., Trans., 28, *1927*, p. 195 ; " Photo-electric Cells and their Applications," Phys. and Opt. Socs., *1930*, p. 118.

79. L. Behr. Opt. Soc. Am., J., 10, *1925*, p. 288.

C. H. Sharp *et al.* Illum. Eng. Soc. N.Y., Trans., 21, *1926*, p. 125 and 23, *1928*, p. 428 ; " Photo-electric Cells and their Applications," Phys. and Opt. Socs, *1930*, p. 110.

E. Gambetta. C.R., 196, *1933*, p. 906.

P. Moon and D. P. Severance. Illum. Eng. Soc. N.Y., Trans., 34, *1939*, p. 801.

F. A. Ryder, J. T. Gier and M. L. K. Boelter. *Ibid.*, p. 941.

R. V. Vosinskij. Jurnal technicheskoi Fisiki, U.S.S.R., 9, *1939*, p. 352 (In Russian).

80. P. R. Gleason. Rev. Sci. Inst., 3, *1932*, p. 556.

L. Bergmann. Z. f. techn. Phys., 13, *1932*, p. 568 ; Phys. Z., 33, *1932*, p. 824.

L. A. Wood. Rev. Sci. Inst., 5, *1934*, p. 295.

B. A. Brice. *Ibid.*, 8, *1937*, p. 279.

J. T. MacGregor-Morris and A. G. Stainsby. Phys. Soc., Proc., 53, *1941*, p. 584.

81. B. A. Brice. Rev. Sci. Inst., 8, *1937*, p. 279.

82. E. D. Wilson. Opt. Soc. Am., J., 29, *1939*, p. 35.

J. T. MacGregor-Morris and A. G. Stainsby. Phys. Soc., Proc., 53, *1941*, p. 584.

See also J. Terrien, C.R., 209, *1939*, p. 300 ; J. de Phys., 6, *1945*, p. 18 ; Mesures, 13, *1948*, p. 111 ; R. Bünnagel and M. Schmidt, Lichttechnik, 3, *1951*, p. 82.

83. N. R. Campbell. *Measurement and Calculation* (Longmans, *1928*), p. 141.

84. J. S. Preston. Illum. Eng. Soc. Lond., Trans., 8, *1943*, p. 121.

85. N. R. Campbell. Opt. Soc., Trans., 32, *1930*, p. 61.

J. S. Preston and L. H. McDermott. Phys. Soc., Proc., 46, *1934*, p. 256.

P. Fleury. C.R., 199, *1934*, p. 195.

86. F. Buchmüller and H. König. Assn. Suisse Elect., Bull., 28, *1937*, p. 89.

J. R. Atkinson, N. R. Campbell, E. H. Palmer and G. T. Winch. Phys. Soc., Proc., 50, *1938*, p. 934.

L. E. Barbrow. Bureau of Standards, J. of Research, 25, *1940*, p. 703.

87. H. Bertling. Licht, 1, *1931*, pp. 359 and 385.

A. Dresler. Licht, 3, *1933*, p. 41.

H. König. Helv. Phys. Acta, 7, *1934*, p. 433.

E. Ferencz *et al.* C.I.E., Proc., 9, *1935*, p. 229.

M. E. Fogle. Illum. Eng. Soc. N.Y., Trans., 31, *1936*, p. 773.

H. König. Assoc. Suisse Elect., Bull., 28, *1937*, p. 385.

R. Fridland. Jurnal technicheskoi Fisiki, U.S.S.R., 9, *1939*, p. 1952 (In Russian).

A. E. Parker. Illum. Eng. Soc. N.Y., Trans., 35, *1940*, p. 833.

L. E. Varden. Opt. Soc. Am., J., 31, *1941*, p. 507.

H. G. W. Harding. J. Sci. Inst., 27, *1950*, p. 132. (See also D. G. Anderson, *ibid.*, p. 131.)

88. J. S. Preston and L. H. McDermott. J. Sci. Inst., 11, *1934*, p. 150.

J. Rieck. Z. f. techn. Phys., 21, *1940*, p. 184.

J. S. Preston. J. Sci. Inst., 23, *1946*, p. 211.

For a filter giving, with a photo-multiplier cell, an approximation to the scotopic luminosity curve of the eye, see W. S. Plymale, Rev. Sci. Inst., 18, *1947*, p. 535.

89. S. English. Illum. Eng., 28, *1935*, p. 94.

Illum. Eng. Soc. N.Y., Trans., 32, *1937*, p. 379.

G. J. Taylor. Illum. Engng., 36, *1941*, p. 1414.

C. L. Dows. *Ibid.*, 37, *1942*, p. 103.

Light and Ltg., 36, *1943*, pp. 32 and 43.

V. S. Khazanov and L. G. Ksentitskaya. Svetotechnika, 3, *1957*, No. 7, p. 15 (In Russian).

90. R. Jouaust and P. Waguet. C.R., 180, *1925*, p. 59.

J. Terrien. C.R., 209, *1939*, p. 300.

See also E. Spiller, Licht u. Lampe, 16, *1927*, pp. 333 and 363.

91. See, e.g. J. Elster and H. Geitel, Phys. Z., 10, *1909*, p. 457.

The spectral sensitivity curve also varies with the state of polarisation of the light (see A. L. Hughes and L. A. DuBridge, *Photo-electric Phenomena*, Chapter V).

92. L. Bergmann. Phys. Z., 33, *1932*, p. 17.

A. W. Smith, H. Newhouse and P. Drake. Rev. Sci. Inst., 7, *1936*, p. 433.

H. Hausner. Licht, 9, *1939*, p. 124 ; Illum. Engng., 38, *1943*, p. 382.

CHAPTER V

THE PRINCIPLES OF PHOTOMETRY

Photometry may be defined as the measurement of light by visual comparison (provided this is made by an eye having the spectral sensitivity curve described on p. 72), or, alternatively, by some method which gives the same results as such a visual comparison [1]. In this chapter the various photometric quantities will be defined and described and their relations to one another will be derived. The formal definitions are quoted from, or based on the those accepted internationally and published by the Commission Internationale de l'Eclairage [2].

Luminous Flux and Luminous Intensity—In any system of photometric definitions it is possible to start either with the luminous intensity (candle-power) of a light source or with the rate of flow of the luminous energy produced by a source. The first of these arrangements possesses the advantage that the only quantity which can conveniently be used for the purpose of standardisation is the luminous intensity of a specified light source [3]. On the other hand the most fundamental notion in photometry is that of the radiant energy which, when it reaches the eye, produces the visual sensation, and very often this radiant energy is considered without reference to its source.

It will be most convenient for the purposes of this chapter to consider both the energy and its source together, and, therefore, the definitions of luminous flux and of luminous intensity are here given as follows :

LUMINOUS FLUX *is that quantity, characteristic of radiant energy flux, which expresses its capacity to produce visual sensation, evaluated according to the values of relative luminous efficiency for the light-adapted eye adopted by the Commission Internationale de l'Eclairage (Symbol F).*

LUMINOUS INTENSITY *(in a given direction) is the quotient of the luminous flux emitted from a source or from an element of a source in an infinitesimal cone containing this direction, by the solid angle of this cone (Symbol I).*

It will be seen that luminous flux is radiant energy flux so far as its purely physical properties are concerned, but as it is luminous flux solely by virtue of its power to evoke visual sensation, it cannot be measured in physical units, viz. ergs per sec. or watts. The measurement must take account of the fact that the visual sensation produced by a given radiant energy flux depends upon the wave-length in a way characteristic of the human eye. The relation between the physical units and the photometric units may be looked upon either as a property of the radiation, its " luminous efficiency ", or as a property of the eye, its " sensitivity ". Thus the curves of Fig. 44 (p. 73) which are, in fact, spectral sensitivity curves of the eye, become, when looked at from the photometric point of view, curves showing the luminous efficiency of radiation. Similarly the values of V_λ given in Appendix IV are equally values of the relative sensitivity of the conventional average eye to radiation of any wavelength [4].

Many analogies have been proposed to illustrate the conception of luminous flux [5]. Magnetic flux is not comparable since it involves no transfer of energy. Perhaps the most satisfactory analogies are to be found either in hydraulics or in electricity. If the energy is regarded as similar to an incompressible fluid such as water [6], then luminous flux corresponds with the flow past a point, and the unit of luminous flux, the lumen (to be defined later), corresponds with gallons of water per hour, the speed of the current being assumed constant. Similarly, if the energy be regarded as analogous to electricity, so that when evaluated photometrically (ergs $\times K_\lambda$) it is represented by quantity of electricity in coulombs, then the luminous flux corresponds with the current, and the lumen is represented by the ampere.

Neither of these analogies is really satisfactory, since the essential fact of the rectilinear propagation of radiant energy is not implied, and therefore the vector nature of luminous flux is not brought out. In order to avoid misconception when using the term " luminous flux," it is often useful to recall the real nature of this quantity, for " it has frequently been loosely used in the past as if it represented the entity itself, and not, as it does in fact, a rate of passage of the real entity, viz. energy. It is true that since the velocity of propagation of this energy may be taken as constant, the rate of passage is proportional to something which may be conveniently looked upon as an entity. In the same way electric current, which is the rate of passage of electricity, is almost invariably looked upon as an entity. Provided its real nature be kept in sight, there is much to be gained in conciseness of expression by using the word ' flux ' in the way proposed. Care must, however, be taken to preserve the distinction between luminous flux, as now defined, and energy " [7].

The difficulty may be avoided by defining luminous flux in terms of radiant power rather than radiant energy as follows :

LUMINOUS FLUX *is radiant power evaluated according to its capacity to produce visual sensation, the basis of the evaluation being the agreed values of relative luminous efficiency throughout the spectrum.*

In the definition of luminous intensity it will be noticed that a point source of light is implied, i.e. a source whose dimensions are negligible in comparison with the distance at which the flux is measured. The nearest practical approach to a point source is a fixed star as viewed from the earth. The energy emitted from such a source may then be regarded as travelling outwards radially in the form of waves which are perfect spheres. It should be noticed, in passing, that the luminous intensity is not here assumed to be the same in all directions. A source of which this was true would be termed a " uniform point source ". A variable star is an illustration of a non-uniform point source, for at any instant its luminous intensity is not the same in all directions in space. Since in this definition the luminous intensity in a single direction only is under consideration it follows that it is only the solid angular flux density in that direction which is referred to.

The luminous intensity in any direction is measured in terms of flux per steradian [8], for it is the limiting case of angular flux density over a cone when the solid angle becomes vanishingly small. This may be regarded as analogous to pressure at a point. The actual flux along a line is the rate of energy transfer across any point of that line, and, like the pressure on a mathematical point, has no meaning, except as a limit [9]. It may be regarded as $\underset{\omega=0}{Lim} F/\omega$, where F represents the flux within a solid angle ω containing the line under consideration.

It will be noticed that in the definitions given above for the quantities " luminous flux " and " luminous intensity " the second of these ideas is made dependent on the first. When the units are defined, however, it is necessary to reverse this relationship, since the unit of luminous intensity (the candela) is the primary reproducible quantity. The units are therefore defined as follows :

The unit of luminous intensity is the CANDELA. *It is of such a magnitude that the luminance of a full radiator (black body) at the temperature of solidification of platinum is* 60 *candelas per square centimetre. The symbol is cd* [10].

The unit of luminous flux is the LUMEN. *It is the flux emitted in unit solid angle by a uniform point source of one candela. Symbol lm.*

The term which has been most commonly used in the past to express the light-giving power of a source is " candle-power." This word, including as it does the name of the unit, is not altogether satisfactory as a general expression for the quantity itself. It is, therefore, preferable always to use the term " luminous intensity."

The method by which the unit of luminous intensity is actually maintained will be considered in detail in Chapter VI. It must be remarked here, however, that in the definition of the lumen a uniform point source is postulated. This is clearly impossible of attainment under practical conditions. The actual standard, therefore, is a source which, under the conditions of use to be defined later, will give results equal to those that would be obtained with a uniform point source to an accuracy well within the limits of experimental error. In this way it may, perhaps, be likened to the unit of length, which is the length between two lines on a bar of metal. Theoretically those lines should be mathematical lines, without breadth, and therefore invisible. Practically, their centres give a value for the unit which is correct within the limits of experimental error.

From the definitions of the lumen and the candela just given the following defining equations result :

$$I = \underset{\omega=0}{Lim}\ F/\omega \quad \text{and} \quad F = \int I\,d\omega.$$

where F is the luminous flux measured in lumens, I is the luminous intensity measured in candelas, and ω is a solid angle measured in steradians.

Distribution of Luminous Intensity—It has already been said that a uniform point source, or even a point source, is unattainable under practical conditions. At the same time it is often sufficiently accurate to regard many small sources, though of appreciable dimensions, as point sources for photometric purposes, the limit to what is allowable being set by (a) the accuracy of measurement desired, and (b) the ratio of the linear dimensions of the source to the distance from it at which the measurements are made. While this is true, the question of *uniformity* is quite another matter. This does not at all depend upon distance, and for many practical purposes a source which may quite well be regarded as a point source can by no means be regarded as uniform. For example, although an electric lamp of ordinary size may often be regarded as a point source at distances exceeding a metre, the luminous intensity of such a lamp in the direction of the cap is very small compared with that in the direction of the pip, and this again often differs considerably from that in a direction perpendicular to the axis of the lamp.

The expression " luminous intensity of a source " is therefore indefinite unless either the value in a single definite direction or the average value within a given region is specified.

The average value of the luminous intensity of a source in all directions, sometimes referred to as the " mean spherical candle-power " (m.s.c.p.) is, by the defining equation given above, equal to the total luminous flux emitted by the source, divided by 4π, since $\omega = 4\pi$ for the total solid angle at a point. The " mean horizontal candle-power " (m.h.c.p.), a term used to denote the average value of the luminous intensity in all directions in a plane passing through the centre of a source and perpendicular to its axis (normally vertical), is sometimes of interest. Methods of measuring these quantities will be described in Chapter VIII. The ratio (m.s.c.p.)/(m.h.c.p.) for a source may be termed its " spherical reduction factor " or, more briefly, its " reduction factor " (see p. 150) [11].

The Polar Curve of Light Distribution—In addition to a knowledge of the luminous flux given by a source it is often desirable, for purposes of illumination calculation, to know the value of luminous intensity in any given direction. This information can only be obtained, theoretically, by means of an infinite number of measurements, but for practical purposes many of the sources ordinarily in use are sufficiently symmetrical about their axes for measurements in a single plane to give the information to as great an accuracy as is desired. The results of such measurements are most conveniently displayed by means of a polar diagram in which the source is considered to be at the origin and the length of the radius vector in any direction represents the luminous intensity in that direction. Such a curve is shown in Fig. 68. The ordinary convention is that the

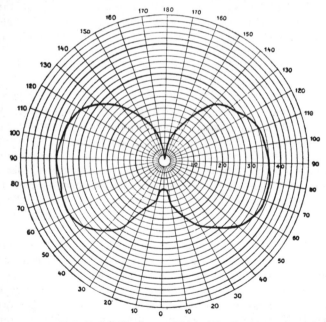

FIG. 68. A Polar Curve of Light Distribution.

vertically downward direction is the zero line, and angles are reckoned upwards, positive on one side and negative on the other, to 180° at the zenith [12]. Sometimes, in order to give a better representation of the average distribution about the source, the radius vector at any angle is drawn to represent the average value of the luminous

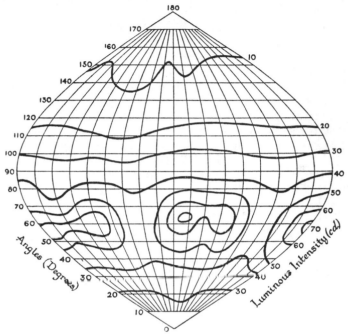

Fig. 69. An Isocandela Diagram.

intensity in all directions along the surface of a cone having its axis coincident with the axis of the source, and its semi-vertical angle equal to the angle of the radius vector on the diagram. For certain purposes a diagram drawn with rectangular co-ordinates is more convenient than a polar diagram (see p. 469).

The Isocandela Diagram—When the source is not sufficiently symmetrical to allow of the use of a polar curve, recourse must be had to an " isocandela " diagram [13]. In constructing this diagram the source is considered to be surrounded with an imaginary sphere whose radius is such that at every point on the surface of the sphere the source may be regarded as a point source. Contour curves are then drawn on this sphere through the points from which the source appears to have the same luminous intensity. These are " isocandela " curves. The spherical diagram thus obtained is reproduced on a flat surface by any of the methods of projection used in map making. It is, however, desirable that some type of equi-area projection should be used so that, if necessary, values of flux can be found by the method to be described later. The sinusoidal equi-area projection [14] is generally convenient and Fig. 69 shows the isocandela diagram on this projection for a source with four opaque bars reducing the luminous intensity at positions 90° apart in the lower hemisphere. Only one-half of the complete diagram is shown.

The methods used for making the measurements necessary for drawing a curve of light distribution or an isocandela diagram will be described in Chapter VIII.

Zone Factors—If the light distribution from a source is symmetrical about an axis, the total luminous flux, or the flux within a given zone, can be calculated from the polar diagram in several ways.

If I_θ is the average luminous intensity over the range θ_1 to θ_2, since the solid angle within the zone bounded by these angles is $2\pi(\cos\theta_1 - \cos\theta_2)$, it follows that the total luminous flux emitted within this zone is $2\pi I_\theta(\cos\theta_1 - \cos\theta_2)$. If, therefore, values of $2\pi(\cos\theta_1 - \cos\theta_2)$ are tabulated for convenient intervals of θ, the total flux can readily be found by summing the products formed by multiplying each such " zone factor " by the appropriate value of I_θ found from the polar diagram.[14a] The following table gives the zone factors for 5 degree zones :

TABLE OF ZONE FACTORS FOR CALCULATION
OF LUMINOUS FLUX

θ (degs.)	Z. factor	θ (degs.)	Z. factor	θ (degs.)	Z. factor
0–5	0·0239	30–35	0·2945	60–65	0·4862
5–10	0·0715	35–40	0·3337	65–70	0·5064
10–15	0·1186	40–45	0·3703	70–75	0·5228
15–20	0·1648	45–50	0·4041	75–80	0·5352
20–25	0·2098	50–55	0·4349	80–85	0·5435
25–30	0·2531	55–60	0·4623	85–90	0·5476

The Rousseau Diagram—It might at first be thought that the total luminous flux given by a source could be found from the area of the polar curve, or the volume of its solid of revolution about the 0°–180° axis, but a moment's consideration will show that this is not the case [15]. If curve ABC of Fig. 70 represents the polar curve of a source, supposed symmetrical about the axis OP, since the radius vector is everywhere proportional to the luminous intensity, the area enclosed by the curve is proportional to $\int_0^\pi I_\theta^2 \, d\theta$, while the volume of the solid of revolution is proportional to $\int_0^{2\pi} \int_0^\pi I_\theta^3 \sin\theta \, d\theta \, d\phi$.

The total luminous flux, however, is $\int_0^{2\pi}\int_0^\pi I_\theta \sin\theta \, d\theta \, d\phi$, i.e.
$2\pi \int_0^\pi I_\theta \sin\theta \, d\theta$, since I_θ is here independent of ϕ.

The value of this expression may be obtained graphically from the polar curve by means of a simple construction due to Rousseau [16] and known as the Rousseau diagram. It is shown in Fig. 70. The

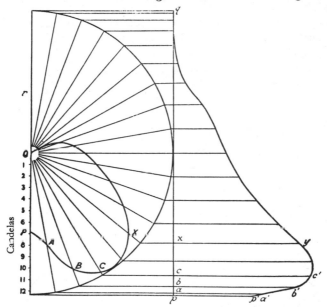

FIG. 70. The Rousseau Diagram.

left-hand part of the diagram is a polar curve. At the ends of the radii vectores $OA, OB, OC, OX, \ldots$ horizontal lines are drawn to cut a vertical axis at $a, b, c, x, \ldots$. Along these lines lengths $aa', bb', cc', xy \ldots$ are cut off equal to $OA, OB, OC, OX \ldots$ and the ends $a', b', c', y \ldots$ joined by a smooth curve. Now if the angle which OX makes with OP is θ, $\overline{px} = r(1 - \cos\theta)$, so that $d\,\overline{px} = r\sin\theta \, d\theta$. Further, $\overline{xy} = I_\theta$, so that the area of the curve $pp'a'b'c'yqp$ is equal to
$r\int_0^\pi I_\theta \sin\theta \, d\theta$, and, therefore, on the scale connecting OP with I, the
area of the Rousseau diagram divided by half its height (r) and multiplied by 2π represents the total flux from the source.

Co-ordinate paper can be obtained with one set of divisions proportional to $\sin\theta$, so that the right-hand part of Fig. 70 can be drawn directly from the observed values of luminous intensity. The area of the Rousseau diagram may be found by means of a planimeter, or by the summation of equidistant ordinates, or by a graphical construction [17].

Instead of drawing the Rousseau diagram and calculating the area by the addition of equidistant ordinates, it is clearly more simple to make the measurements of luminous intensity at the angles which correspond to equidistant ordinates on the diagram, so that the total flux can be found at once from the average of the measured values [18].

In Fig. 71 the same polar curve as that shown in Fig. 70 has been reproduced, but in this case the line *pq* has been divided into a

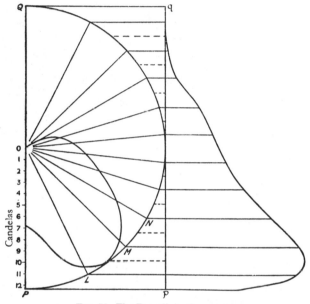

Fig. 71. The Russell Angles.

number of equal parts. Horizontal lines have been drawn through the mid-points of these parts to cut the circle of the polar diagram at *L, M, N* ... and the points *L, M, N* ... have been joined to *O*. It follows that if the luminous intensity is measured in the directions *OL, OM, ON* ... the total flux may be found simply by taking the arithmetic mean of the values thus obtained and multiplying by 4π, for since the values are now the lengths of equidistant ordinates on the Rousseau diagram, their mean is closely proportional to the area of that diagram divided by $2r$. Other sets of angles may be used to obtain an equally good approximation with fewer measurements [19].

The values of the Russell angles for 20, 10, 8 and 6 ordinates are given in the following table :

TABLE OF RUSSELL ANGLES FOR CALCULATION OF
LUMINOUS FLUX *

20 *angles*	10 *angles*	8 *angles*	6 *angles*
18·2	25·8	29·0	33·6
31·8	45·6	51·3	60·0
41·4	60·0	68·0	80·4
49·5	72·5	82·8	99·6
56·6	84·3	97·2	120·0
63·3	95·7	112·0	146·4
69·5	107·5	128·7	—
75·5	120·0	151·0	—
81·4	134·4	—	—
87·1	154·2	—	—
92·9	—	—	—
98·6	—	—	—
104·5	—	—	—
110·5	—	—	—
116·7	—	—	—
123·4	—	—	—
130·5	—	—	—
138·6	—	—	—
148·2	—	—	—
161·8	—	—	—

The general formula for the values of a set of $2n$ angles is, clearly, $\cos^{-1}(\pm x/2n)$ where x has the values $1, 3, 5, \ldots (2n-1)$.

It will be clear from the description given above that the accuracy of the determination of luminous flux by any of these methods depends on (a) the accuracy of the measurements, (b) the degree to which the lamp is symmetrical about the axis, and (c) the absence of sudden variations of luminous intensity in the regions between the angles at which measurements are made, i.e. it depends on the " smoothness " of the polar curve. For most sources in common use the set of twenty Russell angles tabulated above gives a result which is correct within the limits of experimental error [20]. When the source cannot, to the accuracy required, be regarded as symmetrical about its axis, measurements must be made in more than one plane. From theoretical reasoning it can be shown [21] that for a source with two vertical planes of symmetry (e.g. a gas-filled electric lamp or a two- or four-mantle gas lamp) the measurement should be made in one half (0° to 180°) of each of the four vertical planes, which respectively make the following angles with either plane of symmetry:

* N.B.—The angles here given are measured from a vertically downward zero, assuming measurements made in a vertical plane through a vertical axis of symmetry of the source. The angles given in the paper above quoted are measured upwards and downwards from a horizontal zero.

9°, 144°, 236°, and 279°. For a source with three planes of symmetry (e.g. a three-source lighting unit) the corresponding angles are 9°, 150° and 291°.

A number of methods, other than those described above, for finding the total flux given by a source, or the flux emitted within a given zone have been devised [22].

In the case of a source for which the light distribution is so unsymmetrical that it can only be exhibited by means of an iso-candela diagram, the total flux, or the flux emitted within any given zone or angular area, can be found quite simply from the diagram if this is drawn on an equi-area projection. The area between each pair of contour lines is measured, generally with a planimeter, and is multiplied by the mean of the two values of luminous intensity to which those contours refer. The sum of the products thus formed is proportional to the total flux emitted within the angular area over which the sum is taken [23].

Illumination—In the foregoing paragraphs a description has been given of luminous flux and luminous intensity and their relationship with each other. When luminous flux reaches a surface, that surface is said to be illuminated, and the illumination at any point of it is thus defined :

The ILLUMINATION *at a point of a surface is the quotient of the luminous flux incident on an infinitesimal element of surface containing the point under consideration by the area of this element (Symbol E).*

Thus the illumination at any point of a surface is the luminous flux density at the point [24], or the quotient of the flux by the area if the illumination of the surface is uniform. Thus illumination is analogous to pressure at a point in that it is $\underset{s=0}{Lim} (F/s)$, where s is the area (containing the point in question) which receives the flux F. There are several units of illumination, according to the unit of length adopted for the measurement of s. If s is measured in square centimetres, the unit is called the *phot*, but this unit is of an inconvenient magnitude, and the *milliphot* has been proposed for practical use. It is, however, seldom employed. The ordinary metric unit is the *lux*, or *metre-candle*, which is 1 lumen per square metre. The unit on the British system is the lumen per square foot, equal to 10·76 lux. This unit is also known as the *foot-candle* [25]. The defining equation is clearly $E = dF/ds$, where, if F is measured in lumens, and s in square metres or square feet, E is measured in lux or in lumens per sq. ft. respectively.

It was pointed out in Chapter II (p. 19) that, as a consequence of the rectilinear propagation of radiation, the quantity of radiant energy received by any area which is normal to the direction of propagation varies inversely as the square of the distance of this area from the source, it being understood that the area is so small in comparison with its distance from the source that it may be considered as a part of the spherical wave surface emanating from the source, which is regarded, again, as a point source. Since it has been agreed to regard the rate of propagation of light energy as constant in photometric work, it follows that the rate of reception of radiant energy by a surface under the conditions above described, i.e. the luminous flux it receives (see p. 120, *supra*), also varies inversely as the square of its distance from the source [26]. Now if the small area s be at a distance d from a source of which the luminous intensity in the direction of s is I, then the luminous flux incident on s is $F_s = I \times (s/d^2)$, and the illumination $E = F_s/s = I/d^2$, where d is measured in the same units as s [27]. This relationship gives an alternative definition of the unit of illumination as " that illumination which is produced at the surface of a sphere of unit radius, due to a uniform point source of one candela placed at its centre."

In the above definition the illumination of the surface of a sphere is considered, as this avoids the stipulations, necessary in the case of a plane surface, that the area s shall be negligibly small compared with d, and normal to the incident light, for another consequence of the rectilinear propagation of radiant energy is that the rate of energy reception by a surface is proportional to the cosine of the angle between the normal to that surface and the direction of propagation of the incident waves (see p. 19). Hence the above relationship may be widened to include any area s of which the normal makes an angle θ with the direction of the incident light by writing it $E = I \cos \theta/d^2$.

This equation is the symbolic expression of the two fundamental laws of photometry, viz. the inverse square law and the cosine law of illumination [28], which may be formally stated thus :

The illumination of an elementary surface due to a point source of light is proportional to the luminous intensity of the source in the direction of that surface, and to the cosine of the angle between this direction and the normal to the surface, and it is inversely proportional to the square of the distance between the surface and the source.

A point source has been defined as one for which the inverse square law is valid, to the accuracy of measurement, at the distance at which it is used [29]. When it is impossible to regard the surface as small in comparison with its distance from the source, the illumination is different at different parts of the surface, and the average illumination may be found either by calculating the total flux incident at the surface and dividing by the area, or by finding the illumination at each point and averaging over the surface [30].

In the case of a symmetrical arrangement the latter course is often more convenient, and as an example it will be useful to consider the simple case of a circular disc of radius a illuminated by a uniform point source of luminous intensity I placed at a distance d from the disc along the axis of the latter.   Let L (Fig. 72) be the source of

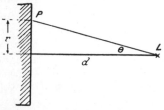

light, and P any point in the plane of the disc distant r from the projection of L on the plane, then the illumination at P is $I \cos \theta/(r^2 + d^2)$, and since $\cos \theta = d/\sqrt{r^2 + d^2}$, this may be written $I \cos^3 \theta/d^2$.   It should be remarked in passing that this result shows that the illumination at any point of a plane due to a source at a

FIG. 72. The " Cosine-cubed " Law.

distance d from the plane is proportional to the cube of the cosine of the angle of incidence θ of the light when the source is uniform, and varies as $I_\theta \cos^3 \theta$ when I varies with θ.   This is sometimes referred to as the " cosine-cubed " law [31].   For the disc, when I_θ is independent of θ, it follows that the average illumination is

$$(1/\pi a^2) \int_0^a (I \cos^3 \theta/d^2)\, 2\pi r \, dr,$$

where $r = d \tan \theta$.   This equals

$$(2I/a^2) \int_0^{\tan^{-1}(a/d)} \sin \theta \, d\theta \quad \text{or} \quad (2I/a^2)\{1 - d/\sqrt{a^2 + d^2}\}.$$

When a is small compared with d, this expression reduces, as it should, to I/d^2.   The same expression may be obtained by the flux method, for assuming the disc to have its edge on a sphere of radius $\sqrt{a^2 + d^2}$ with the source as centre, the flux reaching the disc is $AI/(a^2 + d^2)$, where A is the area of the spherical sector limited by the disc.   Since $A = 2\pi\sqrt{a^2 + d^2}\{\sqrt{a^2 + d^2} - d\}$, the expression for the flux becomes $2\pi I\{1 - d/\sqrt{a^2 + d^2}\}$, so that the average illumination of the disc is $(2I/a^2)\{1 - d/\sqrt{a^2 + d^2}\}$ as before.

The Calculation of Illumination—A very important problem in practical engineering is that of finding the illumination produced at different points on a given plane (e.g. the surface of a street, the level of a table, etc.) by one or more light sources of known luminous intensity situated at known positions with respect to the plane and to the points considered.

From what has been proved above it follows that the illumination of a horizontal plane at a point P, due to a source L situated at a height h above the plane, is $(I_\theta \cos^3 \theta)/h^2$, where θ is the angle between PL and the vertical and I_θ is the luminous intensity of L in the direction of P. If a number of sources mounted at the same height contribute to the illumination at P the total illumination is $(\Sigma I_\theta \cos^3 \theta)/h^2$.

The Illumination Curve—The formula just quoted makes it possible, from a knowledge of the polar curve of a source and its height h above a plane, to calculate the curve of variation of illumination along any line situated in that plane and passing through a point vertically below the source [32]. Such a curve is shown in Fig. 73,

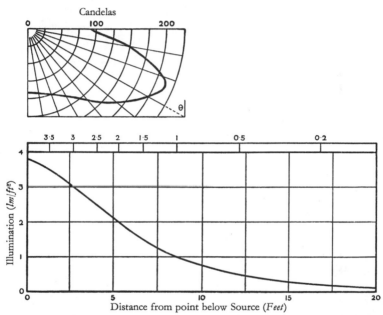

FIG. 73. The Illumination Curve for a Single Source.

where the heavy line is the curve of illumination along a line 5 feet below a source having the polar curve shown in the top left-hand part of the figure. If, now, there is, instead of one source, a number of similar sources spaced at 10-foot intervals over the line for which the illumination curve has been drawn, the curve giving the total illumination due to all the sources is obtained by superposing a number of curves like that of Fig. 73, the maxima being placed at distances apart corresponding to 10 feet. This has been done in Fig. 74, where the full line curve, obtained by adding the ordinates of the simple (broken line) curves, shows the distribution of illumination due to the whole line of sources. Clearly, if the sources are not all similar, a separate illumination curve must be drawn for each single source, and these individual curves, when superposed at the proper intervals, then give the final illumination curve. It will be obvious that a similar method may be applied generally, i.e. when the sources are arranged in any manner whatever with respect to the line considered, but the calculations involved are very much more complicated than in the example given above [33].

The Isophot Diagram—The illumination curve of Fig. 74 shows

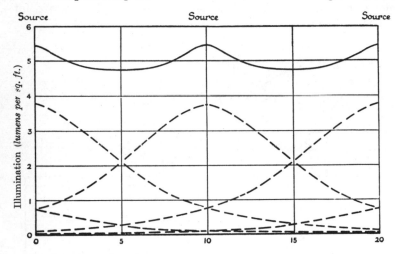

FIG. 74. The Illumination Curve for a Line of Sources Ten Feet Apart.

only the distribution of illumination along a single line. If it is desired to show the distribution over an area, this is most conveniently done by means of a " contour " map of lines of equal illumination. Such lines are known as isophot or equilux curves and the map is an isophot or an equilux diagram.

For a single source with a distribution which is symmetrical about the vertical axis, the isophot curves on a horizontal plane are, clearly, concentric circles with the point vertically below the source as centre. The radii of these circles for the case shown in Fig. 73, for instance, are as indicated at the top of the network with the illumination curve on it.

The illumination at any point on a plane receiving light from a single source may be found at once if a tracing of the isophot diagram to the appropriate scale is placed over a plan showing the point and the position of the source. The centre of the diagram may be placed at the point indicating the source and then the required illumination is found by interpolation between the two isophot curves which pass nearest to the point, one on each side. Alternatively, the diagram

may be placed so that its centre coincides with the *point* and then
the illumination is found by interpolation between the isophot curves
which pass nearest to the point representing the source.   The latter
arrangement is the more convenient if the point receives light from
several similar sources mounted at the same height, for then the total
illumination at the point is the sum of the values read off, as above,
for the several sources [34].   For instance, in Fig. 75, if *P* represents

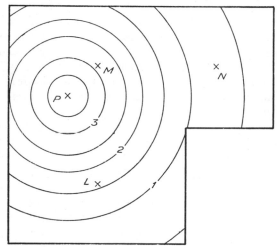

FIG. 75. The Calculation of Illumination by means of the Isophot Diagram.

the point for which the illumination is to be found and *L*, *M* and *N*
the positions on plan of three similar sources mounted at the same
height, the isophot diagram for a single source is placed over the
plan with *P* as centre.   The total illumination at *P* is then found to be
5·2 lumens per sq. ft., made up of 1·6 from *L*, 2·9 from *M* and 0·7
from *N*.

The isophot diagram for a system of sources is prepared by finding
the values of illumination for a sufficient number of points, using the
method just described, and then drawing the isophot curves for
appropriate illumination values by interpolation between these
points [35].

When the light distribution from the source is not symmetrical,
the isophot diagram for a single source can be found from the isocandela diagram [36].   The isophot diagram for a system of such
sources may then be prepared by superposing a number of these
individual diagrams, each placed in its appropriate position and
appropriately oriented on the plan [37].

It is to be noted that in this case the illumination at a point due
to several sources cannot generally be found by placing the isophot

diagram for a single source so that its centre is at the point. This method is, however, applicable so long as (a) the distribution is symmetrical about two mutually perpendicular planes, so that the isophot diagram has two axes of symmetry at right angles, and (b) the sources are all mounted with similar axes parallel.

The preparation of an isophot diagram from measurements of illumination made in an actual lighting installation is described on p. 396.

Brightness and Luminance—While neither luminous flux, luminous intensity nor illumination can be directly perceived by the eye, this is not true of the fourth principal quantity in photometry, luminance, and therefore, as explained in Chapter III (p. 75), it is necessary to draw a distinction between (a) the physical quantity, viz. the luminous intensity of a surface per unit apparent area (i.e. area projected on a plane perpendicular to the direction of view) and (b) the visual effect produced, which may depend on the conditions under which the surface is viewed [38]. For this reason the word " brightness," if unqualified, is ambiguous and when the physical quantity is meant the term *luminance* should be used. This may be defined as follows :

The LUMINANCE, *in a given direction, at a point of a surface is the quotient of the luminous intensity in that direction of an infinitesimal element of the surface containing the point, by the area of the orthogonal projection of this element on a plane perpendicular to the direction considered (Symbol L or B).*

The unit of luminance is one candela per unit area. On the c.g.s. system the unit is the *stilb* (*sb*), equal to one cd/cm^2 [39]. The metric unit is the cd/m^2, at one time called the *nit* (*nt*) [40]. There is no name for the corresponding unit on the British system ; the candela per sq. inch or per sq. ft. is generally employed. The defining equation is, clearly, $B_\theta = Lim_{s=0} I_\theta/(s \cos \theta)$ where θ is the angle of view, measured from the normal to the surface.

For the visual effect the term " subjective brightness," or the word " luminosity," may be used. While it is true that there is no strict correspondence between luminance and subjective brightness (or luminosity) [41], nevertheless surfaces of equal luminance appear equal in luminosity when viewed under identical conditions, so long as the eye is light-adapted. This is, in fact, the basis of nearly all visual photometry. Within the Purkinje range, or under scotopic conditions, however, this simple relationship ceases to hold, as explained in Chapter III (see p. 75) where the convention necessary for expressing subjective brightness observed under these conditions in units of luminance was described.

The subjective brightness of a surface of uniform luminance is independent of the distance from which the surface is viewed, since the quantity which (other things being equal) determines it, viz. the illumination of the retinal image, is unaffected [42]. This follows from the fact that the flux entering the eye from a given area of the surface varies inversely as the square of its distance away, and so does the area of the retinal image illuminated by this flux.

It will be seen that, while illumination is the measure of the light *received* by a surface, luminance is the measure of the light emitted in any given direction [43]. This light may be due either to self-luminosity, as in the case of a flame or other luminous source, or it may be due to reflection by a non-self-luminous surface of some of the light received by that surface from a self-luminous body. In the latter case the surface is sometimes termed a " secondary source " of light.

So far only the luminance of a surface in a given direction has been dealt with, and in practice it is found that all surfaces, to a greater or less extent, vary in luminance according to the direction in which the measurements are made. From the defining equation it will be seen, however, that if $I_\theta = I \cos \theta$, where I is the luminous intensity per unit area in the direction of the normal to the surface, then $B = I/s$, and is independent of θ. Such an ideal surface is known as a " uniformly diffusing surface " or, more shortly, a " uniform diffuser." Although, as has been said above, no such surface is known in practice, a large number of surfaces exist for which the relationship holds approximately over a wide range of values of θ. Such surfaces are said to be " matt ", or " good diffusers," and have many applications in photometry. A uniformly diffusing surface is said to obey the *cosine law of emission*, which was first enunciated by Lambert [44], and may be thus stated :

A uniformly diffusing surface is one for which the luminous intensity per unit area in any direction varies as the cosine of the angle between that direction and the normal to the surface, so that it appears equally bright whatever be the direction from which it is viewed.

The luminance of a uniform diffuser may very conveniently be expressed in terms of the flux emitted by it per unit area, for (Fig. 76)

$$F = \int_0^{\pi/2} I \cos \theta \, d\theta \,.\, 2\pi \sin \theta = \pi I,$$

so that the flux emitted per unit area by a uniform diffuser whose luminance is I candelas per unit area is πI lumens. It follows at once that if a uniform diffuser emits F lumens per unit area, its luminance (in all directions) is F/π candelas per unit area.

In illuminating engineering it is often found very convenient to express the luminance of an actual surface in any given direction in terms of that of a uniform diffuser emitting one lumen per unit

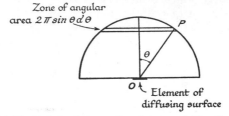

FIG. 76. The Relation between Luminance and Flux Emission.

area [45]. Corresponding to the different units of area in common use there are different names for the unit of luminance on this system, as shown below.

Unit of Area	Unit of Luminance	Equivalent lum. int. per unit area
metre - - -	apostilb (asb) [46]	$1/\pi$ cd/m^2 = $10^{-4}/\pi$ sb.
foot - - -	foot-lambert [47] (ft.-L)	$1/\pi$ cd/ft.^{2}
centimetre - -	lambert [48] = 1000 millilamberts	$1/\pi$ sb.

The lambert and millilambert have now been generally superseded by the other two units which are used respectively where the metric and British systems of units are current.

It is to be noted that, while on the system just described the unit of luminance is the luminance of a uniformly diffusing surface emitting one lumen per unit area, the unit should never be defined in that way, e.g. one apostilb is not equivalent to one lumen per square metre. For any surface except a uniform diffuser, the luminance in any direction is not definitely related to the flux emitted but only to the luminous intensity in that direction.

The "Mechanical Equivalent of Light"—It will have been noticed that there is naturally a close parallelism between the various photometric quantities described above and corresponding quantities used in the measurement of radiation. In particular, luminous flux, measured in lumens, corresponds to radiant flux measured in watts and illumination corresponds to flux density measured in watts per unit area. The factor relating the units in the two systems is the number of lumens corresponding to one watt. This is known as the *luminous efficiency of radiation*, K, which as explained in Chapter III, depends on the wave-length of the radiation. It is a maximum for radiation of wave-length 555 $m\mu$ and the value for any other wavelength is found by multiplying this maximum value by the relative luminous efficiency for that wave-length (see Appendix IV). The value of K_m is determined by the fact that the luminance of a full radiator at the temperature of solidifying platinum is 60 candelas per sq. cm. The spectral distribution of the radiation from the full radiator can be found from its temperature, using the Planck radiation formula (see p. 40), and then the total luminous flux is given by $\int K_\lambda E_\lambda \, d\lambda$,

i.e. by $K_m \int V_\lambda E_\lambda \, d\lambda$ where V_λ is the relative luminous efficiency at wave-length λ. The value of this integral may be calculated by a point-to-point method [49] or, if a close approximation is sufficient, one of the empirical expressions which have been proposed to represent the curve for V_λ may be used with Wien's radiation formula (see p. 40) [50]. The expression for V_λ takes the form $\Sigma A \, (R\lambda^{-1}e^{1-R/\lambda})^n$, there being three or four terms with different values of the constants, A, R and n [51], and thus the integral becomes

$$\Sigma \int A \, (R/\lambda)^n e^{n(1-R/\lambda)} c_1 \lambda^{-5} e^{-c_2/\lambda T} \, d\lambda$$

$$= \Sigma c_1 A R^n e^n \int \lambda^{-(n+5)} e^{-(Rn+c_2/T)/\lambda} \, d\lambda$$

$$= \Sigma c_1 A R^n e^n (Rn + c_2/T)^{-(n+4)} \Gamma(n+4).$$

This may be written

$$\Sigma \alpha (1 + \beta/T)^{-(n+4)},$$

where

$$\alpha = c_1 A R^n e^n (nR)^{-(n+4)} \Gamma(n+4)$$

and

$$\beta = c_2/nR.$$

By Stirling's theorem

$$\alpha = c_1 A \, (\beta/c_2)^4 (n+3)(n+2)(n+1)\sqrt{2\pi n}$$

to an accuracy of 0·1 per cent, since $n > 100$ (see Chrystal's *Algebra*, Vol. II, Ch. XXX).

Since the value of the integral $K_m \int V_\lambda E_\lambda \, d\lambda$, taken over the whole spectrum, is equal to 60π lumens, if E is expressed in watts K_m is found in lumens per watt. Taking 2042·1° K as the temperature of solidifying platinum [52], $c_1 = 3·74 \times 10^{-5}$ erg. cm.² sec.⁻¹ and $c_2 = 1·438$ cm. deg., the value of K_m is found to be 680 lumens per watt. This is the maximum luminous efficiency of radiation. Its reciprocal has been termed, somewhat unfortunately, *the mechanical equivalent of light* and has the value 0·00147 watts per lumen [53].

It is of interest to note that the luminance of a full radiator over a wide range of temperature can be represented by an empirical formula of the type $\log L = A - B/T + C/T^2$ where A, B and C are constants [54]. To an approximation of about 1 per cent over the range 2000 to 3000° K, only two terms are necessary with $A = 7 \cdot 1153$ and $B = 10,899$ where L is in cd/cm² and T in degrees K, the logarithm being to base 10 and the radiation constants having the values stated above.

It will be clear that all the photometric quantities can be defined in terms of energy and luminous efficiency [55] and a unit, called the " light-watt " has been used to express radiant power weighted in accordance with V_λ, so that one watt at wave-length λ is equal to V_λ light-watts, and one light-watt is equivalent to $(1/V_\lambda)$ watts, i.e. to K_m lumens [56]. The luminous efficiency of a source may then be expressed in terms of the number of lightwatts it emits per watt of total energy radiated, i.e. $\int V_\lambda E_\lambda \, d\lambda \Big/ \int E_\lambda \, d\lambda$. The maximum possible value for luminous efficiency, as thus defined, is unity. This is only attained when all the energy is emitted in radiation of the wave-length for which $V_\lambda = 1$. If the energy is uniformly distributed through the visible spectrum, but is zero at all other wave-lengths, the luminous efficiency is the maximum possible for a source giving white (equi-energy) light and is about $0 \cdot 4$ [57].

In practice it is more convenient to express the efficiency of a source of light or a particular radiator somewhat differently. It is, in fact, defined as the ratio of the total luminous flux emitted to the total power consumed and expressed in lumens per watt or in lumens per thermal unit per unit of time.

Illumination from Line and Surface Sources [58]—It has been stated already that no surface obeys the cosine law of emission perfectly. Nevertheless, many of the surfaces dealt with in photometry obey this law to a sufficiently close approximation for the purposes of calculation in certain classes of problems. The closest approximation is that given by a " black body " cavity, the opening

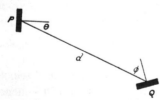

FIG. 77. The Radiation of Flux from one Surface to Another.

of which behaves very accurately as a surface radiating according to the cosine law, so that, at a distance which is large compared with the size of the opening, the luminous intensity may be taken as proportional to the cosine of the angle between the line of measurement and the axis of the surface. If P (Fig. 77) is an element of such a surface, whose area is a and whose normal luminance is B candelas per unit area, then the flux emitted per unit solid angle in any direction PQ is $Ba \cos \theta$, where θ is the angle which PQ makes with the normal to P. The flux incident on an element of surface of area b

situated at Q, and having its normal at an angle ϕ with PQ, is therefore $(b \cos \phi/d^2)$. $Ba \cos \theta$, where $PQ=d$.

The symmetrical form of this expression, $(Bab . \cos \theta . \cos \phi)/d^2$, shows that the flux reaching Q from P is equal to that which P would receive from Q if the latter had a luminance of B candelas per unit area.

The illumination of the surface at Q is the flux received per unit area, i.e. it is $(Ba \cos \theta \cos \phi)/d^2$. This may also be written $Bd\omega \cos \phi$, where $d\omega$ is the solid angle subtended by the element P at Q, for clearly $d\omega = (a \cos \theta)/d^2$. Further, if P and Q are two elements of the surface of a sphere, $\theta = \phi$ and $d = 2r \cos \theta$ where r is the radius of the sphere. Hence the illumination at Q is $Ba/4r^2$. Since this expression is independent of θ, it follows that the illumination is independent of the relative positions of P and Q on the sphere surface. In other words, every part of the surface of a sphere is equally illuminated by the flux emitted or reflected from any given portion of the spherical surface. This principle is made use of in the photometric integrator (see p. 257).

When the radiating surface is not negligibly small compared with the distance d, each element may be taken as radiating according to the cosine law, and the aggregate result may be obtained by integrating the above expression over the surface ; thus in the case of a radiating circular disc [(59)] of radius r the illumination of a parallel and coaxial element is $\pi Br^2/(d^2+r^2)$, where B is the normal luminous intensity per unit area of the disc and d the distance from it at which the elementary area is situated. In

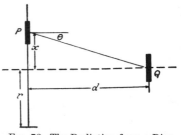

FIG. 78. The Radiation from a Disc.

Fig. 78, if P is an element of the disc at a distance x from the axis and of area a, the illumination of Q due to the flux from P is

$$Ba \cos^2 \theta/(d^2+x^2) = Bad^2/(d^2+x^2)^2.$$

The illumination of Q by an annulus of radius x and breadth dx is therefore $Bd^2 . 2\pi x \, dx/(d^2+x^2)^2$. Thus the total illumination due to the disc is $2\pi B \, d^2 \int_0^r x \, (d^2+x^2)^{-2} \, dx = \pi Br^2/(d^2+r^2)$. It will be seen that this differs from the result which would be obtained according to the simple inverse square, viz. $\pi r^2 B/d^2$, by the factor $d^2/(d^2+r^2)$. It follows that the true luminous intensity, as measured when $d = \infty$, may be deduced from the luminous intensity measured at a finite distance by multiplying by the factor $(d^2+r^2)/d^2$. The values of this factor for different values of r/d are given by curve A of Fig. 79 When the receiving element is not on the axis of the radiating disc, but is at a distance ρ from this axis, the expression for the illumination becomes $\frac{1}{2}\pi B[1 - c/\sqrt{c^2 + r^2}]$, where $c \equiv (d^2 - r^2 + \rho^2)/2d$. This may be written

$$\frac{1}{2}\pi B\{1 - \operatorname{cosec} \theta + (r/\rho) \cot \theta\},$$

where $\sec \theta = (d^2 + \rho^2 + r^2)/2\rho r$.

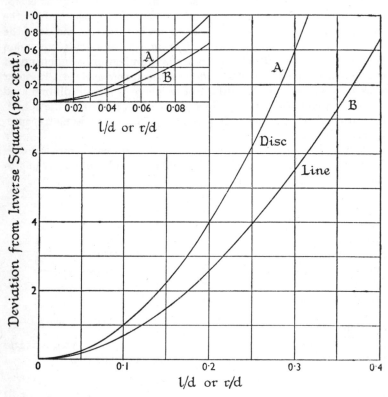

FIG. 79. The Effect of Size of Source on the Inverse Square Rule.

When the receiving element is *perpendicular* to the plane of the disc instead of parallel to it, the illumination can be shown to be $\frac{1}{2}\pi B(d/\rho)\{\operatorname{cosec} \theta - 1\}$. Of this amount the contribution from the half of the disc shown unshaded in Fig. 80 is

$$(Bd/\rho)\{\operatorname{cosec} \theta \tan^{-1}\sqrt{(\sec \theta - 1)/(\sec \theta + 1)}$$
$$+ (\rho/\sqrt{d^2 + \rho^2}) \tan^{-1}(r/\sqrt{d^2 + \rho^2}) - \pi/4\}.$$

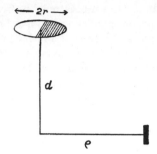

FIG. 80. The Radiation from a Disc to a Perpendicular Surface.

When $\rho = 0$ this gives the illumination of one side of an element situated on the axis of a circular disc and perpendicular to the plane of the disc, viz.

$$B\{\tan^{-1}(r/d) - rd/(r^2 + d^2)\}.$$

This result may readily be obtained by direct integration [60].

From the above results it is quite easy to deduce that the total flux which reaches any disc from another parallel disc radiating according to the cosine law [61] is

$$\tfrac{1}{2}\pi^2 B\{(r_1^2 + r_2^2 + d^2) - \sqrt{(r_1^2 + r_2^2 + d^2)^2 - 4r_1^2 r_2^2}\}.$$

Since the total flux from the radiating disc is $\pi^2 r_1^2 B$, it follows that the fraction of the whole flux which reaches the second disc is

$$(1/2r_1^2)\{(r_1^2 + r_2^2 + d^2) - \sqrt{(r_1^2 + r_2^2 + d^2)^2 - 4r_1^2 r_2^2}\}$$

or, more conveniently for numerical computation,

$$2r_2^2/\{(r_1^2 + r_2^2 + d^2) + \sqrt{(r_1^2 + r_2^2 + d^2)^2 - 4r_1^2 r_2^2}\}.$$

When d is large compared with r_1 and r_2, this becomes, very nearly,

$$r_2^2/(r_1^2 + r_2^2 + d^2).$$

It is easy to show that when two discs are so placed that their edges form small circles of the same sphere, the flux received by either disc from the other is independent of the relative positions of the two discs on the sphere, so that it can be at once found from the formula just given [62]. It may also be shown that the amount reflected back to the radiating disc is

$$\frac{1}{2}\rho\pi^2 B\left[(r_1^2 + r_2^2 + d^2) - \sqrt{(r_1^2 + r_2^2 + d^2)^2 - 4r_1^2 r_2^2}\right.$$
$$\left. - dr_1\tan^{-1}\frac{2dr_1 r_2^2}{(d^2 - r_1^2)r_2^2 + (d^2 + r_1^2)^2}\right],$$

where r_1 is the radius of the radiating disc and r_2 that of the reflecting disc with a reflection factor ρ [63].

It will be clear that an annulus may be treated as a disc from which a concentric disc of smaller radius has been removed [64].

Another important case is that of a radiating cylinder of radius a and length $2l$. The illumination from such a cylinder at an elementary surface P distant d from the axis of the cylinder, and situated on and perpendicular to a line passing through the centre of the cylinder and perpendicular to its axis, has been given by Hyde [65] as (Fig. 81)

$$Ba\iint (d \cos \alpha - a)(d - a \cos \alpha)\{a^2 + d^2 - 2ad \cos \alpha + y^2\}^{-2} d\alpha\, dy$$

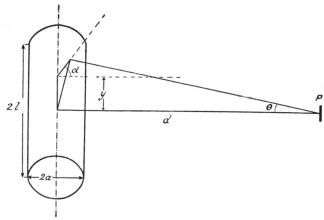

FIG. 81. The Radiation from a Cylinder.

where the limits of y are $\pm l$, and those of α are $\pm \cos^{-1}(a/d)$. This reduces to

$$\frac{B}{d}\left[a \cos^{-1}\frac{d^2 - a^2 - l^2}{d^2 - a^2 + l^2} + l\left\{ \frac{q+1}{\sqrt{q}} \cot^{-1}\sqrt{\frac{p}{q}} - 2 \cot^{-1}\sqrt{p} \right\} \right],$$

where $p \equiv (d+a)/(d-a)$ and $q \equiv \{(d+a)^2 + l^2\}/\{(d-a)^2 + l^2\}$.

When, as is commonly the case in practice, a is small compared with d, the cylinder may be regarded as equal to an elementary strip of breadth $2a$ and length $2l$. The illumination at P due to such a strip is clearly (Fig. 82), putting $\tan^{-1} y/d \equiv \theta$,

$$4aB\int_0^l \{\cos^2 \theta/(d^2 + y^2)\}\, dy = (4aB/d)\int_0^{\tan^{-1}l/d} \cos^2 \theta\, d\theta$$
$$= (2aB/d)\{\tan^{-1}(l/d) + ld/(l^2 + d^2)\},$$

which is also the limiting value of Hyde's expression when a becomes a small quantity so that squares and higher powers of a may be neglected [66].

If l also is small compared with d, this becomes, as it should, $4alB/d^2$. It follows that if l is not small compared with d the result

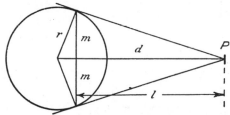

given by the simple inverse square is too large and should be divided by

$$(d/2l)\{\tan^{-1}(l/d) + ld/(l^2+d^2)\} \quad {}^{(67)}.$$

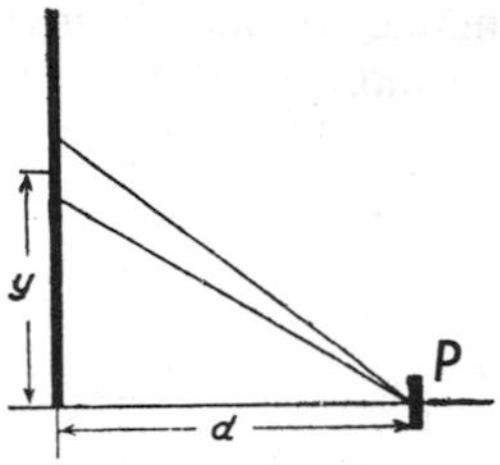

The magnitude of this error for different values of l/d is shown in curve B of Fig. 79, p. 142.

Other results which are of some importance in photometry are (i) the illumination from a spherical diffusing surface and (ii) the illumination due to a plane rectangular source. The former problem is most easily solved by making use of a very important

FIG. 82. Radiation from a Straight Flat Strip, or from a Rod of Flame.

general principle, viz. that the illumination at a point P due to any diffusing surface S (see Fig. 83) is equal to that from any other surface S' of equal luminance if S and S' appear to have the same boundary when viewed from P, and this whether the surfaces be plane or not.

The truth of the statement just made may be regarded as self-evident or it may be demonstrated by dividing the surfaces into corresponding pairs of elements such as ds and ds' (Fig. 83) and applying the formula given on p. 141 for the illumination due to an elementary diffusing surface. It will be clear that if ds and ds' appear congruent from P they must subtend the same solid angle and therefore, since the angle of

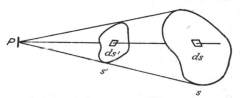

FIG. 83. The Equivalence of Apparently Congruent Surfaces of Equal Luminance.

incidence is the same, they produce the same illumination at that point. Since this is true for each pair of corresponding elements into which the two surfaces S and S' can be divided, it must be true for the entire surfaces.

FIG. 84. The Radiation from a Sphere.

Using the principle just stated, the case of a diffusing sphere of radius r reduces to that of a circular disc of radius m at a distance l (see Fig. 84). The illumination at P is therefore equal to

$$\pi Bm^2/(l^2+m^2) = \pi Br^2/d^2.$$

Thus the sphere is equivalent to a point source of luminous intensity $\pi B r^2$ situated at its centre [68].

The problem of the rectangular source arises in finding the illumination at a point in a room due to a rectangular window through which is visible a sky of uniform brightness (see also p. 410). The solution is [69] (Fig. 85)

$$E_H = \tfrac{1}{2}B\{\alpha - \alpha' \cos \beta\}, \quad \text{and} \quad E_V = \tfrac{1}{2}B\{\alpha' \sin \beta + \beta' \sin \alpha\},$$

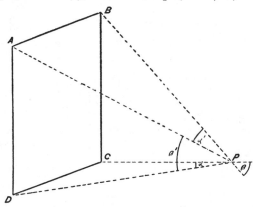

FIG. 85. Radiation from a Rectangular Area to a Point Opposite One Corner.

where B is the normal luminance of the rectangle and E_H or E_V represent respectively the illumination of an elementary horizontal or vertical surface placed at P, a point on the line perpendicular to the source and passing through one corner of it. It is clear that the general case, when the position of P is not restricted, may be treated

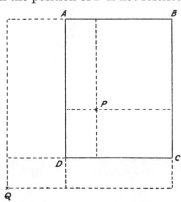

FIG. 86. Radiation from a Rectangular Area to Any Point.

as shown in Fig. 86 where P or Q represents the projection of the illuminated point on the plane of the rectangle. When finding the illumination at P, the rectangle $ABCD$ is divided into the four rectangles PA, PB, PC, and PD. In the case of Q,

rect. $ABCD$ = rect. QB + rect. QD – rect. QA – rect. QC.

It is to be noticed that in finding E_H at P the rectangles PD and PC have to be neglected, since they contribute nothing to the illumination of the upper side of a horizontal surface at P.

Formulae have also been derived for calculating the amount of flux received from a rectangular source by a rectangular area [70].

The Solid-Angle Projection Method—The results given in the preceding section have been obtained by direct integration but there is a principle which may sometimes be usefully employed, either to save the labour of integration or for the graphical determination of the illumination from sources of irregular shape [71].

From the principle of the equivalence of apparently congruent surfaces (see p. 140), it is clear that the illumination produced at a point P on a plane MN (see Fig. 87) by an element ds of a diffusing

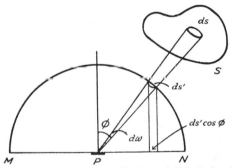

FIG. 87. The Solid-Angle Projection Method of Calculating Illumination from an Extended Surface.

surface S is equal to that produced by an element ds' of a hemisphere of unit radius with P as its centre, if ds' appears congruent with ds as viewed from P. Further, this illumination is equal to $Bd\omega \cos \phi$ which, since the radius of the hemisphere is unity, may be written $Bds' \cos \phi$. This is equal to B multiplied by the area of the projection of ds' on the plane MN. It follows that the illumination due to the whole surface S is equal to B multiplied by the area of the projection on MN of that portion of the hemisphere of unit radius which is contained within the cone having S as its base and P as its apex.

This principle has been applied to the calculation of illumination from windows and other large sources and special networks have been designed [72] to facilitate the graphical solution of such problems in cases where the outline of the source is irregular (see p. 410).

As an example of the application of this method, the illumination at any point on the axis of an elliptical disc may be calculated (see

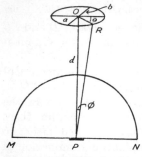

Fig. 88). Let the point P be at a distance d from the centre O of the disc and let the major and minor semi-axes of the ellipse be a and b respectively. The length r of a radius vector OR making an angle θ with the major axis is given by the equation

$$(\cos^2 \theta)/a^2 + (\sin^2 \theta)/b^2 = 1/r^2$$

and $r/d = \tan \phi$, where ϕ is the angle OPR. If R' is the projection on the plane MN of the point at which PR intersects the unit hemisphere about P, then PR' is numerically equal to $\sin \phi$. The equation to the projection of the line of intersection of the hemisphere with the cone generated by PR is therefore

FIG. 88. The Radiation from an Elliptical Disc.

$$1/r'^2 = \operatorname{cosec}^2 \phi = 1 + \cot^2 \phi$$
$$= (\cos^2 \theta + \sin^2 \theta) + (d^2/a^2) \cos^2 \theta + (d^2/b^2) \sin^2 \theta,$$

i.e. this projection is an ellipse of which the semi-axes are equal respectively to $a/\sqrt{a^2+d^2}$ and $b/\sqrt{b^2+d^2}$ units of length. The area is therefore $\pi ab/\sqrt{(a^2+d^2)(b^2+d^2)}$ units and the illumination at P is equal to this expression multiplied by B, the luminance of the disc. This may be written more concisely as $\pi B \sin \alpha \sin \beta$ where α and β are the angles subtended at P by the semi-axes of the disc. It will be noticed that the result for a circular disc is obtained at once as a special case by putting $b - a$ and in fact this result can be obtained by this method almost without calculation.

Another very important result which can be obtained immediately on the solid-angle projection principle is the illumination from a source of infinite extent, such as a sky of uniform brightness. This is clearly equal to πB.

Illumination from Volume Sources—A somewhat different problem is that of finding the illumination due to a so-called " volume source ", i.e. one which can be regarded as transparent to its own radiation [73]. Most flames and the luminous discharge through certain gases are examples of sources in which this condition is approximately fulfilled [74].

It is clear that the illumination of P (Fig. 82) due to the flux from a slender cylindrical luminous rod, each part of which is perfectly transparent, is equal to $I_v \int A d (d^2 + y^2)^{-3/2} dy$, where A is the cross-section of the rod, and I_v the luminous intensity per unit volume of the rod (necessarily the same in all directions). The integral equals $I_vAl/d\sqrt{d^2+l^2}$.

Similarly it can be shown [75] that the illumination due to a disc of radius r and elementary thickness t is $2\pi I_vt\{1 - d/\sqrt{d^2+r^2}\}$, while that due to a rectangular flame of the dimensions shown in Fig. 86 is $I_vt \tan^{-1}(\sin \alpha' \tan \beta)$.

The solution for the cylindrical flame of radius r and semi-height h is less simple, leading to a form containing elliptic integrals. The final result for the illumination due to the whole flame (height $2h$) is (d being measured to the axis of the cylinder)

$$\{4I_vrht/d\sqrt{h^2+(r+d)^2}\}\{K(k) + \Pi_1(n, k) . (d-r)/(d+r)\},$$

where K is the complete elliptic integral of the first kind and

$$k^2 = 4rd/\{h^2+(r+d)^2\}.$$

$\Pi_1(n, k)$ is equal to the expression

$$K(k) + \frac{\sqrt{1-k'^2\sin^2\theta}}{k'^2\sin\theta\cos\theta}\left\{\frac{\pi}{2} + K(k) . F(k', \theta)\right.$$
$$\left. - E(k) . F(k', \theta) - K(k)E(k', \theta)\right\},$$

where $\qquad k'^2 = 1 - k^2 = \{h^2+(d-r^2)\}/\{h^2+(d+r)^2\}$

and $\qquad\qquad k' \sin\theta = (d-r)/(d+r)$.

Analogous to the cylindrical flame is the " squirrel-cage " filament lamp in which the filament consists of a number of vertical limbs disposed on the surface of an imaginary cylinder. With this source, the first order correction on values of illumination found by assuming the light centre of the lamp to coincide with its geometrical centre is reduced to zero if the semi-height of the filaments and the radius of the cylinder are related by the equation $h = 0\cdot865r$ [76].

Inter-reflections—When finding the luminous flux reaching one surface from another, inter-reflection between the surfaces is very frequently neglected. Sometimes, however, this reflected flux is important and it is then necessary to use special methods of analysis to take account of it. A very simple case, which occurs in the theory of the spherical photometric integrator, can be solved from first principles (see p. 258) but others of more complexity are met with in the theory of the cylindrical form of full radiator (see p. 178) and in other similar problems and these require more advanced mathematical treatment [77].

The Vector Method—A very general method for finding the illumination due to an extended source or system of sources is based on the fact that illumination may be regarded as a vector quantity in a " light field " established by the sources [78]. This method is useful for dealing with generalised problems of surface and volume sources, including inter-reflections, whereas only special cases, such

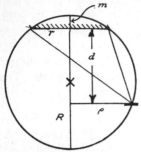

as those described in the immediately preceding sections, lend themselves to solution by simple integration. For example, it can be shown at once by the vector method that the illumination produced by a circular disc on an elementary surface parallel to it is the same as that of the surface of a sphere containing the edge of the disc and passing through the elementary surface (see Fig. 89). It is therefore the same wherever this surface may be situated on the sphere [79] and so is equal to $\pi B r^2/\{(2R-m)^2+r^2\}$.

FIG. 89. Radiation from a Disc (Vector Method).

Since $m(2R-m)=r^2$ this reduces to $\pi Bm/2R$, a result which also follows from appropriate transformation of the formula given on p. 142, viz. $\frac{1}{2}\pi B[1-c/\sqrt{c^2+r^2}]$ since $\rho^2+(d+m-R)^2=R^2$, so that $c=R-m$.

Light Distribution Curves and Reduction Factors—Since for a perfectly diffusing plate of area s and luminance B, the luminous intensity at any angle θ from the normal is $Bs \cos \theta$, the polar curve is a circle touching the plate as shown in Fig. 90 where the plate is supposed perpendicular to the plane of the paper. The diameter of the circle represents the luminous intensity in the normal direction, Bs, and since the total flux emitted is πBs, the average luminous intensity (m.s.c.p.) is $\frac{1}{4}Bs$, i.e. one quarter of the maximum.

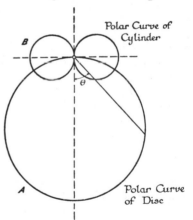

In the case of a diffusing rod the axis of symmetry is the axis of the rod and the polar curve is a pair of touching circles of which this axis is the common tangent. In Fig. 90 the axis is represented by the vertical line in the plane of the paper. The diameter of each

FIG. 90. Polar Curves for a Disc and a Cylinder.

circle is proportional to the luminous intensity of the rod in the normal direction, viz. Ba where a is the projected area of the rod. Since the total area is πa, the total flux emitted is $\pi^2 Ba$ and the average luminous intensity (m.s.c.p.) is therefore $\frac{1}{4}\pi Ba$, i.e. the normal luminous intensity multiplied by $\pi/4$. For a source consisting of one or more vertical rods or filaments, therefore, the spherical reduction factor (see p. 124) is $\pi/4$ [80].

It will be seen that if a plate and a rod emit equal amounts of total flux, their maximum luminous intensities will be in the ratio of π to 1. The curves of Fig. 90 have been drawn to represent this condition and illustrate very forcibly the difficulty of judging total flux from a polar curve (see p. 126).

Photometry of a Screened Source—When a diaphragm is placed in front of a uniformly bright diffusing source, the illumination at any point in front of the diaphragm may be found by regarding the opening in the diaphragm as a plane diffusing source of luminance equal to that of the surface behind it, whatever the shape of this latter surface may be, for it is clear that to an eye placed anywhere in front of the diaphragm the opening appears to have a uniform brightness equal to that of the source. It follows that if the finite size of the opening can be neglected the illumination varies inversely as the square of the distance from the *diaphragm* [81]. This is a principle often used in photometry. It can naturally be applied only as long as the diaphragm aperture is completely filled by the source when the combination is viewed from the point where the illumination is being considered. In the case of a vertical diffusing strip masked by a diaphragm with a long horizontal opening, the position of the " effective light-centre " is not definite. It may generally be taken as approximately half way between the strip and the diaphragm [82], for if l is the distance from the photometer to the diaphragm, and d the separation from diaphragm to source, the distance of the effective light source from the photometer is clearly

$$\sqrt{\overline{l(l+d)}} = \left(l + \frac{1}{2}d\right)$$

approximately so long as d is small compared with l.

A similar principle may be used to find the light distribution from an opaque *diffuse* reflector placed over a light source. If the total flux intercepted from the source by the reflector is Φ and the reflected flux $\rho\Phi$, it follows that the reflector, if its edge is plane and internal reflections negligible, has a luminous intensity in the direction θ equal to $(\rho\Phi/\pi)\cos\theta$, where θ is measured from the normal to the plane containing the edge of the reflector [83].

Illumination of an Image formed by a Lens or Mirror—When a lens or mirror is used to form an image of a source or other bright object on a diffusing surface, the illumination of this image is proportional to the luminance of the source, B, and to the aperture of the lens or mirror [84]. It is independent of the area s of the source, for the flux reaching a lens of area a from the source is Bsa/u^2, if s and a are both small compared with u, the distance of the source from the lens. The flux transmitted to the image is therefore $\tau Bsa/u^2$, where τ is the transmission factor (see p. 160) of the lens. Since the area of the image is v^2s/u^2 (see p. 25 ; s is assumed to be the projected area of the source as viewed from the lens), its illumination is $\tau Ba/v^2$. This principle is used in some forms of photometer in which a variable diaphragm is placed over a lens so that the value of a can be changed at will (see p. 231).

Luminance of a Projector System: The Maxwellian View— Another principle which is sometimes useful in photometry is that, if a lens or mirror be caused to form a real image of a small source at the pupil of the eye, the whole surface of the lens or mirror appears to have a uniform luminance proportional to the luminous intensity of the source in the direction of view. The case of a biconvex lens may be considered by reference to Fig. 91. Let S be the source and

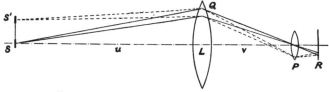

Fig. 91. The Principle of the Maxwellian View.

L the lens forming an image of S at P. Let P and R be respectively the pupil and retina of the eye. The eye is focused on L so that an image of the surface of L is formed on R. If both S and L are small compared with the distance between them, the flux reaching an element (area a) of the lens at Q is Ia/u^2. Hence the flux reaching P from S through Q is $\tau Ia/u^2$. Now if L were replaced by a diffusing surface of luminance B, the flux reaching P from Q would be paB/v^2 where p is the area of P (the pupillary aperture). Hence the apparent luminance of Q is $\tau Iv^2/pu^2$. It is here assumed that the size of the image of S is smaller than P, otherwise the iris acts as a stop, and in this case the apparent luminance of L is $\tau B'$ where B' is the luminance of the source.

This principle is made use of in some photometric instruments designed to measure sources of light of low luminous intensity, or those which are situated at a considerable distance, a lens being arranged to form an image of the source at the pupil of the eye. The arrangement is sometimes termed the " Maxwellian view ", it having been adopted by Clerk Maxwell in his colour-mixing apparatus [85]. By its use an extended field of view may be obtained, with a lumin- ance very much greater than that of the ordinary photometric comparison surface used in most instruments. In spectrophotometry or colorimetry the Maxwellian view is used to obtain an extended field of uniform colour.

Referring again to Fig. 91, if S and S' are neighbouring elements of the same source, the light reaching R from S' through Q is shown by the broken lines. It will be seen that the rays by which Q is viewed at R pass through different parts of P. If, however, the source is very small indeed, the light from each part of L only passes through a very small area of P. In consequence, when the Maxwellian view is used with a source which subtends a very small angle at the lens, the field of view is marred by the imperfections in P, such as variations in transmission which cause patchiness, and specks or other opaque bodies which give shadows moving apparently across the field of view [86].

There is a precaution to be observed in photometric instruments in which the Maxwellian view is employed, particularly when the photometric balance is achieved by rotation of part of the optical train. If, as is generally the case, some shift of the image is liable to occur during the rotation, it is necessary to ensure that the eye-piece does not act as a stop of variable aperture. This is achieved either by making the image so small that it is always completely within the aperture, or, alternatively, by having the image more than large enough to cover the aperture completely with a patch of uniform illumination. Generally this can be arranged by using as the object a small diffusing surface of uniform luminance or a small uniform patch of an extended diffusing surface.

Reflection—When light is incident on the surface of a body, some of it is, in general, directly reflected according to the laws of specular reflection, some is diffusely reflected, while the remainder passes on into the substance of the body. The two types of reflection are known respectively as direct reflection[87] and diffuse reflection and the extent to which reflection of either kind takes place at any given surface is expressed by means of a ratio, the reflection factor [88], defined as follows :

The reflection factor *of a body is the ratio of the luminous flux reflected by the body to the luminous flux incident upon it.*

The flux reflected according to the laws of specular reflection is called directly reflected flux, and the corresponding reflection factor is called the direct reflection factor. The flux diffused, i.e. that sent out in directions other than that of direct reflection, gives the diffuse reflection factor. The total reflection factor is obtained by considering the whole of the flux reflected by the body.

From some surfaces very little of the reflected light is diffused ; surfaces of this kind are termed " polished " or " specular ". From

others practically all of it is diffused and these surfaces are called
" unpolished " or " matt ". No real surface behaves either as perfectly polished or as perfectly diffusing, but it is convenient to consider the behaviour of these two classes of theoretical surfaces and
thence to deduce the general behaviour of surfaces met with in practice.

Direct Reflection—When reflection takes place in a perfectly
polished surface, this behaves as a mirror and the reflection is wholly
direct. If the mirror is plane and has a reflection factor ρ, it can be
shown that the image of an elementary surface of luminance B,
viewed by reflection in the mirror, has a luminance ρB. Let P (Fig.
92) be the elementary surface, seen by reflection in MQ, and let P' be

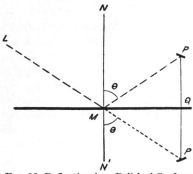

its image situated symmetrically on the other side of the
mirror. The flux emitted from
P in the direction PM appears
at L to come from P'. If the
luminance of P in the direction
PM is B, the flux reaching L is
the same as that from an equal
element of surface, also of luminance B but situated at P', assuming reflection without loss.
If the reflection factor is ρ, however, the flux is reduced in this
ratio, i.e. it is now the same as

FIG. 92. Reflection in a Polished Surface.

that which would be received from a surface at P' of luminance ρB.
It is to be noted that this is also the apparent luminance of the reflecting surface at M.

For transparent materials the reflection factor of a polished surface depends on the angle of incidence and, if the light is polarised,
on the angle between the plane of incidence and the plane of polarisation. Fresnel's law [89] states that if ρ_1 and ρ_2 are respectively the
reflection factors for light polarised in and perpendicular to the plane
of incidence, then

$$\rho_1 = \sin^2 (i - r)/\sin^2 (i + r)$$
and $$\rho_2 = \tan^2 (i - r)/\tan^2 (i + r),$$

where i and r are the angles of incidence and *refraction*. For perpendicular incidence it follows that $\rho_1 = \rho_2 = (n - 1)^2/(n + 1)^2$, where
n is the refractive index and for glancing incidence $(i = 90°)$ $\rho_1 = \rho_2 = 1$.

With glass of refractive index 1·5 the values of ρ_1 and ρ_2 are given
in the following table [90] :

$i =$	$0°$	$15°$	$30°$	$45°$	$56.3°$	$60°$	75	
$\rho_1 =$	0·040	0·044	0·058	0·092	0·148	0·177	0·39	
$\rho_2 =$	0·040	0·036	0·025	0·008	0·000	0·002	0·107	
$\tau_1 =$	0·960	0·956	0·942	0·908	0·852	0·823	0·601	0·000
$\tau_2 =$	0·960	0·964	0·975	0·992	1·000	0·998	0·893	0·000

Light polarised in a plane making an angle ϕ with the plane of incidence may be regarded as consisting of two components, whose intensities are proportional to $\cos^2 \phi$ and $\sin^2 \phi$, polarised respectively in and perpendicular to the plane of incidence, so that the reflection factor of the surface is in this case $\rho = \rho_1 \cos^2 \phi + \rho_2 \sin^2 \phi$. Unpolarised light may be regarded as made up of equal components polarised in two perpendicular directions, so that in this case $\rho = \frac{1}{2}(\rho_1 + \rho_2)$. Values of the reflection factor for unpolarised diffused light have been calculated [91].

From the table given above it will be seen that at a certain angle, for which $\tan i = n$ (known as the polarising angle), the reflection factor is zero for light polarised perpendicular to the plane of incidence, so that ordinary light reflected at this angle should be completely polarised in the plane of incidence [92]. This phenomenon was made use of in some early forms of polarisation photometer (see p. 3). In practice the polarisation is never complete, owing, probably, to the fact that the transition from one medium to another does not take place with absolute suddenness, but that there is an extremely thin transition layer [93].

Coating a glass surface with a very thin layer (a quarter of a wavelength of light in thickness) of a suitable material of low refractive index reduces very considerably the amount of light reflected at a glass surface [94]. This process is known as " blooming."

In the case of metals the reflection factor varies with the state of polish of the surface, as well as with the wave-length and angle of incidence of the light. It is practically independent of the plane of polarisation. For silver it may be as high as 0·9 or more. Some values of reflection factors are given in Appendix VII, p. 528.

Diffuse Reflection—A uniform diffusing surface has been defined (p. 137) as one which emits light according to the cosine law. Similarly, a uniform diffusely reflecting surface may be defined as one which redistributes the light it receives in such a manner that, whatever be the directional distribution of the incident light, the light reflected from each element of the surface in any given direction is proportional to the cosine of the angle which that direction makes with the normal to the surface. In other words, the uniformly diffuse reflector acts as if it absorbed all the incident radiation and then re-emitted a definite fraction of it in accordance with the cosine law of emission. Such a surface, therefore, appears equally bright in all directions [95] and is known as a uniform diffuser. If its illumination is E lm/ft^2 it emits ρE lumens per sq. ft. and so has a luminance of $\rho E/\pi$ candelas per sq. ft. or ρE foot-lamberts. It may be treated in exactly the same way as a diffuse radiator (see pp. 140 et seqq.).

A uniform diffuser for which ρ is unity, so that it reflects diffusely all the luminous flux it receives, is known as a perfect diffuser. The nearest practical approximation to this ideal surface is a freshly prepared coating of magnesium oxide obtained by " smoking " a sheet of metal or other material over burning magnesium ribbon until a sufficiently thick layer of MgO has been deposited (see p. 372).

Reflection from Matt Surfaces—All real surfaces show reflection that is neither wholly direct nor uniformly diffuse. In every case, if the incident light is directional, the reflection tends to a maximum in the direction of specular reflection [96] while some surfaces also exhibit a much smaller secondary maximum in directions close to that of the incident light [97]. In general, the specular maximum becomes more pronounced as the angle of incidence of the light increases. This kind of reflection is sometimes referred to as " preferential diffuse reflection ".

There is no physical reason why the reflection from a matt surface should follow, even approximately, the cosine law, unless it is assumed that the reflected or emitted light emanates equally in all directions from particles within the substance of the reflecting or emitting body. In this case, if α' is the absorption factor of the material, the light emitted in the direction θ from the particles at a distance x below the surface is proportional to $e^{-\alpha' x \sec \theta}$ if refraction is ignored (see p. 160). Hence the total light emitted in this direction is [98]

$$\int_0^\infty e^{-\alpha' x \sec \theta} \, dx = (\cos \theta)/\alpha'.$$

Bouguer supposed that a matt surface was made up of innumerable elementary surfaces, each acting as a mirror, and this theory was later elaborated by assuming that the surfaces were distributed, as to slope, according to the Gaussian probability law [99]. The resulting expression for the distribution of the reflected light was somewhat complicated, like others put forward from time to time by various workers [100].

For many purposes in photometry it is desirable to use surfaces which approximate as nearly as possible to a uniform diffuser. Those principally employed are mentioned in the sections dealing with (a) the internal coating of photometric integrators (p. 270), (b) test plates for visual illumination photometers (p. 381) and (c) the determination of reflection and transmission factors of diffusing materials (p. 421).

Luminance Factor—It will be seen that for a matt surface, both the reflection factor and the distribution of the reflected light are very dependent on the directional characteristics of the light incident on the surface. This makes it impossible to assign to such a surface a definite value of reflection factor, unless the illumination conditions are precisely specified. Further, the value of reflection factor so defined gives no information as regards the distribution of the reflected light, whereas for many purposes it is the luminance of the surface when viewed in a particular direction that is of interest.

It is therefore often convenient to use, instead of a figure of reflection factor, the ratio of the luminance of the surface to that of a perfect diffuser when both are viewed under the same illumination conditions. This ratio is known as the *luminance factor* (β). It will be seen that for shiny surfaces, and even for matt surfaces in directions close to that of specular reflection, the luminance factor may greatly exceed unity, whereas the reflection factor must always be less than unity. The luminance factor always refers to specified conditions of illumination of the surface and a stated angle of view [101]. It is clearly equal to the luminance in foot-lamberts, or in apostilbs, divided by the illumination in lumens per square foot, or in lux, respectively.

Reflection from Coloured Surfaces—The reflection factor of a surface may vary with wave-length ; in fact, the colour of a non-self-luminous surface depends entirely upon the power of the surface to reflect at some wave-lengths more strongly than at others. A blue-green surface, for example, has a higher reflection factor for wave-lengths in the neighbourhood of $500m\mu$ than for any other part of the visible spectrum. A curve showing the reflection factor of a surface at all wave-lengths is called the spectral reflection curve for that surface.

It will be seen at once that the colour of a surface is dependent upon the colour of the light it receives, for it is obvious that wave-lengths which are absent from the incident light cannot be present in the reflected light [102]. Thus, for example, a normally " blue-green " object, if illuminated by a light containing little radiation of wave-lengths less than about $600m\mu$ appears very dark, since its reflection factor for the longer wave-lengths is very small. A white or a grey surface has the same reflection factor at all wave-lengths ; it therefore appears to be of exactly the same colour as the light illuminating it.

Spectral Distribution Curves—The foregoing general statements can be given more precision by making use of spectral distribution curves for energy or for luminous flux. These are curves which show for each wave-length within a given range (e.g. the visible

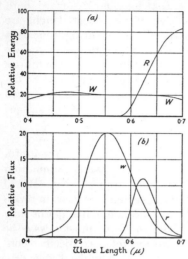

FIG. 93. Spectral Distribution Curves : (a) Energy, (b) Flux.

spectrum) the relative amounts of energy, or of luminous flux, within a definite small wave-length interval centred on that wave-length. Some spectral energy distribution curves are shown in Fig. 93 (a) ; the curve marked R refers to a red light, i.e. one in which only the longer wave-lengths are present, while W refers to a white light which has a much more uniform distribution of energy throughout the spectrum. If each ordinate of a spectral energy distribution curve is multiplied by the appropriate value of V_λ (see p. 72), the corresponding spectral flux distribution curve is obtained. The curves marked r and w in Fig. 93 (b) are the spectral flux distribution curves corresponding to the energy curves marked R and W in Fig. 93 (a).

The spectral distribution curve of either energy or flux for the light reflected from any given surface can be obtained from the corresponding curve for the incident light by multiplying each ordinate by the appropriate value of reflection factor. For example, if the curve B in Fig. 94 represents the spectral reflection curve of a blue-green surface, and if the spectral energy distribution of the incident light is that indicated by curve R in Fig. 93 (a), the spectral energy distribution of the reflected

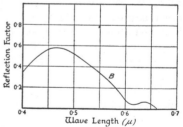

FIG. 94. The Spectral Reflection Curve of a Blue-Green Surface.

light is found by multiplying the corresponding ordinates of the two curves B and R. The result is shown by the curve marked BR in Fig. 95 (a) ; similarly BW represents the spectral energy distribution of the light reflected by the surface when illuminated by the white light to which W refers. A spectral flux distribution curve for reflected light is obtained in an exactly similar way. Clearly, it may also be found from the spectral energy distribution curve of the reflected light by multiplying each ordinate by the appropriate value of V_λ. Fig. 95 (*b*) shows spectral flux distribution curves, *Br* and *Bw*, for the light reflected from the surface to which *B* refers when the incident light has the spectral flux distribution shown by curves *r* and *w* respectively.

The modification of spectral distribution brought about by repeated reflections is found, either by corresponding repetitions of the process described above, or by constructing a new spectral reflection curve from the individual reflection curves by multiplication of the ordinates. For example, the curves 2*B* and 3*B* in Fig. 96 have been drawn by respectively squaring and cubing the ordinates of curve *B* in Fig. 94 and these

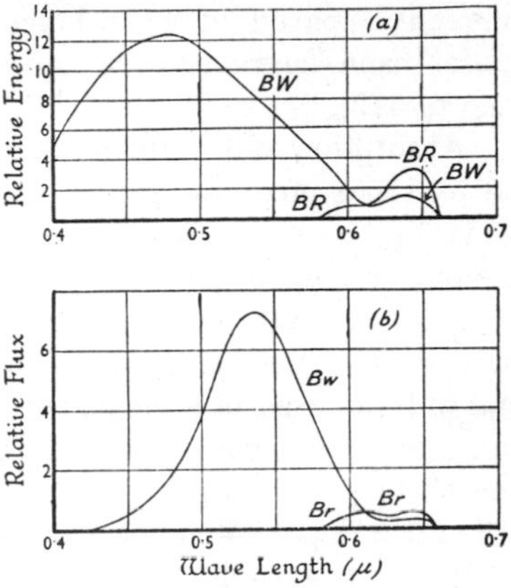

FIG. 95. Spectral Distribution Curves for Light reflected from a Blue-Green Surface : (*a*) Energy, (*b*) Flux.

curves are therefore the composite spectral reflection curves for double and triple reflection respectively from the surface to which

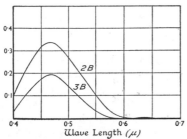

FIG. 96. The Effect of Repeated Reflections.

curve *B* refers. It will be seen that the maxima of these curves are more pronounced than those of curve *B* and, generalising, it is clear that both maxima and minima in the spectral reflection curve are accentuated by repeated reflections. This fact is of importance in connection with the choice of an inner coating for a photometric integrator (see p. 270).

The reflection factor of a surface for a composite light of any given spectral distribution is the ratio of the area under the spectral flux distribution curve of the reflected light to that under the corresponding curve for the incident light. Thus the reflection factor of the blue-green surface referred to in the foregoing examples is, for the white light represented by *W* and *w*, the ratio of the area under *Bw* to that under *w* when both curves are drawn to the same scale, viz. 28 per cent. For the red light *R* the reflection factor of the same surface is only 5 per cent, the ratio of the area under *Br* to that under *r*.

The reflection factor can be found directly from the spectral energy distribution curves for the incident and reflected light by plotting these on special co-ordinate paper in which the ordinates are unevenly spaced in accordance with the function V_λ. The area under each curve is then proportional to the corresponding flux (see p. 372).

Absorption and Transmission—Of the light entering a body from an external medium, part is absorbed within the substance of the body, and its energy is converted into other forms, e.g. heat, chemical action, or some other process requiring the supply of energy. If the body absorbs all the light entering it, it is said to be opaque ; otherwise it is termed transparent or translucent. Clearly these terms can only be used in a very general and ill-defined way. The absorption factor of a body is defined as the ratio of the flux absorbed by the body to the flux incident upon it. As in the case of reflection, this ratio depends on the wave-length of the radiation entering the body, some wave-lengths being more readily absorbed than others. The definition of transmission factor is exactly analogous to that of reflection factor (see p. 516).

It will be noticed that the above definition of absorption factor concerns a particular body, and not a material in general. It is, therefore, dependent on the form of the body, and, in fact, depends entirely on the length of path travelled by the radiation within the body. This, again, depends on the thickness ; therefore for any given material it is the absorption factor per unit thickness which must be employed. This is known as the *absorptivity*.

In the case of homogeneous transparent materials, the light passes straight through them, while in translucent bodies it suffers internal reflections, so that the length of its path may be many times the thickness of the body. In the former case, if the absorptivity is α and the luminous flux entering any given area of the body is F, then the flux absorbed in passing through unit thickness is αF and the amount transmitted is $(1 - \alpha)F$. The fraction transmitted through a single layer of unit thickness is known as the *transmissivity* of the material and is frequently denoted by τ, so that $\tau = 1 - \alpha$. The flux transmitted through a thickness t is clearly equal to $F(1 - \alpha)^t$. If, instead of using the absorptivity α, the absorption in a very thin layer δt is expressed as a multiple of the thickness of that layer, $\alpha'\delta t$, the flux transmitted through a thickness t is

$$F(1 - \alpha'\delta t)^{t/\delta t} = Fe^{-\alpha't} \quad \text{(103)}$$

and the transmissivity τ is therefore $e^{-\alpha't}$. The quantity α' is known as the *absorption coefficient* of the material [104]. It is clearly equal to the logarithm to base e of the reciprocal of the transmissivity.

For colourless optical glass the value of α' is in the neighbourhood of 0·01 to 0·02 when t is in centimetres, so that the transmissivity is about 98 to 99 per cent per centimetre, since $\tau = 1 - \alpha' t$ to a first approximation when $\alpha' t$ is small [105].

For substances in homogeneous solution in a solvent it might be expected *a priori* that increase in concentration would be exactly equivalent to increase in thickness, i.e. that the transmission factor would be proportional to k^{tc}, where t was the thickness, and c the concentration [106]. Generally however, this relation, known as Beer's law, is not strictly obeyed [107].

A perfectly absorbing body is one that absorbs all the radiation incident upon it; it must, therefore, be not only perfectly opaque, but it must not reflect any of the incident radiation. It follows that it must have the same index of refraction as the medium surrounding it, and, in fact, the only perfect absorber is a " black-body " cavity (see p. 35).

Transmission through a Plate—When light reaches the second bounding surface of a body, reflection takes place at this surface and it will be seen, from the form of the expression given earlier, that the reflection factor here is the same as it is at the first bounding surface [108]. Thus the final transmission factor for a plate of transparent material is $(1 - \alpha)(1 - \rho)^2$ where ρ now denotes the reflection factor for a single surface and $1 - \alpha$ the ratio of the flux reaching the second surface to that entering at the first. If α and ρ are small this may be simplified to $(1 - \alpha - 2\rho)$. Usually, part of the light reflected at the second surface is added to the light absorbed, and the remainder to the light reflected at the first surface, so that the relationship is written in its usual form, $\tau = 1 - \alpha - \rho$, in which α denotes the fraction of the flux absorbed and ρ the fraction returned from both surfaces in the direction opposite to that of the incident light.

The reciprocal of the transmission factor of a plate is sometimes termed the *opacity* of the plate and the logarithm to base 10 of the opacity is often known as the *optical density* of the plate. If surface reflections are neglected the optical density is proportional to the thickness of the plate, for $D = \log_{10}(1/\tau)$ and $1/\tau = e^{\alpha' t}$.

The light transmitted by a single transparent plate of glass may be calculated fairly simply thus : If the incident light follows the direction LA in Fig. 97, the incident flux is F. Of this $F\rho$ is reflected and $F(1 - \rho)$ enters the glass along the path AB. Of the part $F(1 - \rho)\tau$ which reaches B, $F(1 - \rho)\rho\tau$ is reflected along BC, and $F(1 - \rho)^2\tau$ emerges. Of the part reaching

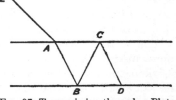

FIG. 97. Transmission through a Plate.

C, viz. $F(1-\rho)\rho\tau^2$, one part, $F(1-\rho)\rho(1-\rho)\tau^2$, emerges and $F(1-\rho)\rho^2\tau^2$ is reflected along CD to D, where $F(1-\rho)^2\rho^2\tau^3$ emerges. Hence the total light emerging on the side BD is

$$F(1-\rho)^2\{\tau+\rho^2\tau^3+\rho^4\tau^5+\ldots\}=F(1-\rho)^2\tau/(1-\rho^2\tau^2)$$

which, if $\rho=0{\cdot}04$ and $\tau=0{\cdot}9$, is equal to $0{\cdot}83F$ [109].

When light traverses two or more plates in succession, the expressions for the transmission factor become more complicated. G. G. Stokes has given the formula [110].

$$\rho_N/(b^N-b^{-N})=\tau_N/(a-a^{-1})=1/(ab^N-a^{-1}b^{-N})$$

where ρ_N and τ_N are respectively the reflection and transmission factors for N parallel plates, and a, b are constants found from the equations

$$\rho_1/(b-b^{-1})=\tau_1/(a-a^{-1})=1/(ab-a^{-1}b^{-1}).$$

This formula applies no matter what the angle of incidence of the light or the absorption factor of the substance of the glass. When there is no absorption the above expressions become indeterminate. In this case, writing ρ' for $(1-n)^2/(1+n)^2$

$$\rho_N/2N\rho'=\tau_N/(1-\rho')=1/\{1+(2N-1)\rho'\} \quad [111].$$

The light transmitted by a triangular prism of base-length t is clearly equal to $(1/t)\displaystyle\int_0^t e^{-\alpha't}\,dt$, i.e. to $(1-e^{-\alpha't})/\alpha't$ if reflection at the surfaces be neglected [112]. In the case of a constant deviation prism (Fig. 17) of which the length of the reflecting side is $t\sqrt{2}$, the transmission is, similarly, found to be $e^{-4\alpha't3}(1-e^{-\alpha'nt})/\alpha'nt$, where $n\equiv 2/\sqrt{3}$.

Values of the transmission factor of a glass plate for light incident at any angle and for unpolarised diffused light have been calculated [113]. It can be shown from first principles that for any plate, whether transparent or translucent and whether the surfaces are matt or polished, the transmission factor for diffused light is the same in both directions [114].

Transmission of Coloured Media—Absorption and transmission, like reflection, frequently vary with the wave-length of the incident radiation and it is this variation which determines the colour of a material as seen by transmitted light. A blue glass has its highest transmission factor for wave-lengths in the blue part of the spectrum, while most of the red light is absorbed.

The relation between the spectral transmission of a body (as represented by its spectral transmission curve) and the spectral distributions of the incident and of the transmitted light are exactly the same as in the case of reflection and in fact the discussion of reflection given on pp. 157 to 159 may be directly applied, *mutatis mutandis*, to transmission through a transparent medium. If the curves of Fig. 93 represent the spectral distribution of the light incident on a transparent medium, for which the spectral transmission curve is that shown in Fig. 94, the spectral distribution of the transmitted light is represented by the appropriate curves in Fig. 95.

In the case of transmission, the effect of increasing the thickness of the medium traversed by the light is exactly analogous to the effect of repeated reflections, except that the treatment can be generalised so as to apply to any increment of thickness and not only to multiples of the original, as in the case of two or more reflections from a single surface. The greater the thickness, the greater the accentuation of maxima and minima in the spectral transmission curve (see Fig. 96). This observation is of importance in connection with the use of coloured media, either glass or chemical solutions in heterochromatic photometry (see Chapter IX).

It will be clear that the expressions for absorption and transmission given in the previous section apply only to light of a single wave-length although, if the absorption of the material is the same for a range of wave-lengths, they may be applied to a composite light containing only those wave-lengths. In the special case of a neutral material, i.e. one for which the absorption factor is the same throughout the visible spectrum, the expressions remain valid for light of any spectral distribution. The remarks in the last paragraph with regard to the effect of thickness on spectral transmission explain why a material which is satisfactory for use as a neutral filter when in moderate thickness, may show a marked departure from neutrality when the thickness is considerably increased.

The spectral transmission curve of a plate of homogeneous material of any given thickness t_1 can be calculated from that of a plate of the same material of any other thickness t_2, since, for a given wave-length,

$$\tau_1 = 1 - e^{-\alpha' t_1} - 2\rho \quad \text{and} \quad \tau_2 = 1 - e^{-\alpha' t_2} - 2\rho$$

so that

$$\log (1 - 2\rho - \tau_1) = (t_1/t_2) \log (1 - 2\rho - \tau_2).$$

For coloured glass filters it is usual to assume that $\rho = 0.04$ [115].

Diffuse Transmission—In the case of a translucent body, or of a transparent body in which one or both surfaces have been rendered matt, diffusion of the incident light takes place to a greater or less extent and the expressions found for the transmission through a transparent medium do not hold [116].

The transmitted light, as might be expected, is not distributed according to the cosine law of emission, the intensity being always a maximum in the direction of the incident light if the substance is in the form of a plate [117]. The approximation to uniform diffusion increases with the density of the substance and the thickness of the plate, and the nearest approach to a uniformly diffuse transmitter is a sheet of dense opal glass sand-blasted or etched on both sides. Diffuse and colourless transmission is required for the window of any form of photometric integrator (see Chapter VIII), but it is difficult to obtain a material which combines a sufficiently high transmission factor with a satisfactory degree of diffusion.

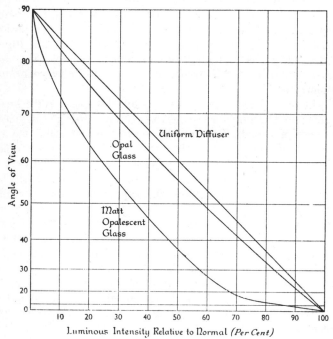

FIG. 98. The Definition of Diffusing Power.

Definition of " Diffusing Power "—The " diffusing power " of a substance, opaque or translucent, may be qualitatively defined as the degree to which the light it reflects or transmits is distributed according to the cosine law. A satisfactory quantitative definition of diffusing power is, however, very difficult to arrive at, and it has generally been expressed by means of a polar curve showing the luminous intensity of a given element of surface as viewed from all directions in a plane passing through the normal to that element. This curve, sometimes termed the indicatrix [118], becomes a circle touching the element in the case of a uniform diffuser. For all other surfaces it is distorted in a manner depending on the nature of the surface and on the direction of the incident light. Various attempts have been made to define a " figure of merit " for expressing the diffusing power of a substance [119]. Probably the most convenient system is that of Halbertsma [120], in which, with light incident normally on the surface, the luminous intensities at different angles of view, θ, are plotted as abscissae, the corresponding ordinates being proportional to $(1 - \cos \theta)$, as in Fig. 98. For a uniformly diffusing surface the resulting curve clearly becomes a straight line. The area enclosed by the axes of co-ordinates and the representative curve for any surface may be termed the " diffusing power " of the surface, the area for a uniformly diffusing surface being taken as unity. Imperfect diffusion is sometimes referred to as " spread " reflection or transmission [121].

Volume Diffusers—When light passes through a considerable thickness of a diffusing material, so that the diffuser can no longer be regarded as a thin sheet, the sum of the transmissivity and the absorptivity as defined above is not unity. The difference is due to scatter without absorption and may be termed the *scattering coefficient* of the medium. If a term is needed for the loss by both scatter and absorption, this may be termed the *attenuation coefficient* which is thus the difference between unity and the transmissivity [122].

The reduction in visibility of an object seen through a diffusing medium is, to a large extent, caused by loss of contrast between the object and its background due to the superposition of a " veil " of uniform luminance. If B_1 is the luminance of the object, B_2 that of its background and B that of the veil of diffusing material the contrast, defined for this purpose as $(B_1 - B_2)/B_1$ is reduced to $(B_1 - B_2)/(B_1 + B)$. The ratio of these two functions is $1 + B/B_1$ so that B/B_1 may be used as a measure of the effect. It has been termed the *haze factor* because the matter is of considerable importance in meteorology and the visibility of distant objects in the open depends mainly on the diffusing power of the intervening atmosphere. Instruments, usually called " visibility meters " [123], have been designed for measuring this quantity on an arbitrary scale by finding the amount of additional diffusion necessary in order to cause a given object just to become invisible. This additional diffusion is usually obtained by inserting a number of sheets of material of graded diffusing power between the observer's eye and the selected object [124]. The methods used for measuring the transmission factor of the atmosphere will be described in Chapter XIII (see p. 444).

BIBLIOGRAPHY

Most of the books included in the Bibliography in Appendix I deal with the general principles of photometry. Additional references are :

A. Beer. *Grundriss des Photometrische Calcüles*. (Vieweg, Brunswick, *1854*.)

N. A. Halbertsma. Z. f. Bel., 26, *1920*, pp. 83, 97, 104, 112, 121, 132 and 142.

E. L. J. Matthews. *Etude critique des procédés graphiques ou analytiques pour la détermination du flux lumineux des sources de lumière.* (Philips, Eindhoven, *1928*.)

H. H. Higbie. *Lighting Calculations.* (Wiley, New York, *1934*.)

P. Moon. *Scientific Basis of Illuminating Engineering.* (McGraw-Hill, *1936*.)

H. Zijl. *Manual for the Illuminating Engineer on Large Size perfect Diffusers.* (Philips Technical Library, *1951*.)

REFERENCES

1. On the implications of a statement such as this, see J. Guild, " Discussion on Vision," Phys. and Opt. Socs., *1932*, p. 60. See also V. Ronchi, Elettrot., 43, *1946*, p. 217.

2. The official definitions are in French ; the English version used is that given, with the German version, in the " *Vocabulaire International de l'Eclairage* ".

3. Illumination is a possible alternative, but a standard of illumination can only be set up through the medium of a standard source. (See, on this subject, U. Bordoni, Elettrot., 6, *1919*, p. 430, and 15, *1928*, p. 243 ; C.I.E., Proc., 5, *1921*, p. 53 ; N. R. Campbell and B. P. Dudding, Phil. Mag., 44, *1922*, p. 577 ; J. W. T. Walsh, *ibid.*, p. 1165; M. Eskenazi, Helv. Phys. Acta, 28, *1955*, p. 395.)

The primary standard (see p. 174) is, strictly, a standard of luminance, but as this is simply luminous intensity per unit area, the standard may legitimately be regarded as one of luminous intensity.

4. The term " luminous energy " has been proposed for the photometric quantity which corresponds to radiant energy in radiometry (Report of Committee on Colorimetry, Opt. Soc. Am., J., 34, *1944*, p. 246 ; see also *ibid.*, 4, *1920*, p. 230). The unit is the " talbot " equal to the lumen-second. On the international system " luminous energy " is termed " quantity of light " (see p. 515). See also note (56) *infra*.

5. See, e.g., L. Bloch, Illum. Eng., 2, *1909*, pp. 516 and 682.

6. The compressibility of water may be neglected for the purposes of illustration.

7. Report of the National Illumination Committee of Gt. Britain, Illum. Eng., 15, *1922*, p. 225.

8. The unit of solid angle, often called a steradian, is the angle subtended at the centre of a sphere of unit radius by unit area of the surface of the sphere. It follows that the total solid angle at a point is 4π steradians.

9. For a curious example of the confusion which may arise from a misconception of flux, see Electrician, 29, *1892*, p. 170.

10. This unit replaces both the old international candle, to which it is very nearly equal in magnitude, and the unit formerly used in Germany and some other countries, the Hefnerkerze, or Hefner candle, the value of which was about 0·9 international candles (see p. 177).

11. G. B. Dyke. Phys. Soc., Proc., 19, *1904*, p. 399.

12. British National Illumination Committee, C.I.E., Proc., 5, *1921*, p. 98.

13. F. A. Benford. Gen. El. Rev., 28, *1925*, p. 271 ; Illum. Eng. Soc. N.Y., Trans., 21, *1926*, p. 129.

J. W. T. Walsh. Illum. Eng., 26, *1933*, p. 169.

B. Monash. Illum. Eng. Soc. N.Y., Trans., 35, *1940*, p. 374.

J. Dourgnon. Rev. Gén. de l'El., 53, *1944*, p. 119.

See also G. F. Freeman, Light and Ltg., 30, *1937*, p. 222 ; A. Marsat, C.R., 199, *1934*, p. 275 ; F. Benford and J. E. Bock, Opt. Soc. Am., J., 31, *1941*, p. 239 ; R. Nampon, Soc. Franç. des Elect., Bull., 4, *1944*, p. 131 ; H. J. Turner, Light and Ltg., 42, *1949*, p. 218.

14. See, e.g., G. P. Kellaway, *Map Projections* (Methuen, *1946*), p. 66.

14a. D. A. Toenjes. Illum. Engng., 46, *1951*, p. 335.

15. See, e.g. F. Uppenborn, J.G.W., 48, *1905*, p. 272 ; A. P. Trotter, *Illumination, etc.*, p. 151.

Different forms of polar diagram in which the area is proportional to the m.s.c.p. or flux have been described by E. S. Oberndorf (El. World, 101, *1933*, p. 132), by E. Meyer (Licht, 7, *1937*, p. 247) and by F. A. Benford (Opt. Soc. Am., J., 32, *1942*, p. 307).

A planimeter for finding the total flux directly from the ordinary polar diagram has been described by G. Weber (Licht, 3, *1933*, p. 145). See also R. Roggan, Z. f. techn. Phys., 11, *1930*, p. 207.

16. E. Rousseau. C.R. des essais photométriques à l'exposition d'Anvers, *1885*. R. H. Ledeboer. Ecl. El. 26, *1887*, p. 58.

See also H. Krüss, Central-Ztg. f. Opt. u. Mech., 5, *1884*, p. 110.

17. See, e.g., A. E. Kennelly, Illum. Eng. Soc. N.Y., Trans., 3, *1908*, p. 243.

On the calculation of the flux from small projection apparatus see G. K. Ustjugov, State Opt. Inst., Leningrad, Trans. (Trudui), 6, *1931*, No. 59, p. 31 (in Russian).

18. A. Russell. Inst. El. Eng., J., 32, *1903*, p. 631.

See also N. Macbeth, Illum. Eng. (N.Y.), 3, *1908*, p. 27 ; E.T.Z., 35, *1914*, p. 274 ; C. E. Greenslade, Light and Ltg., 42, *1949*, p. 205 ; W. A. Hedrich. Illum. Engng., 50, *1955*, p. 170.

19. H. Buckley. Illum. Eng., 18, *1925*, pp. 69 and 93.

Z. Yamauti. C.I.E., Proc., 7, *1928*, p. 409.

20. See also E. Liebenthal, *Prakt. Phot.*, pp. 272 *et seqq.* and J. Ondracek, E. u. M., 36, *1918*, p. 77.

21. H. Buckley. Illum. Eng., 18, *1925*, pp. 69 and 93.

22. See the refs. in note (22) on p. 121 of *Photometry (1926)*. To ref. A. A. Wohlauer add Illum. Eng. Soc. N.Y., Trans., 23, *1928*, p. 551 and H. Lingenfelser and A. A. Wohlauer, Licht, 1, *1931*, p. 287.

H. S. Bull. El. World, 91, *1928*, p. 807.

E. L. J. Matthews. Rev. Gén. de l'El., 24, *1928*, p. 275.

H. J. Helwig. Licht, 4, *1934*, p. 79.

A. Sellerio. Z. f. techn. Phys., 15, *1934*, pp. 267 and 366.

R. Sewig. Licht, 8, *1938*, p. 12.

See also note (15) *supra*.

23. See also K. S. Weaver, Illum. Eng. Soc. N.Y., Trans., 22, *1927*, p. 547.

24. See e.g., J. Teichmüller, J.G.W., 57, *1914*, p. 193.

25. Originally "candle-foot." On the objections to a name of this form for the unit of illumination see, e.g. A. P. Trotter, *Illumination, etc.*, p. 16.

26. It may, perhaps be thought that this assumption of constant rate of propagation is invalid, in view of the fact that light travels in water, for example, with a velocity which is only three-quarters of its velocity in air, but it will be clear that although it travels more slowly in water, as much energy must reach a surface immersed in water as would reach it were the water absent (neglecting losses due to surface reflection and absorption), otherwise there would be an accumulation of energy in the body of the water. In this respect the energy propagation may be likened to a number of balls dropped from a height at regular intervals. The rate of their arrival at the bottom will be the same as the rate at which they are dropped, but owing to the increased velocity at the end of their journey, they will be farther apart (less concentrated) at the bottom than at the top of their path. Similarly, decreased velocity of the light will be compensated by the decrease in the wavelength, the frequency, and therefore the number of waves arriving at the surface in any given time, being unchanged.

27. For an account of an experimental investigation of the inverse square law see F. Carstaedt, Ann. d. Phys., 150, *1873*, p. 551.

28. To be distinguished from the cosine law of emission (see p. 137).

29. J. Ondracek. E.u.M., 42, *1924*, Lichttech., p. 336.

30. See, e.g. A. Gouffé, C.I.E., Proc., 7, *1928*, p. 57 and Int. Illum. Congress, *1931*, Proc., Vol. I, p. 544.

31. Tables of $\cos^3 \theta$ are given in most text-books on illumination.

Nomograms for the calculation of illumination have been described. See, e.g.,

L. Bloch, E.T.Z., 43, *1922*, p. 73 ; A. Fischer, Licht u. Lampe, 20, *1931*, p. 209 ;
E. Meyer, Licht, 3, *1933*, p. 176 ; W. J. G. Davey, Light and Ltg., 28, *1935*, p. 18
and 29, *1936*, p. 46 ; P. Noël and A. Vallat, Rev. Gén. de l'El., 38, *1935*, p. 11 ;
R. Sewig, Licht, 8, *1938*, p. 33 ; W. M. Armstrong, Illum. Engng., 36, *1941*, p. 503 ;
A. Quesnel, Rev. Gén. de l'El., 51, *1942*, p. 387. (See also K. Franck, Illum. Engng.,
39, *1944*, p. 245.)
Special slide-rules have been designed by O. Höpcke and E. Summerer (Licht u.
Lampe, 19, *1930*, p. 1183), by G. F. Freeman (J. Sci. Inst., 14, *1937*, p. 411) and by
E. Meyer (Licht, 9, *1939*, pp. 144 and 166).
For earlier papers on this subject see the refs. in note (57) on p. 375 of *Photometry*
(1926).

32. A. P. Trotter. Inst. Civil Eng., Proc., 110, *1892*, p. 69.
See also J. Wetzel, Rev. Gén. de l'El., 18, *1925*, p. 857 and 20, *1926*, p. 31.

33. A number of different graphical methods of constructing illumination curves
have been described. See, e.g., F. Loppé, L'Electricien, 14, *1890*, p. 936 ; C. H. Lees,
Phil. Mag., 40, *1895*, p. 463 ; E. C. White, Illum. Eng. (N.Y.), 1, *1906*, pp. 333 and
640 ; F. A. Benford, Illum. Eng. Soc. N.Y., Trans., 7, *1912*, p. 695 ; E. Meyer, Licht
u. Lampe, 21, *1932*, p. 99 ; F. Nitzsche, *ibid.*, p. 195 ; R. Mühlig, Licht, 6, *1936*,
pp. 23 and 49 ; E. R. Andersson, Licht u. Lampe, 25, *1936*, p. 45 ; P. Behret, *ibid.*, 27,
1938, pp. 753 and 781 ; W. v. Langen, Licht, 9, *1939*, p. 146 ; J. H. Dean, Illum.
Engng., 37, *1942*, p. 417 ; I. Goodbar, *ibid.*, 41, *1946*, p. 39 ; J. G. Holmes, Light
and Ltg., 39, *1946*, p. 158.
See also A. A. Wohlauer, El. World, 88, *1926*, p. 1270 ; E. R. Andersson, Licht u.
Lampe, 25, *1936*, p. 605 ; T. W. Rolph, Illum. Engng., 41, *1946*, p. 775.

34. J. G. Holmes. Light and Ltg., 39, *1946*, p. 158.

35. See also A. P. Trotter, *Illumination, etc.*, p. 46.
Examples of isophot diagrams calculated for different arrangements of sources
may be found in the literature of illumination, especially of streets. See, e.g., A. P.
Trotter, *loc. cit.*, pp. 47⁻51 ; H. Maréchal, *L'Éclairage à Paris* (Baudry, *1894*),
pp. 474 *et seqq.* ; A. Blondel, Electrician, 37, *1896*, pp. 14 and 42 ; H. Lux, Z. f. Bel.,
2, *1896*, p. 282 ; H. Bohle, *Electrical Photometry and Illumination* (Griffin, *1925*),
p. 119.
An alternative form of diagram has been proposed by R. R. Holmes (Illum. Eng.,
28, *1935*, p. 186).

36. R. C. Putnam. Gen. El. Rev., 36, *1933*, p. 539.
R. Nampon. Rev. Gén. de l'El., 34, *1933*, p. 791 and 42, *1937*, p. 67. (The
second paper describes an extension to the determination of curves of equal luminance.)

37. F. C. Smith. Illum. Eng., 25, *1932*, p. 287.

38. See, e.g., A. Blondel, Rev. Gén. de l'El., 31, *1932*, p. 333.

39. C.I.E., Proc., 5, *1921*, p. 89 and 6, *1924*, pp. 156 and 167.

40. C.I.E., Proc., 11, *1948*, p. 145.

41. W. D. Wright. Illum. Eng. Soc. Lond., Proc., 4, *1939*, p. 1 and 6, *1941*,
p. 23.
See also W. D. Wright and J. H. Nelson, J. Sci. Inst., 12, *1935*, p. 373.

42. E. Liebenthal. Art. " Photometrische Gesetze und Formeln " in *Physikalisches Handwörterbuch*, ed. Berliner and Scheel (Springer, Berlin, *1924*).

43. The notion of luminance is not necessarily dependent on the presence of a
surface. See, e.g. J. Dourgnon, Rev. Gén. de l'El., 30, *1932*, p. 747 or C.I.E., Proc.,
10, *1939*, Vol. I, p. 12 and, for the contrary view, A. Blondel, Rev. Gén. de l'El., 31,
1932, p. 333 and 32, *1932*, p. 3.
See also P. Moon and D. E. Spencer, Illum. Engng., 39, *1944*, p. 507.

44. *Photometria*, p. 324.

45. H. Reinhardt. Illum. Engng., 39, *1944*, p. 521.
See also R. P. Teele, Soc. Motion Picture Eng., J., 26, *1936*, p. 554 ; J. Pawli-
kowski, Rev. trimestrielle Canadienne 32, *1946*, p. 45.

46. Licht u. Lampe, 20, *1931*, pp. 241 and 335.
O. Reeb. *Ibid.*, 21, *1932*, p. 298 ; C.I.E., Proc., 9, *1935*, p. 164.
See also L. Schneider, Licht u. Lampe, 16, *1927*, p. 335.

47. C.I.E., Proc., 6, *1924*, p. 175 ; Illum. Eng. Soc. N.Y., Trans., 19, *1924*,
p. 512.

48. El. World, 65, *1915*, pp. 332, 460 and 715.

49. E. F. Caldin. Phys. Soc., Proc., 57, *1945*, p. 440.

50. H. E. Ives. Frank. Inst., J., 188, *1919*, p. 217 ; Opt. Soc. Am., J., 12, *1926*, p. 75.

51. See J. W. T. Walsh, Opt. Soc. Am., J., 11, *1925*, p. 111 ; P. Moon and D. E. Spencer, *ibid.*, 33, *1943*, p. 89 and J. of Maths. and Phys., 25, *1946*, p. 111.
See also the refs. quoted in notes (12) to (14) on p. 311 of *Photometry (1926)*.

52. Com. Int. des Poids et Mesures, Procès-verbaux, 21, *1948*, pp. T26 and T47. See also W. F. Roeser, F. R. Caldwell and H. T. Wensel, Bureau of Standards, J. of Research, 6, *1931*, p. 1119 ; F. H. Schofield, Roy. Soc., Proc., 146, *1934*, p. 792 ; F. Hoffmann and C. Tingwaldt, Phys. Z., 35, *1934*, p. 434 ; H. F. Stimson, Bureau of Standards, J. of Research, 42, *1949*, p. 209.

53. B. Lohse and U. Stille. Z. f. Phys., 125, *1948*, p. 133.
H. T. Wensel. Bureau of Standards, J. of Research, 22, *1939*, p. 375 (see also Opt. Soc. Am., J., 34, *1944*, p. 657).
G. Heller. Philips Techn. Rev., 5, *1940*, p. 1.
D. MacAdam. Opt. Soc. Am., J., 35, *1945*, p. 615.
E. F. Caldin. Phys. Soc., Proc., 58, *1946*, p. 207.
See also E. Lax, Licht, 5, *1935*, p. 76.
It will be clear that the value of K can be found experimentally from measurements of the luminous flux and of the corresponding energy rate, either for monochromatic radiation of any convenient wave-length (see, e.g. H. Buisson and C. Fabry, C.R., 153, *1911*, p. 254 ; H. E. Ives, W. W. Coblentz and E. F. Kingsbury, Phys. Rev., 5, *1915*, p. 269 ; H. Krofft and M. Pirani, Z. f. techn. Phys., 13, *1932*, p. 367 ; G. A. W. Rutgers, Physica, 15, *1949*, p. 985) or for any source of light whatever provided the spectral distribution of the energy is known (see, e.g., the literature cited in notes (16) to (23) on p. 312 of *Photometry (1926)*, esp. E. P. Hyde, C.I.E., Proc., 5, *1921*, p. 160 and H. E. Ives, Opt. Soc. Am., J., 9, *1924*, p. 635 ; also E. Brodhun and F. Hoffmann, Z. f. Phys., 37, *1926*, p. 137 ; L. S. Ornstein *et al.*, Amsterdam Acad., Proc., 34, *1931*, p. 212). The value given in the text follows directly from the definition of the candela and is independent of experimental determinations.

54. E. F. Caldin. Phys. Soc., Proc., 57, *1945*, p. 440.
W. Geiss. Licht, 13, *1943*, p. 33.
G. A. W. Rutgers and J. C. de Vos. Physica, 20, *1954*, p. 715.
See also K. S. Weaver, Opt. Soc. Am., J., 26, *1936*, p. 339 ; W. de Groot, Philips Tech. Rev., 10, *1948*, p. 150.

55. See, e.g., S. Maisel, State Optical Inst. Leningrad, Trans. (Trudui), 5, *1929*, No. 44, p. 1 (In Russian) and Int. Illum. Congress, *1931*, Proc., Vol. I, p. 1 ; S. Maisel and A. Gerschun, Licht u. Lampe, 19, *1930*, p. 84 ; P. Moon, *Scientific Basis of Illuminating Engineering*, Appendix B.

56. Opt. Soc. Am., J., 4, *1920*, p. 230.
Alternatively, energy weighted in the same way may be expressed in terms of a unit, the *lumerg*, which corresponds to the erg, so that 1 lightwatt $= 10^7$ lumergs per sec. (see Opt. Soc. Am., J., 34, *1944*, p. 245). See note (4) *supra*.

57. See, e.g. C. Fabry, Soc. Franç. des Elect., Bull., 7, *1927*, p. 376.

58. See, on this subject, the books listed at the end of this Chapter ; also P. Moon and D. E. Spencer, *Lighting Design* (Addison-Wesley Press, Cambridge, Mass., U.S.A., *1948*), Chapter IV ; G. Bethe, Optik, 8, *1951*, pp. 476 and 489 ; J. H. McGuire. D.S.I.R. Fire Research, Special Report No. 2 (H.M.S.O., *1953*) ; A. I. Mahan and W. F. Malmborg, Opt. Soc. Am., J., 44, *1954*, p. 644.

59. See A. F. Salanson, Soc. techn. de l'indust. du gaz, C.r., 16, *1889*, p. 200 and the other papers cited in note (46) on p. 122 of *Photometry (1926)*.

60. See also U. Bordoni, Rivista d'ottica e mechanica di precisione, 2, *1922* (II), p. 1.

61. *Photometria*, p. 99.
J. W. T. Walsh. Phys. Soc., Proc., 32, *1920*, p. 59.
E. A. Milne. Phil. Mag., 7, *1929*, p. 273.

62. J. W. T. Walsh. Phys. Soc., Proc., 32, *1920*, p. 59.
The principle may be extended to non-planar surfaces (O. A. Saunders, Phil. Mag., 8, *1929*, p. 213).

63. J. W. T. Walsh. Phys. Soc., Proc., 32, *1920*, p. 315.

64. See also S. P. Owen, Phil. Mag., 39, *1920*, p. 359 and A. C. Bartlett, *ibid.*, 40, *1920*, p. 111.

65. E. P. Hyde. Bureau of Standards, Bull., 2, *1906*, p. 1 and 3, *1907*, p. 81. For the mathematical treatment see A. S. Chessin, Am. Math. Soc., Bull., 14, *1908*, p. 212.

66. On the illumination from long cylindrical sources see, e.g., K. Norden, E.T.Z., 28, *1907*, p. 757 and 29, *1908*, p. 883 ; J. Pole, Illum. Eng. Soc. N.Y., Trans., 6, *1911*, p. 306 ; E. L. J. Matthews, Licht, 1, *1931*, pp. 141 and 165 ; R. C. Whipple, Illum. Eng. Soc. N.Y., Trans., 30, *1935*, p. 492 ; A. A. Wohlauer, *ibid.*, 31, *1936*, p. 695 ; Light and Ltg., 29, *1936*, p. 212 ; E. Meyer, Licht u. Lampe, 27, *1938*, p. 259 ; H. Zijl, Philips Techn. Rev., 6, *1941*, p. 147 ; M. Cohu, Rev. Gén. de l'El., 52, *1943*, p. 92. See also A. Hnatak, Z. f. Phys., 22, *1924*, p. 186; G. Parolini and M. Calzini, Elettrot., 37, *1950*, p. 182.

67. G. B. Dyke. Phys. Soc., Proc., 19, *1905*, p. 616.

J. A. Fleming. *Ibid.*, p. 681.

E. W. Weinbeer. Z. f. Bel., 15, *1909*, p. 305.

68. W. Saltzmann. E.T.Z., 8, *1887*, p. 430.

E. B. Rosa. Bureau of Standards, Bull., 6, *1910*, p. 543.

E. L. J. Matthews. Licht u. Lampe, 17, *1928*, p. 7.

69. B. Jones. Illum. Eng. Soc. N.Y., Trans., 4, *1909*, p. 216 (formula (13) in this paper is incorrect), 5, *1910*, p. 281 (formula (20) is incorrect) and 6, *1911*, p. 365 (gives the polar curve for a rectangle).

U. Bordoni. Assoc. El. Ital., Atti., 12, *1908*, p. 265 and 17, *1913*, p. 554.

R. Böker. Z. f. Bel., 25, *1919*, p. 95.

H. H. Higbie. Illum. Eng. Soc. N.Y., Trans., 20, *1925*, p. 433.

H. H. Higbie and A. Levin. *Ibid.*, 21, *1926*, p. 273.

J. Ondracek. E. u. M., 44, *1926*, Lichttech., p. 93.

W. Viets. Licht, 12, *1942*, p. 102 and 14, *1944*, p. 87.

See also K. Hisano, Electrotech. Lab., Tokyo, Researches No. 353, *1933* ; J. Dourgnon, Rev. Gén. de l'El., 36, *1934*, p. 227 ; J. Ondracek, E.u.M., 56, *1938*, p. 585 ; D. E. Spencer, Opt. Soc. Am., J., 32, *1942*, pp. 274 and 539 ; P. Moon and D. E. Spencer, Frank. Inst., J., 241, *1946*, p. 195 ; M. Cohu, Rev. Gén. de l'El., 56, *1947*, p. 167.

A nomogram for finding E_H has been described by H. S. Bull (Illum. Eng. Soc. N.Y., Trans., 23, *1928*, p. 547). See also H. H. Higbie and W. Turner-Szymanowski, *ibid.*, 25, *1930*, p. 213.

70. J. Ondracek. E.u.M., 44, *1926*, Lichttech., p. 93.

L. F. Richardson *et al.* Phil. Mag., 6, *1928*, p. 1019 ; 7, *1929*, pp. 419 and 946 and 8, *1929*, p. 126.

Z. Yamauti. Electrotech. Lab. Tokyo, Researches No. 250, *1929*.

See also J. Dourgnon, Rev. Gén. de l'El., 23, *1928*, p. 271 ; E. Carlevaro, Elettrot., 18, *1931*, p. 89 ; K. Hisano, Electrotech. Lab. Tokyo, Researches No. 367, *1934*.

71. J. Ondracek. Z. f. Bel., 28, *1922*, p. 64 (see also Chr. Wiener, *Lehrbuch d. darstellenden Geometrie*, Vol. 1 (Teubner, Leipzig, *1884*), pp. 399 *et seqq.* and R. Mehmke, Z. f. Math. u. Phys., 43, *1898*, p. 41).

Z. Yamauti. Electrotech. Lab. Tokyo, Researches No. 194, *1927*.

A. C. Stevenson. Int. Illum. Congress, *1931*, Proc., Vol. II, p. 1167.

See also J. Dourgnon and P. Waguet, C.R., 189, *1921*, p. 361 ; Soc. Franç. des Elect., Bull., 9, *1929*, p. 939 ; S. O. Maisel, State Opt. Inst., Leningrad, Trans. (Trudui), 3, *1923*, No. 16, p. 12 (In Russian) ; J. Ondracek, E.u.M., 49, *1931*, Lichttech. p. 49 ; Rev. Gén. de l'El., 41, *1937*, p. 811 ; A. Gouffé, *ibid.*, p. 815 ; J. Ondracek, Licht, 9, *1939*, p. 180 ; V. H. Cherry, D. D. Davis and L. M. K. Boelter, Illum. Eng. Soc. N.Y., Trans., 34, *1939*, p. 1085 (describes a mechanical integrator) ; B. F. Greenberg, *ibid.*, 35, *1940*, p. 629 ; Licht, 11, *1941*, p. 167 ; S. G. Yurov, Jurnal technicheskoi Fisiki (U.S.S.R.), 18, *1948*, p. 1073 (In Russian).

72. A. C. Stevenson. Int. Illum. Congress, *1931*, Proc., Vol. II, p. 1167.

O. Höpcke. Licht, 2, *1932*, pp. 113 and 133.

M. Goldmann. *Ibid.*, pp. 136 and 153.

P. Hartill. Illum. Eng. Soc. Lond., Trans., 11, *1946*, p. 253.

See also A. Burchard, Zentralbl. d. Bauverwaltung, 39, *1919*, pp. 38 and 597.

73. The case of the transparent radiator may, clearly, be treated as a problem in gravitation. See A. Beer, Ann. d. Phys., 88, *1853*, p. 114 ; W. von Bezold, *ibid.*, 141, *1870*, p. 91 ; Phil. Mag., 41, *1871*, p. 241 ; H. Ebert, Gesell. deut. Naturforscher u. Aerzte, Tagebl., 62, *1889*, p. 200.

See also A. A. Gershun, Phys. Z. Sowjetunion, 2, *1932*, p. 149 ; Licht, 2, *1932*, p. 221.

74. E. Allard. C.R., 82, *1876*, p. 1300.
R. W. Wood. Phil. Mag., 11, *1906*, p. 782.
M. Laporte. Rev. d'Opt., 12, *1933*, p. 21.

75. Gas World, 25, *1896*, p. 284.

76. U. Tanaka. Dept. of Communications, Tokyo, Researches. " On the Use and Selection of Standard Electric Lamps " (In Japanese), Feb., *1921*.

77. H. Buckley. Phil. Mag., 4, *1927*, p. 753 and 6, *1928*, p. 447 ; C.I.E., Proc., 7, *1928*, p. 888.
Z. Yamauti. Opt. Soc. Am., J., 13, *1926*, p. 561 ; Rev. Gén. de l'El., 42, *1937*, p. 293.
See also J. Dourgnon, Rev. Gén. de l'El., 23, *1928*, p. 609 ; V. Genkin, *ibid.*, 29, *1931*, p. 369 ; W. F. Whitmore, J. of Maths. and Phys., 17, *1938*, p. 218 ; P. Moon, Opt. Soc. Am., J., 30, *1940*, p. 195 and 31, *1941*, pp. 223, 301 and 374 ; W. T. White, *ibid.*, p. 308.

78. V. Fock. Z. f. Phys., 28, *1924*, p. 102.
A. Gershun and M. M. Gurevick. Russkoe Fisiko-Khimicheskoe Obschestvo, Jurnal (Chast Fisicheskaya), 60, *1928*, p. 355 (In Russian).
A. A. Gershun. State Opt. Inst., Leningrad, Trans. (Trudui), 4, *1928*, No. 38, p. 10 (In Russian).
M. M. Gurevic. Phys. Z., 30, *1929*, p. 640.
Z. Yamauti. Electrotech. Lab. Tokyo, Researches Nos. 148, *1924*, 194, *1927* and 339, *1932*.
J. Dourgnon. Rev. Gén. de l'El., 41, *1937*, p. 619. (See also *ibid.*, 45, *1939*, p. 437.)
A. Gerschun. *Ibid.*, 42, *1937*, p. 5 and 44, *1938*, p. 307.
A. Blondel. *Ibid.*, 42, *1937*, p. 579 and 44, *1938*, p. 312.
G. W. O. Howe. El. Rev., 123, *1938*, p. 679.
A. Gerschun. J. of Maths. and Phys., 18, *1939*, p. 51.
P. Moon. Opt. Soc. Am., J., 29, *1939*, p. 108 and 33, *1943*, p. 115.
A. Gershun. Elektrichestvo, *1947*, No. 10, p. 5.
H. J. Helwig. Lichttechnik, 2, *1950*, p. 14.

79. A. S. McAllister. El. World, 56, *1910*, p. 1356 ; Illum. Eng. Soc. N.Y., Trans., 6, *1911*, p. 703.
F. Benford. Opt. Soc. Am., J., 30, *1940*, p. 33.
A. A. Wohlauer. Frank. Inst., J., 231, *1941*, p. 49.

80. J. A. Fleming. Phys. Soc., Proc., 19, *1905*, p. 681.

81. E. Liebenthal. *Prakt. Phot.*, p. 93.

82. A. G. Vernon-Harcourt. J. of Gas Lighting, 51, *1888*, p. 371.
C. H. Sharp. El. World, 27, *1896*, p. 54.

83. See, e.g., N. A. Halbertsma, E.T.Z., 38, *1917*, pp. 482 and 494 ; E.u.M., 37, *1919*, p. 197.

84. A. Cornu. Ann. de l'Observatoire de Paris, 13, *1876*, p. A76.

85. J. Clerk Maxwell. Phil. Trans., 150, *1860*, p. 57. It has also been called the Rayleigh method (see, e.g., C.R. 181, *1925*, p. 310)

86. A. A. Michelson. Opt. Soc. Am., J., 9, *1924*, p. 197.

87. This has also been called regular (or specular) reflection.

88. In the U.S.A. the terms " reflectance ", " transmittance " and " absorptance " are preferred to " reflection factor ", etc.

89. A. J. Fresnel. Ann. Chim. Phys., 17, *1821*, p. 167 (paged in error as 267) and 46, *1831*, p. 225.
T. Preston, *Theory of Light*, §§ 208 and 209 ; A. Schuster and J. W. Nicholson, *Theory of Optics*, §§ 27 and 143 ; R. A. Houstoun, *Treatise on Light*, Ch. XXIII.

90. E. Liebenthal. *Prakt. Phot.*, p. 397.
More extended tables are given by P. Moon (J. of Maths. and Phys., 19, *1940*, p. 1) and by J. G. Holmes (Illum. Eng. Soc. Lond., Trans., 12, *1947*, p. 108.)
Experimental values have been obtained by Rayleigh and others. See, e.g., Roy. Soc., Proc., 41, *1886*, p. 275.

91. " Transmission Factor of Commercial Window Glasses." Illum. Research Tech. Paper No. 2. (H.M. Stationery Office, *1926*), Appendix. (See also J. W. Ryde, Roy. Soc., Proc., 131, *1931*, pp. 462 and 466.)
F. A. Benford. Gen. El. Rev., 37, *1934*, p. 414.
D. B. Judd. Bureau of Standards, J. of Research, 29, *1942*, p. 329.

See also A. Gershun, State Opt. Inst., Leningrad, Trans. (Trudui), **4**, *1928*, No. 38, p. 1 (In Russian) ; Opt. Soc. Am., J., **35**, *1945*, p. 162.

92. It does not follow that this is the direction of maximum polarisation for the transmitted light. See T. Erhard, Ann. d. Phys., **12**, *1881*, p. 655.

93. L. V. Lorenz. Ann. d. Phys., **111**, *1860*, p. 460 and **114**, *1861*, p. 238.

P. Drude. *Lehrbuch d. Optik*, p. 266 (287).

R. C. Maclaurin. Roy. Soc., Proc., **76**, *1905*, p. 49.

94. See, e.g., D. H. Jacobs, *Fundamentals of Optical Engineering* (McGraw-Hill, *1943*), Chap. VIII ; F. Kollmorgen, Illum. Eng. Soc. N.Y., Trans., **11**, *1916*, p. 220 ; J. Strong, Opt. Soc. Am., J., **26**, *1936*, p. 73 ; K. B. Blodgett, Phys. Rev., **55**, *1939*, p. 391 ; C. H. Cartwright, Opt. Soc. Am., J., **30**, *1940*, p. 110 ; H. W. Lee and E. A. Neumann, Photog. J., **84**, *1944*, p. 223 ; P. Jacquinot, Rev. d'Opt., **21**, *1942*, p. 15.

95. J. H. Lambert. *Photometria*, Part 3, Chap. II.

96. P. Bouguer. *Traité d'Optique*, p. 175.

97. C. Dunbar. Opt. Soc., Trans., **32**, *1931*, p. 184.

L. W. J. Holleman and H. J. Hardon. Chronica Naturae, **106**, *1950*, p. 1.

98. J. C. F. Zöllner. *Photometrische Untersuchungen* (Engelmann, Leipzig, *1865*), E. Lommel. Ann. d. Phys., **10**, *1880*, pp. 449 and 631. [p. 17.

L. V. King. Phil. Mag., **23**, *1912*, p. 237.

99. P. Bouguer. *Traité d'Optique*, p. 161.

E. M. Berry. Opt. Soc. Am., J., **7**, *1923*, p. 627.

See also L. Grabowski, Astrophys. J., **39**, *1914*, p. 299.

100. H. Seeliger. Munich Ber., **18**, *1888*, p. 201.

E. Lommel. Ann. d. Phys., **36**, *1889*, p. 473.

F. Jentzsch. Ann. d. Phys., **39**, *1912*, p. 997.

B. Fessenkoff. C.R., **158**, *1914*, p. 1271.

F. Henning and W. Heuse. Z. f. Phys., **10**, *1922*, p. 111.

G. I. Pokrowski. Z. f. Phys., **30**, *1924*, p. 66 ; **34**, *1925*, p. 496 ; **35**, *1925*, pp. 34 and 390 ; **36**, *1926*, p. 472.

W. W. Barkas. Phys. Soc., Proc., **51**, *1939*, p. 274. (See also Appendix by R. F. S. Hearmon.)

101. C.I.E. Proc., **11**, *1948*, pp. 6 and 18.

See also note (20) on p. 449.

102. Photo-luminescence (see p. 45) is not considered here since it is not a pure reflection phenomenon.

103. P. Bouguer. *Essai d'Optique*, p. 44 ; *Traité d'Optique*, pp. 229 *et seqq.*

J. H. Lambert. *Photometria*, pp. 222 *et seq.*

See also J. Bottomley, Manchester Lit. and Phil. Soc., Mem., **28**, *1884*, p. 198 ; F. H. Perrin, Opt. Soc. Am., J., **38**, *1948*, p. 72.

104. Also called the " extinction coefficient " but this name was used by R. W. Bunsen and H. E. Roscoe (Phil. Trans., **147**, *1857*, p. 601) to denote the quantity ϵ where $10^{\epsilon} = e^{\alpha'}$. ϵ is then the reciprocal of the thickness having a transmission factor of 0·1. See also E. Hagen and H. Rubens, Ann. d. Phys., **8**, *1902*, p. 432.

105. Int. Critical Tables, Vol. V, p. 264.

H. C. Vogel. Berlin Ber., **11**, *1896*, p. 1219.

W. D. Haigh. Opt. Convention, *1926*, Proc., Vol. I, p. 327.

On the calculation of the transmissivity of optical glass, see, e.g. A. A. Gerschun, Z. f. techn. Phys., **10**, *1929*, p. 18.

A method of measuring the transmissivity of optical glass has been described by T. Smith (Rev. d'Opt., **27**, *1948*, p. 371).

106. A. Beer. Ann. d. Phys., **86**, *1852*, p. 78.

107. E. C. C. Baly. *Spectroscopy* (Longmans, *1927*), Vol. II, p. 350.

H. S. Taylor. *Treatise on Physical Chemistry* (Macmillan, *1931*), p. 1461.

108. See also D. S. Perfect, Opt. Soc., Trans., **27**, *1926*, p. 324.

109. It is to be noted that no allowance need generally be made for the light reflected by a glass bulb or chimney surrounding a light source, for clearly the amount lost by reflection at the surfaces of the front glass is exactly compensated by the light gained owing to reflection in the surfaces of the back glass, neglecting absorption in the flame and in the substance of the glass itself. See R. A. Fessenden, El. World, **33**, *1899*, p. 231.

110. Roy. Soc., Proc., 11, *1862*, p. 545 ; Math. and Phys. Papers, vol. 4, p. 145.
F. A. Benford. Opt. Soc. Am., J., 7, *1923*, p. 1017.
T. Smith. Opt. Soc., Trans., 27, *1926*, p. 317.
H. Goldschmidt. Ann. d. Phys., 82, *1927*, p. 947.
L. B. Tuckermann. Opt. Soc. Am., J., 37, *1947*, p. 818.
H. Brinkman. Rev. d'Opt., 27, *1948*, p. 31.

111. H. Lunelund. Phys. Z., 10, *1909*, p. 222.
T. Y. Baker. Opt. Soc., Trans., 22, *1921*, p. 88.
R. A. Hull. Phys. Soc., Proc., 48, *1936*, p. 574.
See also F. de la Provostaye and P. Desains, Ann. Chim. Phys., 30, *1850*, p. 159 ;
J. A. Fresnel, Œuvres (Paris, *1868*), vol. 2, p. 789.

112. F. Paschen. Berlin Ber., *1899*, p. 405.
113. J. G. Holmes. Illum. Eng. Soc. Lond., Trans., 12, *1947*, p. 108.
A. A. Gershun and N. G. Boldyrev. State Opt. Inst., Leningrad, Trans.
(Trudui), 6, *1931*, No. 59, p. 17 (In Russian).
See also N. G. Boldyrev, *ibid.*, p. 1 ; A. A. Gershun, *ibid.*, 11, *1936*, No. 99, p. 43.

114. A. A. Gershun. Acad. Sci. U.R.S.S., C.r. (Doklady), 18, *1938*, p. 31.
See also A. I. Mahan, Opt. Soc. Am., J., 33, *1943*, p. 621.

115. H. P. Gage. Opt. Soc. Am., J., 27, *1937*, p. 159.
116. H. J. Channon, F. F. Renwick and B. V. Storr, Roy. Soc., Proc., 94, *1918*,
p 222.

G. I. Pokrowski. Z. f. Phys., 31, *1925*, pp. 14 and 514.
J. W. Ryde *et al.* Roy. Soc., Proc., 131, *1931*, pp. 451 and 464 ; Int. Illum.
Congress, *1931*, Proc., Vol. I, p. 387 ; Illum. Eng., 26, *1933*, pp. 33 and 41.
J. S. Preston. Int. Illum. Congress, *1931*, Proc., Vol. I, p. 373.
S. Q. Duntley. Opt. Soc. Am., J., 32, *1942*, p. 61.
See also L. Silberstein, Opt. Soc. Am., J., 15, *1927*, p. 125 ; M. Gurevic, Phys. Z.,
31, *1930*, p. 753 ; G. M. Dreosti, Phil. Mag., 11, *1931*, p. 801 ; W. Hartel, Licht, 10,
1940, pp. 141, 165, 190, 214 and 232 ; F. Benford, Opt. Soc. Am., J., 36, *1946*, p. 524

117. T. W. Rolph. Illum. Eng. Soc. N.Y., Trans., 11, *1916*, p. 1144.

118. *Traité d'Optique*, p. 170.
A. Blondel. Ecl. El., 3, *1895*, pp. 406 and 583.

119. Illum. Eng. Soc. N.Y., Trans., 10, *1915*, pp. 353 and 366 and 34, *1939*, p. 109.
A. Boutaric. Rev. d'Opt., 10, *1931*, p. 485.
J. Dourgnon. Rev. Gén. de l'El., 37, *1935*, p. 819.
C.I.E., Proc., 9, *1935*, pp. 4 and 322 ; 10, *1939*, Vol. I, pp. 201 *et seqq.* and
Vol. III, p. 4.

120. N. A. Halbertsma. J.G.W., 60, *1917*, p. 651 ; E.u.M., 36, *1918*, p. 225.
H. Schönborn. Int. Illum. Congress, *1931*, Proc., Vol. I, p. 361.
R. Kurosawa. *Ibid.*, p. 452 ; Congrès Int. d'Electricité, Paris, *1932*, C.r.,
Vol. VIII, p. 133.

121. T. W. Rolph. Illum. Eng. Soc. N.Y., Trans., 8, *1913*, p. 268 and 11, *1916*,
p. 1144.
Report on Spectrophotometry, Opt. Soc. Am., J., 10, *1925*, p. 169.

122. J. M. Waldram. Illum. Eng. Soc. Lond., Trans., 10, *1945*, p. 147.
See also W. E. K. Middleton, *Vision through the Atmosphere* (Univ. of Toronto Press,
1952), p. 13.

123. This name has also been applied to instruments designed to measure the
facility with which a given visual task can be performed. See, e.g., C. Dunbar,
Illum. Eng. Soc. Lond., Trans., 5, *1940*, p. 33.

124. For a treatment of this subject (with extensive bibliography) and a description of the instruments used, see W. E. K. Middleton, *Vision through the Atmosphere*,
Chap. IX ; also Opt. Soc. Am., J., 32, *1942*, p. 139.

CHAPTER VI

STANDARDS AND SUB-STANDARDS

As stated at the beginning of the last chapter, the most practical photometric standard is one of luminous intensity. The standards now to be described include two groups : (a) primary standards by reference to which the luminous intensities of all sources are expressed, and (b) secondary standards for practical use in everyday photometry as temporary custodians of the unit fixed by the primary standards.

The conditions which a primary standard of light should fulfil are those required of any physical standard, viz. ease of reproducibility from specification, maintenance of value over long periods and convenience in use. In addition to these, a standard of luminous intensity should fulfil, as far as possible, the conditions that its luminous intensity should be of a convenient magnitude, and that the spectral distribution of its light should approximate to that of the light sources to be measured by comparison with it [1]. This is important owing to the difficulties encountered in making a photometric comparison between lights which are not of the same colour (see Chapter IX).

Many suggestions were made at different times for the production of a satisfactory primary standard of luminous intensity (see Chapter I, pp. 5 et seq.). None of these fulfilled all the conditions outlined above. Most were difficult to reproduce with sufficient accuracy, and were, moreover, greatly affected by change of exterior conditions such as barometric pressure, temperature, etc. Those which were actually employed at one time or another were (a) the flame of a candle of specified dimensions burning at a given rate (the standard candle, from which the unit derives its name) ; (b) the flame of a lamp of specified construction burning a specified fuel at a given rate ; (c) a certain area of a specified radiating surface held at a specified temperature ; and (d) electric lamps mutually compared so as to preserve an arbitrarily agreed value of luminous intensity as the unit. Nothing further need be said about the flame standards or the earlier incandescence standards, as these have already been described in Chapter I [2].

The Primary Standard—It has repeatedly been proposed to use as the primary photometric standard a specified area of a full radiator (see p. 35) at some definite temperature [3]. The great advantage of such a standard is its reproducibility and its independence of small variations in construction. Moreover its radiation follows

definite and well-established laws, not only as regards the total
energy emitted but also as regards the distribution of that energy
throughout the spectrum (see p. 40). Unfortunately, however, at a
temperature of, say, 2000° K. a change of 10° produces a change of

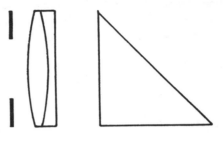

about 5 to 6 per cent in
luminous intensity so that,
for the reproducibility
necessary in a standard,
the temperature control
must be exceedingly pre-
cise. It is, in fact, impossible to ensure the necessary
accuracy of repetition by
means of any form of tem-
perature measurement and
therefore the control is
applied by immersing the
whole radiator in molten
platinum and maintaining
this at the temperature of
solidification. So long as
the purity of the platinum
can be ensured, the tem-
perature of the radiator is
defined in this way much
more precisely than it can
be measured [4].

The construction of the
standard, as it has been
widely used [5] is shown in
Fig. 99. The radiator itself
consists of a small cylinder
of pure fused thoria, about
45 mm. long, with an in-
ternal diameter of about
2·5 mm. and a wall thick-
ness of 0·2 to 0·3 mm.
The bottom of this cylinder
is packed with powdered

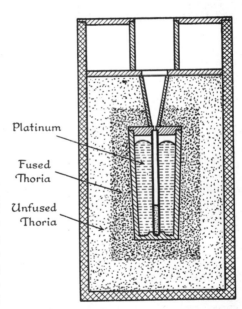

Platinum

Fused
Thoria

Unfused
Thoria

FIG. 99. The Primary Standard of Light.

fused thoria to a depth of 10 to 15 mm. and it is supported vertically
in a fused thoria crucible of about 20 mm. internal diameter nearly
filled with pure platinum, as shown in Fig. 99. This crucible has a lid
with a small hole in the centre, about 1·5 mm. in diameter and this
hole, which is the source of light, is surrounded above by a funnel-

shaped sheath forming part of the crucible lid. The crucible is embedded in powdered fused thoria in a larger refractory container and is heated by enclosing it in a high-frequency induction furnace. The power required to melt the platinum is about 7 kilowatts at a frequency of the order of one million cycles per second. With this arrangement it is possible to regulate the temperature so closely that the period required for the solidification of the platinum may exceed 20 minutes. The purity of the platinum is controlled by taking samples before and after use and determining the ratio of the electrical resistance at 100° and 0° C. A minimum value of 1·390 for this ratio is required to ensure that the temperature of solidification is sensibly the same as that of pure platinum. This corresponds to an impurity of less than 3 parts in 100,000.

The method by which the standard is used is shown in Fig. 100. Since the crucible has to be kept upright, a total reflection prism and

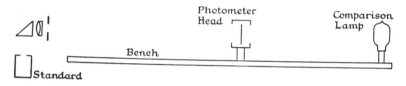

FIG. 100. Method of Use of the Primary Standard.

a cemented doublet lens are placed above it, as shown in Fig. 99, the transmission factor of this lens-prism combination (τ) having been carefully determined by a subsidiary measurement [6]. The whole system is then mounted near one end of a photometer bench and an enlarged image of the hole in the lid of the crucible is formed by the lens on one side of the diffusing disc in a Lummer-Brodhun photometer head (see p. 202), the other side of this disc being illuminated by a comparison lamp. When a diaphragm with an aperture of accurately known area (a) is placed close to the lens, the illumination of the image at the photometer head is equal to $Ba\tau/d_s^2$, B being the luminance of the hole, i.e. of the radiator, and d_s the distance between the diaphragm and the photometer disc (see pp. 151 and 152).

The luminous intensity of any sub-standard lamp of suitable type, such as that to be described later in this chapter, can now be found in terms of the unit established by the standard, using the normal photometric procedure described in the next chapter (pp. 205 et seqq.). The lamp is mounted on the photometer bench (the standard having been screened off or removed) and the distance, d, at which it gives an illumination on the photometer disc equal to that of the image of the standard radiator is noted. The luminous intensity of the sub-standard (I) is then given by the equation $I/d^2 = Ba\tau/d_s^2$. As stated in the last chapter (p. 122), the candela has been defined by giving B the value 60 candelas per square centimetre and thus I is measured in candelas to an accuracy determined by that with which the other quantities can be evaluated.

The greatest uncertainty arises in finding the transmission of the lens and prism. It is not sufficient to measure the transmission factors of these elements separately and to take the product, because of the inter-reflections between the various glass-air surfaces. It is therefore necessary either to allow for these inter-reflections or to measure the transmission of the combination exactly as it is used [7]. One way of doing this is to measure the luminance of an extended diffusing surface when viewed (a) directly and (b) through the lens-prism combination (see also p. 441).

The procedure followed in using the standard is first to raise the temperature of the crucible and its container well above the melting point of platinum. Then the whole is allowed to cool very slowly, by carefully controlling the supply of heat, and the distance d_s is continually adjusted to maintain a balance in the photometer head. As soon as solidification starts the distance d_s ceases to diminish and successive settings vary slightly about a constant value. At this stage the heat supply is controlled so as to prolong this " arrest period " as much as possible and a large number of readings of d_s are noted. As soon as the arrest point is passed, d_s again diminishes continuously. The mean of the values obtained during the arrest period is taken for the purpose of calculating the illumination of the image on the photometer disc. The period of solidification of the platinum is used in preference to the period of fusion as it has been found to give more consistent results.

The International Candle—The unit based on the standard just described was introduced on 1st Jan., 1948 as a result of action by the Comité International des Poids et Mesures [8]. Until that date the unit used in most parts of the world, except Germany and other central European countries, was the " international candle," originally established in 1909 by agreement between the national standardising laboratories of France, Great Britain and the U.S.A. [9] and adopted by the Commission Internationale de l'Eclairage (C.I.E.) in 1921 [10]. This unit was not defined by means of any primary standard. It was based on units previously in use in the different countries and derived from the Carcel and pentane lamps (see p. 5), but it was maintained by means of carbon filament electric lamps of special construction [11]. The unit used in Germany was the Hefner-kerze (symbol HK) derived from the Hefner lamp (see p. 8); its value was about nine-tenths of that of the international candle [12].

The value found for the luminance of the primary standard was $58 \cdot 9 \pm 0 \cdot 2$ int. candles per sq. cm. [13]. It follows that, by adopting the value of 60 for this quantity in establishing the new unit, the candela, a reduction of about $1 \cdot 9$ per cent was made in the magnitude of the unit. The change involved in the case of lamps operating at higher temperatures was, however, less. This was due to the fact that the sub-standards originally used at these higher temperatures, were prepared by a photometric procedure which did not give results strictly in accordance with the international table of values of V_λ which, in fact, had not been established at that time. For lamps operating at a colour temperature of about 2360° K (see p. 42) the new unit was approximately $0 \cdot 6$ per cent smaller than the old, while for a colour temperature of about 2800° K it was slightly larger [14].

Approximation to Ideal Conditions—The form of the standard described in the last section but one is that originally used in establishing the value of the unit, but it is to be noted that the definition refers to an ideal full radiator and not to a cavity radiator of any particular shape or dimensions. It is therefore important to know to what extent the form in which the standard has been realised affects the value obtained for the unit. The difference between the luminance of a full radiator and that of a cavity radiator of cylindrical form at the same temperature has been studied [15] and it has been found that, for the radiator described above, this difference is very much less than the estimated probable error in the photometric measurements.

Sub-standards and Working Standards [15a]—It is clear that the primary standard described above is quite unsuitable for everyday use in the measurement of light sources and it is therefore necessary to prepare sub-standards (preferably called secondary standards) and working standards for this purpose. Further, it is necessary to have sub-standards and working standards of luminous flux as well as of luminous intensity.

A sub-standard may be described as a suitable lamp which has been measured by comparison with the primary standard or with other sub-standards so that its luminous intensity in a defined direction, or its luminous flux output, is known to an accuracy which approaches the highest normally attainable in photometric measurement.

A working standard is a lamp which has been measured by comparison with a sub-standard, so that its luminous intensity or luminous flux output is known to an accuracy sufficient for ordinary photometric work.

As might be expected, the type of lamp which is suitable for use as a sub-standard is, in many cases, also the best to use as a working standard. Sometimes, however, this is not the case and the type, size or rating of a working standard may be dictated by the conditions under which it has to be used rather than by the considerations which are paramount in the case of a sub-standard, viz. constancy and any other quality which facilitates the attainment of a high degree of accuracy in standardisation. For example, in the routine measurement of discharge lamps, working standards of the same type as the lamps to be measured are often used [16].

For sub-standards of luminous intensity the form of tungsten filament vacuum electric lamp shown in Fig. 101 has been found

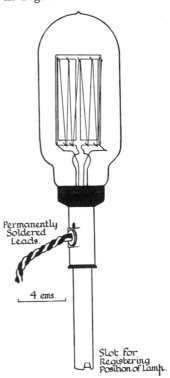

satisfactory [17]. The tungsten filament is mounted in a single plane so that this may be used for defining the zero of the distance measurements. When the lamp is in use this plane is arranged to be perpendicular to the axis of the photometer bench (see next chapter). The lamps are carefully " aged " before being standardised, i.e. they are run for at least 100 hours at an efficiency equal to or greater than that at which they are to be used in practice[17a]. They are usually operated either at a specified current or at a specified potential (see p. 183). In the latter case the potential is measured at the ends of leads which are soldered to the contact plates, and so form a permanent part of the lamp [18]. The process of measuring the luminous intensity, and the electrical adjustment, will be described in Chapter VII. One of the most important precautions in using a sub-standard lamp is to ensure that no potential which is even slightly in excess of that at which the lamp is standardised can ever be

Permanently
Soldered
Leads.

4 cms.

Slot for
Registering
Position of Lamp.

FIG. 101. A Sub-standard of
Luminous Intensity.

applied to it, even for a fraction of a second. If this should happen inadvertently, the lamp should be re-standardised.

There are many precautions which have to be observed in the manufacture of sub-standard lamps. The joint by which the filament is connected to the leading-in wires should be welded, and not simply " pinched," so that any possibility of uncertain contact may be avoided. Further, hooks and supports which are loose, so that they sometimes touch the filament and sometimes do not, cause a variation in luminous intensity due to local cooling of the filament by conduction. The glass bulbs are considerably larger than those that would be used for lamps of the same luminous intensity designed for ordinary work. This is in order to reduce the fall of luminous intensity due to " blackening," i.e. the fine deposit on the glass which takes place gradually in all filament lamps, and which produces a marked increase in the absorption factor of the bulb [19].

It is of the first importance that sub-standard lamps should be used so that the light which reaches the photometer from them is that emitted in a certain direction, for not only does the luminous intensity of the filament differ slightly in different directions, but the inevitable slight variations of thickness in the glass bulb give rise to lens effects which produce small local variations of intensity. Reflections in the bulb and in the glass framework supporting the filament are also responsible for unevenness in the light distribution [20]. If this unevenness is so marked that it produces noticeable " streaks " or " blotches " on a featureless white surface held in the path of the light, the lamp, though perhaps perfect in other respects, is valueless as a sub-standard. Uniformity of distribution can conveniently be examined photo-electrically [21].

The " registering " of a lamp so as to ensure that its position with respect to the photometer is always the same, is most conveniently achieved by mounting the lamp permanently in a holder provided with a stem which fits into the carriage of the photometer bench, and registers in its correct position in that holder by means of a small slot, such as that shown at the bottom of the stem of the lamp illustrated in Fig. 101. A further advantage of a permanent mounting of this kind for sub-standard lamps is that the potential can be measured at the ends of terminals which are permanent and fixed points in the lamp circuit. All uncertainty of contact at the lamp terminals, which is so frequently a source of unsteadiness when lamp sockets are used, is thus completely avoided, and, further, if the lamp is carefully " lined up " when it is mounted, so that the plane of the filament passes through the axis of the stem, no further lining up is necessary when the lamp is used on the bench. When it is impossible to use a self-registering mounting for a sub-standard the best method of " lining-up " is to etch on opposite sides of the bulb two small circles, so placed that when the lamp is in the correct position the line passing through the centres of these circles also passes through the photometer head. In other words, this line defines the direction in which the sub-standard has the measured luminous intensity. When the lamp is set up for use on the bench it is first placed with its axis vertical (either upright or pendent), and it is then turned about this axis until the two circles are in line with the photometer head. It is very desirable that a sub-standard should be used in the position in which it has been standardised, viz., either always upright or always pendent, as the case may be.

It has been found that lamps of this type may be used at colour temperatures (see p. 42) up to about 2360° K. After the initial ageing period which was mentioned earlier, the fall of luminous intensity should not exceed about 2 per cent per 100 burning hours, so that if a lamp is used only occasionally for the preparation of working standards it needs re-standardisation only at long intervals. The steadiness and day-to-day reproducibility are good, although it has been found that, even when the lamp is most carefully constructed, the luminous intensity is not completely free from small fluctuations of the order of one-quarter of one per cent. These, however, are apparently quite fortuitous and so are largely eliminated during the course of a set of observations. Any lamp which is intended for use as a sub-standard should be examined for steadiness and rejected if the variations found are much in excess of the figure just mentioned. Some form of simple photo-electric photometer is particularly convenient for this purpose.

It has been found that the luminous intensity of a lamp does not steady down to its final value immediately after switching on; in fact uniplanar vacuum lamps of the type described above should be burnt for at least 5 minutes to ensure that their luminous intensities at the commencement of the measurements are within 0·2 per cent of the final steady values [22].

One disadvantage of the type of lamp shown in Fig. 101 is the formation of a real image of the filament by reflection in the curved surface of the bulb. If the filament is centrally placed, the image, the luminance of which is approximately 8 per cent of that of the real filament, will lie very nearly in the same plane as the filament, and so will not produce any appreciable shift in the position of the effective light centre. A badly placed filament may, however, give an image which is considerably displaced, and which therefore gives rise to unsuspected errors, particularly if the lamp is used at short distances from the photometer (see p. 469) [23]. This trouble has been overcome by mounting the filament in a conical bulb, sometimes with the axis of the cone tilted as shown in Fig. 102 [24].

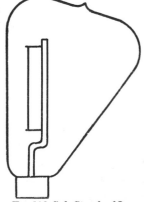

FIG. 102. Sub-Standard Lamp in which Reflections of the Filament are avoided.

Lamps with the "squirrel-cage" form of filament have been used as sub-standards [25]. They are rotated, cap upwards at about 60 r.p.m. and distances are measured from the axis of rotation. Special precautions have to be taken to ensure steadiness of the current supplied to the lamp while it is rotating (see p. 253).

Sub-standards giving light of the same colour as the primary standard may be measured, either by direct comparison with that standard, or by comparison with other sub-standards which have been so measured. It is generally convenient to have, as well, sub-standards which operate at higher colour temperatures, so that large colour differences may be avoided in the photometry of ordinary light sources. Since the measurement of these sub-standards involves a colour difference it must be carried out by one of the methods described in Chapter IX. The method used must be one which gives results in accordance with the internationally agreed values of V_λ (see p. 72) and it has been recommended that the colour step be bridged by using a blue glass in combination with the lamp of lower colour temperature to give a colour match with the lamp of higher colour temperature [26].

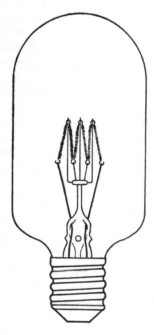

FIG. 103. Sub-Standard Lamp for Higher Colour Temperatures.

It has already been stated that lamps of the type illustrated in Fig. 101 can be used as sub-standards at colour temperatures up to about 2360° K. For higher temperatures some form of gas-filled lamp must be employed and it has been found that lamps of the type shown in Fig. 103, usually known as uniplanar grid filament projector lamps (class A1) [27], are satisfactory for the purpose at colour temperatures not exceeding about 2850° K. Lamps in the low voltage range, viz. 100 to 115 volts, are generally preferable to those operating at 200 to 250 volts, especially at the higher colour temperatures, but in all cases the rate of fall of luminous intensity is greater than in the case of the vacuum lamps described earlier and more frequent re-standardisation is therefore necessary. Further, these lamps frequently have a less uniform light distribution in directions close to that used for the standardisation, viz. normal to the plane of the grid, so that greater care is necessary to ensure that

a lamp is always precisely aligned when in use. To overcome difficulties due to uneven light distribution, lamps in opal glass bulbs
have been used, the light centre being assumed to coincide with the
geometrical centre of the bulb [28].

Sub-Standards of Luminous Flux—Sub-standards of luminous
flux are prepared from sub-standards of luminous intensity by the
method described on p. 257 [29]. Tungsten filament vacuum lamps
are generally employed for the purpose since they can be rotated
without any effect on the light distribution. The lamp to be measured is mounted in a rotator, with the axis horizontal, and measurements of luminous intensity are then made in a number of directions,
with the lamp rotating at a convenient speed, so that the mean polar
curve can be accurately drawn. Then, by constructing the Rousseau diagram, the total luminous flux from the lamp, can be found
(see p. 126). This lamp may now be used as a sub-standard of luminous flux and other sub-standards may be prepared by comparing
them with it in some form of integrating photometer (see p. 259).

Since a flux sub-standard obtained as described above by direct
comparison with a sub-standard of luminous intensity is necessarily
a vacuum lamp, its colour temperature cannot exceed about 2360° K,
whereas the colour temperature of ordinary gas-filled electric lamps
is considerably higher than this and may approach 3000° K. Gas-
filled lamps similar in construction to ordinary " general service "
lamps may be used as sub-standards of luminous flux at colour
temperatures up to about 2850° K [30]. The constancy may be
improved by spot-welding the filament to its supports and by careful
selection during a period of ageing carried out at a current equal to
or slightly greater than that at which the lamp is to be operated.
Gas-filled lamps should always be used in their normal burning position, viz. with the cap uppermost in the case of general service lamps
or with the cap down in the case of class A1 projector lamps. The
colour difference between flux sub-standards at 2360° K and gas-
filled sub-standards at higher colour temperatures is bridged by
means of a blue glass, as in the case of sub-standards of luminous
intensity [31].

In laboratories where much photometric work is carried out, the
sub-standards are usually divided into two or more groups, those in
one group being used only occasionally for checking the remainder
from which the working standards are prepared [32].

Sub-standard lamps may be set either by voltage or by current.
The percentage change of luminous intensity or luminous flux is
about 3·6 times that of the voltage, or about 6 to 7 times that of the
current, so that voltage control is the more sensitive. On the other
hand it necessitates either separate leads to the lamp or measurement

across the ends of a pair of leads permanently connected to the lamp. Current control is independent of changes of resistance in the circuit [33] and it tends to compensate for the slow fall of luminous intensity of a lamp due to the very gradual thinning of the filament which takes place as the lamp is used [34]. For gas-filled lamps it is usually found that current control gives greater constancy of the light output.

High-Temperature Sub-Standards—It has been pointed out above that in order to obtain a sub-standard giving an approximate colour match with ordinary light sources it is necessary to bridge the colour step from the primary standard by some means such as the use of a blue glass of accurately known transmission factor. Proposals have been made to avoid this difficulty by using either a high temperature source of a luminance which is so constant that it can be measured once for all or, alternatively, one for which the luminance can be determined by means of a subsidiary measurement involving no colour difference.

Many years ago it was suggested that the luminance of the positive crater of a carbon arc, operating under controlled conditions, would be sufficiently constant to be used as a standard of light and a considerable amount of work on this subject was done by many investigators [35]. The form which has been most studied is the three-electrode arc (Fig. 104) in which two negatives are employed,

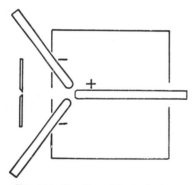

FIG. 104. The Three-Electrode Arc.

each at an angle of about 130° with the positive. With this arrangement, and using pure amorphous carbon electrodes of 10 mm. diameter, the luminance at the centre of the positive crater increases with increase of current until it reaches a steady value of about 155 candelas per sq. mm. at a current of about 11 amps. With a graphite anode the luminance is higher, viz. about 165 candelas per sq. mm., the current in this case being about 18 amps. [36]. A diaphragm, with a small aperture of accurately known area, is placed in front of the positive crater, as shown in the figure, and this aperture then serves as the standard. The colour temperature, in the case of amorphous carbons, is about 3820° K [37].

Another high temperature standard which has been proposed is a full radiator operating at some temperature which is definitely fixed but need not be accurately known, e.g. the solidifying point of iridium (about 2712° K). The form of the radiator may be the same as that used for the primary standard [38]. The ratio of the luminance of the radiator at some convenient wave-length (λ_R) to that of the primary standard at the same wave-length is measured by means of an optical pyrometer. By Wien's formula (see p. 40) [39] this ratio $R = (e^{-c_2/\lambda_R\theta_2})/(e^{-c_2/\lambda_R\theta_1})$, where θ_2 is the temperature of the radiator and θ_1 that of the standard, and therefore

$$c_2/\theta_2 = c_2/\theta_1 - \lambda_R \log_e R.$$

The ratio of the total brightness of the radiator to that of the primary standard is equal to $\int V_\lambda \lambda^{-5} e^{-c_2/\lambda\theta_2} d\lambda$ divided by $\int V_\lambda \lambda^{-5} e^{-c_2/\lambda\theta_1} d\lambda$. Substituting for c_2/θ_2 this becomes $\int V_\lambda \lambda^{-5} e^{-a} d\lambda / \int V_\lambda \lambda^{-5} e^{-b} d\lambda$ where

$$a \equiv (c_2/\theta_1 - \lambda_R \log_e R)/\lambda \quad \text{and} \quad b \equiv c_2/\lambda\theta_1.$$

It will be noticed that the expression for the ratio involves θ_1, the temperature of the primary standard, but a small uncertainty in this is negligible since a change of 10° only alters the luminance ratio by about 0·1 per cent. The same remark applies to the small uncertainty which exists in the value of c_2.

The Acetylene Sub-Standard.—For approximate work in laboratories where a steady source of electric supply is not available, a screened acetylene flame has been found useful as a sub-standard [40]. This form of standard, known as the Eastman-Kodak standard is shown in section in Fig. 105. The burner is a Bray air-mixing burner, consuming about $\frac{1}{4}$ cub. ft. of gas per hour and giving a cylindrical flame about 3 mm. in diameter and 50 mm. high. The flame is surrounded with a blackened cylindrical hood of metal having at one side a small rectangular opening C. From this opening metal leaves extend inward to within about 2 mm. of the flame. The inner edges of these leaves form an aperture about 3 mm. high so that the light source is a horizontal section of the flame of this height. The position of C is adjusted vertically until the portion of flame visible through the aperture is that which is least affected in luminance by small changes in gas pressure. The centre of the aperture is then usually between 18 and 20 mm. above the tip of the burner. The pressure of the gas worked with is 9 cm. of water. Each burner requires standardisation by comparison with a tungsten lamp. The colour temperature is about 2360° K [41].

Fig. 105. The Acetylene Sub-standard

Absolute Standards—It will be clear that, at any rate in theory, there is no necessity for a standard of light [42]. The value of the unit of luminous flux may be derived from the watt by giving some convenient value to the constant K in the equation $F = K \int V_\lambda E_\lambda \, d\lambda$ or, in other words, adopting a particular value for the so-called mechanical equivalent of light (see p. 139). If this is done, the measurement of light of any known spectral energy distribution is reduced to a measurement of energy at some convenient wavelength or range of wave-lengths [43]. The value of E_λ being then known for all values of λ throughout the visible spectrum, the value of the integral written above can be calculated. As a sub-standard, some source of well-defined energy distribution, such as a sodium vapour lamp or a tungsten filament lamp of known colour temperature, could be used.

BIBLIOGRAPHY

P. Fleury. *Etalons Photométriques.* (Revue d'Optique Press, Paris, *1932.*)

REFERENCES

1. E. Liebenthal. *Prakt. Phot.*, p. 102.
   P. Fleury. Soc. Franç. des Elect., Bull., 5, *1925*, p. 700.
   W. Dziobek. Congrès Int. d'Electricité, Paris, *1932*, C.r., Vol. VIII, p. 1.
2. See also Licht, 7, *1937*, p. 176 ; Roy. Soc., Proc., 186, *1946*, p. 204.
3. C. E. Guillaume. Ecl. El., 8, *1896*, p. 55.
   J. Violle. C.R., 141, *1905*, p. 1188.
   W. Nernst. Phys. Z., 7, *1906*, p. 380.
   E. Warburg. Deut, Phys. Gesell., Verh., 19, *1917*, p. 3.
   E. C. Crittenden. C.I.E., Proc., 5, *1921*, p. 46.
   C. Müller. Z. f. Bel., 28, *1922*, pp. 76, 89 and 130 ; Z. f. Phys., 47, *1928*, p. 751 ; C.I.E., Proc., 7, *1928*, pp. 1116 and 1125 ; Z. f. techn. Phys., 14, *1933*, p. 107.
   C.I.E., Proc., 6, *1924*, p. 67.
   P. Fleury. Ann. de Phys., 5, *1926*, p. 265 ; C.I.E., Proc., 7, *1928*, p. 1102.
   H. Abraham. C.I.E., Proc., 8, *1931*, p. 598.
   G. A. Homès. Rev. d'Opt., 13, *1934*, p. 273. See also *ibid.*, 12, *1933*, p. 392.
4. C. W. Waidner and G. K. Burgess. El. World, 52, *1908*, p. 625.
   H. E. Ives. Phys. Rev., 8, *1916*, p. 250 (see also p. 177) ; Frank. Inst., J., 186, *1918*, p. 122 and 197, *1924*, pp. 147 and 359.
   E. Brodhun and F. Hoffmann. Z. f. Phys., 37, *1926*, p. 137.
5. H. T. Wensel, W. F. Roeser, L. E. Barbrow and F. R. Caldwell. Bureau of Standards, J. of Research, 6, *1931*, p. 1103.
   Illum. Eng. Soc. N.Y., Trans., 27, *1932*, p. 738.
   Comité Int. des Poids et Mesures, Procès-verbaux, 13, *1930*, p. 175 and 14, *1931*, p. 249 and 16, *1933*, pp. 254, 256 and 261.
   G. Ribaud. Rev. d'Opt., 12 *1933*, p. 289.
   J. W. T. Walsh. World Power, 20, *1933*, p. 68 and 21, *1934*, p. 19.
   H. Buckley and W. Barnett. Comité Int. des Poids et Mesures, Procès-verbaux, 18, *1937*, p. 247.
   H. Willenberg. Phys. Z., 40, *1939*, p. 389.
   F. Hoffmann, H. Korte and H. Willenberg. Licht, 11, *1941*, p. 207.
   M. Debure and N. Leroy. Rev. d'Opt., 31, *1952*, p. 529.
   C. L. Sanders, B. A. Stevens and W. E. K. Middleton. Opt. Soc. Am., J., 44, *1954*, p. 88.
6. H. T. Wensel *et al. Loc. cit.* note (5).
   H. Buckley and W. Barnett. *Loc cit.*, note (5).

7. J. W. T. Walsh. World Power, 20, *1933*, p. 68 and 21, *1934*, p. 19.
See also refs. in note (6) *supra*.

8. Comité Int. des Poids et Mesures, Procès-verbaux, 18, *1937*, pp. 64 and 236 and 20, *1946*, p. 119.
    A. Pérard. Rev. d'Opt., 28, *1949*, p. 1.
    See also W. Köhler. Licht, 10, *1940*, p. 175; Amtsblatt der P.T.R. 16, *1944*, p. 48; M. Jacob and E. Befahy, Soc. Belge d'El., Bull., 60, *1944*, pp. 20 and 46; Assn. Suisse des Elect., Bull., 41, *1950*, p. 1 ; H. Korte, Lichttechnik, 1, *1949*, p. 43.

9. Illum. Eng., 2, *1909*, p. 393 ; Illum. Eng. Soc. N.Y., Trans., 4, *1909*, p. 526 ; Lum. El., 6, *1909*, p. 275 ; Z. f. I., 29, *1909*, p. 264.

10. C.I.E., Proc., 5, *1921*, p. 41.

11. J. A. Fleming. Inst. El. Eng., J., 32, *1902*, p. 119.
    C. H. Sharp and P. S. Millar. Illum. Eng. Soc. N.Y., Trans., 5, *1910*, p. 457.
    C. C. Paterson and B. P. Dudding. Phys. Soc., Proc., 27, *1915*, p. 263.
    E. C. Crittenden and J. F. Meyer. C.I.E., Proc., 7, *1928*, p. 1138.
    J. F. Meyer. *Ibid.*, 8, *1931*, p. 588.
See also note (51) on p. 145 of *Photometry, 1926*.

12. See the references in notes (22) and (23) on p. 142 of *Photometry (1926)*.
    See also C.I.E., Proc., 7, *1928*, pp. 18 and 1088 ; E. König and F. Buchmüller, Assn. Suisse des Elect., Bull., 18, *1927*, p. 618 ; W. Dziobek, Licht u. Lampe, 17, *1928*, p. 77 ; W. Geiss, Assn. Suisse des Elect., Bull., 19, *1928*, p. 198 ; Licht, 12, *1942*, p. 35 ; Licht u. Lampe, 31, *1942*, p. 196.

13. Comité Int. des Poids et Mesures, Procès-verbaux, 18, *1937*, pp. 231 and 247.

14. Light and Ltg., 40, *1947*, p. 122 ; Nature, 159, *1947*, p. 325.
    Opt. Soc. Am., J., 37, *1947*, p. 402.
    See also W. Geiss, Assn. Suisse des Elect., Bull., 33, *1942*, p. 395 ; G. A. W. Rutgers, J. A. H. Kersten and J. Boersema, Electro-techniek, 25, *1947*, p. 311; J. Netusil, Elektrotechniky Obzor, 36, *1947*, p. 413 (In Czech).

15. H. Buckley. Phil. Mag., 4, *1927*, p. 753 and 6, *1928*, p. 447 ; C.I.E., Proc., 7, *1928*, p. 888 ; Opt. Soc. Am., J., 18, *1929*, p. 216 ; Phil. Mag., 17, *1934*, p. 576.
    Z. Yamauti. Comité Int. des Poids et Mesures, Procès-verbaux, 16, *1933*, p. 243 ; Electrotech. Lab. Tokyo, Researches No. 378, *1934* (In Japanese).
    F. A. Cunnold and M. Milford. Phil. Mag., 8, *1934*, p. 561.
    P. Moon. Opt. Soc. Am., J., 31, *1941*, p. 223.
    F. A. Benford. Gen. El. Rev., 46, *1943*, p. 377.
    A. Gouffé. Rev. d'Opt., 24, *1946*, p. 1.
    C. L. Sanders and B. A. Stevens. Rev. d'Opt., 33, *1954*, p. 179.
    J. C. de Vos, Physica, 20, *1954*, p. 669.
See also G. Ribaud and S. Nikitine, Ann. de Phys., 11, *1929*, p. 451 ; G. Liebmann, Z. f. techn. Phys., 12, *1931*, p. 433.

15a J. Terrien and H. Moreau. C.R., 234, *1952*, p. 2267 (see also p. 2269).
    J. W. T. Walsh. N.P.L. Symposium, *Maintenance of Standards* (H.M.S.O., *1953*), p. 63.
    J. Terrien. *Ibid.*, p. 68.
    J. Terrien. Soc. Franç. Elect., Bull., 4, *1954*, p. 463 and 5, *1955*, p. 347.
    R. E. Leeds and G. T. Winch. G.E.C. Journ., 22, *1955*, p. 232.

16. E. Rulla and W. Trojok. Licht, 12, *1942*, pp. 13 and 33.

17. C. C. Paterson and B. P. Dudding. Phys. Soc., Proc., 27, *1915*, p. 263.
    W. Barnett. Opt. Convention, *1926*, Proc., I, p. 277.
    B. P. Dudding and G. T. Winch. *Ibid.*, p. 275.
    Z. Yamauti. Comité Int. des Poids et Mesures, Procès-verbaux, 19, *1939*, p. P82.

17a W. R. Blevin, W. J. Brown and K. S. Sarma. Illum. Eng. Soc. Lond., Trans., 20, *1955*, p. 99.
    W. Barnett, R. G. Berry and J. S. Preston. J. Appl. Phys., 8, *1957*, p. 363 and 9, *1958*, p. 317.

18. P. Good. Electrician, 55, *1905*, p. 430.

19. J. A. Fleming. Electrician, 55, *1905*, p. 515.

20. Z. Yamauti. Int. Illum. Congress, *1931*, Proc., Vol. I, p. 275.

21. H. Willenberg. Phys. Z., 41, *1940*, p. 234.
    W. E. K. Middleton and E. G. Mayo. Opt. Soc. Am., J., 41, *1951*, p. 513.

22. L. H. McDermott and F. W. Cuckow. J. Sci. Inst., 12, *1935*, p. 323.
See also J. Terrien, Rev. d'Opt., 27, *1948*, p. 351.

23. B. F. Thomas. Int. El. Congress, Chicago, *1893*, Proc., p. 198.

24. P. M. Tikhodéef. Illum. Eng., 24, *1931*, p. 220.
J. W. T. Walsh. Light and Ltg., 29, *1936*, p. 76.
H. Willenberg. Phys. Z., 41, *1940*, p. 234.
H. J. Helwig. Lichttechnik, 1, *1949*, p. 110.

25. E. C. Crittenden and J. F. Meyer. C.I.E., Proc., 7, *1928*, p. 1138.

26. Comité Int. des Poids et Mesures, Procès-verbaux, 18, *1937*, p. 223.
See also C.I.E., Proc., 8, *1931*, p. 138 ; J. W. T. Walsh, Illum. Eng. Soc. Lond.,
Trans., 5, *1940*, p. 89.

27. J. N. Aldington. Illum. Eng. Soc. Lond., Trans., 10, *1945*, p. 1.
See also E. Ferencz and J. Urbanek, Int. Illum. Congress, *1931*, Proc., Vol. I,

28. W. Dziobek and M. Pirani. Licht u. Lampe, 16, *1927*, p. 473.   [p. 159.

29. H. J. Helwig. Licht, 3, *1933*, p. 243.

30. R. P. Teele. Illum. Eng. Soc. N.Y., Trans., 25, *1930*, p. 78.

31. For an alternative method, in principle spectrophotometric, see L. S. Ornstein, J. G. Eymers and D. Vermeulen, Rev. d'Opt., 12, *1933*, p. 390.

32. J. Cahen. Soc. Franç. des Elect., Bull., 4, *1934*, p. 1055.

33. N. R. Campbell and M. K. Freeth. Opt. Convention, *1926*, Proc., I, p. 253.

34. Constant power consumption instead of either constant voltage or constant current has also been proposed. See, e.g. C. Fabry, Ecl. El., 37, *1903*, p. 411 ; E. B. Rosa and G. W. Middlekauff, Am. I.E.E., Proc., 29, *1910*, p. 1191.
See also J. Terrien, Rev. d'Opt., 27, *1948*, p. 351.

35. See, e.g. J. E. Petavel, Roy. Soc., Proc., 65, *1899*, p. 469 ; J. F. Forrest, Electrician, 71, *1913*, pp. 729 and 1007 ; see also the other references in notes (31) and (32) on p. 143 of *Photometry (1926)*.

36. J. T. MacGregor-Morris. Inst. El. Eng., J., 91, *1944*, p. 183.
See also H. Kohn and M. Guckel, Z. f. Phys., 27, *1924*, p. 305 ; N. K. Chaney, V. C. Hamister and S. W. Glass, Electrochem. Soc., Trans., 57, *1935*, p. 107 ; C. Krygsman, Physica, 5, *1938*, p. 918 ; W. Finkelnburg, Phys. Z., 41, *1940*, p. 559 ; J. T. MacGregor-Morris, Illum. Eng. Soc. Lond., Trans., 5, *1940*, p. 123.

37. H. G. MacPherson. Opt. Soc. Am., J., 30, *1940*, p. 189.

38. H. T. Wensel, W. F. Roeser, L. E. Barbrow and F. R. Caldwell. Bureau of Standards, J. of Research, 13, *1934*, p. 161.

39. This simplification is justifiable, since Wien's formula gives the same results as Planck's to within 0·1 per cent so long as $\lambda\theta$ is less than 0·21 cm. deg., i.e. for λ up to 0·7μ so long as $\theta < 3000°$ K.

40. C. E. K. Mees and S. E. Sheppard. Photog. J., 50, *1910*, p. 287 ; Congrès Int. de Photog., 5, *1910*, p. 287.
L. A. Jones. Illum. Eng. Soc. N.Y., Trans., 9, *1914*, p. 716.

41. A. R. Pearson and B. Pleasance. Phys. Soc., Proc., 47, *1935*, p. 1032.

42. C. P. Steinmetz. Am. I.E.E., Trans., 27, *1908*, p. 1319.
R. A. Houstoun. Roy. Soc. Proc., 85, *1911*, p. 275.
H. E. Ives. Illum. Eng. Soc. N.Y., Trans., 6, *1911*, p. 258 and 7, *1912*, p. 376 ; Astrophys. J., 36, *1912*, p. 322.
H. Strache. C.I.E., Proc., 3, *1911*, p. 107.
H. E. Ives. Frank. Inst., J., 180, *1915*, p. 409.

43. L. S. Ornstein and D. Vermeulen. Int. Illum. Congress, *1931*, Proc., Vol. I, p. 115.
C. Zwikker. *Ibid.*, p. 136.
L. S. Ornstein. Rev. d'Opt., 12, *1933*, p. 385.
G. T. Winch. Illum. Eng. Soc. Lond., Trans., 21, *1956*, p. 91.

CHAPTER VII

THE MEASUREMENT OF LUMINOUS INTENSITY

PHOTOMETRY may conveniently be divided into two branches, according to the nature of the information which it is desired to obtain. " Bench " photometry has for its object the measurement of the output of light sources, expressed either in luminous intensity or in luminous flux, while " illumination photometry " is only incidentally concerned with the sources, and has for its principal object the measurement of the illumination which they produce at a given point. Illumination photometry will be dealt with in a later chapter of this book (Chapter XII) while this and the following chapters are devoted to a description of the apparatus and methods of measuring luminous intensity and flux. The measurement of luminous intensity in a single direction will be dealt with in the pages immediately following, while the determination of the distribution of light from a source and its total flux output, and the apparatus special to that particular branch of the subject, will be described in Chapter VIII.

General Considerations—It has been said already that the eye is the ultimate judge in all photometry, since the sensation of light is essentially a psycho-physiological phenomenon inseparable from that organ of special sense. Nevertheless, methods of photometry have been devised in which purely physical apparatus is used to measure radiant energy in such a manner that the energy at any given wave-length is weighted according to the value of V_λ at that wave-length (see p. 72), so that the physical apparatus becomes, in reality, a representative of what it has been universally agreed to accept as the *average* human eye. Both visual and physical methods can be used for most types of photometric measurement and in what follows a description of the process adopted when the measurement is made visually will be followed by an indication of the modifications required when physical methods are used.

In common with all the other organs of sense, the eye cannot *measure* with any degree of accuracy [1] ; in fact, its power of adaptation (p. 64) is so great that it is probably the worst of all the sense organs in this respect. Measurements must therefore depend on the judgment of equality [2]. Under the most favourable conditions a difference of luminance of about 1 to $1\frac{1}{2}$ per cent (see p. 61) can be detected, and it is found that by a practised judgment of the midway point between the first appearance of lack of equality in either direction a measurement accurate to about 0·2 per cent can be obtained by taking the mean of a large number of readings. This, then, represents the limit of accuracy of visual photometry. The art of photometry and the design of photometric apparatus have for their object the attainment of this limit by enabling the eye to be used under the most favourable conditions [3]. It may be said, in fact, that every visual photometer is a combination of two principal parts, viz. : (a) some device for enabling the eye to compare, as accurately as possible, the luminance of two surfaces, one of which is illuminated by the source to be measured ; and (b) means for varying the luminance of the other surface according to some known law. The only exceptions to this general rule are the so-called " absolute " photometers, which depend on such physiological phenomena as (i) the relation between the retinal illumination and the diameter of the pupil (see p. 54), (ii) the amount of reduction required to bring the measured light just to the threshold of visibility (" extinction " photometers, see p. 3), (iii) the relation between visual acuity and luminance (" acuity " photometers, see p. 291), or (iv) critical frequency (see p. 70).

A physical photometer is not restricted to the establishment of the condition of equality. It can be used as a measuring instrument in the ordinary sense of the word, at any rate within the limitations imposed by the characteristics of the photocell, the photographic plate or other apparatus which is being employed for making the measurement.

Classification of Photometers—It is convenient to divide apparatus for visual photometry into several classes according to the method used for obtaining the variation of luminance of one of the surfaces to be compared. By far the most important of these classes is that in which the inverse square law of illumination is used. In the other classes various other laws are employed, such as the tangent-squared law of polarisation, Talbot's law of the transmission factor of a sector disc, the law of transmission of an absorbing medium, the cosine law of illumination, etc. This classification is by no means a rigid one, for apparatus belonging to two or more classes may be, and frequently are, used together, but it will be useful for the purposes of this chapter, and will be adopted in what follows.

Photometry by the Inverse Square Method—The simplest, and at the same time most commonly used, form of photometer depending upon the inverse square law of illumination consists of two essential parts, viz. :

(i) A specially designed piece of apparatus termed a " photometer head " (sometimes, for brevity, a " photometer " [4]), the function of which is to enable the eye to judge when equality of brightness is attained between the two comparison surfaces within it, each of these surfaces being illuminated by one of the two sources of light to be compared.

(ii) A graduated bench upon which the photometer head and the sources may be mounted in such a manner that the distances of one or both of the sources from the head may be varied and measured readily and accurately.

If I_1 and I_2 are the luminous intensities of the sources, while ρ_1 and ρ_2 are the reflection factors of the surfaces, and d_1 and d_2 their distances from the sources, it follows that when the two surfaces are equally bright $\rho_1 I_1/d_1{}^2 = \rho_2 I_2/d_2{}^2$. Hence, if ρ_1 and ρ_2 are known or equal, I_1/I_2 can be found from a measurement of d_1 and d_2. The simplest arrangement is that in which the photometer head and the sources are in one straight line, as shown in Fig. 106, one or both

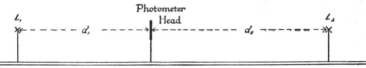

FIG. 106. Photometry by the Inverse Square Method.

of the distances d_1 and d_2 being variable at will by moving one of the sources (L_1, L_2) or the photometer head, or both, along the " photometer bench ".

The Photometer Bench—From the equation given above it is clear that the distances d_1 and d_2 must be measured to an accuracy superior to that of the photometric comparison. Since the distance enters as a square, an accuracy of 0·2 per cent in the photometric measurement demands an accuracy of at least 0·1 per cent in distance, and since it is desirable that the total of the various errors involved may not be much in excess of the 0·2 per cent theoretically attainable, it is clear that the distance measurement should be accurate to at least 0·05 per cent, i.e. half a millimetre in 1,000 mm. The photometer bench, then, must be graduated accurately in millimetres, and should allow of the use of distances in excess of 1 metre on either side of the photometer head. This is further necessary on account of the dimensions of the sources to be measured and the possible range of values of I_1/I_2.

The bench may consist of a simple vertical wooden beam carrying movable saddles, on which are mounted the light sources and the photometer head. It is, however, necessary to have the movements of these saddles as smooth and easy as possible, so as to enable the observer to pass through the balance point quickly and without much manual effort [5], and also to avoid any vibration of the sources.

Rigidity is essential in order that the true distance between each source and the comparison surface in the photometer may be accurately measured on the bench [6]. These requirements are more fully met in a bench such as that shown in Figs. 107 and 270 (p. 488) [7]. The particular pattern illustrated in Fig. 107 was designed by Messrs. Alexander Wright & Co., of Westminster, in co-operation with the National Physical Laboratory. It is a modification of the bench made by Messrs. Franz Schmidt and Haensch, of Berlin [8]. The bars B, B are parallel steel rods of 32 mm. diameter, placed at a distance of 178 mm. between centres. These bars are supported at four or five points, according to the length of the bench and provision is made for levelling them accurately throughout. This is very important since, if there is any tilt of the carriages, one way or the other, as they move along the bench, the actual distances between the lamps and the photometer head may differ slightly from the distances read on the scale. Close to one bar a broad brass strip bearing a scale of millimetres is mounted at an angle of 45° with the vertical.

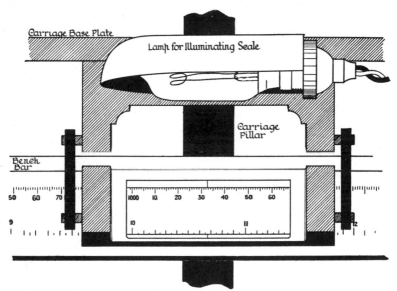

FIG. 108. The Photometer Bench Scales.

The figuring of this scale is from a left-hand zero and is marked at every 10 mm., the dimensions of the graduations being shown to two-thirds scale in Fig. 108. The graduation should be continued for a few millimetres to the left of the zero for convenience in making the correction for screen thickness (see p. 208). The length of the bench may be from 3 to 5 metres. The brass strip sometimes bears a

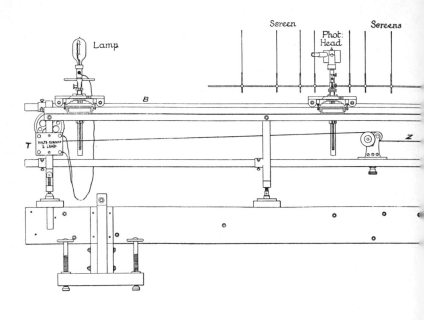

Lamp

Screen

Phot: Head

Screens

B

T

VOLTS CIRCUIT 2 LAMP

Z

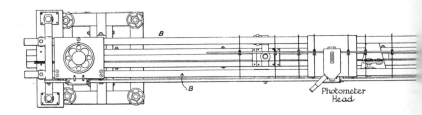

B

B

Photometer Head

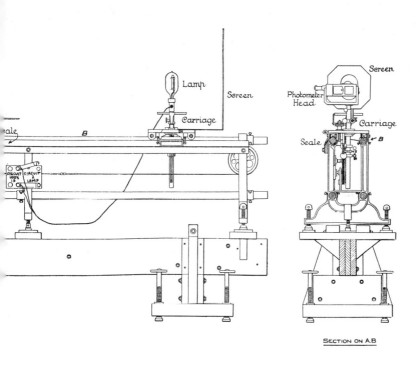

Lamp

Screen

Carriage

Scale

B

CIRCUIT LAMPS   CIRCUIT & LAMP

Screen

Photometer Head

Carriage

Scale

B

SECTION ON A.B

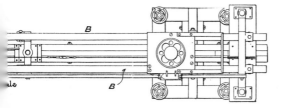

B

B

Scale

25 CMS

second, "squared," scale, graduated in such a way as to indicate
the square of the distance from the zero point. The 1,000 mm. mark
of the millimetre scale is marked 10 on the squared scale, so that if
the standard illumination is 10 lux, and a distance of 1,000 mm.
therefore corresponds to a luminous intensity of 10, the luminous
intensity of any source may be read directly on the squared scale
when this source is giving the standard illumination at the photometer head. The necessity for squaring the reading of the millimetre
scale is thus avoided [9].

The Photometer Bench Carriage—The carriages which travel
on the bars of the bench and bear the standard lamps, photometer
head, etc., are all similar in general design. One of them is shown in
Fig. 109. The primary essentials of these carriages are, as has been

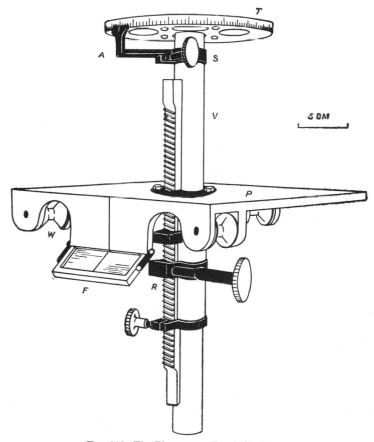

Fig. 109. The Photometer Bench Carriage.

said, lightness and ease of motion, combined with rigidity and
steadiness. Upon the ease and rapidity with which a carriage can
be moved depends, to a very great extent, the accuracy of the
photometric measurement which can be made by means of the
movement of this carriage, for inside a region of about 2 per cent,
where contrast is unperceived by the eye, photometric measurement
depends on the judgment of the half-way position between the just
perceptible limits on either side. The accuracy of this judgment
naturally depends on the rapidity with which the limit on each
side can be presented to the eye. The less the physical effort involved
in this operation (down to a limit well below that ordinarily attainable in photometric apparatus), the more accurate will be the mid-
point judgment [10]. The necessity for rigidity and steadiness have
been mentioned already.

The secondary requirements of a carriage will be best understood
from the following description of the design actually employed on
the bench already described. A broad aluminium base plate P
(Fig. 109) runs on the photometer bench by means of three wheels W,
which are spool-shaped so as to ride easily on the bars B, B (Fig. 107).
This plate carries at its centre a vertical pillar V, into which fits the
tubular stem of a circular table T. The pillar V is capable of a
vertical motion of about 130 mm. by means of a diagonal rack and
pinion R, while the table T is capable of rotation about a vertical
axis within the pillar V. Each of these motions is provided with a
clamp which, in the case of the table T, takes the form of a small
split-collar S bearing a key-piece, which can be tightened on to T
in any desired position and which fits down into a similarly shaped
slot in the upper edge of the pillar V. The table T is graduated in
degrees round its outer edge, while the pillar V carries an arm A
with a mark on it which is in the same vertical plane with the axis
of the pillar and the fiducial mark on the framework F which moves
over the brass scale of the photometer bench. The base plate P
also carries (i) a clamp for clamping the carriage to the bench at
any desired position, (ii) a short pillar, which grips the wire Z
(Fig. 107) by which the carriage is moved when in use, and (iii) a
second pillar, which carries a split-ring for clamping the carriage
to a brass tube used for fixing two carriages at a definite distance
apart so that they can be moved as one unit.

The same pattern of carriage is used for mounting the various
pieces of apparatus which have, for different purposes, to be used on
the bench. Sub-standard lamps, mounted as shown in Fig. 101
(p. 179), fit down into the central stem of the circular table T, and
the slot at the bottom of the lamp mounting fits into a key-piece
fixed inside the bottom of the stem of the table. This key-piece is

in such a position that, when the zero graduation of the table is over the mark on the arm A of the carriage, the mean plane of the lamp filament is at right angles to the axis of the bench.

When electric lamps are to be measured they are accommodated in sockets of bayonet, screw, or any other required pattern, specially constructed for rigidity and mounted on a stem which fits into the circular table of the photometer carriage. Gas burners are similarly mounted on holders attached to stems which, again, fit into the carriage tables, and these are so arranged that the axis of the table passes through the centre of the burner. Various other pieces of apparatus for obtaining measurements of luminous intensity in different directions are similarly mounted so that they can be used in the standard form of photometer carriage. These will be described later, particularly in Chapter VIII.

The photometer head (Fig. 107) is used on a carriage which only differs from the others in that it has no circular table. The stem attached to the head fits down into the pillar V, which in this case has also at its upper end a slot to receive a key-piece which can be clamped to the stem bearing the photometer head. It follows that when this key-piece is tightened on the photometer stem the position of the head is automatically fixed in relation to the carriage. The pillar which bears the photometer head is also provided with a side clamp holding an aluminium tube of about 12 mm. diameter, on which are mounted the screens, to be described later (see Fig. 107 and p. 216). Since the most convenient sub-standards and other lamps used as temporary standards of luminous intensity in modern photometry are electric lamps, provision has to be made on the photometer bench for the ready connection of these lamps to a source of supply, and to apparatus for the adjustment and accurate measurement of potential and current. Methods by which this may conveniently be arranged will be described in Chapter XVI.

The apparatus described above is suitable for all classes of measurement of luminous intensity, both precise standardisation and ordinary commercial photometry. If the latter work alone is contemplated certain simplifications of detail may be introduced, provided always that the principal requirements outlined above are adequately met.

The Photometer Head—As already stated, it is the function of this piece of apparatus to present to the eye, side by side, the two surfaces between which a comparison of brightness is to be made. The methods by which this object may be achieved and the instruments which have been designed for the purpose are exceedingly numerous (see Chapter I) [11]. For accuracy of measurement it is necessary that the line of division should be as fine as possible ;

hence the surfaces should neither overlap in such a way as to produce a bright band between them, nor, on the other hand, should they be separated by a dark band or line of appreciable breadth [12]. Another requirement is that either the surfaces should be perfectly matt or else they must be looked at from a fixed direction, to avoid differences of luminance due to lack of fulfilment of the cosine law of emission. It is desirable that the luminance of the surfaces should not be greatly affected by a small alteration in the angular position of the photometer head. For this reason they should be arranged as nearly as possible perpendicular to the incident light, for $\cos \theta$ is equal to unity (to an accuracy of 0.1 per cent) up to a value of 2.5° and hence, if the light is incident normally, the photometer head may be turned through angles smaller than this without affecting the accuracy of measurement as long as the surfaces are matt. If, however, the light is incident at an angle of from 20° to 45°, as in the case of the Ritchie wedge or its modifications [13], a change of 2° in the position of the head produces an alteration of from 1 to 3 per cent in the illumination of the photometer surface, and this alteration is in opposite directions on the two sides, so that the total error is twice as great [14].

The Bunsen Photometer Head—The first really accurate photometer head to be devised was that of Bunsen [15]. In this head, which is still in common use, a piece of thin opaque white paper, with a translucent spot obtained by treating the paper locally with oil or wax, is mounted between the lamps to be compared, and at right angles to the line joining them (Fig. 106, p. 191). Then if the illumination of the left-hand side of the paper is E_L, while that of the other side is E_R, it follows that the luminance of the opaque part of the Bunsen disc on the left is $\rho E_L/\pi$, while the luminance of the translucent part is $(\rho' E_L + \tau' E_R)/\pi$, where ρ, ρ' and τ' are respectively the reflection factor of the opaque part, and the reflection and transmission factors of the translucent part of the disc.

There are several methods of using this photometer. In one (the substitution method) E_R is kept constant by means of a subsidiary source, and the luminous intensities of two other sources, I_S and I_T, say, are then compared by finding the respective distances, d_S and d_T, at which these sources must be placed from the photometer in order that the translucent spot may disappear. When disappearance takes place $\rho E_L = \rho' E_L + \tau' E_R$, so that E_L has a constant value, and therefore $I_S/d_S^2 = I_T/d_T^2$.

In the second method the two sources to be compared are placed one on each side of the photometer, and the points of disappearance of the translucent spot on each side are noted. In this case

$$\rho E_L = \rho' E_L + \tau' E_R, \quad \text{and} \quad \rho E'_R = \rho' E'_R + \tau' E'_L,$$

if ρ and ρ' are *the same for both sides of the Bunsen disc.* Hence,

$$E_L/E_R = \tau'/(\rho - \rho') = E_R'/E_L',$$

and hence $(I_S/d_S{}^2)(d_T{}^2/I_T) = (I_T/d_T{}'^2)(d_S{}'^2/I_S)$

or $I_S/I_T = d_S d_S'/d_T d_T'.$

If absolute symmetry of the photometer head cannot be assumed, then the head must be reversed and the same process gone through again. It is easy to show that the true value of I_S/I_T is the geometric mean of the values obtained with the photometer (*a*) direct and (*b*) reversed [16].

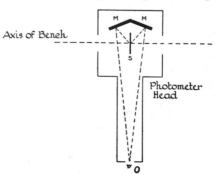

FIG. 110. The Bunsen Photometer.

The third method of using the Bunsen photometer is that of comparing the contrast between the translucent and opaque parts on the two sides where these are viewed simultaneously. This can easily be achieved by placing the disc in a box containing two mirrors M, M (Fig. 110) slightly inclined towards the disc S, so that images of the two sides are seen in close juxtaposition by an observer at O [17]. When there is equality of contrast on the two sides it follows that $\rho E_L^{\cdot}/(\rho' E_L + \tau' E_R) = \rho E_R/(\rho' E_R + \tau' E_L)$, or $E_L^{\cdot} = E_R$. If symmetry of the disc and mirrors cannot be assumed, the photometer head is reversed and the process repeated, the geometric mean of the two results again giving the true value. The separation of the two fields, inevitable when mirrors are used, may be avoided by the use of the prism system, shown in Fig. 111 [18].

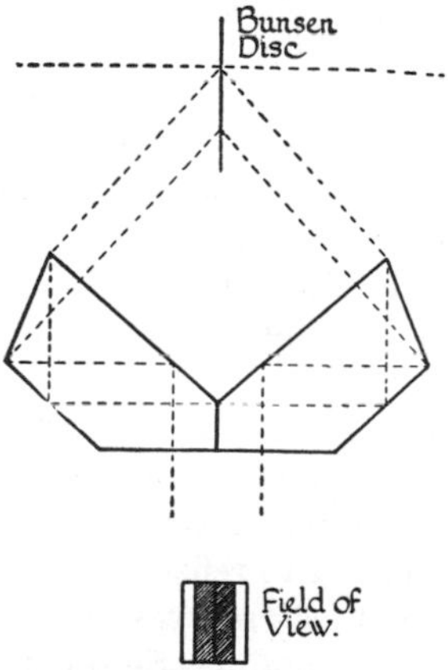

It will be noticed that in this method of using the Bunsen screen the criterion is equality of *contrast* instead of equality of *brightness*, and it has been found that in favourable circumstances the eye is capable of appreciating contrast equality even more accurately than it can appreciate brightness equality. This principle has, therefore, been adopted in the accurate form of photometer head to be described in a later section of this chapter (see p. 202).

FIG. 111. Prism System for Viewing the Bunsen Disc.

Since the values of ρ, ρ' and τ' vary considerably with the angle of emergence of the light, it is essential that, whatever method be followed in using the Bunsen disc, the line of sight should always make the same angle with the normal to the disc.

The theory of the Bunsen disc has been worked out very completely by Weber and others [19]. It has frequently been described quite wrongly in text-books [20], it being stated that, with the sources to be compared one on each side of the photometer head, the balance point is the position of disappearance of the translucent spot *when the disc is viewed from one side*. A simple experiment will serve to demonstrate that the points of disappearance on the two sides are separated by a distance which is far from negligible even in rough photometric work [21].

Methods of preparing the Bunsen disc have been described by many writers [22], and the translucent spot has been given many different forms, including a circular disc, a star, and a vertical band. In any case, the dimensions of the translucent part should not be large. When an actual " grease-spot " is used, a sheet of suitable white paper [23] is stretched on a board, and a disc of brass of the form and dimensions desired for the spot is heated, plunged into molten paraffin wax, and, after draining, is placed on the sheet of paper and then removed. The superfluous wax is absorbed with a sheet of blotting paper and an iron, moderately heated so as not to spoil the edges of the spot. The Leeson disc consists of a sheet of white paper in which a star-shaped hole has been cut with the sharpest possible edge. A sheet of thin translucent paper is then pressed on to each surface of this sheet, and a Bunsen disc with a very fine line of demarcation is obtained. Töpler's disc is similar, but has a circular spot.

It is important that any Bunsen disc in which a paper surface is used should be kept in a dustproof and dark enclosure when not actually in use ; otherwise dirt and the discoloration due to exposure to light will gradually produce a lack of equality between the two comparison surfaces [24].

The Disadvantage of Mixed Light on the Comparison Surfaces— It will be noticed that there is one defect in the Bunsen photometer head. This is the fact that the luminance of the translucent portion of the field is due partly to transmitted and partly to reflected light, i.e. each comparison surface receives light from *both* sources, with a consequent reduction of sensitivity. When the photometric setting is obtained, the luminance of this part of the field is porportional to $\tau' E_R + \rho' E_L$, while the luminance of the opaque part of the field is ρE_L. It follows that if the photometer head is displaced by a small distance x to the left of its balanced position, the percentage *increase* of luminance of the opaque part will be $200x/d_L$, while the percentage *decrease* of luminance of the translucent part will be

$$200x\,(\tau'E_R/d_R - \rho'E_L/d_L) \div (\tau'E_R + \rho'E_L).$$

Dividing through by $\tau'E_R$ and putting $E_L/E_R \equiv m$, where m is very nearly unity, this becomes

$$200x\left(\frac{1}{d_R} - \frac{\rho'}{\tau'} \cdot \frac{m}{d_L}\right) \div \left(1 + \frac{\rho'm}{\tau'}\right).$$

Clearly the accuracy with which the photometric setting can be made increases with the percentage change of contrast for a given movement of the photometer head, i.e. with increase in the value of the expression written above. Hence, since the ratio of d_R to d_L is governed entirely by the ratio of the luminous intensities of the two sources, while m is very nearly unity, it follows that the sensitivity increases as ρ'/τ' diminishes, and attains its limiting value when $\rho' = o$, i.e. when the translucent part of the field derives its light from one source only.

This is clearly a particular case of a more general principle that the sensitivity of a photometer is reduced if either comparison field receives light from both the sources being compared. For example, if one field A receives the whole of its light from a source L_A, while the other field B receives a fraction p of its light from the same source L_A, and the rest from a second source L_B, then any movement from the position of balance which produces an increase of x per cent in the illumination of A produces a simultaneous increase of px per cent in the illumination of B. If this same movement produces a decrease of y per cent in the illumination of B due to L_B, the aggregate contrast produced by the movement is $(y - px)$ per cent, and this clearly increases as p decreases. The principle just proved shows once again the necessity for a sharp boundary between the two comparison fields, for the presence of an intermediate region owing its luminance to both sources, and therefore less affected by any given movement of the photometer head, causes an undesirable separation between those portions of the surfaces which alone the eye should compare in making its equality setting.

Thus the following may be laid down as the conditions to be fulfilled in a sensitive photometer head [25] :

(*a*) The light should be incident normally at the comparison surfaces.

(*b*) The surfaces should either be perfect diffusers or else be viewed from a fixed direction.

(*c*) The surfaces should be presented to the eye with the sharpest possible boundary between them. There should be no overlapping nor any appreciable separation.

(d) Each surface should receive its light from one only of the sources to be compared.

(e) The size of the comparison field should be as large as is practicable ; a minimum dimension of 8° to 10° is satisfactory [26].

The Lummer-Brodhun Photometer Head—The conditions above laid down are best met in the form of photometer head due to O. Lummer and E. Brodhun [27]. The principle of this photometer depends on the use of a so-called " cube " made up of two right-angled glass prisms, as shown in Fig. 112. In one of the prisms the

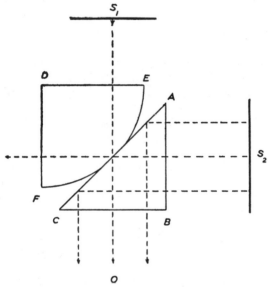

FIG. 112. The Lummer-Brodhun Cube.

principal surface is spherical instead of flat, but it has a small region at the centre which is flat, and which makes optical contact with the central portion of the flat surface of the other prism, while the outer parts of the surfaces are separated by air. It follows that light entering the prism system at the surface AB passes undeviated through the central portion in optical contact, while over the outer portion it is totally reflected, and emerges at BC. On the other hand, light entering DE is transmitted through the central portion and emerges at BC. Hence, if S_1 and S_2 are two comparison surfaces, the central part of S_1 is seen directly by an eye placed at O, while the outer part of S_2 is seen by total reflection at the surface AC, and the two together form a ring and disc field with a very fine and sharp line of demarcation if the prism DEF is skilfully constructed [28]. For photometric purposes the cube and comparison surfaces are arranged as shown in Fig. 113. *S* is a sheet, about 4 mm. thick, of plaster of Paris or some other white diffusing substance, held in a

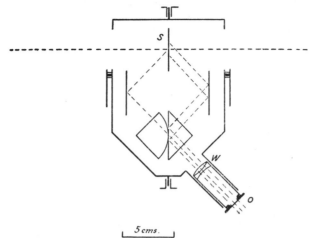

FIG. 113. The Lummer-Brodhun Head. (Equality of-Brightness Type.)

brass framework, the plaster surface being circular and about 52 mm. in diameter. The two sides of this disc are illuminated by the light from the two sources whose luminous intensities are being compared, and the light from them is brought to the two prisms of the cube by means of silvered glass mirrors or auxiliary total reflection prisms, as shown in the figure. The field of view seen by the eye at *O* is then as shown in Fig. 114. The eyepiece is provided with a lens at *W*, so that the surface of the cube may be brought to a focus and the necessary sharpness of the boundary between the two parts of the field obtained. The plaster screen, mirrors, cube, and eyepiece are mounted rigidly inside a brass box provided with two openings by which the light from the sources may reach *S* (see Fig. 120). These windows are provided with brass cover-plates, which are used to close the windows when the photometer is not in use, and thus prevent, as far as possible, the entrace of dust. This, by settling on the glass surfaces, produces dark specks on the field which are very annoying to the eye when it is endeavouring to make a photo-metric balance. The interior of the photometer box is lined with black velvet or optical black [29] in order to absorb stray light due to reflection from the glass surfaces. The screen *S* is removable, so

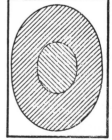

FIG. 114.
The Lummer-Brodhun
Equality-of-Brightness
Field.

that it can be reversed, or taken out altogether for the purpose of testing the screening, etc. (see p. 217). The whole photometer box is pivoted about its axis by means of two steel bearings working in a solid brass semi-rectangular framework, so that it can be completely reversed. It is also provided with a degree scale, which works under a clamp and pointer attached to the framework, so that the photometer may be used at any desired angle. The framework has at the bottom a short stem which fits into a tubular holder, and is thus mounted on a carriage travelling on the photometer bench.

A slight modification, due to H. Krüss [30] and shown diagrammatically in Fig. 115, is the introduction of a reflection prism, by means of which the light is re-directed in such a way that the eyepiece can be situated either along or parallel to the axis of the photometer box. Further, by means of the prism system shown in Fig. 116, binocular vision of the photometer field may be obtained [31].

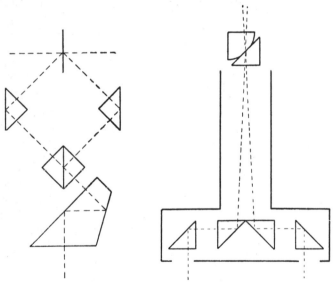

Fig. 115. Prism System for Direct-Vision Lummer-Brodhun Head.

Fig. 116. Binocular Vision Lummer-Brodhun Head.

The Lummer-Brodhun Photometer (Contrast Type)—In the photometer above described the equality of brightness of the two comparison fields at the position of balance causes the boundary between these fields practically to disappear when this setting is made, so long as the condition (c) set out on p. 199 above is fulfilled and the lights compared are of the same colour. Disappearance of the boundary, however, is not that condition which enables the eye to judge most accurately of equality between two fields, and for this reason, as already remarked with regard to the third method of using the Bunsen disc, the contrast photometer, in which equality of contrast is the criterion instead of equality of brightness, possesses a greater sensitivity. The Lummer-Brodhun cube may be adapted for use in this way by altering the form of the surface of contact of the two prisms [32]. The faces of both prisms are flat, and that of the prism ABC (see Fig. 117) is sand blasted or etched with the pattern shown shaded in Fig. 118. The result is that when the

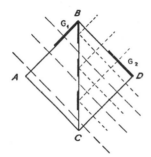

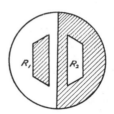

Fig. 117. The Lummer-Brodhun
Contrast Cube.

Fig. 118. The Lummer-Brodhun
Contrast Field.

prisms are pressed together, either with or without balsam, so that the smooth parts are in optical contact, the light passes straight on in the region shown unshaded in Fig. 118, while the light entering at BD is totally reflected over the region shown shaded in that figure. It follows that if the cube is mounted as in Fig. 119 the luminance of the unshaded region is due to the left-hand side of S, while the luminance of the shaded region is due to the right-hand side of S. If thin sheets of glass G_1, G_2 are added as in Fig. 117, then owing to reflection at the two additional glass surfaces thus introduced, the luminance of the trapezoidal patch R_1 in Fig. 118 will be about 8 per cent less than that of the background to R_2, while the luminance of R_2 will similarly be 8 per cent less than that of the background to R_1. Thus at the position of balance the difference of luminance between trapezoid and background will be

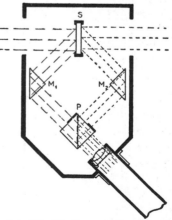

Fig. 119. The Lummer-Brodhun
Contrast Head.

8 per cent on both sides of the field of view, and this contrast will be increased on one side and diminished on the other as the photometer is moved away from the position of balance. Thus the criterion is equality of contrast. The most suitable difference of luminance for maximum sensitivity has been investigated by Lummer and Brodhun [33], who found that the sensitivity was a maximum (0·2 per cent) with a difference of about 3 to 4 per cent, while with a difference of 8 per cent it was only half as great (0·4 per cent). Nevertheless, the great simplicity of the two fixed glass plates has led to their general adoption. The correct difference of luminance could be readily obtained by substituting for the plain glasses G_1, G_2 two neutral glasses having an absorption factor of 4 per cent (apart from surface losses) and cementing these to the cube [34] or by " blooming " both faces of G_1 and G_2 (see p. 157) [35]. It has also been proposed to use a field in which the contrast is graduated, increasing from below upwards on one side, and from above downwards on the other [36]. The position of balance is then found by adjusting to equality of contrast at the middle parts of the two trapezoidal patches.

The component parts of the Lummer-Brodhun contrast head are shown in Fig. 120.

The Martens Photometer—There are several other forms of photometer head which are used on the bench in the same way as the Bunsen or Lummer-Brodhun form. One of these, designed by F. F. Martens [37], is shown diagramatically in Fig. 121. Light from each side of the photometer screen passes through a series of lenses and a Fresnel biprism F, so that two images of each surface are formed in the plane of the exit pupil of the eye-piece E. The positions of these images are shown in the diagram, those of surface S_1 being a_1 and a_2, formed respectively by light from the halves 1 and 2 of the biprism. Similarly, the images of S_2 are b_1 and b_2, and the angle of the biprism is so related to the separation of the total reflection prisms and to the distance FE that a_1 and b_2 coincide ; a_2 and b_1 are stopped by a diaphragm, while an eye placed at E sees the two halves 1 and 2 of F bright by reason of the light from S_1 and S_2 respectively. The dividing line, formed by the

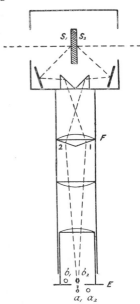

Fig. 121. The Martens Photometer.

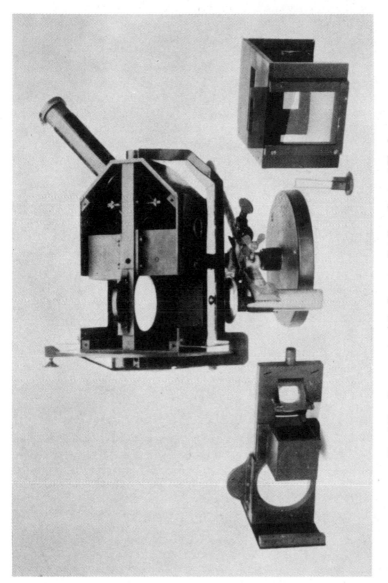

Fig. 120. Components of the Lummer-Brodhun Contrast Head.

edge of the biprism, can be made very sharp. The use of a bip
for photometry was first suggested by M. v. Frey and J. v. Kries [38],
and was adopted by König in his spectrophotometer (see p. 358). The
arrangement can be adapted to give a contrast field [39]. A somewhat similar arrangement is the Hüfner rhomb, shown in Fig. 122.

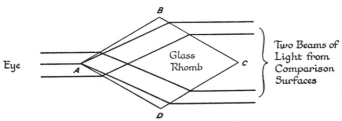

FIG. 122. The Hüfner Rhomb.

This consists of a glass rhomb $ABCD$, the angles of which are such
that two beams of light, one from each of the surfaces to be compared,
are caused to emerge at A in juxtaposition, the line of demarcation
being the fine edge of the rhomb.

Use of the Photometer Bench—The preceding sections of this
chapter have been devoted to a description of the photometer bench
and its accessories, and to an account of the various forms of photometer head which have been designed for use with it. The most
obvious method of applying the inverse square law to the comparison
of the luminous intensities of two sources is that of placing the sources
on carriages fixed at any convenient positions on the bench, and then
moving the photometer head to and fro between them until the
position of balance is found. This simple method is, however, open
to various objections. In the first place, it assumes absolute symmetry in the photometer head. Equality of brightness of the
comparison field results from equality of illumination of the two
surfaces exposed to the light from the sources only if these surfaces
have equal reflection factors, and if the light from them is equally
treated as regards reflection, transmission, etc., before it reaches the
eye [40].

Another objection, of less importance, is the amount of calculation necessitated by this method, for if one source is fixed at the zero
mark on the bench, while the other is at a distance d from it, then,
if the photometer setting is x, the ratio of the luminous intensities is
$(d-x)^2/x^2$.

To overcome the first objection it is usual to employ the substitution method, so often used in accurate physical measurement [41].
In this a third source, whose luminous intensity need not be known,
is used as a comparison lamp on one side of the photometer head,

rces to be compared are placed in turn on the other
neter. A photometric balance with the comparison
ach case. Clearly, if the luminous intensity of the
is assumed to be I_C, then the required ratio of the
intensities of the other two sources $I_1/I_2 = (I_1/I_C)/(I_2/I_C)$,
and this is quite independent of the value of I_C, and therefore of any
symmetry in the photometer head, for this must affect equally both
of the ratios I_1/I_C and I_2/I_C.

The second difficulty is overcome by fixing the distance between
the photometer and the comparison lamp, so that the luminance of
one comparison surface is a constant. If, then, photometric balance
is obtained with the photometer head at distances d_1, d_2, d_3...
respectively from a number of other sources in turn, it follows that
$I_1/d_1^2 = I_2/d_2^2 = I_3/d_3^2 = \ldots$. Much calculation is therefore avoided
when a number of measurements have to be made in succession,
especially if each of the expressions I/d^2 is made equal to some convenient figure, say 10^{-5}, with d in millimetres, so that $I_n = 10^{-5}d_n^2$.
This method is often described as the " fixed distance " method.

There are some cases in which it is impossible or inconvenient to
adopt the fixed distance method, as, for instance, when working
with flame sources [42]. The substitution method must still be
employed, in order to avoid errors due to asymmetry in the photometer head [43], but the sources are fixed and the head is moved
between them (Fig. 123a). The sub-standard and test lamp are
placed in turn at the zero of the bench, while the comparison lamp
is fixed at a distance d. If the positions of balance of the head are
d_1 and d_2 for two lamps whose luminous intensities are respectively
I_1 and I_2, it follows that $I_1/I_2 = d_1^2(d - d_2)^2/d_2^2(d - d_1)^2 \ldots$ [44].

In most cases, however, it is possible to fix the photometer head
either with respect to the comparison lamp or in relation to the test
lamp and sub-standard. The latter arrangement is by far the more
convenient when the light distribution of a source is being measured
by means of mirror apparatus, or when the source is enclosed in an
integrating sphere (see Chapter VIII). The carriage holding the
photometer head is then clamped at the zero of the bench (Fig. 123b),
and the comparison lamp is moved by means of the cord and pulley
arrangement previously described (Z in Fig. 107). By this method
$I_1/I_2 = d_2^2/d_1^2$, where d_1 and d_2 are respectively the positions of the
comparison lamp when sources of luminous intensities I_1 and I_2 are
in the test lamp position.

For simplicity in calculation the method first described, viz. that
in which the photometer is fixed with respect to the comparison
lamp, is much to be preferred. Either of two methods may be used,
according to circumstances. When the zero of the bench is near its

left-hand extremity, the carriages bearing the photometer head and the comparison lamp are clamped together by means of a stout bar so that they move together as a single unit (Fig. 123c). The sub-standard and the test lamp are placed at the *zero* of the bench, and

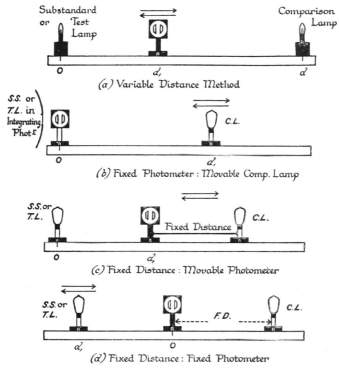

Fig. 123. Methods of Bench Photometry.

the fixed distance between the photometer head and comparison lamp is so adjusted by means of the bar that $I_S/d_S{}^2 = 10^{-5}$, d_S being the position of balance of the photometer head for a sub-standard of luminous intensity I_S. For approximate work a "squared" scale (see p. 193) may be used. The photometer is fixed at the mark I_S on this scale and the comparison lamp is moved until a balance is obtained in the photometer head. The comparison lamp is then clamped to the photometer at this distance and a test lamp is sub-stituted for the sub-standard. The position to which the photo-meter has then to be moved in order to restore the balance in the head, gives I_T at once on the "squared" scale. The disadvantages of this arrangement are (i) the observer has to move his head to and fro with the photometer in making a setting, and (ii) the unit to be moved is heavy, since it consists of *two* carriages and the connecting bar.

These disadvantages may be avoided by fixing the photometer and the comparison lamp to the bench and moving the sub-standard or test lamp. To avoid complicating the calculations, it is desirable to have the zero mark at or near the centre of the bench and to scale in both directions from this zero (Fig. 123*d*). The disadvantage of this method is that the centre zero implies the waste of a considerable part of the bench length when any illumination higher than normal has to be used at the photometer head, as, for instance, in measuring sources of high candle-power, when the use of a sector disc or absorbing medium is not desirable. The various bench methods just described are shown diagrammatically in Fig. 123.

It is usually found that the method in which the photometer head and comparison lamp are moved together is the most generally useful. The necessity for moving the observer's head is not found to cause any noticeable inconvenience. The movement, in any case, is a slight one. The weight to be moved may be reduced by using aluminium in place of brass wherever possible in the construction of the carriages and photometer head. This method will, therefore, be described in detail, and the modifications necessary if either of the other methods be employed can easily be inferred. First, however, two sources of error common to all methods of bench photometry must be considered.

Separation of Photometric Comparison Surfaces: Thickness of Photometer Screen—It will be seen that as long as the substitution method is employed, symmetry of the photometer head, never completely attainable in practice, need not even be aimed at. The assumption is made, however, that the vertical plane of each comparison surface in the head passes through the fiducial mark on the photometer carriage. This condition is frequently not fulfilled. For example, in the case of the ordinary Lummer-Brodhun head the plaster screen is 4 mm. thick, so that each comparison surface is 2 mm. right or left of the carriage mark. It follows that with this instrument the actual distance between each source and the surface of the screen which it illuminates is $(d-2)$ mm. when the distance between the source and the centre of the photometer as measured on the bench is d mm. Hence the true illumination is $E = I/(d-2)^2$.

If the left-hand comparison surface is t_l mm. to the left of the fiducial mark, while the right-hand surface is t_r mm. to the right of this mark, the allowance for " screen thickness " may be made as follows, according to the method of working chosen :

(*a*) *Variable Distance Method*—The sub-standard or test lamp is placed t_l mm. to the *left* of the bench zero, while the comparison lamp is placed at the position $(d + t_r)$, although the value d is used in the calculations.

(b) *Comparison Lamp alone Moved*—The photometer head is placed with its fiducial mark t_r mm. to the left of the bench zero. If any calculations are based on the distance between the sub-standard (or test lamp) and the photometer, the distance $(t_l + t_r)$ mm. must be subtracted in each case.

(c) *Photometer and Comparison Lamp moved together*—The sub-standard or test lamp is placed t_l mm. to the left of the bench zero. The effective distance between the comparison lamp and the photo-meter is t_r mm. less than the fixed distance as read on the bench, but this distance usually does not enter into the calculations.

(d) *Centre Zero*—The photometer head is placed t_l mm. to the right of the bench zero, assuming that the comparison lamp is on the right. The effective distance of the comparison lamp from the photometer is $(t_r + t_l)$ mm. less than the distance as read on the bench.

The magnitude of the error involved in the neglect of this correction clearly increases as the ratio I_S/I_T departs from unity; for, taking the fixed distance method as an example, the illumination due to the sub-standard is $I_S/(d_S - t_l)^2$, and this is equal to the illumination due to the test lamp $I_T/(d_T - t_l)^2$.

The true value of I_T/I_S is $(d_T - t_l)^2/(d_S - t_l)^2$, and this equals $(d_T/d_S)^2[1 + 2t_l(1/d_S - 1/d_T)]$ approximately. Since the value of the expression enclosed within the square brackets does not differ from 1 by more than 0·1 per cent so long as $2t_l(d_S - d_T)/d_S d_T < 10^{-3}$ numerically, it follows that if, when d_S and d_T are of the order of 1,500 mm., the difference between them does not exceed about 500 mm., i.e. the ratio between the luminous intensities is not greater than 2, then the correction need not be made so long as t_l does not much exceed 2 mm., i.e. in the case of the Lummer-Brodhun head. In some other photometer heads, however, t_l is much in excess of this value [45], so that the correction for screen thickness is always necessary in such cases. The extra work involved in making it is, moreover, so small that there is no justification for neglecting it in work having any pretensions whatever to accuracy.

Importance of Exact Positioning of the Photometer Head— Owing to the fact that no surface is perfectly diffusing, there is a source of error in all the ordinarily used forms of photometer head, if proper care is not taken to ensure that the comparison surfaces are perpendicular to the incident light. Fig. 124, which is exaggerated for the sake of clearness, shows the effect of twisting the photometer head through a small angle. The light which reaches the eye from the left-hand side of the disc S leaves the surface of the disc in the direction SA, while that from the other surface leaves it in the direction SB. It follows that, if the surface is not perfectly diffusing, the reflection factor will be different in the two cases (see pp. 158, 381), and in the case of most surfaces, when both sides of S are equally illuminated, the right-hand side will appear the brighter in the photometer. This effect may amount to as much as 0·4 per cent for an angle of twist of 2° in the case of a plaster screen. Although this error is avoided in the substitution method of photometry if the twist of the head is not altered between the readings on the different lamps, it is clearly desirable to remove all possibility of error from this cause by adjusting the screen to be exactly perpendicular to the bench axis and then clamping the registering collar on the pillar attached to the photometer framework. The adjustment may be made quite accurately by placing a small piece of mirror on the top of the photometer so that it is exactly in the plane of the screen S. The image, in this mirror, of the lamp L will be in line with the lamp itself when viewed from a point on the axis of the bench, if S is properly adjusted. A slight vertical tilt of the head is clearly less important, owing to the fact that the plane of SA and SB is perpendicular to the plane of S.

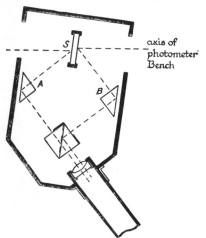

FIG. 124. The Effect of Twisting the Photometer Head.

Procedure in making Measurements on the Bench, using the Substitution Method and a Fixed Distance between the Photometer and the Comparison Lamp—In the following detailed description of the method used in measuring luminous intensities by the fixed distance method, the source to be measured will be referred to as the "test lamp" (luminous intensity I_T), while the lamps used as the basis of the measurement will be termed "sub-standards." Each such sub-standard will be assumed to be an electric lamp of the type illustrated in Fig. 101, p. 179, and its luminous intensity, as determined by comparison with a standard at one of the national standardising laboratories, will be taken as I_S. For the sake of convenience in description, it will be assumed that the test source is also an electric lamp, and that it is to be measured in a single direction. The modifications in procedure necessary in the testing of other sources will be indicated later in this section. The photometer head used will be assumed to be the Lummer-Brodhun contrast head, with a screen 4 mm. thick.

The test may be divided into four parts, as follows :

(i) A comparison lamp L_C is placed in the carriage on the right of the photometer. This lamp is preferably of the same type as the sub-standard, but it may be of any convenient type so long as its position can be maintained quite rigidly in the carriage mounting and there is no possibility of even slight changes of luminous intensity over a burning period of a few hours. A comparison lamp of adjustable luminous intensity is sometimes useful. This may consist of a lamp of sufficiently high luminous intensity in a whitened box having, on the side facing the photometer, a ground glass window fitted with a variable diaphragm [46]. The electrical connections may be as described in Chapter XVI. The function of this lamp is to maintain a constant illumination of the comparison surface on the right-hand side of the photometer head.

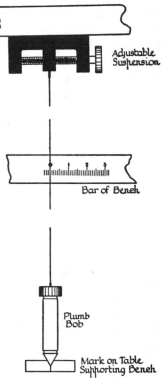

FIG. 125. Arrangement for setting Lamps on the Bench Zero.

(ii) A sub-standard L_S is placed in the carriage on the left of the photometer head, and its leads are connected as shown on p. 491. The mean plane of the filaments is adjusted to be accurately over a line 2 mm. to the left of the zero mark of the bench. For the purpose of this adjustment it is convenient to have a plumb line hanging at a short distance in front of the zero mark, as shown in Fig. 125. The suspension of this plumb line should be capable of a small movement in the direction of the bench axis. When the carriage is placed with its fiducial mark 2 mm. left of the zero of the bench, the plumb line may be adjusted by sight so that it lies in the plane passing through this − 2 mm. mark and the axis of the carriage pillar. The lamp filaments should then be also in this plane. If they are not, the carriage must be moved until, with the eye placed so that the plumb line still covers the − 2 mm. mark on the bench, the filaments are seen to be directly behind the line. During this adjustment a low potential should be applied to the lamp terminals so that the filament is just glowing, although not sufficiently to dazzle the eye and prevent clear vision of the plumb line and the bench scale. When the position of the lamp has been correctly fixed, the carriage is firmly clamped to the photometer bench.

(iii) The lamps L_S and L_C are now switched on, at first with their adjusting resistances fully in, so that there is no chance of even a momentary excess of potential above that at which these lamps are to run, especially in the case of the sub-standard. The potentials on the lamps are then gradually raised to their correct values, and the photometer carriage is clamped at the position on the bench given by the relation $I_S/d_S^2 = 10^{-5}$, supposing that 10 lux is being taken as the working illumination. The distance d_C between the photometer carriage and the comparison lamp carriage is then adjusted so that as good a balance as possible is obtained in the photometer, and these carriages are then clamped together by means of the brass bar previously referred to. The distance d_C is noted, and the photometer carriage is then unclamped from the bench [47].

A series of photometric settings is now made with the lamps carefully maintained at a constant potential. Supposing two observers to be working together, each one in turn makes five or ten settings without looking at the readings he obtains, while the other observer notes down these readings to the nearest half millimetre and watches the instruments which indicate the potentials (or currents) on the comparison lamp and the sub-standard circuits. It is to be noticed that the observer does not see his own readings until after the completion of the set, so that he cannot be unconsciously biassed in either direction [48]. The mean reading for observer A may be denoted by $_A d_S$, and that for observer B by $_B d_S$. It will generally be found that these mean distances are not exactly equal to each other or to $\sqrt{10^5 \times I_S}$, which may be denoted by d_S. The usual procedure is to find the alteration which would be necessary in d_C in order to bring these quantities into agreement. Since $I_S/_A d_S^2 = I_C/d_C^2$, it follows that $I_S/d_S^2 = I/_C (d_C + x)^2$, where

$$x = (d_C/_A d_S)(d_S - _A d_S),$$

so that, since $_A d_S$ is nearly equal to d_S, the " correction " for A is $d_C(d_S - _A d_S)/d_S$, and similarly that for B is $d_C(d_S - _B d_S)/d_S$.

Several more sub-standards, L_2, L_3, L_4, etc., are now inserted in turn in place of L_S and the different corrections to d_C found by A and B are tabulated on opposite page.

The figures in the extreme right-hand column should show about the same degree of consistency for each observer as that shown in

Date   Comp. lamp No.   at   volts.

$$d_C = 1{,}739 \cdot_0 \text{ mm.}$$

Observer (1)	Sub-standard (2)	d_S (true) (3)	d_S (observed) (4)	(3) – (4) (5)	$(d_C/d_S) \times (5)$ (6)
A	L_S	$1{,}364\cdot_3$	$1{,}362\cdot_6$	$+1\cdot_7$	$+2\cdot2$
	L_2	$1{,}326\cdot_4$	$1{,}326\cdot_2$	$+0\cdot_2$	$+0\cdot2$
	L_3	$1{,}358\cdot_0$	$1{,}359\cdot_0$	$-1\cdot_0$	$-1\cdot3$
	L_4	$1{,}359\cdot_2$	$1{,}357\cdot_7$	$+1\cdot_5$	$+1\cdot9$
			Mean correction for A		$+0\cdot7$
B	L_S	$1{,}364\cdot_3$	$1{,}364\cdot_8$	$-0\cdot_5$	$-0\cdot6$
	L_2	$1{,}326\cdot_4$	$1{,}332\cdot_0$	$-5\cdot_6$	$-7\cdot3$
	L_3	$1{,}358\cdot_0$	$1{,}361\cdot_6$	$-3\cdot_6$	$-4\cdot8$
	L_4	$1{,}359\cdot_2$	$1{,}359\cdot_4$	$-0\cdot_2$	$-0\cdot2$
			Mean correction for B		$-3\cdot2$

the above example. If they do not, more sub-standards should be taken. If the inconsistencies are too large to be accounted for by personal errors, defects in the comparison lamp or in the electrical circuits should be looked for.

The correction to the fixed distance d_C is generally made according to the results obtained by one observer. Subsequent measurements of test lamps made by this observer (A, say) with this corrected fixed distance do not then require any correction. The results obtained by B require correcting, however, to bring them to the values which that observer would have obtained if his value had been adopted for the fixed distance. The amount of this correction is clearly xd/d_C, where x is the difference between the fixed distance actually used and the fixed distance found by B, i.e. $x = (_B d_C - d_C)$. In the example given above $x = -3 \cdot 9$ mm. with d_C reset to suit A.

(iv) Test lamps may now be put in the position formerly occupied by the sub-standards, each being lined up so that its " photometric centre of symmetry " (i.e. the centre line of the light-giving system) is in the plane perpendicular to the axis of the bench and passes through the -2 mm. mark on the scale. Photometric measurements are then made on each lamp by both observers as before. After the correction to the distances found by B has been made as described at the end of the last paragraph [49], the mean of the results of both observers is found for any one test lamp, and the luminous intensity I_T found by squaring this distance (in mm.) and dividing by 10^5. A convenient method of booking the readings is shown in the following scheme :

Date . Comp. lamp No. at volts.

Fixed distance, 1,739·7 mm.

Test Lamp (1)	Observer (2)	d_T (observed) (3)	d_T (corrected) (4)	Mean (5)	I_T (6)
T_1	A B	1,493·$_2$ 1,495·$_6$	1,493·$_2$ ⎫ 1,492·$_2$ * ⎬	1,492·$_7$	22·2$_8$
T_2	A B	832·$_7$ 835·$_1$	832·$_7$ ⎫ 833·$_2$ ⎬	833·$_0$	6·9$_4$

For approximate work one observer is often considered to be sufficient. In this case the fixed distance is set to suit this observer, and no correction is necessary. The luminous intensities of the test lamps are found, either by direct reading on a " squared " or luminous intensity scale, or by squaring the reading on an ordinary millimetre scale.

In the above description of photometric procedure it has been assumed that what is required is the luminous intensity of a lamp at a given potential or current. Sometimes it is required to determine the potential or current at which a lamp has a given luminous intensity I_T. This is obtained by fixing the test lamp at the – 2 mm. mark, and the photometer head at the point d_T ($= \sqrt{I_T \times 10^5}$). The electrical conditions are then adjusted to give a fairly close photometric balance in the photometer head. Two sets of measurements are made in the ordinary manner, with the test lamps at potentials respectively about one half of 1 per cent above and below the potential thus obtained. These measurements enable the correct value of potential or current at the specified luminous intensity to be obtained at once by interpolation (see Appendix X). For approximate work it is sometimes sufficient to set the photometer head at the distance which corresponds with the definite luminous intensity, and to obtain the photometric balance by altering the potential on the test lamp. This is done by means of a resistance inserted in the test lamp circuit, and placed so as to be conveniently under the control of the observer at the photometer head.

When the source to be measured is not electrical, the photometric procedure is exactly the same for operations (i), (ii) and (iii). For (iv) the lining-up of the test lamp is also similar, but the control conditions necessarily depend on the particular nature of the source. In the case of a gas flame, mantle, or similar source, the pressure of the gas must be controlled by some form of regulator [50]. The

* $1,492·_2 = 1,495·_6 - (d_T/d_C) \times 3·9.$

rate of consumption must be adjusted to the scheduled value, or to the value at which the maximum luminous intensity is obtained. This rate should be measured while the photometric measurements are in progress. Adjustment of the air inlet may also be required. No photometric measurement should be made until the lamp has been burning for at least thirty minutes, and a final slight adjustment of the gas and air inlets may be required at the end of this period before the observations are begun. Other factors which affect the luminous intensity of gas lamps are the calorific value of the gas used and, to a less extent, the humidity and pressure of the surrounding atmosphere [51]. The centre plane of a flat flame, and the axis of a gas mantle, are usually adopted for lining-up over the zero mark of the bench. Although the gas mantle is very nearly opaque, the ordinary inverted mantle may be regarded as a rough approximation to a diffusing sphere so that the error made in assuming its photometric centre to be on the mechanical axis is usually very small (see p. 146). A flame is usually so transparent that the mean plane of a duplex flame may be taken as the plane midway between the two individual flames (see also p. 148).

When a measurement of luminous intensity is made in a single direction, unless this direction is specified beforehand (as, for example, by the position of the leading-in wires in an electric lamp), it is usual to choose a direction in which the illumination is even and as free as possible from bright or dark lines or spots. A piece of white paper placed in front of the photometer head will generally show considerable unevenness of illumination in the case of an ordinary commercial electric lamp, for instance. As the lamp is rotated in the carriage pillar light and dark vertical lines will be seen to move across the paper owing to images of the filaments in the bulb and slight lens effects due to vertical striations in the walls of the bulb. If these are included in the field covered by the photometer head the luminous intensity may be found very sensitive to exact positioning of the lamp.

To define the direction of measurement it is generally sufficient in approximate work to mark an arrow on the lamp cap on the side of the lamp facing the photometer. For more accurate work the procedure described in connection with the preparation of sub-standards (see p. 180) may be followed.

Measurement of Sub-standards—The process by which the value of luminous intensity is assigned to a sub-standard at a standardising laboratory is very similar to that described above. This sub-standard now becomes the " test lamp," while the standardising laboratory's master sub-standards are used for the comparison. The only important difference is, in fact, the number of measurements made on each lamp, the final value assigned to it being the mean of the values obtained on at least three separate occasions by two or more observers. The master sub-standards used at the standardising laboratory are compared in a similar manner with the international standards, a large number of observers making measurements on many separate occasions, so that their mean values are probably correct to at least 0·1 per cent.

For approximate work in laboratories where the amount of photometric work done is considerable, as, for example, in a lamp factory, it is usual for a number of lamps to be compared at the laboratory with sub-standards obtained from a standardising laboratory. Such lamps then become working standards, and, if compared at frequent intervals with the real sub-standards, they may be used until they fracture or develop some other defect.

When a sub-standard is measured, the current taken by it at the standard potential is usually measured by means of a potentiometer and standard resistance (see p. 492). This current value will then serve as a check on the constancy of the lamp in subsequent work. The correction to be applied to the measured current when the potentiometer is in the sub-standard circuit (p. 492) should be noted.

Screening—A very important precaution to be observed in all photometry is that of preventing stray light from reaching the photometer screen [52]. Stray light may be regarded as any light which reaches the photometer otherwise than directly from the source being measured. It may be due either to the other sources of light in the room or, more frequently, to reflections, by objects near the bench, of light from either of the lamps being compared.

Clamp to Bar on Photometer Carriage

FIG. 126. Form of Screen for Use on the Photometer Bench.

There are several methods of avoiding stray light, though all depend on the same principle, viz. the interposition of opaque black screens which completely shield the photometer except in the direction of the lamp. These screens may be of the general form shown in Fig. 126, with apertures of various sizes. They are supported at intervals along a light aluminium tube which is clamped to the carriage holding the photometer. The distances between the screens are adjusted in relation to the sizes of the apertures, as shown diagrammatically in Fig. 127, so that no light can reach the photometer except from the region AB. The lamp is situated in the centre of this region, and some 50 cm. behind it is placed a large screen covered with clean black velvet,* so that in effect the photometer and lamp are enclosed in a light-tight box. Sometimes, as an additional precaution, black curtains are hung along

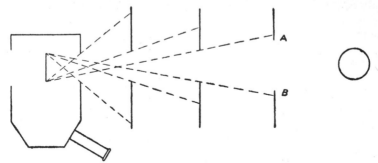

FIG. 127. Arrangement of Screens on the Bench.

the bench on either side to prevent too much light from reaching the screens, and so finding its way by reflection to the photometer, for the reflection factor of even a matt-black paint may be from 3 to 5 per cent.

In a slightly different method of screening a light-tight box is actually used. Two rectangular frameworks, one near the photometer, and the other near the lamp, are connected by a square tube of black material which, being pleated like an accordion bellows, elongates or contracts as the photometer moves away from or towards the lamp. Here, again, a black velvet screen is placed at a sufficient distance behind each lamp.

In order to test the effectiveness of the screening arrangements, the photometer disc should be removed and each lamp looked at from the window on the opposite side of the photometer. Nothing should be visible in any direction except the lamp itself; the remainder of the field of view should be completely occupied by black surfaces.

Sometimes trouble is experienced from light reflected by the polished metal bars of the photometer bench itself. In the direction of specular reflection this light, unless completely stopped by the screens, may cause a considerable error in the photometric measurements. It can be avoided completely by covering the bars with a piece of black velvet at the region half-way between the lamp and the photometer.

Too much emphasis cannot be placed on the importance of adequate screening in accurate photometry. It is no exaggeration to

* It should be noted that velvet readily collects dust and may, when sufficiently coated, reflect an appreciable amount of light.

say that half the inconsistencies in the photometric measurements made in an ordinary laboratory are due to imperfect screening.

Transportable Photometers—Many different types of so-called " portable " photometers have been designed for use outside the laboratory or testing room [53]. These consist, generally, of a short bench of simplified form in the centre of which is fixed a photometer head. A working standard is used on one side, and the lamp under test is moved along the bench on the other side of the photometer.

The accuracy of instruments of this kind is not great, and for most purposes for which a portable photometer is required it is preferable to abandon the bench altogether and use one of the illumination photometers described in Chapter XII. The test surface of the photometer is placed at one end of a blackened tube, and the test lamp at a certain fixed distance d from it. If E is the illumination measured by means of the photometer, $I = d^2E$.

The Weber Photometer—A very convenient form of portable photometer in which the inverse square law is employed without the use of a bench is that first designed by L. Weber in 1883 [54], and subsequently modified by the introduction of a Lummer-Brodhun cube, and still later by the substitution of an electric lamp for the benzine comparison lamp originally used. This photometer, since the scale employed for the distance measurement is short compared with that of a photometer bench, is most useful for work of moderate accuracy and in places where a bench is not available. It is shown in sectional elevation in Fig. 128. T_2 is a stout wide

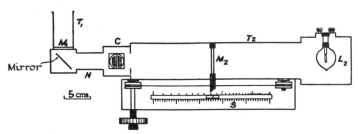

FIG. 128. The Weber Photometer.

horizontal tube along which moves an opal glass plate M_2. This is illuminated by a small electric glow lamp L_2 contained in a square box at the end of T_2. The distance of M_2 from this lamp is measured by means of a pointer moving over a scale S. The current through L_2 is maintained constant by means of an external rheostat and battery. At the other end of the instrument is a smaller tube T_1 containing a second opal glass plate M_1, fixed in position. M_1 is illuminated by the lamp L_1 (not shown) which is to be measured.

The brightnesses of M_1 and M_2 are compared by means of the mirror system and the Lummer-Brodhun cube C. The photometric balance is obtained by adjustment of the position of M_2, and if the distance of M_2 from L_2 is d_2 when a balance is obtained, while the constant distance between L_1 and M_1 is d_1, then $I_1/d_1{}^2 = \kappa I_2/d_2{}^2$, where κ is a constant of the instrument [55]. κI_2 is found by standardising with sub-standards in the usual way ; in fact, it plays the same part as the luminous intensity of the comparison lamp in the substitution method of photometry. For increasing the range of the photometer, absorbing glasses are introduced in front of M_1 to increase the value of κ (see p. 230).

Polarisation Photometers—In certain problems of photometry, notably the comparison of the luminous intensity of two sources wave-length by wave-length (spectrophotometry, see Chapter XI), it is not generally practicable to vary the distance between the source and the photometer head, so that the inverse square law cannot be applied. For such problems recourse is had to one of the other laws governing the luminance of a surface illuminated by a source, notably the squared tangent law of polarisation, referred to in Chapter II (p. 32).

The principle of a polarisation photometer is, briefly, the production of contiguous (or, occasionally, superposed) images of the two comparison surfaces by means of an optical train which includes a device for plane polarising the light which forms one or both of these images. The polarising device may consist of a pile of glass plates upon which the light is incident at or near the polarising angle (see p. 157), or, more conveniently, it may consist of a doubly-refracting prism, such as a Nicol or Wollaston (see p. 30) [56]. If the beams of light forming the two images be polarised in mutually perpendicular planes, then the interposition of a second, or analysing, Nicol prism reduces the intensity of one image by the factor $\cos^2 \theta$, and that of the other image by the factor $\sin^2 \theta$, where θ is the angle between the optic axis of the Nicol prism and the plane of polarisation of the light forming the first image (see p. 32).

If, therefore, the analysing Nicol is capable of rotation and photometric balance is obtained at the angle θ, it follows that the ratio between the luminances of the two images, supposing no Nicol interposed, would be $\tan^2 \theta$.

The Martens Polarisation Photometer—The methods of producing the two contiguous images with the finest possible dividing line are different in the various polarisation photometers that have been designed from time to time. In the Martens polarisation photometer [57] a Fresnel biprism is used, as in the ordinary form of Martens photometer already described (see p. 204). The polarisation instrument is shown diagramatically in Fig. 129. Here a and b are the two comparison surfaces. The light from a passes through a

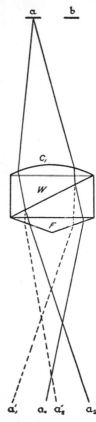

FIG. 129. The Martens Polarisation Photometer (general principle).

plano-convex lens C_1 into a Wollaston prism W. Here it is split up into two beams, one, shown by the full line, being polarised in the plane of the paper, while the other, shown by the broken line, is polarised in a plane perpendicular to this. Each of these two beams passes through the biprism F and, in consequence, is again split into two parts, so that the light from a is now divided into four beams which, on passing through a suitable lens system, form four separate images of a in the plane of the entrance pupil of the eyepiece. Of these four images two, viz. a_1 and a_2, are polarised in the plane of the paper, while the other two, a'_1 and a'_2, are polarised in the perpendicular plane. The light from b is treated similarly, and the angle of the biprism is designed in relation to the relative positions of object and image, and to the separation of a and b, so that a'_1 and b_2 coincide at the eye, while the remaining six images are stopped by a diaphragm. It follows that one half of the biprism F appears bright due to the light from a, which is polarised in the plane of the paper, while the other half appears bright due to light from b, which is polarised in a perpendicular plane. The interposition of a Nicol prism in a holder capable of rotation about the axis of the instrument therefore gives the complete photometer, which in its actual form is shown in Fig. 130.

T is a hollow tube, open at one end and closed at the other with a small cap holding a white plaster screen S. This tube is capable of rotation about the horizontal axis of the instrument ZZ', while the instrument itself is mounted on a vertical pillar capable of rotation in azimuth, so that the tube T can be moved to such a position that the light from the lamp to be measured, L_1, passes along the tube and is incident normally at S. The light from S is deflected by the totally reflecting prisms P and Q, and a lens cemented to P forms an image of S at a position a, which is close to the second surface of Q. The comparison lamp used for the measurements, L_2, is placed at one end of a horizontal tube T', and illuminates a small sheet of translucent opal glass b. The image a and the surface b form the

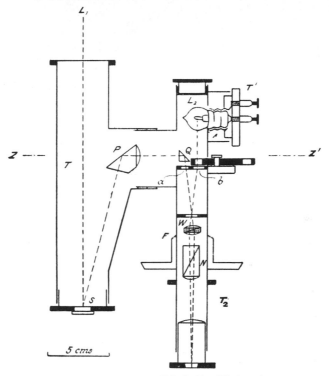

FIG. 130. The Martens Polarisation Photometer.

two comparison surfaces, and the remainder of the instrument is seen to be arranged as just described. Now the luminance B_a of image a'_1 is proportional to the illumination of S (E_s, say), while that of b_2, B_b, is a constant, so that if θ is the angle on the scale of the Nicol prism, $E_s = \kappa \tan^2 \theta$, where κ is a constant of the instrument. κ is obtained by calibration with a sub-standard of luminous intensity I placed at a distance d from S. If, then, α is the value of θ with this arrangement, $I/d^2 = \kappa \tan^2 \alpha$, so that $\kappa = I \cot^2 \alpha / d^2$.

A modification of the Weber photometer (see p. 218) has been designed [58] in which two Nicol prisms, crossed at a measurable angle, are employed instead of the movement of the plate M_2.

Since the polarisation photometer makes use of the squared tangent law [59], it follows that the scale of the instrument becomes very inaccurate when the ratio of luminance of the comparison surfaces B_a/B_b is far removed from unity, for

$$d(\tan^2 \theta)/\tan^2 \theta \, d\theta = 4 \operatorname{cosec} 2\theta,$$

which becomes infinite when $\theta = 0°$ or $90°$, and has its minimum value when $\theta = 45°$ ($B_a/B_b = 1$). The angular movement for a given contrast is reduced to one-half of its maximum value when B_a/B_b is equal to about 15. The maximum absolute accuracy is 1 per cent for a movement of 0·1 mm. on an angular scale of 80 mm. diameter, so that it is clear that the accuracy attainable with this form of photometer, using a scale of practicable dimensions, does not approach that obtainable with a photometer bench of even 3 metres total length. Further, the instrument possesses the two errors common to all apparatus involving accurate measurement of angular rotation, viz. (a) error of centering of the Nicol prism in relation to the axis of rotation, and (b) zero error due to lack of exact coincidence of the optic axis with the plane of polarisation of the ordinary ray transmitted by the Wollaston prism when $\theta = 0$. The first error is overcome by taking readings on the scale in opposite quadrants. The second error is eliminated by taking as the true value of θ the mean of the angles measured on each side of the zero line.

It is clear that in this form of photometer the light from the comparison surfaces must be quite free from polarisation [60]. Since specular reflection produces polarisation, it follows that the comparison surfaces must be as matt as possible, and the direction of specular reflection must be carefully avoided.

The Martens photometer may be used for determining the plane of polarisation of partially polarised light as well as the ratio between the intensities of the polarised and unpolarised parts. The tube T_2 is removed from the rest of the instrument and closed at the end by a diaphragm with a single hole admitting unpolarised light from an exterior surface. The balance point of the analyser N is found, and it is clamped in this position. The tube T_2 is then directed towards the surface giving partially polarised light, and is rotated *as a whole* to find the four positions of photometric balance. The plane of polarisation of the light bisects the angle between the lines joining the pairs of mutually opposite positions found, and the correct bisector is determined by the direction in which the photometric balance is disturbed as the tube is slightly rotated from the balance point.

The tube T_2 is then placed at an angle of 45° with the plane of polarisation thus found, and the Nicol N is unclamped and rotated until a balance is obtained, at an angle α, say. The percentage of polarised light is 100 sin 2α, for the unpolarised part of the light U can be resolved into two components, each of magnitude $\frac{1}{2}U$, and polarised respectively in and perpendicular to the plane of polarisation of the polarised part P and since the analyser makes an angle $(45° + \alpha)$ with the plane of polarisation of P, at the position of balance

$$(\tfrac{1}{2}U + P)/\tfrac{1}{2}U = \tan^2(45 + \alpha),$$

whence $P/(U + P) = \sin 2\alpha$.

Photometers depending upon Talbot's Law—By Talbot's law (see p. 67), if a disc with an aperture in it, such as that shown in Fig. 131, is set rotating between a lamp and a photometer head so that the light from the lamp only reaches the photometer for a certain fraction of the whole time, and if the rotation is so fast that all sense of flicker is lost when the eye looks into the photometer, the effective luminous intensity of the lamp is reduced in ratio of the time of exposure to the total time [61], i.e. if the aperture in the disc has the form of a sector of angle $n°$ the effective luminous intensity is $I(n/360)$. It was long thought that Talbot's law did not apply when n was small [62],

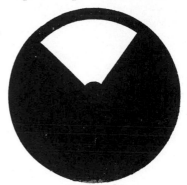

FIG. 131. The Simple Sector Disc.

but it is probable that the deviations found were due to small inaccuracies in the measurement of n (which naturally became more important as n was reduced), since Hyde, in a very careful series of measurements [63], found that the deviations lay within the limits of experimental error (0·3 per cent) for values of n as low as 10°.

Sector discs have been used in photometry in two ways. The original form of disc with fixed apertures, or with apertures that are adjustable only when the disc is stationary [64] reduces the light reaching the photometer in a fixed ratio. The chief use of such a disc is therefore to extend the range of a given working standard, either upwards or downwards according to the side of the photometer on which the disc is placed. Discs have been constructed, however, so that the angle of the aperture can be altered while the disc is in rotation [65] and such discs have been used to obtain the balance in a photometer head.

The Napoli-Abney form is illustrated in Fig. 132. The shaft H carries near one end a grooved pulley, which may be driven at any desired speed by an electric motor. At the other end is a disc A, of which two (or sometimes three) equal sectors have been removed, except by the shaft and the rim. A second, exactly similar, disc is placed behind this one, and is rigidly attached to a sleeve which slides on the shaft. Fixed to this sleeve is a pin, which engages in a spiral groove cut in the shaft so that the longitudinal position of the sleeve along the axis of the shaft controls the relative positions of the two discs. The width of the sector openings is thus capable of control by means of a wheel W attached to the sleeve and acted upon by a groove in a lever L, which moves over a divided scale S.

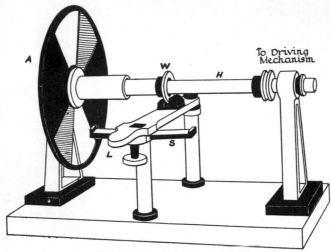

FIG. 132. The Napoli-Abney Sector Disc.

The use of a variable sector of this type for obtaining a photometric balance is not generally to be recommended. Apart from the difficulty of avoiding back-lash in the mechanism used to vary the aperture, the chief drawback is the high accuracy needed in determining the total angle of opening. With a ratio as high as one-quarter, the total angle must be measured to less than one degree to obtain an accuracy of one per cent in the photometric measurement. Further, the rotation of the disc has to be stopped for every reading unless the scale is illuminated by some form of intermittent illumination synchronised with the rotation of the disc [66].

A different form of apparatus, in which some of the difficulties mentioned above are overcome, consists of a stationary sector with an optical device for rotating the beam of light to be reduced [67]. One form of this is the double total-reflection prism system in Fig. 133. This prism system is mounted on a double disc which rotates

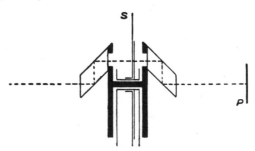

FIG. 133. The Brodhun Sector Disc.

about the axis of the stationary sector disc S. The light follows the path shown by the broken line, so that the illumination of the screen P is proportional to the opening. It is to be noticed that in this device the Fresnel prisms must not act as a stop on the beam of light, i.e. the whole of the source must be clearly visible from every part of P when the sector disc is not acting as an obstruction. A particular application of this form of the variable sector disc is in the design of transportable photometers [68] which are otherwise somewhat similar to the Weber photometer described above (see p. 218).

When the beam of light to be reduced is of small cross-section as, for example, in spectrophotometry (see p. 356), a special form of sector disc in which the openings have curved edges is sometimes used (see Fig. 134) [69]. The reduction ratio of the disc then depends on the distance of the beam of light from the axis of the disc, so that lateral move-ment of either can be used to adjust the intensity of the beam. The curves forming the edges of the apertures are usually designed so as to give an approximately uniform percentage rate of change in the reduction ratio for a given change in the distance of the beam from the disc axis. This distance may conveniently be varied by mounting the disc on a carriage which can be moved by means of a screw along a

FIG. 134. Sector Disc for Spectrophotometry.

vee-shaped track in a casting to which the apparatus giving the light beam is rigidly attached. It is clearly most important that there should be no possibility of relative movement of the disc and the beam, except by deliberate rotation of the screw.

For ordinary photometric purposes discs with fixed apertures are required. It is very important that the edges of each aperture should be exactly radial [69a], especially where the total angular opening is small, and sometimes the openings cut in the disc are made rather larger than required so that a separate strip of metal can be attached near each edge. These strips can then be adjusted in position so that the working edges are exactly radial and give an aperture of the desired angle. The edge of the metal should be ground quite straight and should be bevelled on the side facing the photometer in order to avoid possible reflection from a flat edge. The number of apertures is usually one, two or three. They are not carried to the edge of the disc and if thin metal is used for the sake of lightness this edge should be dished or otherwise prevented from deforming during rotation. Although the disc is painted black on both sides, the paint is not carried over the edges of the apertures, as otherwise the angle of opening is diminished.

A convenient set of discs is one for which the nominal ratios are 1/5, 1/10, 1/20 and 1/50. The exact ratio for each disc is best obtained by direct calibration on the photometer bench, a lamp of convenient luminous intensity being balanced against a comparison lamp both with and without the disc. If the distances of the lamp from the photometer in the two cases are d_1 and d_2 respectively, it is clear that the reduction ratio is equal to $(d_1/d_2)^2$. For ratios below 1/10 it is generally best to calibrate " in cascade," using, say, the known 1/5 or 1/10 disc in the first photometric balance, and then substituting the disc of unknown ratio. Care must be taken to arrange the disc between the lamp and photometer so that the whole of the lamp may be seen from the photometer as an aperture passes, while, on the other hand, no part of the lamp is visible except through an aperture in the disc.

It should be noted that a sector disc cannot, in general, be used in flicker photometry (see p. 308). Further, when a sector disc is used to reduce the light from a lamp which shows rapid periodical fluctuations, such as a discharge lamp or a low-wattage tungsten filament lamp operating on an alternating current supply, care must be taken to ensure that the speed of the disc is not a multiple or sub-multiple of the supply frequency [70] (see p. 236).

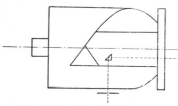

FIG. 135. Cylindrical Form of " Sector Disc."

For certain purposes, particularly in spectrophotometry, a cylinder with one or more apertures, rotated about its axis, has been used instead of a sector disc [71]. The principle will be clear from Fig. 135 which shows a cylinder in which the reduction ratio is varied during operation by a longitudinal movement in the direction of the axis.

Neutral Filters—Yet another method of varying the illumination of a photometer comparison surface is to insert between it and the source of light a piece of transparent medium the transmission of which can be varied in a known manner [72]. The simplest form of apparatus for achieving this consists of two thin wedges of neutral glass, or of lampblack in gelatine enclosed between glass plates, arranged as in Fig. 136, so that one wedge can be moved over the other. The transmission factor thus remains uniform over the whole surface of overlap, but changes as one wedge is moved over the other, so that the thickness of the combination is altered. It is

clear that, if the angle ϕ of each wedge is very small, then a movement δl of one wedge over the other produces a change of $\phi\delta l$ in the

FIG. 136. The Double-wedge Absorbing Filter.

thickness t. If α is the absorption coefficient of the wedge material,
the rate of change of transmission is $d\tau/dt = -\alpha\tau$ (see p. 160). Hence
$(1/\tau)(d\tau/dl) = \phi\alpha$.

If α is 1 mm.$^{-1}$ (2·3 mm. for 10 per cent), then $\phi\delta l = \delta\tau/\tau$, so
that for a movement of 1 mm. to produce a 1 per cent change in τ,
ϕ must be 0·01 radian, or about half a degree. Clearly, since
$(1/\tau)(d\tau/dl)$ is a constant, the scale connecting l and τ is logarithmic,
i.e. it gives the same percentage accuracy throughout. It must be
remembered, however, that in practice the absolute accuracy will
depend on (a) the constancy of α throughout the body of the filter,
and (b) the constancy of ϕ, which is extremely difficult of attainment
in such a very small angle. In general, therefore, it is advisable
to calibrate any given pair of wedges by other photometric methods,
and not to rely on the theoretical relation given above.

In cases where the accuracy required is not great, or the breadth
of the beam of light which traverses the wedge is small, a single
wedge of neutral glass may be used in combination with a wedge
of clear glass, for in this case the variation of transmission over the
length of wedge occupied by the beam may be neglected.

Instead of neutral glass, a Goldberg wedge, made of gelatine
containing a very fine lampblack in suspension, is often used [73].
A small amount of diffusion cannot be avoided in the case of this
material [74], but it is more truly neutral than most so-called
" neutral " glass [75].

Instead of a wedge, a strip of photographic plate may be used.
The gradation of transmission may be obtained (i) by exposing the
plate through a Goldberg wedge, (ii) by grading the time of exposure
from one end to the other, or (iii) by using a wedge-shaped diaphragm
over a diffusing source of light, so as to produce a gradation of
illumination from one end of the plate to the other [76]. The objection to this form of wedge is the diffusion of light inseparable from
an exposed photographic film. A graded filter may also be obtained
by the cathodic sputtering of platinum on glass [77].

A layer of liquid, adjustable in depth, has been used as a variable
absorbing filter for photometric purposes [78] while two sheets of
polarising material, mounted so that the angle between the planes
of polarisation can be varied at will, also provide a filter of variable
transmission [79].

A device in which the difficulties due to diffusion or to lack of neutrality are avoided altogether consists of a pair of exactly similar gratings having, say, sixty lines to the inch, mounted face to face at a distance apart approximately equal to the breadth of a line. The lines are parallel to each other and the transmission of the combination can be varied by moving the gratings relatively so that the lines of one cover more or less of the spaces of the other or by tilting the pair of gratings with respect to the incident light [80].

Even the best variable absorbing filter is but a poor substitute for a photometer bench, and, just as in the case of the sector disc, the chief field of usefulness for an absorbing filter in photometry is in conjunction with a photometer bench, where a filter of fixed and accurately known transmission may be used to reduce the luminous intensity of a powerful source so as to bring it within a range convenient for comparison with the sub-standards available [81]. A coloured filter may be used to alter the spectral distribution of the light from the source, but this will be dealt with later in Chapter IX. For the purposes considered in this chapter a filter should be as neutral as possible, i.e. its transmission factor should be the same for light of all wave-lengths. It should also be truly transparent, i.e. it should not diffuse any of the light passing through it. Neither of these conditions is fulfilled in practice by any homogeneous absorbing filter [82]. So-called " neutral " glasses always have a somewhat higher transmission factor in one region of the spectrum or another. This is clearly seen when several are placed together for the purpose of looking at a bright source, such as the sun.

The effect of diffusion in an absorbing filter may be minimised by placing the filter close to and at a fixed distance from either the photometer or the lamp. It should *not* be so placed between the photometer and the lamp that its distance from either or both is liable to change, since the light which is diffused by the filter acts as if it emanated from the filter as a source. The necessity for the fulfilment of these conditions may be shown theoretically as follows. Let τ and τ' be respectively the " regular " and " diffuse " transmission factors of the filter, and let the distances of the filter and of the photometer surface from the source be respectively x and d. The illumination at the filter is I/x^2. That at the photometer is $\tau I/d^2 + (I/x^2)\tau' f/\pi (d - x)^2$, where f is the area of the filter. This equals

$$(I/d^2)[\tau + \tau' f d^2/\pi x^2 (d - x)^2].$$

Now if $(d - x)$ is small compared with d, x is nearly equal to d, and the right-hand term of the expression in the brackets reduces to $\tau' f/\pi (d - x)^2$, which is constant as long as $(d - x)$ is constant. Similarly, if x is small compared with d, this term becomes $\tau' f/\pi x^2$, which is constant as long as x is constant. Thus constancy of effective transmission can only be obtained when the filter is close to and at an invariable distance from either the source or the surface it illuminates.

When the filter is close to the photometer, it may be necessary to make a small correction for the inter-reflection of light between the filter and the photometer surface. The amount of this correction can be calculated by assuming that the filter forms a mirror image of the surface, this image having a luminance equal to that of the surface multiplied by the reflection factor of the filter, ρ. The value of ρ may be taken as equal to $0.04 (1 + \tau^2)$ in the case of a filter with two glass-air surfaces and a transmission factor of τ. The reflections at the glass-liquid surfaces in a liquid filter may usually be neglected. The illumination of the photometer surface due to the light from its mirror image may usually be calculated to the necessary accuracy by one of the methods described on pp. 141 *et seqq.*

Absorbing filters may be used in two ways. A single plane filter may be used to reduce the illumination from a source of very high luminous intensity so that it may conveniently be balanced against a comparison lamp of normal intensity; alternatively it may be used on the comparison lamp side of the photometer when very small sources are being measured. In any case, the transmission factor must be known for light of the same spectral distribution as that given by the source with which it is to be used (see p. 298). It is convenient in the photometric laboratory to have a set of neutral filters of this kind with transmission factors of the order of 10, 5 and 2 per cent. These will enable sources up to about 2,000 candelas to be measured with a bench distance of 2 metres when the standard illumination at the photometer is 10 lux. The transmission factors of such filters must be accurately determined, either at a standardising laboratory or by using a high intensity source of the same kind as that with which the filters are to be used. For instance, if they are required for work with gas-filled lamps operating at an efficiency of about 15 lumens per watt, then such a lamp, with a luminous intensity of about 250 cd., may be used on the test lamp end of the photometer bench, while a similar lamp of about 30 cd. will serve as a comparison lamp, and if used at a distance of about 1 metre from the photometer will give a comparison illumination of about 30 lux. It will be noticed that the exact value of this illumination does not matter. With no filter on the test lamp side, the reading of the photometer at the balance point will be d, about 3 metres. With the 10 per cent filter in place the reading d' will be about 1 metre. The transmission factor of the filter will clearly be $(d'/d)^2$. The other filters may now be measured in a similar way, either directly, or " in cascade " by using the already determined factor of the 10 per cent filter and placing this filter on the comparison lamp side when the filter being measured is on the test lamp side. The correction for the thickness of the photometer screen should be made as described on p. 208 [83]. It is to be noted that the transmission factor of a number of filters in series is not exactly equal to the product of the transmission factors of the individual filters, owing to inter-reflection of light between the surfaces [83].

The range of many portable illumination photometers is increased by the use of neutral filters which can be inserted in suitable positions (see p. 384). The instrumental constant must be determined with each filter or set of filters in position.

It is usually safe to assume that a lampblack-gelatine neutral filter is sufficiently neutral for its transmission factor to remain quite constant over the whole range of colour given by electric lamps, from ordinary vacuum lamp efficiency (6·7 lumens per watt) upwards. The value determined with such sources should not, however, be assumed to hold with great accuracy when the filter is being used with such sources as the electric arc, incandescent gas mantles, or electric discharge lamps [84]. The transmission factor of filters for use with sources of different colours will be referred to again in Chapter IX.

Whenever filters of appreciable thickness are used in photometry, it should be remembered that, owing to refraction, the effective distance of the light source from the photometer screen is reduced by the quantity $(n-1)t/n$, where t is the thickness of the filter and n its refractive index (see p. 24). Thus for a filter of glass $(n = 1·5)$ of 3 mm. thickness the measured distances must be reduced by 1 mm. in order to find the true luminous intensity of the source.

Instead of reduction by transmission, reduction by reflection may be used, the light from the high intensity source being reflected once or several times from a polished surface of black glass [85].

Other Methods of Varying the Photometer Illumination—Methods of photometry have at various times been based on a large number of devices, other than those enumerated above, for altering the luminance of the photometer comparison surface according to a known law [86]. In some forms of photometer the variation of luminance according to the cosine law of illumination has been used [87]. This method is still employed in certain portable photometers for measuring illumination (see p. 384). Since for every known surface the reflection factor varies with the direction of the incident light, the cosine law cannot be assumed to hold accurately, and the instrument therefore requires calibration by a more fundamental form of photometer.

Diaphragms of variable opening, have also been used. A source of light is placed behind a translucent screen, which illuminates one surface of the photometer head. The illumination is directly proportional to the area of a diaphragm which may be placed (*a*) directly in front of a translucent surface acting as the effective source [88], (*b*) close to a lens which forms an image on the photometer surface [89], or (*c*) close to a lens which serves as an objective to an optical system so designed that the light entering the eye is proportional to the area of the diaphragm [90]. Forms of diaphragm in which the area of the opening can be readily determined are shown in Fig. 137.

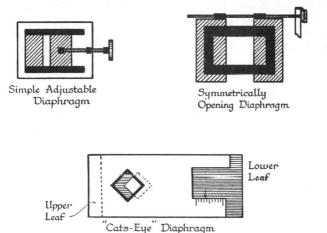

Simple Adjustable
Diaphragm

Symmetrically
Opening Diaphragm

Lower
Leaf

Upper
Leaf

"Cats-Eye" Diaphragm

FIG. 137. Forms of Variable Diaphragm.

A negative lens may be used to reduce the illumination of a screen placed behind it, for if L be the source (Fig. 138), P the lens of focal

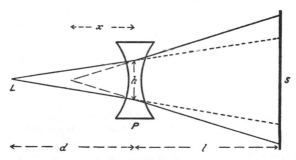

FIG. 138. The Reduction of Illumination by a Negative Lens.

length f, and S the screen, the light flux, which without the lens would occupy an area on the screen equal to $\pi h^2 (d + l)^2 / d^2$, actually occupies an area $\pi h^2 (x+l)^2/x^2$ where $1/x - 1/d = 1/f$ (see p. 23), so that the ratio of reduction of illumination is

$$\left[\frac{(d+l)x}{d(x+l)} \right]^2 = \left[1 + \frac{dl}{f(d+l)} \right]^{-2}$$

on account of lens action. This ratio must be further reduced on account of losses due to reflection at the glass surfaces and absorption within the substance of the lens [91]. This effect has been the basis of a so-called " dispersion " photometer in which the brightness of the screen is varied by changing the position of a negative lens placed between it and the source to be measured [92].

Photometers have been designed in which the light from the two comparison surfaces is caused to traverse two prisms of glass separated at the interface by a very thin air film (see p. 28). The interference bands formed by the transmitted light from one comparison surface are superposed on those formed by the reflected light from the other surface, so that the light bands of one set coincide with the dark bands of the other set. When both sets are of equal intensity the field of view appears uniformly bright [93].

A visual effect which has been applied to photometric measurement is the apparent curvature of the path of an object which is really moving in a straight line, but which is unequally illuminated on the two sides [94]. The effect is due to the relation between the brightness of an object and the lag in the visual impression produced by that object [95].

The Accuracy of Visual Photometry [96]—Several investigations have been made with the object of finding the relative sensitivity of different types of photometer head [97]. It seems to be the general conclusion that for photometry in which there is little or no colour difference between the sources being compared the Lummer-Brodhun contrast field gives the best results, although the Bunsen, if properly designed and used, may be almost as good. When there is a marked colour difference, the results are less definite (see p. 311). The brightness of the field of view has a considerable influence on the sensitivity of the eye to small contrasts (see p. 62), and it is therefore only to be expected that it will also affect the precision of photometric measurements [98]. In cases where the comparison field is very small (of the order of $2°$ to $4°$) the use of an evenly illuminated background with a luminance equal to or slightly less than that of the comparison field has been found to improve the accuracy of the settings [99]. Both these matters have already been dealt with in Chapter III (see p. 61). In general it may be said that the luminance of the comparison field as seen by the observer should never be less than about one foot-lambert and whenever possible it should be 2 or 3 times as great as this.

High accuracy can never be combined with great simplicity of construction, with portability, or with cheapness.   On the other hand, one or more of these latter characteristics may, in some problems, be more important than the last $\frac{1}{4}$ per cent in accuracy. For work of the highest precision a photometer bench, Lummer-Brodhun contrast type head, sub-standards obtained from a standardising laboratory, and the best possible electrical equipment must be used.   Nearly all the so-called " portable " photometers have to be calibrated with such an arrangement, but if carefully treated after calibration the best can be relied upon, usually, to 1 or 2 per cent and are often convenient for use in positions where it would be impossible to set up a bench.

With regard to the various personal factors inseparable from visual observations of any kind [100] it may be remarked that the experience of all those who have done much visual photometry shows that accuracy is impaired by anything which tends to diminish the power of concentrating the attention.   Thus unfamiliarity with the instrument used, or any source of discomfort while observing such, for instance, as a cramped attitude, may well reduce the accuracy of photometric observations.

It has already been pointed out (see p. 67) that the glare which results from looking at an object brighter than the photometric field, even for a short period, will vitiate readings for a length of time dependent on the brightness of the object and the time during which it has been looked at [101].   The importance of quick and almos effortless transition from one side to the other of the point of photometric balance has been mentioned earlier in this chapter [102].

The unconscious mental bias which may result if an observer becomes aware of any progressive tendency in his readings is avoided in most laboratories by arranging that the observers shall work in pairs, each one noting down the readings obtained by the other.   In accurate work not more than about a dozen settings should be made by a single observer without at least a brief period of rest.   A very definite " settling-in " effect is often noticeable in photometry.   At the beginning of a day's work the first few readings made by an observer may differ noticeably and in a definite direction from his subsequent observations, owing, apparently, to a preliminary uncertainty of criterion which is not resolved until after the first half-dozen or more observations have been made.   This effect is naturally more pronounced when the colour difference worked with is considerable.   Some observers, however, find that with an equality of brightness photometer a small colour difference is more troublesome than one which is large enough to be immediately apparent. The same is sometimes said when working with the contrast type of head, but in that case the difficulty is generally found to arise from the fact that the observer has, consciously or unconsciously, used as his criterion of balance the disappearance of the central dividing line instead of the equality of contrast between patch and background in the two halves of the field ; in fact, the head has been used as an equality of brightness instead of as a contrast head.

Under the best conditions, particularly as regards brightness and size of field and the absence of any considerable colour difference, the coefficient of variation * of single settings by a practised observer is usually between 0·5 and 1 per cent [103].

Photo-electric Measurements of Luminous Intensity—When a photocell is used for measuring the luminous intensity of a source there are at least three methods which may be adopted (see also p. 109). The simplest consists in illuminating the cell, first with the test lamp and then with a sub-standard of convenient intensity, the distance from the cell being precisely the same in both cases. The ratio of the luminous intensities is then equal to the ratio of the photo-currents so long as the response of the cell is linear (see p. 95).

In the second method the cell is mounted at one end of a photometer bench so that the sensitive surface is precisely over the zero mark on the scale. The sub-standard and the test lamp are placed in turn in a carriage on the bench and the respective distances are found at which a certain convenient value of photo-current is obtained (see also p. 110). The luminous intensities are then in the ratio of the squares of these distances. Two or more values of photo-current may be adopted and the mean of the ratios thus found may be taken in calculating the luminous intensity of the test lamp.

In the third method the photo-current is again adjusted to the same value both for the sub-standard and for the test lamp but instead of varying the distance and using the inverse square law, some other means, such as a sector disc or a neutral filter, is used for making the adjustment.

Although these three methods have been described as alternatives, it is clear that they may be combined. In particular, since the first method depends entirely on accurate linearity of the photocell, it is frequently combined with one of the other two methods so that linearity over only a limited range, e.g. a ratio of 3 to 1, is necessary. A fixed sector disc or a neutral filter of accurately known transmission may be used with the lamp of higher luminous intensity so as to

---

* If a large number of settings are made, the chance that any one will depart from the arithmetic mean of all the settings by more than the coefficient of variation is slightly less than 1 in 3. See, e.g. E. S. Pearson, " Statistical Methods in Standardisation " (British Standards Instn., 1935, p. 120.)

bring the ratio to be measured by the cell well within the range over which linearity may be relied upon. If two sector discs or filters are available, with reduction ratios such as to bring the higher luminous intensity to values respectively above and below the lower luminous intensity, the error due to slight non-linearity of the cell may be almost entirely eliminated. It is to be noted that the use of a sector disc is subject to the condition that the photocell and circuit employed are such that Talbot's law is rigorously obeyed (see pp. 98 and 107).

In describing the second method of using a photocell it was mentioned that the cell was placed with its sensitive surface exactly over the zero of the photometer bench. In some types of photo-emissive cell the sensitive surface is not in one plane and there is therefore some doubt as to the point from which measurements of distance should be made. Further, in many cells there is a wire mesh or grid which casts a shadow on the sensitive surface and the area shadowed depends on the dimensions of the source and on its distance from the cell [104]. For these reasons it is sometimes not possible, when using photo-emissive cells, to apply the inverse square law except over a very limited range of distances. The difficulty does not arise in the case of photo-voltaic cells since in these the sensitive surface is in a well-defined plane.

When a filter is used between a lamp and a photocell it should be placed close to either the lamp or the cell, as in the case of visual photometry, and the distance between the lamp and the filter should be corrected for the shortening of the light path (see p. 230). This applies not only to any neutral filter used for reducing the luminous intensity of one of the lamps to be compared but also to the colour filter which is necessary to correct the spectral sensitivity of the cell to that of the normal eye unless the lamps to be compared have precisely the same spectral distribution curve (see p. 112).

Careful screening to prevent stray light from reaching the photocell is most important and it is to be noted that some photo-emissive cells used in photometry are quite sensitive to radiation of wavelengths outside the visible spectrum. The screens used should, therefore, be made of a material that is opaque for all wave-lengths to which the cell is sensitive.

Measurement of Variable Sources [105]—It has so far been tacitly assumed that the source of light to be measured is, for all practical purposes, invariable in intensity but this is not always the case. It is sometimes necessary to measure sources which are varying and the variation may be periodic, as in the case of a discharge lamp or a low-wattage filament lamp on an alternating current supply, or it may be a single rise to a peak value followed by a fall to zero, as in the case of a source giving a single flash or a series of isolated flashes.

In the former case, it may be the average value of the luminous intensity throughout the cycle that is required, or a series of instantaneous values at different parts of the cycle. If the frequency is above the critical frequency of the eye (see p. 70) the average luminous intensity can be measured visually in exactly the same way as the intensity of a steady source of light, the sole restriction being that mentioned on p. 226 in connection with the use of a sector disc. The instantaneous luminous intensity at any part of the cycle can be measured by placing a single-aperture sector disc, synchronised with the electric supply, between the test lamp and the photometer [106]. Photometric readings are then taken in the ordinary way, allowance being made for the transmission of the sector disc. Since the disc is synchronised with the intensity fluctuations, it follows that the light reaches the photometer from the test lamp only during a brief interval of time and always at the same part of a cycle. By changing the angular position of the disc opening, the luminous intensity can be measured at any point on the cycle. It is clear that the same method may be used when the measurements are made photoelectrically [107] and in this case the restriction on the lower limit of frequency of the intensity variations does not apply. Care must, however, be taken to ensure that the circuit used has a sufficiently high time constant (see p. 103).

When the variation is non-periodic and not too rapid, or when the frequency is low, rough visual measurements may be made by using a shutter so timed as to give an exposure at any selected instant [108]. A photo-electric method is, however, much to be preferred and is not subject to the limitations just mentioned. In fact, by using a vacuum photo-emissive cell and a cathode ray tube with a long persistence screen, the whole time-intensity curve for a flash, even if it lasts only for a few milliseconds, can be obtained at once [109]. The photocell, colour corrected by means of a filter, is connected to the vertical deflection plates of the c.r. tube, so that the vertical deflection of the trace is proportional to the photocurrent and hence to the illumination of the cell. A tripping circuit may be used to synchronise the initiation of the sweep with the operation which produces the flash. The vertical scale is obtained by exposure to a source of known and suitable luminous intensity. Time-intensity curves have also been determined by photographic photometry (see p. 364) [110]. Such curves do not represent the visual effect produced because the response of the eye is not instantaneous (see Chap. III, p. 68), so that the intensities cannot, except by extension, be expressed in ordinary photometric units. It has been suggested [111] that an appropriate unit in this case is the lumerg (see note (56), p. 169).

Photo-electric methods can also be used to determine directly the maximum luminous intensity of a flashing source [112] or the time-integral of the luminous intensity (candela-seconds). For the latter purpose a circuit of the kind described on p. 100 may be used [113].

Measurement of Point Sources—This type of measurement is most frequently met with in the photometry of projection apparatus and will therefore be dealt with in Chapter XIV (p. 472).

BIBLIOGRAPHY

All the books listed in Appendix I describe methods of measuring luminous intensity. In addition there are articles on the subject in most of the larger works of reference or those dealing with pure or applied physics. A list of general papers, many of them of historical interest, will be found on pp. 186–7 of *Photometry (1926)*.

REFERENCES

1. F. Uppenborn-B. Monasch. *Lehrbuch der Photometrie* (Berlin, *1912*), p. 182.

2. See note (41) on p. 85. A photometer not dependent on a judgement of equality has been described by O. Reeb, Lichttechnik, 4, *1952*, p. 188.

3. " Der Zweck des Photometers ist demnach lediglich, die günstigsten Bedingungen herzustellen für die Sichtbarmachung kleinster Helligkeitsdifferenzen." (O. Lummer, J.G.W., 38, *1893*, p. 233.)

4. Also " photoped." See the " Notification of the Metropolitan Gas Referees," *1916*, p. 22.

5. A. P. Trotter. *Illumination, etc.*, p.192.
P. Lasareff. Pflüger's Archiv. f. d. ges Physiol., 158, *1913*, p. 371.
See also J. Guild, " Discussion on Vision," Phys. and Opt. Socs. *1932.* p. 17 ; J. Terrien, Comité Int. des Poids et Mesures, Procès-verbaux, 20, *1946*, p. 72.

6. J. Terrien. J. de Phys., 7, *1946*, p. 8 S.

7. For a description of earlier forms of photometer bench, e.g. the Evans, Letheby, Edinburgh, etc., see the literature cited in note (6) on p. 187 of *Photometry (1926)*. On bench design see J. F. Sutton, J. Sci. Inst., 5, *1928*, p. 184 (also p. 231).

8. J. of Gas Lighting, 104, *1908*, p. 33 ; El. World, 60, *1912*, p. 1058.

9. A convenient system for computing this scale has been described by G. Thompson, Illum. Eng. Soc. N.Y., Trans., 14, *1919*, p. 286.
See also J. F. Skogland and R. P. Teele, Bureau of Standards Technol. Paper No. 325, *1926*, p. 681 ; Z. Yamauti and J. Nishikawa, Electrotechn. Lab. Tokyo, Researches No. 272, *1929*.

10. See note (5) *supra*.

11. For the early history of photometry see also Baden Powell, Ann. of Phil., 27, *1826*, p. 371. The first chapter of W. J. Dibdin's *Practical Photometry* (W. King, London, *1889*), articles by E. Durand in Le Gaz (Paris), 2, *1858*, pp. 65 *et seq.*, and a series in Engineering, 35, *1883*, pp. 1 *et seqq.*, also give much information concerning early forms of photometers.

12. See note (13), p. 12.
O. Lummer and E. Brodhun. Z. f. I., 9, *1889*, p. 42.
P. Lasareff. Rev. d'Opt., 3, *1924*, p. 65.
See, however, W. E. K. Middleton, Opt. Soc. Am., J., 27, *1937*, p. 112.

13. See p. 3.

14. L. Wild *et al.* Electrician, 57, *1906*, pp. 529 *et seqq.* The above statement assumes that the substance forming the photometer surface behaves as a perfect

diffuser but A. P. Trotter has pointed out (Electrician, 57, *1906*, p. 627) that in the case of dulled Bristol board, owing to the peculiar nature of the diffusion curve for this surface, the angle error in a Ritchie wedge on which the light is incident at an angle of less than 35° is less than one half of one per cent per degree tilt. The error is avoided altogether in a form of photometer described by P. Yvon (C.R., 75, *1872*, p. 1102) in which the lamps are placed so that each illuminates its respective side of the wedge perpendicularly. This arrangement, however, clearly cannot be adopted on a straight bench.

15. R. Bunsen. Ann. d. Phys., 60, *1843*, p. 402.
    W. T. Casselmann. *Ibid.*, 63, *1844*, p. 576.
16. H. Krüss. Repertorium d. Phys., 18, *1882*, p. 54.
    L. Weber. Ann. d. Phys., 31, *1887*, p. 676.
17. A. Boutan. Acad. des Sci., etc., Rouen, Précis anal. des travaux, *1851–2*, p. 101.

    H. B. Leeson. J. of Gas Lighting, 2, *1852*, p. 273.
    F. Rüdorff. J.G.W., 12, *1869*, p. 283.
18. H. Krüss. Central-Ztg. f. Opt. u. Mech., 5, *1884*, p. 181.
19. L. Weber. Ann. d. Phys., 31, *1887*, p. 676.
See also the other papers cited in note (21) on p. 188 of *Photometry (1926)*.
20. C. Bohn. Ann. d. Chem. u. Pharmacie, 111, *1859*, p. 335.
21. C. Hajech. R. Istituto Lombardo di Sci., etc., Rend., 4, *1867*, p. 77.
    H. Krüss. Z. f. angewandte Electricitätslehre, 3, *1881*, p. 460.
However, disappearance may be caused to occur simultaneously on both sides if the viewing mirrors are so arranged that the disc is seen obliquely. See T. Erhard, Central-Ztg. f. Opt. u. Mech., 10, *1889*, p. 280.
22. A. Fyfe. Roy. Scottish Acad. Arts, Trans., 3, *1848*, p. 220.
    R. Bunsen and H. E. Roscoe. Phil. Trans., 149, *1859*, p. 879.
    A. Töpler. Ann. d. Phys., 8, *1879*, p. 640.
See also other refs. in note (24) on p. 188 of *Photometry (1926)*.
23. O. Lummer. J.G.W., 33, *1890*, p. 574.
24. See also S. Elster, J.G.W., 12, *1869*, p. 416.
25. O. Lummer and E. Brodhun. Z. f. I., 9, *1889*, p. 42.
    Y. Le Grand. Rev. d'Opt., 12, *1933*, p. 145.
26. On the effect of form of the field see H. Schober, Z. f. I., 54, *1934*, p. 305 and G. A. Fry, Opt. Soc. Am., J., 37, *1947*, p. 166.
27. Z. f. I., 9, *1889*, pp. 23 and 41 and 12, *1892*, p. 41.
See also W. Swan, Roy. Soc. Edin., Trans., 22, *1859*, p. 33 ; C. G. Knott, Phil. Mag., 49, *1900*, p. 118 ; O. Lummer and E. Brodhun, *ibid.*, p. 541.
28. Instead of a double prism, a sheet of glass silvered over portions of its surface has been used. See L. Wild, Illum. Eng., 3, *1910*, p. 303 ; H. P. Gage, Phys. Rev., 32, *1911*, p. 627 ; Illum. Eng. Soc. N.Y., Trans., 19, *1924*, p. 508 ; also C. S. M. Pouillet, C.R., 35, *1852*, p. 373.
29. A very good surface is obtained by dusting a black powder on to a coating of matt black enamel.
30. J.G.W., 37, *1894*, p. 61.
31. H. Krüss. Z. f. I., 30, *1910*, p. 329 ; Z. f. Bel., 18, *1912*, p. 437.
On the advantage of binocular vision in photometry, see A. Broca, J. de Phys., 3, *1894*, p. 206 and R. Stigler, Wien Ber. (IIa), 120, *1911*, p. 1069. It is essential that *both* comparison surfaces should be presented simultaneously to each eye for this advantage to be gained. See E. L. Nichols, Am. I.E.E., Trans., 6, *1889*, p. 335.
32. O. Lummer and E. Brodhun. Z. f. I., 9, *1889*, p. 461.
See also H. Krüss, J.G.W., 54, *1911*, p. 121.
33. Z. f. I., 9, *1889*, p. 461.
See also A. Boltzmann, Phys. Z., 15, *1914*, p. 718.
34. E. P. Hyde and F. E. Cady. Opt. Soc. Am., J., 6, *1922*, p. 615.
See also A. H. Pfund, *ibid.*, 19, *1929*, p. 387.
35. Comité Int. des Poids et Mesures, Procès-verbaux, 20, *1946*, p. 72.
36. A. H. Pfund. Phys. Rev., 4, *1914*, p. 477.
    E. P. Hyde and F. E. Cady. Opt Soc. Am., J., 6, *1922*, p. 615.
See also P. Lob, Kinotechnik, 15, *1933*, p. 57.

37. Deut. Phys. Gesell., Verh., 1, *1899*, p. 278.

38. Archiv f. Anatomie u. Physiologie, Physiol. Abth., *1881*, p. 336.
See also E. Brodhun and O. Schönrock, Z. f. I., 24, *1904*, p. 70.

39. E. Liebenthal. *Prakt. Phot.*, p. 191.

40. On asymmetry in a judgement of equality by the eye, see J. Terrien, Rev. d'Opt., 22, *1943*, p. 1.

41. See, e.g. L. Weber, Ann. d. Phys., 31, *1887*, p. 676. See also E.T.Z., 18, *1897*, p. 473.

42. C. Carpenter and J. W. Helps. C.I.E., Proc., 1, *1903*, p. 143.
J. G. Clark. J. of Gas Lighting, 92, *1905*, p. 826.
For the measurement of many flame sources an under-run tungsten filament lamp can be used as a comparison lamp. See C. H. Sharp and A. H. Schaaf, Am. Gas Inst., Proc., 8, *1913* (II), p. 324 and H. L. Farrar, Am. Gas Light J., 98, *1913*, p. 318.

43. In those cases where a substitution method cannot be used, lack of symmetry must be compensated by taking the geometric mean of the values given by two sets of readings, one with the photometer head in its normal position and one with it reversed (see p. 197).

44. Tables for facilitating this calculation have been given by L. Ubbelohde (*Tabelle f. Lichtstärkemessungen*, published by Fr. Schmidt u. Haensch, Berlin) and by others (see the refs. in *Photometry* (*1926*), on p. 474 and in note (8) on p. 187). Graphs have been given by N. A. Halbertsma (Archiv. f. Elektrot., 1, *1912*, p. 136) and in *Photometry* (*1926*), p. 475 and a nomograph by L. Bloch (E.T.Z., 43, *1922*, p. 73).

45. See e.g. the description of the Joly head on p. 4 ; also E. W. Lehmann, Ann. d. Phys., 49, *1893*, p. 672 and M. M. Gurevich, Elektrichestvo, *1930*, p. 928 (In Russian).

46. H. E. Ives and L. R. Woodhull. Bureau of Standards, Bull., 5, *1909*, p. 555.

47. It is a useful practice to move the combined carriages after unclamping and to check the distance between them in order to make sure that there is no possibility of their moving relatively to each other during subsequent work.

48. Alternatively, a recording device may be attached to the photometer carriage so that at the conclusion of each setting the observer himself may, by depressing a key, cause an electrically operated pen to mark a dot on a paper scale carried on a cylinder attached to the bench.
C. P. Matthews. Phys. Rev., 7, *1898*, p. 239.
A. P. Trotter. *Illumination, etc.*, p. 132.
G. W. Middlekauff. Bureau of Standards, Bull., 7, *1911*, p. 11.

49. If a candle-power scale is used on the bench instead of the ordinary millimetre scale, this correction may conveniently be made by means of a device described by G. W. Middlekauff (Bureau of Standards, Bull., 7, *1911*, p. 11).

50. See, e.g., J. H. Coste, *The Calorific Power of Gas* (Griffin, *1911*), p. 186.

51. R. S. McBride et al. Bureau of Standards, Technol. Paper No. 110, *1918*.
Inst. Gas Eng., Trans., *1918–19*, pp. 44 and 267 and *1919–20*, p. 167.
Increase of humidity has been found to cause a reduction of candle-power (C. O. Bond, Am. Gas Inst., Proc., 7, *1912*, p. 291).

52. P. Krüss. Illum. Eng., 1, *1908*, p. 380.

53. See, e.g., H. Korte, Art. " Visuelle Photometer " in *Handbuch der Lichttechnik* (Springer, *1938*), and the refs. in note (57) on p. 190 of *Photometry* (*1926*).

54. Ann. d. Phys., 20, *1883*, p. 326 ; J.G.W., 41, *1898*, p. 193.
H. Korte. *Loc. cit.*, note (53), *supra*, p. 322.
See also the refs. in note (58) on pp. 190–1 of *Photometry* (*1926*).

55. K. Satori (E.u.M., 24, *1906*, p. 859) finds that a small constant must be subtracted from d_2 as measured.
See also L. Djomkina, State Opt. Inst., Leningrad, 4, *1928*, No. 42, p. 1. (In Russian.)

56. For references to the many different forms of polarisation photometers, see notes (20) to (31) on p. 12.

57. F. F. Martens. Phys. Z., 1, *1900*, p. 299 ; Deut. Phys. Gesell., Verh., 5, *1903*, p. 149.
H. Beck. Z. f. techn. Phys., 24, *1943*, p. 226.

See also F. E. Wright, Opt. Soc. Am., J., 14, *1927*, p. 339; Instruments, 2, *1929*, p. 245; R. Sewig, Arch. f. techn. Messen, 4, *1935*, T 153.

58. L. Weber. Z. f. I., 11, *1891*, p. 6.

59. A slide-rule for facilitating the calculations involved in the use of the polarisation photometer has been described by M. Richter (Z. f. techn. Phys., 13, *1932*, p. 493).

60. A. Cornu. C.R., 103, *1886*, p. 1227.

61. See note (59), p. 86.

62. See, e.g. E. S. Ferry, Phys. Rev., 1, *1894*, p. 338.

63. E. P. Hyde. Bureau of Standards, Bull., 2, *1906*, p. 1.
See also O. Lummer and E. Brodhun, Z. f. I., 16, *1896*, p. 299.

64. H. Fox Talbot. Phil. Mag., 5, *1834*, p. 321.
See also R. W. Ditchburn, Cambridge Phil. Soc., Proc., 23, *1927*, p. 959.

65. D. Napoli. Soc. Franç. de Phys., Séances, *1880*, p. 53; Lum. El., 2, *1880*, p 133.
W. de W. Abney and E. R. Festing. Roy. Soc., Proc., 43, *1887–8*, p. 247.
E. Brodhun. Z.f.I., 24, *1904*, p. 313.
J. R. Milne. Roy. Soc. Edin., Proc., 31, *1911*, p. 656.
H. E. Ives. Opt. Soc. Am., J., 7, *1923*, p. 683.
E. Karrer. Opt. Soc. Am., J., 7, *1923*, p. 893 and 8, *1924*, p. 541.
G. Kortüm. Z.f.I., 54, *1934*, p. 373.
P. Périlhou. Rev. d'Opt., 21, *1942*, p. 235.
A. Bayle. Rev. d'Opt., 27, *1948*, p. 314.

66. E. Brodhun. Z.f.I., 17, *1897*, p. 10.
A. H. Pfund. Frank. Inst., J., 193, *1922*, p. 641.
L. Harris and J. A. Kyger. Opt. Soc. Am., J., 30, *1940*, p. 505.

67. E. Brodhun. Z.f.I., 27, *1907*, p. 8.
W. Bechstein. *Ibid.*, p. 178.

68. L. Bloch. E.T.Z., 26, *1905*, p. 1051.
W. Bechstein. Z.f.I., 27, *1907*, p. 178.
E. Liebenthal. *Prakt. Phot.*, p. 224.

69. E. P. Hyde. Phys. Rev., 31, *1910*, p. 183; Astrophys. J., 35, *1912*, p. 237.
G. F. Wood. Nature, 114, *1924*, p. 466 (see also p. 683).
See also note (71) *infra*.

69a. A. F. A. Harper and A. J. Mortlock. Brit. J. Appl. Phys., 4, *1953*, p. 220.

70. J. J. B. Moerman. Electrotechniek, 28, *1950*, p. 49.

71. F. L. Dunn. Rev. Sci. Inst., 2, *1931*, p. 807.
M. F. Hasler and R. W. Lindhurst. *Ibid.*, 7, *1936*, p. 137.
J. R. Platt *et al*. *Ibid.*, 14, *1943*, p. 85.
J. L. Steinberg and B. Vodar. Rev. d'Opt., 27, *1948*, p. 611.

72. R. Sabine. Phil. Mag., 15, *1883*, p. 22.
E. J. Spitta. Roy. Soc., Proc., 47, *1890*, p. 15.
H. Krüss. Z.f.I., 33, *1913*, p. 339.
C. Fabry and H. Buisson. J. de Phys., 9, *1919*, p. 371.

73. E. Goldberg. British J. of Photog., 57, *1910*, p. 648; Faraday Soc., Trans., 19, *1923*, p. 349.
F. C. Toy. Photog., J., 62, *1922*, p. 110.
P. Lob. Kinotechnik, 14, *1932*, p. 276.
These wedges are supplied by Messrs. Ilford, Ltd., Ilford.

74. British J. of Photog., 59, *1912*, p. 668 (see also F. F. Renwick, *ibid.*, p. 717).

75. F. C. Toy and J. C. Ghosh. Phil. Mag., 40, *1920*, p. 775.
Very good neutral glass may be obtained from Messrs. Chance Bros., Birmingham (W. D. Chesterman and H. G. W. Harding, J. Sci. Inst., 26, *1949*, p. 175).

76. E. S. King. Harvard Observatory, Annals, 41, *1902*, p. 237.
F. F. Renwick. Photog., J., 35, *1911*, p. 414.
G. Nidetsky. Photog. Korrespondenz, 73, *1937*, p. 141.
M. H. Sweet. Opt. Soc. Am., J., 33, *1943*, p. 194.
See also E. Spiller, Phys. Z., 35, *1934*, p. 753.
On a convenient method for producing an illumination graded according to any prescribed law, see T. Guilloz, C.R., 148, *1909*, p. 164.
See also G. Haase, Z.f.I., 52, *1932*, p. 529.

77. F. Artigas. Rev. d'Opt., 5, *1926*, p. 217.
H. Kienle and H. Siedentopf. Z. f. Phys., 58, *1929*, p. 726.

78. See, e.g., L. A. J. Quetelet, Bibl. Univ., 52, *1833*, p. 212 ; J. B. Albert
(E. W. Finck), Dingler's Polytechn. J., 100, *1846*, p. 20 and 101, *1846*, p. 342 ;
F. H. Hänlein, J.G.W., 24, *1881*, p. 659 ; M. Uibe, Leipzig Abh., 35, *1918*, p. 319 and
Z.f.I., 40, *1920*, p. 27.
The composition of a neutral inorganic solution has been given by L. C. Thomson,
Faraday Soc., Trans., 42, *1946*, p. 663.

79. M. Grabau. Opt. Soc. Am., J., 27, *1937*, p. 420.

80. H. E. Ives. El. World, 59, *1912*, p. 598.
E. F. Kingsbury. Frank. Inst., J., 181, *1916*, p. 369.
H. Krüss. Z.f.I., 37, *1917*, p. 109.
See also E. Karrer, Frank. Inst., J., 185, *1918*, p. 539.

81. H. Krüss. J.G.W., 49, *1906*, p. 109.

82. See, e.g., M. Banning, Opt. Soc. Am., J., 37, *1947*, p. 686.

83. F. Benford. Opt. Soc. Am., J., 25, *1935*, p. 136.
F. Buchmüller and H. König. Assoc. Suisse des Elect., Bull., 28, *1937*, p. 89.

84. H. P. Gage. Illum. Eng. Soc. N.Y., Trans., 11, *1916*, p. 1050.

85. A. Lehmann. Kongelige Danske Videskabernes Selskabs, Forhandlinger
Oversigt, *1909*, p. 541.

86. E.g. multiple reflection (see A. Quetelet, Ann. d. Phys., 29, *1833*, p. 187),
or oblique reflection (see R. Potter, Edin. J. of Sci., 3, *1830*, p. 278 ; Phil. Mag., 1,
1832, p. 174).

87. See, e.g., T.-S. Hawker. Electrician, 13, *1884*, p. 253 ; R. Arnoux (E. Dieu-
donné), Lum. El., 23, *1887*, p. 555 ; F. Bothe, Ann. d. Phys., 128, *1866*, p. 628 ;
H. Schickert, J.G.W., 11, *1868*, p. 522 ; S. P. Thompson, J. of Gas Lighting, 70,
1897, p. 526 ; R. H. Collins, J. of Gas Lighting, 93, *1906*, p. 162 ; J. S. Dow, Phys.
Soc., Proc., 21, *1907*, p. 36 ; G. D. Yarnold, Phil. Mag., 37, *1946*, p. 534.

88. A Crova, C.R., 99, *1884*, p. 1115.
See also A. H. Munsell, Technol. Quarterly (Mass. Inst. Technol.), 18, *1905*, p. 60 ;
H. Korte, loc. cit., note (53) *supra*, pp. 330 and 332.

89. P. Bouguer. Traité d'Optique, p. 35.
A. Blondel and A. Broca. Ecl. El., 8, *1896*, p. 52 and 10, *1897*, p. 145.

90. A. Cornu. J. de Phys., 10, *1881*, p. 189 ; C.R., 103, *1886*, p. 1227.
C. Pulfrich. Z.f.I., 45, *1925*, pp. 35, 61 and 109 (see also C. Hansen, Opt.
Soc. Am., J., 36, *1946*, p. 321).
M. Ponton (Roy. Soc. Edin., Trans., 21, *1857*, p. 363) used a variable artificial
pupil.
This method has been used extensively in stellar photometry. See note (8), p. 483.

91. H. Krüss. J. G. W., 49, *1906*, p. 137.

92. W. E. Ayrton and J. Perry. Phys. Soc., Proc., 3, *1880*, p. 184 and 5, *1882*,
p. 109.
A. Voller. Naturwiss. Verein, Hamburg, Abh., 7 (2), *1883*, p. 40.

93. F. Fuchs. Ann. d. Phys., 11, *1880*, p. 465.
O. Lummer. Phys. Z., 3, *1902*, p. 219.
L. Santon. Rev. d'Opt., 7, *1928*, p. 487.

94. C. Pulfrich. Die Naturwissenschaften, 10, *1922*, pp. 553, 569, 596, 714, 735
and 751 (see also *ibid.*, 11, *1923*, p. 461).
L. C. Martin. Optical Measuring Instruments (Blackie, *1924*), p. 235.
J. Jaumann. Z. f. Phys., 69, *1931*, p. 153.

95. S. Exner. Wien Ber. (II), 58, *1868*, p. 601.
See also H. Schober, Akad. Wiss. Wien, Anzeiger (Math.-naturwiss. Kl.), 69,
1932, p. 190.

96. C.I.E., Proc., 7, *1928*, p. 1091.
O. Reeb and H. J. Hentschel. Lichttechnik, 1, *1949*, p. 75.

97. K. Strecker. E.T.Z., 7, *1886*, p. 146.
Dutch Photometric Commission. [Bunsen] J.G.W., 37, *1894*, p. 613 ;
Z.f.I., 14, *1894*, p. 447.
F. F. Martens and W. Bechstein. [Lummer-Brodhun] J.G.W., 43, *1900*,
p. 251.

L. W. Wild. [Bunsen] Electrician, 60, *1907*, p. 122.

A. E. Kennelly and S. E. Whiting. [Lummer-Brodhun] N.E.L.A. Convention, Proc. (1), *1908*, p. 208 ; El. World., 51, *1908*, pp. 1104 and 1152.

E. J. Edwards and H. W. Harrison. [Lummer-Brodhun] Illum. Eng. Soc. N.Y., Trans., 8, *1913*, p. 633.

A. Utzinger. E.T.Z., 36, *1915*, p. 115.

F. K. Richtmyer and E. C. Crittenden. [Lummer-Brodhun] Opt. Soc. Am., J., 4, *1920*, p. 371. This paper also summarises the previous work on the subject. The name in square brackets is that of the photometer found to give the greatest precision *at colour match*.

98. F. Uppenborn-B. Monasch. *Lehrbuch d. Photometrie*, p. 212.

A. Broca. J. de Phys., 3, *1894*, p. 206.

J. S. Dow. Illum. Eng., 3, *1910*, p. 236.

L. Simek. Int. Illum. Congress, *1931*, Proc., Vol. I, p. 157.

See also the references quoted in note (30) on p. 84.

99. L. C. Martin. Roy. Soc., Proc., 104, *1923*, p. 302.

S. A. Emerson and L. C. Martin. Roy. Soc. Proc., 108, *1925*, p. 483.

See also Chapter IX, p. 304 and the references cited in note (29) on p. 84.

100. See, e.g., C. C. Paterson, El. World, 56, *1910*, p. 338.

101. L. Bell. Illum. Eng. Soc. N.Y., Trans., 6, *1911*, p. 671.

J. Blanchard. Phys. Rev., 11, *1918*, p. 81.

102. On the effect of time taken in making a setting, see P. Lasareff, Rev. d'Opt., 3, *1924*, p. 65 and *loc. cit.*, note (5) *supra*.

103. C.I.E., Proc., 8, *1931*, p. 419.

See also J. Hrdlicka, Int. Illum. Congress, *1931*, Proc., Vol. I, p. 146 ; Int. Congress on Photog., Proc., 8, *1931*, p. 135 and 9, *1935*, p. 508 ; W. F. Little, Int. Illum. Congress, *1931*, Proc., Vol. I, p. 154 ; R. Kövesligethy and P. Selényi, *ibid.*, p. 164 ; B. P. Dudding and G. T. Winch, *ibid.*, p. 170.

104. L. Piatti. N. Cimento, 8, *1931*, p. 29.

P. Fleury. Rev. d'Opt., 11, *1932*, p. 385.

105. M. Moreau-Hanot. *Photométrie des lumières brèves ou variables.* (Rev. d.Opt. Press, Paris, *1934*.)

106. C. H. Sharp. Am. I.E.E., Trans., 25, *1906*, p. 815.

J. T. Morris. Electrician, 58, *1906*, p. 318.

H. Frühling. Licht u. Lampe, 15, *1926*, p. 368.

See also E. Karrer and A. Poritsky, Frank. Inst., J., 198, *1924*, p. 93.

107. J. M. Sandford and J. M. Waldram. Illum. Eng., 28, *1935*, p. 109.

G. Blet. Mesures, 10, *1945*, p. 237.

G. Nidetsky (E.u.M., 51, *1933*, Lichttechn., p. 9) has described a photographic method similar in principle.

See also T. v. Nemes, Arch. f. Elektrot, 26, *1932*, p. 403.

108. Cambridge Inst. Co. Engineering, 111, *1921*, p. 104.

A. G. Worthing. Frank. Inst., J., 191, *1921*, p. 231.

On the visual measurement of the light from a flash, see A. Masson, C.R., 18, *1844*, p. 289 and 19, *1844*, p. 325.

See also A. P. Trotter, Illum. Eng., 11, *1918*, p. 253.

109. W. E. Meserve. Illum. Eng. Soc. N.Y., Trans., 24, *1929*, p. 671.

H. J. Reich and G. S. Marvin. Rev. Sci. Inst., 2, *1931*, p. 814.

J. A. M. van Liempt and J. A. de Vriend. Philips Techn. Rev., 1, *1936*, p. 289 ; Physica, 4, *1937*, p. 353 (see also p. 811).

J. D. Kelley. Opt. Soc. Am., J., 28, *1938*, p. 27.

B. Chance. Electronics, 13, *1940*, Feb., pp. 24 and 63.

C. Butt and R. S. Alexander. Rev. Sci. Inst., 13, *1942*, p. 151.

R. D. Rawcliffe. *Ibid.*, p. 413.

T. H. Projector and L. E. Barbrow. *Ibid.*, 16, *1945*, p. 51.

G. H. Dieke, H. Y. Loh and H. M. Crosswhite. Opt. Soc. Am., J., 36, *1946*, p. 185.

For a description of a photographic method see N. H. Brachman and C. W. Kendall, Rev. Sci. Inst., 2, *1931*, p. 111.

110. H. Beck and J. Eggert. Z. wiss. Photog., 24, *1927*, p. 367.

N. H. Brachman and C. W. Kendall. Rev. Sci. Inst., 2, *1931*, p. 111.

W. E. Forsythe and M. A. Easley. *Ibid.*, p. 638.

See also G. Nidetzky. E.u.M., 51, *1933*, Lichttechn., p. 9.

111. W. D. Wright. *Photometry and the Eye.* (Hatton, *1949*), p. 120.

112. W. E. Forsythe and M. A. Easley. Rev. Sci. Inst., 3, *1932*, p. 488.
L. Wijnberg Rev. Sci. Inst., 27, *1956*, p. 94.
On definitions of the various quantities needed for describing the performance of a flash source, see J. A. M. van Liempt and J. A. de Vriend, Physica, 7, *1940*, p. 255.

113. J. S. Anderson. Opt. Soc., Trans., 32, *1931*, p. 197.
L. R. Koller. Rev. Sci. Inst., 2, *1931*, p. 551.
M. Kornetzki, V. Fomin and R. Steinitz. Z. f. techn. Phys., 14, *1933*, p. 274.
H. E. Edgerton. Electronics, 21, *1948*, June, p. 78.
T. B. Davenport. J. Sci. Inst., 26, *1949*, p. 305.
W. Hartnagel. Z. f. angewandte Phys., 6, *1954*, p. 310.
Y. M. Kutev. Elektrichestvo, *1955*, No. 1, p. 66 (In Russian).

CHAPTER VIII

LIGHT DISTRIBUTION AND TOTAL FLUX MEASUREMENT

Since no source of light used in practice has the same luminous intensity in all directions, it follows that a measurement of this quantity in a single direction gives, by itself, but little information as to the performance of a source, i.e. the total amount of luminous flux which it emits or the manner in which that flux is distributed. The total flux given by a source is most conveniently measured by means of some form of integrating photometer, but information as to flux distribution can only be obtained by means of a large number of measurements of luminous intensity made in different directions about the source. It is true that for sources in which the design of the light-giving elements is more or less invariable it may sometimes be sufficient for practical purposes to make a measurement of the luminous intensity in a single specified direction, and to infer from this the intensity in other directions on the assumption that the distribution remains nearly the same from specimen to specimen. This, however, only simplifies the problem in so far that the determination of light distribution need only be made for a *type* instead of for each individual source. The necessity for a method of measuring the distribution still remains, and the first part of this chapter will, therefore, be devoted to a description of the various methods most commonly employed for the purpose in modern photometric practice. The results obtained are usually exhibited in the form of a polar curve (see p. 124) when a planar distribution is determined, and a solid of light distribution [1] or, more usually, an isocandela diagram (see p. 126) in the case of a determination of space distribution.

Horizontal Luminous Intensity Distribution—The determination of the light distribution curve of a source in a horizontal plane can be carried out very simply by making a sufficient number of measurements of luminous intensity, as described in Chapter VII. If the source is fairly uniform (e.g. an electric lamp of any ordinary type, an incandescent gas mantle, etc.), thirty-six measurements at intervals of 10° will be sufficient for all ordinary purposes. For sources such as a flat flame burner, measurements are required at more frequent intervals over the regions of maximum variation (end-on to the flame). The angle scale on the table of the photometer carriage (Fig. 109, p. 193) is used for setting the source in the required positions.

Distribution of Luminous Intensity in a Vertical Plane—The determination of the light distribution curve of a source in a vertical plane is less simple. If the source can be tilted without altering its luminous intensity, it may be mounted with its axis horizontal and then the measurements can be made in a horizontal plane, exactly as described in the last section [2].

This method, however, clearly cannot be used in the case of flame sources, and indeed most sources of light in common use, other than *vacuum* filament lamps [3], show a change of luminous intensity when tilted out of their normal burning position. For such sources, therefore, some method of measurement must be employed which does not involve tilting the source. The simplest, perhaps, is that in which the source is raised or lowered bodily on a bracket attached to a vertical pillar, as shown in Fig. 139. The photometer

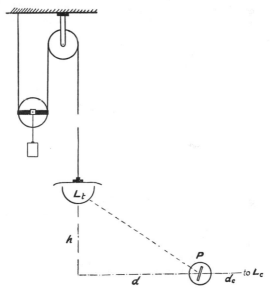

FIG. 139. The " Radial Photometer."

screen P is then tilted so as to bisect the angle between the lines joining the photometer to the two sources being compared, L_t and L_c, the plane of P being perpendicular to the plane L_tPL_c. Since the light is incident at the same angle on both sides of P, $I_t/(h^2 + d^2) = I_c/d_c^2$. Different modifications of this method have been used by various workers [4]. It has the great disadvantage that the light is not incident normally on the photometer screen, so that a very slight inaccuracy in the setting of P produces large errors in the measured luminous intensity (see p. 196).

Another method is that involving the use of a movable mirror system. When only one mirror is used, it may be arranged to occupy the position of P in Fig. 139, and to move about a horizontal axis so as to deflect the light from the source along the axis of the photometer bench which is now to the left of P instead of to the right [5].

The reflection factor of the mirror cannot, however, be assumed to be constant at all angles of incidence [6], and a better scheme is that shown diagrammatically in Fig. 140 [7]. The source to be measured remains fixed at L_t, while the mirror M is carried on a rigid arm by means of which it can be moved round a horizontal axis passing through the centre of L_t. This axis coincides with the axis of the photometer bench, passing through the

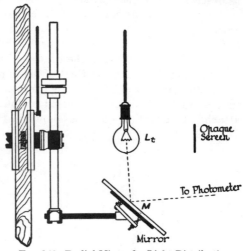

FIG. 140. Radial Mirror for Light Distribution Measurement.

photometer and the comparison lamp. The inclination of M to this axis is capable of adjustment so that the light from L_t can be directed to the photometer when the latter is at different distances. Very frequently two mirrors are used, one on each side of L_t [8].

For sources of small dimensions apparatus which can be accommodated on a portable framework, or even on a photometer bench, has been designed [9].

The chief disadvantage of this method is the fact that the light from M reaches the photometer obliquely, so that as M is moved

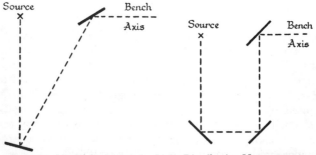

FIG. 141. Mirror Apparatus for Light Distribution Measurement.

round the error mentioned in Chapter VII (p. 209) is introduced. This defect may be avoided by causing the light to suffer two [10] or three [11] reflections before reaching the photometer (see Fig. 141), but since each mirror must be large enough to ensure that the whole of the light source is visible from the position of the photometer head, apparatus of this kind becomes very heavy and cumbersome in the case of large sources.

The most satisfactory device is that in which the source and mirror of Fig. 140 are interchanged, so that the source moves in a vertical circle around the axis of the photometer bench, while the mirror, fixed at an angle of 45° to this axis, rotates so as always to face the source [12]. The light is then incident on the mirror at a constant angle of 45°, and is reflected along the axis of the bench. The apparatus may take the form shown in Fig. 142, which gives a

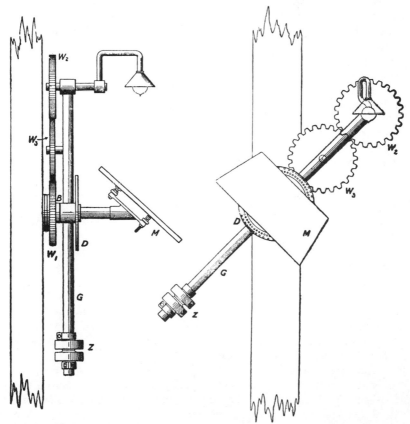

FIG. 142. Mirror Apparatus for Light Distribution Measurement.

view from the position of the photometer. Fixed to a strong upright is a toothed wheel W_1, and one race of a ball and roller bearing B of $3\frac{1}{2}$ inches diameter. The other race of this bearing carries a brass disc D of 14 inches diameter, to which is rigidly attached the steel tube G and a fitting for the mirror M. At one end of G is a collar for the axle of a second toothed wheel W_2, of the same size as W_1 and in gear with it by means of an idler wheel W_3 (or a chain may be used instead). The forward part of this axle carries a swan-neck bracket, on which is supported the light source [13]. The counterweight Z can be adjusted on G so that the whole system ZGW_2 can be moved about B with very little effort. It can be clamped at any angle which is an even multiple of 5° by means of a pin engaging in one of the outer ring of holes seen near the outer edge of the brass disc D. The pin is carried on a long rigid arm (not shown) which swings from a fixed point above the apparatus. A second row of holes in D enables G to be set at either of the Russell angles (see p. 128). The angle which M makes with the axis of W_1 (which is also the axis of the photometer bench) is normally 45°, but it is capable of adjustment to allow for cases in which the source projects unusually far in front of G. The dimensions of M must be sufficiently great to accommodate the largest source for which the apparatus is likely to be required, and it is clear that when measurements are being made no part of the effective light source, including any reflector or other surface contributing to the total light, may be cut off by the mirror. This is tested by viewing the image of the source in the mirror from the position of the comparison surface in the photometer. For sources such as street lighting fittings or large semi-direct bowls with reflectors, a mirror measuring 36 × 24 inches is required.

Where sources of high luminous intensity have to be measured it is necessary to place the photometer at a considerable distance from the source, and on account of the large range of intensities met with in practice it is convenient to have, instead of a very long photometer bench, a short bench of about 2,500 mm. in length mounted on a table provided with small wheels which move along a track in the floor. A pointer on the table leg, and a series of marks at 1 metre intervals on the floor, enable the bench to be fixed at any convenient position for the particular magnitude of luminous intensity being measured at any time.

The range of luminous intensity covered by a single lamp in different directions is often considerable, and in order to avoid the necessity for moving the table too frequently it is often convenient to clamp the photometer at the zero of the bench and move the comparison lamp independently. If the fixed distance of this lamp, found by standardisation in the usual manner (see p. 212), is d_C, while the distance of the photometer from the light source *via* the mirror is d_T, then the luminous intensity corresponding to a position x of the comparison lamp is $(d_T{}^2/\rho)(d_C/x)^2 \times 10^{-5}$, where ρ is the reflection factor of M [14]. ρ may be determined most conveniently either by placing G in the horizontal position and using a lamp of which the horizontal luminous intensity in the direction facing the mirror is known, or by making a measurement of the horizontal luminous intensity of the source in the ordinary way, the azimuth being the same as that facing M when the distribution was determined. In either case ρ is equal to the ratio

(lum. int. measured *via* M)/(true lum. int.).

The constant distance d_T is measured by means of a steel tape or otherwise, as follows : one observer places his eye in the position of the photometer head and directs a second observer to make a mark on the mirror M in the position of the photometric centre of the lamp image which he sees. The distances from this mark to the centre of the photometer and to the lamp centre are added together, and this sum, increased by 1·5 times the thickness of the mirror glass, is the value of d_T required [15]. For a determination of the light distribution in a vertical plane, measurements are made with the mirror M at angular intervals of 10° for most sources of fairly uniform distribution. In some sources large changes of luminous intensity may take place near the axis (0° or 180°) or in the horizontal direction. It is then necessary to reduce the intervals between the readings in these regions.

While measurements are being made the photometer is screened from the direct light from the source by means of a large black screen in the form of an annulus, the centre aperture in which is sufficiently large to avoid any interference with the light reaching the photometer from M. All metal and wooden parts in the apparatus itself must either be painted a dull black or covered with black cloth while measurements are in progress.

It will have been noticed that one set of measurements only gives the distribution curve in a single vertical plane. Very often this is sufficient to give the information required, since for many sources the distribution in every vertical plane may be assumed to be the same to the order of accuracy desired. A really accurate knowledge of the light distribution in all directions in space can, however, only be obtained by making a series of sets of measurements in planes at, say, every 10° of azimuth. This is the most fundamental method of finding the total luminous flux for a source [16].

For approximate work a portable illumination photometer with detached test plate may be used (see Chapter XII). The plate is mounted on a light arm so that it can be moved in a circular track having the source as centre. The illumination of the test plate at any position clearly gives the corresponding luminous intensity of the source [17]. When this method is used it is necessary to have the arm which carries the test plate of such a length that the inverse square law may safely be applied to calculate the luminous intensity of the source from the illumination of the plate (see p. 142) [18].

Photo-electric Measurement of Light Distribution—The simplest method for determining the light distribution curve of a source by means of a photocell is exactly similar to that described in the last paragraph, the cell, usually of the photo-voltaic type, being substituted for the test plate of the illumination photometer [19]. This method is naturally subject to the same limitation as regards the relation between the length of the arm and the dimensions of the source and where, on this account, an inconveniently long arm would be required, mirror apparatus such as that illustrated in Figs. 140 to 142 is used and a photocell is substituted for the photometer head [20]. In this case either a photo-emissive or a photo-voltaic cell may be used.

Since, in general, the spectral distribution of the light from the source is the same in all directions, the form of the light distribution curve can be determined without using any colour correction filter with the photocell. The scale of the curve can be found by making a separate measurement of luminous intensity in one or two convenient directions, either visually or with a colour corrected cell. A source which cannot be tilted from its normal working position, for example, may be measured visually in the horizontal direction, and the values of luminous intensity in all other directions, relative to the value in this direction, can be found with an uncorrected cell [21].

By means of photo-electric apparatus used in combination with a suitable form of recording device, the curve of light distribution from a source may be obtained as a continuous trace instead of point by point. The photo-current, generally after amplification, passes through a galvanometer and the resulting deflection is recorded as a trace on a sheet of sensitized paper [22]. Fig. 143 illustrates the principle. G is the galvanometer and S the sensitized paper, mounted so that it can be rotated in its own plane inside a light-tight box. The axis of rotation A coincides with the direction of zero deflection so that, if the rotation of S is synchronised with the rotation of the photocell or mirror apparatus about the light source, the beam from the galvanometer traces on S the polar curve of the source. In the apparatus shown in the figure the same axle carries both S and the

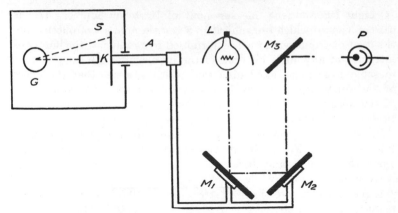

Fig. 143. Photo-electric Apparatus for Tracing Polar Curves of Light Distribution.

mirror system $M_1M_2M_3$. S rotates in its own plane in a light-tight box as the mirrors move round the source and reflect the light from L so that it reaches the photocell P at normal incidence. The photocurrent from P, amplified if necessary, passes through G and deflects the spot of light reaching S so that its distance from K is proportional to the luminous intensity of L in the direction LM_1. An alternative arrangement is to cause the beam of light from G to fall on a sheet of sensitive paper mounted on a drum similar to that used in many recording instruments. This drum is rotated in synchronism with the mirror system and the trace then gives the curve of light distribution in rectangular co-ordinates.

It will be seen that in either case the curve recorded on the sensitive paper only represents the curve of light distribution directly so long as the response of the cell, with its amplifier if one is used, is linear over the range covered. Otherwise it is necessary to calibrate the apparatus by placing a source of convenient luminous intensity at L and, with the mirrors fixed, noting the positions of the galvanometer spot when a graded series of neutral filters (or sector discs) of known transmission factors are placed one after the other in front of the photocell [23]. In all cases it is necessary to establish the scale of the curve by placing a sub-standard or a working standard at L and fixing the mirrors so that LM_1 is the direction for which the luminous intensity is known.

In the case of small sources it is possible to use a mirror system which is sufficiently light to be rotated at a fairly high speed (e.g. about 1000 r.p.m.) about L. The photo-current may then be used to give in a cathode ray oscillograph a trace which represents the light distribution curve of the source [24].

Light Distribution: Measurement of Unsteady Sources—In the case of sources which are subject to a certain amount of fluctuation, the light distribution curve is determined by measuring the luminous intensity at any angle in terms of the intensity at the same instant in some convenient fixed direction. This assumes that the effect of the fluctuations on the luminous intensity is the same in all directions and, clearly, it is only to the extent to which this assumption can be made that the curve has any meaning.

One form of apparatus for measurement of this kind is shown in Fig. 144, where M_1 and M_2 are two exactly similar mirrors, movable along the arms A and B.

A remains horizontal, while B moves round in a vertical plane. A link motion maintains the photometer screen P in the plane bisecting the angle between A and B. C is a graduated circle, behind which is placed the source of light at a distance which

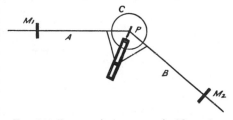

Fig. 144. Rousseau's Apparatus for Measuring Unsteady Sources.

is small compared with M_1P and M_2P. Photometric balance is obtained with M_2 at any angle, by moving M_2 along B. Thus $I_\theta/(M_2P)^2 = I_H(M_1P)^2$ where I_θ is the luminous intensity of the source in the direction PM_2 and I_H is the horizontal luminous intensity at the same instant [25].

An alternative arrangement is that shown diagrammatically in Fig. 145 [26]. The light from L in the direction θ reaches the photometer P by way of the pair of mirrors M_1 and M_2, which can be moved round the axis LP, and the stationary mirror M_3. The light from L in the horizontal direction reaches P by way of M_4, M_5 and M_6. The mirrors are so arranged that the length of path traversed by the light is the same in both cases. The photometric balance may be obtained by means of a sector disc or variable absorbing filter placed in the path of one beam, or comparison may be made with a polarisation photometer, if the polarisation due to the reflections in the mirrors is destroyed. I_θ/I_H may thus be obtained.

Measurement of Axial Luminous Intensity and Mean Luminous Intensity—Measurements of luminous intensity have sometimes to be made in specified directions other than the horizontal and if the source is one which must be operated in its normal burning position, it is usually necessary to employ some form of mirror apparatus. Any of the apparatus described above as suitable for finding light distribution curves can be used, but for measuring luminous intensity in the direction of the downward vertical, the " axial

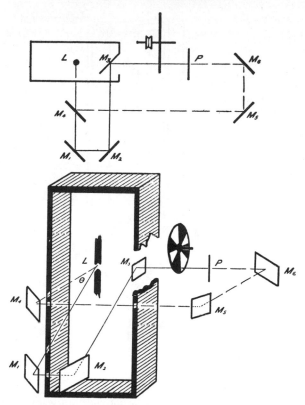

FIG. 145. Light Distribution Measurements on Unsteady Sources
(Fleming's Apparatus).

luminous intensity ", the fitting shown in Fig. 146 is convenient.
The mirror M rotates about a line passing through its silvered surface, and the scales A and B have their zeros on this line so that by
sighting the light-centre of the lamps between the scales its exact
distance from the mirror can be found.

The mean horizontal luminous intensity of a source can be
obtained from the curve of light distribution in the horizontal
plane, determined as described earlier in this chapter, but in the case
of a source that can be spun on its axis, such as a filament vacuum
lamp, it can be found more simply from a single measurement made
with the lamp rotating about its axis sufficiently fast to avoid flicker
in the photometer head [27].   A speed of about 120 to 180 r.p.m. is
usually sufficient [28].

The lamp may be rotated about a vertical axis [29] or a horizontal
axis [30]. The latter arrangement has the advantage that the appara-

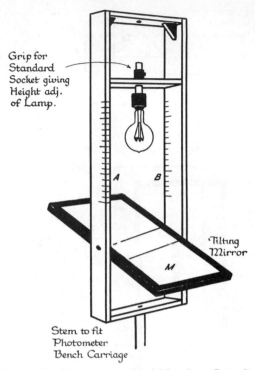

Grip for
Standard
Socket giving
Height adj.
of Lamp.

A B

Tilting
Mirror

M

Stem to fit
Photometer
Bench Carriage

FIG. 146. The Measurement of Axial Luminous Intensity.

tus can be designed so that it can be moved bodily about a vertical
axis passing through the light-centre of the lamp and in this way
not only the mean horizontal luminous intensity, but also the average
value of the luminous intensity at any angle from the lamp axis
can be measured. An essential feature of the apparatus is the
provision of two pairs of mercury contacts, one to carry the current
for the lamp and the second to enable the voltage across the lamp
contacts to be measured directly. Fig. 147 shows the general
design of a rotator of this kind. A is a solid metal arm which can
be moved by hand about the vertical axis of the heavy supporting
pillar P. It carries the motor M which, through a shaft with a pulley
and belt system at each end, drives the hollow shaft R carrying the
lamp L. R rotates within a support S which is also carried on the
arm A and can be moved in guides towards or away from P so as to
bring the light-centre of L over the vertical axis of rotation of A.
The pulley W is not fixed to the shaft but slides along it in grooves
so that it can be moved with S. The rear part of R is fitted with
four insulated copper discs D which, by means of four leads, are

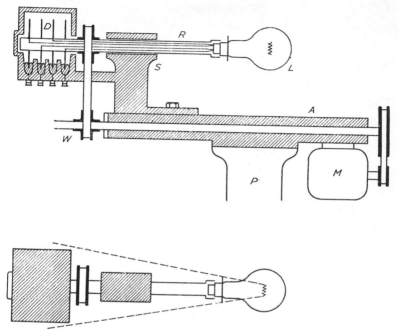

FIG. 147. Rotator for Measuring Mean Luminous Intensity at any Angle
with the Lamp Axis.

connected in pairs, as shown, to the two plungers making contact
with the lamp L. The discs dip into four insulated mercury troughs,
two of which are connected to the supply and two to the leads
used for measuring the voltage across the lamp. It is found that
if the mercury troughs and copper discs are kept scrupulously clean,
there is generally no difficulty in maintaining the current through
the lamp perfectly steady, always a somewhat difficult problem
when measurements have to be made through moving contacts.
If the efficiency of the contacts is suspected, the values of current
and potential obtained with the lamp in the rotator are compared
with those found when the lamp is in a standard socket (see p. 491).
Differences between the values obtained with the lamp rotating
and the lamp stationary are sometimes found to be due to internal
construction of the lamp, such as a very slight looseness of contact
at the pinch where the filament is joined to the leading-in wire.

The mirror apparatus shown in Fig. 148 has been designed so
that the lamp can be rotated about a vertical axis, the three-mirror
system, carried on a light framework, being movable about the
horizontal axis [31].

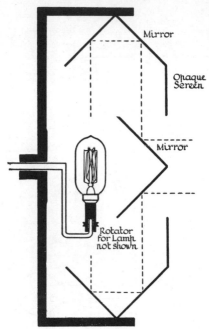

Fig. 148. The Measurement of Mean Luminous Intensity.

For measuring the mean horizontal luminous intensity only, rotation of the source can be avoided by using a pair of mirrors, arranged as shown in Fig. 149, and rotated about the lamp axis [32].

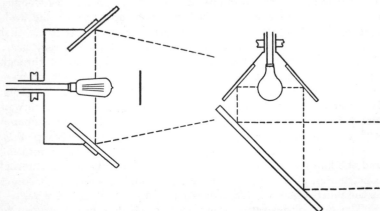

Fig. 149. The Measurement of Mean Horizontal Luminous Intensity.

This method avoids any difficulties due to moving contacts or to the distortion of the filament by centrifugal force [33] but in the arrangement shown on the left the lamp is not measured in its normal burning position.

Total Flux Measurement—It has now become customary to rate light sources in terms of their total output of luminous flux [34]. The fundamental method of determining this quantity for any given source of light is to measure its luminous intensity in a large number of directions uniformly distributed in space about the source [35]. Various methods were devised for obtaining the same result from a limited number of measurements, generally by the use of mirrors [36], but these have now all given place to the integrating sphere which enables the total flux given by a source to be measured by comparison with a sub-standard of flux just as simply as the luminous intensity of a lamp is found by comparing it with a sub-standard of known luminous intensity.

Sub-standards of luminous flux are derived from sub-standards of luminous intensity by means of lamps which can be measured in a rotator of the type described above and illustrated in Fig. 147 [37]. Such lamps, usually of the tungsten filament vacuum type, after a period of ageing to ensure that they are constant and otherwise suitable, are measured on the rotator with the arm A at a number of different positions, e.g. at every 5 degrees, from the axis of the lamp to the direction at which a plate, rigidly attached to the lamp cap, reduces the luminous intensity to zero. This plate should be large enough to ensure that no direct light from the lamp to the photometer is intercepted by the rotator (see the plan in Fig. 147). From the mean polar curve thus obtained the total flux from the lamp is calculated by means of the Rousseau construction (see p. 126) or otherwise, and the lamp, with its plate, then becomes a sub-standard of luminous flux.

The Integrating Sphere—The principle of the integrating sphere, now almost universally used for the measurement of luminous flux, depends on a principle first enunciated by Sumpner in 1892 in connection with work on the reflection factors of various surfaces [38]. He showed that if a source of light were placed inside a hollow sphere coated internally with a perfectly diffusing material, the luminance of any part of the surface due to light reflected from the remainder of the sphere was the same, and was proprotional to the total flux emitted by the source. It has been mentioned already (see p. 141) that the flux received per unit area by one part of the surface of a sphere from a given area of any other part which has a given luminance is the same, whatever be the relative positions of the two parts on the sphere. Thus the flux reflected from each part of the spherical surface is equally distributed over the other parts, and, conversely, the flux received at each part of the surface by reflection from the remainder is everywhere the same and bears a fixed relation to the total flux received by the whole sphere. The theoretical expression for this relation in terms of the reflection factor of the spherical surface is very easily obtained ; for if the luminance of any portion of the sphere surface is B, and the reflection factor, assumed uniform over the whole surface, is ρ, the flux received at any element of area δs of the sphere due to a first reflection from the remainder of the sphere is equal to $(\delta s/4r^2)\int B\,ds$, the summation being made over the whole surface of the sphere. Now the luminance B of any area is equal to the flux reaching that area multiplied by ρ and divided by π, so that, if the total flux given by the source is F, $\int B\,ds=\rho F/\pi$, and hence the flux received by $\delta s=\rho F\,\delta s/4\pi r^2$ or $\rho F/4\pi r^2$ per unit area. Thus the luminance of any part of the surface due to the direct light and light which has suffered one reflection is $B+\rho^2 F/4\pi^2 r^2$. The flux reaching δs by the first and second reflections is, therefore, $(\delta s/4r^2)\int(B+\rho^2 F/4\pi^2 r^2)\,ds$, which is equal to $\rho\,\delta s F/4\pi r^2+\rho^2\,\delta s F/4\pi r^2$, so that the flux received per unit area by one and two reflections is $(F/4\pi r^2)(\rho+\rho^2)$. Similarly, it may be shown that the flux received per unit area due to any number of reflections is $(F/4\pi r^2)\{\rho+\rho^2+\rho^3+\ldots$ to infinity$\}$, so that the total flux received per unit area by reflection is $F\rho/4\pi r^2(1-\rho)$, i.e. the illumination of the sphere by reflected light is equal to the average illumination by direct light multiplied by the factor $\rho/(1-\rho)$, which for $\rho=0.8$ becomes equal to 4 [39].

It will be seen that this expression for the reflected flux is independent of the position of the source and of the distribution of the light from it, and this fact is the theoretical basis underlying the use of the integrating sphere, for it follows that a measurement of the illumination *due to reflected light* of any part of the sphere wall gives at once a measure of the total flux from the source, irrespective of its distribution. The proposal to use the sphere in this way as a photometer was first made by Ulbricht in 1900 [40], and much work, both practical and theoretical, has been devoted to the problem since that time [41].

Practical considerations make it impossible to use the expression found above for the relation between the total flux emitted by a source inside a sphere and the illumination of the sphere surface due to reflected light. In the first place, it is supposed not only that ρ is constant for the whole surface of the sphere, but also that this surface is perfectly diffusing. Further, it is assumed in the above theoretical treatment that the sphere is perfectly empty, so that the reflected flux is entirely undisturbed by the presence of objects within the sphere. Clearly, the very presence of a light source of finite dimensions is a violation of this condition, while the necessary provision of an aperture or window in the sphere wall for the purposes of measuring the illumination due to reflected flux, and the introduction of a disc to prevent direct light from the source from being included in this measurement, are further departures from the ideal conditions.

All these elements of uncertainty naturally put absolute measurements of total flux by means of the sphere quite out of the question, but they do not prevent its use for finding the relative values of the flux given by two sources if suitable precautions are taken. This, after all, is the sole function of any photometric apparatus used for making measurements by the substitution method, and it does not, therefore, imply any important restriction of the usefulness of the integrating sphere. The precautions to be taken arise from the necessity for ensuring that the departures from theory above mentioned affect equally the measurements on the two sources to be compared. These precautions will be dealt with in some detail in later sections of this chapter, but first it will be convenient to give a brief account of the two methods of using the sphere most commonly adopted.

The Substitution Method—In the simpler of these, which may be called the true " substitution " method, a sub-standard lamp of known flux is placed in the sphere, and the reflected flux incident at some part of the sphere wall is measured. This measurement may be made with some form of photometer arranged to receive light

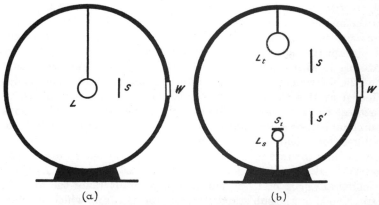

Fig. 150. Methods of using the Sphere.
(a) The Substitution Method.   (b) The Simultaneous Method.

only from a comparatively small area of the sphere. Alternatively a small translucent diffusing window may be provided at a convenient position in the sphere wall (W in Fig. 150). The luminance of the outer surface of this window is assumed to be proportional to the reflected flux received by its inner surface and is measured as described in a later section. In either case the measurement is repeated with the test lamp substituted for the sub-standard and the measurements are repeated. If B_S and B_T are respectively the values of luminance found in the two cases, the flux from the test lamp $F_T = F_S(B_T/B_S)$.

As will be shown later, the best position for the source in making measurements by this method is the centre of the sphere (see p. 269). Direct light from the source must be prevented from reaching the window (or the portion of sphere viewed by the photometer), since only the reflected flux is to be measured. Between the source L and the window W, therefore, is placed a screen S in the form of a disc, just large enough to prevent the window from receiving any but reflected light. The best position for the screen will be discussed later (see p. 266).

The Simultaneous Method—In the other method of using the sphere, termed for convenience the " simultaneous " method, both sub-standard and test lamp are in the sphere throughout the measurements, as shown diagrammatically in Fig. 150 (b). B_S is first measured with only L_S alight ; L_S is then extinguished and B_T is measured with only L_T alight. As before, $F_T = F_S(B_T/B_S)$. This method is generally used in the measurement of large fittings or of sources which necessitate the presence of auxiliary apparatus of considerable bulk in the sphere. The disturbance of the reflected flux distribution by this apparatus is then approximately the same for the measurements of both B_S and B_T. The extent of this disturbance may be reduced considerably by whitening the external surface of the apparatus, either by painting it with a white paint or by covering it with a white material. Care must be taken to ensure that the distribution of the flux directly emitted by the lamp is not affected by this whitening, which should, therefore, be confined to surfaces which receive no direct light from the actual luminous source under normal working conditions. Two screens, S and S', are required for shielding the window from direct illumination by L_T and L_S, and a third screen S_1 is needed between the sub-standard and the test lamp in order to prevent direct light from L_T from reaching any part of L_S.* This screen generally takes the form of a small hood on the sub-standard lamp, the flux from which is determined with the cap in position.

It is desirable that the positions of the two lamps L_T and L_S should be as nearly as possible symmetrical with respect to the

---

* This precaution is necessary, for otherwise the opaque parts of L_T would absorb *direct* light from L_S as well as light reflected by the walls of the sphere. It is this latter absorption only that takes place when L_T is alight.

sphere window, but they should not be too close together, or the size of S_1 will be such as to produce an excessive distortion of the light distribution from the sub-standard. Further, as will be shown later, the lamps should not be too close to the surface of the sphere (see p. 269), so that the best compromise is, generally, to place each about midway between the centre of the sphere and its surface.

An alternative method, involving two measurements with the sub-standard and two with the test lamp in the sphere, has been devised for the measurement of fittings which are so large that the disturbance of the reflected flux distribution is considerable. This method will be described in a later section (see p. 269).

Sphere Details—From the above general description of the theory and practical application of the sphere it will be clear that in the design and use of any particular instrument of this nature very careful consideration must be given to (a) the nature and size of the window, if one is used, (b) the size and position of the screen or screens, (c) the effect of objects within the sphere (including the source itself) and their position, and (d) the nature of the paint used for coating the interior surface. These details will, therefore, be considered one by one, and the application of the conclusions arrived at will then be shown by reference to spheres used in current photometric practice.

The Sphere Window—When the surface of the sphere is viewed directly the photometer may be arranged as shown in Fig. 151 (a). L-B is a Lummer-Brodhun contrast cube, viewed through the eyepiece E, and D is a diffusing surface illuminated by a comparison lamp mounted on a photometer bench [42]. The size of the field of view must be small in order to restrict the area of sphere included, for this has to be entirely screened from direct light and the screen should be as small as possible. The Maxwellian view is therefore frequently used (see p. 152).

When a window is used it should be viewed normally and the arrangement may be of the kind shown in Fig 151 (b). The ordinary Lummer-Brodhun head may be adapted by inserting a thin sheet of silvered glass as shown in Fig. 151 (c). Alternatively, if the luminance of the window is sufficiently high, it may be regarded as a light source and its luminous intensity measured by means of a bench, photometer head and comparison lamp as described in the last chapter (pp. 210-214). Generally, however, this is not possible [43] but the photometer head is fixed rigidly at a short distance from the window and the photometric balance is obtained by moving the comparison lamp. A distance of from 10 to 30 cm. is often convenient, although this naturally depends on the luminance and size of the window and on the illumination desired at the photometer

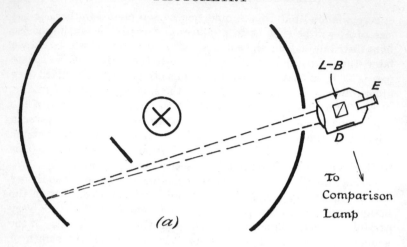

(a)

L-B

E

D

To
Comparison
Lamp

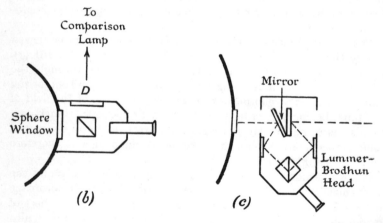

To
Comparison
Lamp

D

Sphere
Window

(b)

Mirror

Lummer-
Brodhun
Head

(c)

Fig. 151. Forms of Photometer Head for use with the Integrating Sphere.

screen. Departures from the inverse square law due to the size of the window are quite immaterial so long as the distance from window to photometer head remains unaltered between the measurement of the sub-standard and the test lamp.

Whichever method is employed for measuring the luminance of the sphere window, it is convenient to have an iris diaphragm close to the outer surface, so that the effective area may be reduced when sources of high luminous intensity are being measured. When the

luminous intensity of the window is measured directly, it is necessary
to keep the aperture of the diaphragm constant between the test
lamp measurement and the standardisation. If the photometer
head is not fixed in position, it must be remembered
that the distance to be used for calculation by the
inverse square law is that between the photometer
head and the diaphragm (see p. 151) [44]. It is clear
that a diaphragm cannot be employed in this way
when the window forms one of the comparison surfaces in the photometer. In this case it is often
found convenient to use two widely separated
diffusers with an iris close to that one which forms
part of the sphere surface (see Fig. 152). The second
diffuser, W_2, then forms the comparison surface. A
more satisfactory arrangement is that in which W_2
is a window in a small auxiliary white sphere with
an opening in the plane of D. The luminance of W_2 is then approximately proportional to the flux admitted into this sphere, i.e. to the
area of the opening in D.

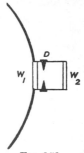

Fig. 152.
The Double Win-
dow for a Sphere.

In all cases it is desirable that the window should be readily
removable from the sphere so that it can be cleaned effectively, and
so that the sphere wall can be repainted without damage to the
window surface. Some form of shallow cylindrical framework is
generally used to carry the window. This fits into a circular aperture
in the sphere wall, and a register is provided to ensure that, when the
window is replaced, its surface is exactly flush with the inner surface
of the sphere. The inside of the cylinder should be painted a matt
black or covered with black velvet to avoid reflection of light from
the window towards the photometer.

The choice of a suitable material for the window presents some
difficulty. Since the function of the window is to enable the total
flux received by its inner surface to be deduced from a measurement
of the luminance of its outer face, it is clearly necessary that these
two quantities should bear a constant ratio to each other, no matter
what the angle of incidence of the flux at the inner surface. The
window must therefore give as close an approximation as possible
to perfectly diffuse transmission, though since it is generally viewed
in a constant direction it is more important that the luminance in a
fixed direction should be independent of the direction of the incident
flux than that it should be the same at all angles of view. This
condition is very difficult to satisfy without reducing the transmission factor to an inconveniently small figure. Opal glass depolished
on the inner surface is often used, while two pieces of glass ground
on their adjacent surfaces and on the surface forming the inner face

of the window have also been employed. In any case the inner surface of the window should be matt, and it should be absolutely flush with the inner surface of the sphere, otherwise part of the incident flux will fail to reach the window (see Fig. 153, (*a*) and (*b*)).

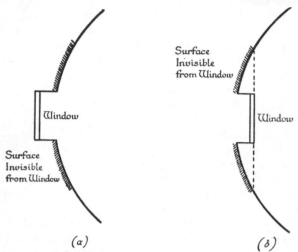

Fig. 153. The Effect of Displacement of the Sphere Window.

The edges of the glass or other translucent material forming the window should be painted white so that as little light as possible is lost by diffusion from them.

The material used should be one that can readily be cleaned. Further, it must not alter the colour of the light transmitted through it, and it must therefore be as non-selective as possible. Opal glass usually shows a selective absorption at the blue end of the spectrum. If this material is used, it follows that the thickness should be the minimum consistent with adequate diffusion of the transmitted light. It has been found that a thickness of less than 1 mm. is generally sufficient, or a flashed opal may be used. If ground glass is employed, the kind of glass selected should be as colourless as possible. A slight tinge of green may be corrected by placing an equal thickness of clear glass of the same kind on the comparison lamp side of the photometer. In any case this artifice may be employed for the purpose of avoiding the introduction of a colour difference in the photometer head due to slightly selective transmission of the window.

The Screen—It has already been pointed out (see p. 260) that one or more screens have to be placed in the sphere in order to shield the window (or area whose luminance is to be measured) from direct

illumination by the source. The size and position of the screens
naturally affect the distribution of the flux within the sphere, and
therefore exert a noticeable effect on the performance of the sphere
as an integrator. It will be clear from Fig. 154 that the first reflected

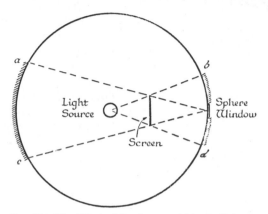

FIG. 154. The Effect of the Screen within the Sphere.

light cannot reach the window from the zones ac and bd ; in the
latter case because no direct light reaches this part of the sphere,
in the former because the screen shields this portion of the sphere
wall from the window. The influence of this on the window illumination can readily be calculated as follows [45] :

The average illumination of the sphere wall by both direct and
reflected light $E = E_d/(1-\rho)$, where E_d is the average value of the
direct component. Hence $E = E_d + \rho E$, which shows that the reflected
component is ρE. By multiplying both sides of this equation by ρ
the value of this component is found to be $\rho E_d + \rho^2 E$, so that this
expression represents the theoretical illumination of the window.
If δ represents the fraction of the total flux from the source which
falls upon the screened areas, the actual illumination of the window
is $E' = (1-\delta)\rho E_d + \rho^2 E$, if the absorption by the screens of the flux
in the second and subsequent reflections may be neglected. It
follows that the departure from the theoretical value is

$$E'/\rho E = (1-\delta)(1-\rho) + \rho, \quad \text{or} \quad E' = \rho E \{1 - \delta(1-\rho)\}.$$

If E_s and E_s' are the theoretical and actual values of window illumination in the case of a sub-standard lamp for which the screened
flux is δ_s, $E_s' = \rho E_s \{1 - \delta_s(1-\rho)\}$. Thus the error introduced into a
measurement by comparison with a sub-standard is

$$(E'/E_s')(E_s/E) - 1 = (\delta_s - \delta)(1-\rho) \text{ approx.}$$

This is zero when $\delta = \delta_s$. If the substitution method is used the screened areas are equal for both lamps, a, say, and δ and δ_s are then respectively equal to $a\theta$ and $a\theta_s$, where θ represents the ratio of the average illumination over the screened area to the average illumination over the whole sphere. It should be noticed that the error diminishes as ρ increases (as might be expected *a priori*), so that the paint used for the sphere should have a high reflection factor (see p. 270).

So long as the test lamp and the sub-standard give approximately the same distribution of light $(\delta - \delta_s)$ is very small. For all other cases, however, it is clearly desirable to reduce both δ and δ_s as much as possible. This can only be done by reducing the size of the screen and adjusting its position in relation to the lamp and the window. The minimum size of screen which can be used is fixed by the sizes of the source and of the window. The latter must be completely shielded from all direct light, not only from the filament, fluorescent tube, etc., but also from every part of the lamp structure which is to be regarded as contributing anything towards the flux emitted in the direction of the window. For example, in the case of an incandescent lamp with a shallow translucent shade over it, not only the lamp filament, but also the whole of the shade, should be invisible from any point of the sphere window.

When the light source is at the centre of the sphere, it has been calculated [46] that the minimum value of the screened area is obtained if the screen is placed at a distance from the lamp of from 0·3 to 0·4 times the sphere radius [47]. If the screen diameter does not exceed one-sixth of the sphere diameter $a = 0·12$, and the error is therefore equal to $0·024(\theta - \theta_s)$, if $\rho = 0·8$. Hence if an accuracy of 1 per cent is aimed at, $(\theta - \theta_s)$ must not exceed 0·4, and as the value of θ_s is generally known, the limits between which θ must lie are readily ascertainable. An approximate idea of the value of θ may be obtained from the "spherical reduction factor" of the source under consideration, if this is known (see p. 124). In other cases the luminous intensity may be measured in the two horizontal directions concerned, and for all sources but those of exceptional distribution the ratio of the mean of these two values to the mean luminous intensity (m.s.c.p.) as deduced from measurements in the sphere will give a good approximation to the value of θ.

When both test lamp and sub-standard are in the sphere together, it will be clear from Fig. 150 that the areas screened by S and S' are different in area and differently placed, according as L_t or L_s is alight. For accurate compensation it is necessary that the fraction of the direct flux from L_t which reaches the areas shaded by S and S' when that lamp is alight should be the same as the fraction of the direct flux from L_s which reaches the areas shaded by these screens when L_s is alight. Compensation of this kind is difficult to arrange, and all that can generally be done is to have the screens as small as is compatible with efficient shielding of the window and to place them at distances from the lamps equal to between $0 \cdot 3d$ and $0 \cdot 4d$, where d is the distance between lamp and window [48].

The use of translucent screens has been recommended in order to compensate for the error due to shading by the addition of a certain amount of transmitted light [49]. Although very good compensation may be achieved, for a given arrangement of source and screen, by suitably adjusting the transmission factor of the latter, the method may lead to results which are in considerable error if the distance between source and screen, or the light distribution of the source, is materially altered from the standard arrangement [50]. A reflecting screen with foliated black patches has also been devised with the object of producing compensation [51]. There is but little advantage to be gained by the use of such devices, for the conditions which it has been shown to be necessary to fulfil when using an opaque screen are readily complied with in all cases likely to be met with in practice.

Effect of Objects within the Sphere—It is clear that any object placed within the sphere will not only disturb the distribution of the reflected flux, but will also reduce the amount of this flux if it receives direct light from the source. It will be convenient to deal with these two effects separately.

If A is the superficial area of the object [52] relative to that of the sphere it can be shown that, *if the object receives no direct light from the source*, the average illumination of the sphere wall due to reflected light is reduced in the ratio $1 : 1 + \{\alpha' A / \alpha (1 - \alpha' A)\}$, where α and α' are the absorption factors of the sphere wall and of the object respectively. If E_D is the average direct illumination of the sphere wall and E_R the illumination by reflected light when the sphere is empty, the total flux from the source $F = 4\pi r^2 \alpha E_D + 4\pi r^2 \alpha E_R$. When the object is in the sphere the flux it absorbs is equal to the total reflected flux, $4\pi r^2 \rho (E_D + E_R')$, multiplied by $\alpha' A$, so that now

$$F = 4\pi r^2 a E_D + 4\pi r^2 \alpha E_R' + \alpha' A \cdot 4\pi r^2 (1 - \alpha)(E_D + E_R').$$

From these equations it follows [53] that

$$E_R / E_R' = 1 + \{\alpha' A / \alpha (1 - \alpha' A)\}. \qquad \ldots\ldots\ldots\ldots\ldots(i)$$

If $\alpha' = \alpha$, the percentage reduction becomes approximately $100A$ so long as α and A are both small. If, however, $\alpha' = 1$, the percentage reduction is approximately $100A / \alpha$.

If, now the object receives direct light from the source it is clear that the amount of flux lost due to absorption by the object is $\alpha'I\omega$, where ω is the solid angle subtended by the object at the source, and I is the luminous intensity of the source in the direction of the object. There is thus a further reduction of the illumination of the sphere walls in the ratio $(F - \alpha'\omega I) : F$, i.e. in the ratio

$$\{1 - \alpha'\omega I/F\} : 1. \quad\ldots\ldots\ldots\ldots\ldots\ldots\ldots\text{(ii)}$$

It will be seen that both the corrections represented by (i) and (ii) vanish when $\alpha' = 0$, so that the effect of any object can be minimised by painting it a dead white of the highest attainable reflection factor. In the case of the screen between lamp and window, however, the side facing the window should be coated with the same paint as that used for the sphere.

The above expressions (i) and (ii) give an indication of the probable magnitude of the effect produced by any given object in a sphere photometer. With regard to expression (i) it must be remembered that, since the distribution of the reflected light is disturbed by the presence of the object, it can no longer be assumed that the illumination of the sphere walls due to reflected light is everywhere the same. The above expressions only indicate the *average* reduction in illumination. The amount of the reduction at any particular region of the sphere due to a specific object must depend upon the proximity of that object to the region in question. For example, it has been found that with a disc of area A (i.e. superficial area $2A$) relative to the area of the sphere the percentage reduction of the illumination of the sphere window is about $1000A$ in the case of black discs, and about $300A$ in the case of white discs $(\alpha' = \alpha)$, when the source is in the centre of the sphere and the disc is approximately half-way between the source and the window [54]. These figures serve to confirm the theoretical formulae deduced above if it is assumed that $\alpha = 0.2$, and that $I \backsimeq F/4\pi$.

It must not be forgotten that the lamp itself, particularly if it includes reflectors or other opaque parts, must be regarded as disturbing the *reflected* flux, and therefore altering the illumination of the window [55]. Those parts which do not receive direct light from the actual luminous source should therefore be whitened, and, further, the correction calculated from the formula given above should be made except when a sub-standard of exactly the same type as the test lamp (i.e. having similar shades, opaque parts, etc.) is available, so that all necessity for correction is avoided owing to exact equality of the disturbing effect in the case of both test lamp and sub-standard. Generally no such sub-standard is available, and the correction must be made. From the nature of the case however, the amount of this correction is difficult to estimate with accuracy, and it has therefore been recommended that in cases where the correction is found to be large the simultaneous method of measurement should be used. By this method sources may be measured for which the area of the opaque surfaces does not exceed one-fortieth of the area of the sphere.

Even a simple electric incandescent lamp without shade or reflector may cause appreciable absorption of light if the bulb is noticeably blackened [56]. For example, if such a lamp has an absorption factor in the single glass thickness (excluding surface reflection losses) of 10 per cent, it follows from the formula given on p. 267 that the change produced in the illumination of the window is 1 per cent if the bulb is spherical and of radius one-tenth that of the sphere, the absorption factor of the sphere surface being taken as 0·2. If such a lamp is compared with a sub-standard in which the blackening of the bulb is negligible, an error of 1 per cent will be introduced into the measurements.

As mentioned above, the uniformity of the (reflected) flux distribution over the surface of the sphere, postulated in the simple theory, is disturbed by the presence of an absorbing object, and this disturbance is greater the nearer the object is placed to the surface of the sphere. It follows that the source to be tested and its auxiliary apparatus should be placed as near the centre of the sphere as may be possible having regard to other considerations [57].

The Auxiliary Lamp Method—An alternative method of making the measurements, a combination of the substitution and simultaneous methods, has been proposed for use when the absorption of reflected flux by the source being measured is large [58]. An auxiliary lamp with a hood is mounted in the integrator, as in the simultaneous method except that it is closer to the wall and opposite the window, while the sub-standard and test lamp are placed in turn near the centre of the integrator. Four measurements of the luminance of the window are made under the following conditions : (a) with the sub-standard in the integrator and the auxiliary lamp only alight, (b) as in (a) but with the sub-standard only alight, (c) and (d) as (a) and (b) respectively but with the test lamp in place of the sub-standard. On the assumption that the disturbance of the reflected flux due to the presence of the test lamp in the integrator is the same when the auxiliary lamp is alight as when the test lamp is alight, this effect may be allowed for by applying the correction factor B_a/B_c to the ordinary expression for F_T/F_S. Thus by this method $F_T/F_S = (B_d/B_b) \times (B_a/B_c)$ where B_a, etc., represent the measured values of luminance of the window under the four conditions described above.

Paint for Integrators—It will be evident from the foregoing

paragraphs that a satisfactory paint for integrating spheres should fulfil, as far as possible, the following conditions :

(a) It should have a matt surface when dry [59].

(b) It should be quite non-selective, so that the repeated reflections within the sphere do not appreciably alter the colour of the light [60].

(c) It should have a high reflection factor in order to reduce the effect of the screens and other objects within the sphere (see p. 265). A high reflection factor also assists in the diffusion of the flux within the sphere, and so helps to compensate for imperfect fulfilment of condition (a) [61]. On the other hand, if the reflection factor is close to unity, so that α is very small, the effect of objects within the sphere is unduly exaggerated (see p. 267). The compromise usually adopted is to aim at a reflection factor of about 80 per cent.

(d) It should be easy to apply, tenacious and permanent, particularly as regards freedom from colour change with lapse of time.

Of these four requirements, the second and third are the most important. So far no paint which fulfils the other three conditions sufficiently for practical purposes has been found to be absolutely non-selective. Many different paints have been used by various workers [62]. It is necessary to use an undercoat which adheres well to the primary coat used on the material of the integrator and to cover this undercoat with a finishing coat which has the required optical properties. An aluminium paint is suitable for the priming coat and the undercoat may consist of a non-yellowing polyvinyl-acetate paint pigmented with anatase titanium dioxide. A very little ivory black has to be added to reduce the reflection factor to about 80 per cent. The amount required (of the order of 0·2 per cent. by weight) will depend on the particular sample of paint.

The finishing coat consists of a pigment grade of barium sulphate (blanc fixe) mixed with water containing sodium carboxymethyl-cellulose (C.M.C.) in the proportion of about 1 part by weight to 40 parts of the pigment. Zinc oxide has sometimes been used in place of barium sulphate. Again a small amount of ivory black has to be added to give a reflection factor of about 80 per cent. Several coats of this material may be required ; the final one should be highly diffusing and the amount of C.M.C. may be reduced with advantage.

The formula for a suitable paint has been given in some detail

as it is necessary to renew the surface of an integrator quite frequently. Repainting should be carried out at least once a year [63],
all the finishing coats being washed off with water before the
new coats are applied. The period which is allowed to elapse
between repainting must necessarily depend on the amount of use
made of the sphere and the nature of the sources measured in it.
Flame sources and arcs, which produce a very marked upward
current of heated air, soon cause a noticeable blackening of the top
of the sphere. The fact that this blackening is more or less localised
makes it far more important than a general uniform darkening of
the whole surface of the sphere, for if one portion of the sphere surface has a lower reflection factor than the remainder, the flux reaching that portion will receive less than its proper weight in the
estimation of the total flux. Hence, if the light distribution of the
two sources is not exactly the same, an error will be introduced into
the measurements [64].

A gradual change of reflection factor of the sphere paint sometimes occurs during the course of a series of measurements, owing
to the evaporation of absorbed moisture by the heat of the lamps
placed in the sphere [65]. This effect can be allowed for if sub-
standards are measured at intervals during the course of the work.

The extent to which any paint is selective as regards colour
may be tested quite simply on the photometer bench [66]. Two lamps,
adjusted to colour match, are placed so that one of them illuminates
one side of the photometer directly, while the other illuminates a
flat surface coated with the paint under examination. The light
reflected from this surface illuminates the other side of the photometer, and the difference in colour introduced by the paint is seen
as soon as adjustment to equality of brightness has been made.
It must be remembered that, owing to the repeated reflections which
take place in an integrator, the effect of any slight selectivity of the
paint is multiplied four or five times, so that what appears as a very
slight coloration on the bench is quite important in the integrator [67].

It will be clear that the effect of selectivity of the sphere window,
if one is used, is exactly similar to that of selectivity of the paint so
that both can be considered together in what follows [68]. If the
spectral distribution of the light given by the test lamp is the same
as that of the light from the sub-standard, selectivity of the paint
and window is unimportant but in all other cases an error is introduced of a magnitude which depends on the difference between the
colours of the lights to be compared [69]. The amount of the error
committed in comparing two sources giving respectively lights which
match a black body at two different temperatures may be determined by means of an electric incandescent lamp. The luminous

intensity of the lamp is measured in any convenient single direction at two different efficiencies, viz. the efficiencies at which it gives lights of the colours in question. The total flux is then measured at the same two efficiencies and, since it may be assumed that the ratio of the flux to the luminous intensity is unchanged by the change in efficiency, it follows that the difference between the ratio of the values of flux and the ratio of the values of luminous intensity is the error due to the selectivity of the paint and window. This is clearly equal to the error which would be made in comparing two lamps giving respectively lights matching in colour the light given by the electric lamp operating at the two efficiencies used in the experiment.

If the change of colour caused by the selectivity of the paint and window is not large, it may be corrected by placing over the sphere window a colour filter which, as nearly as possible, neutralizes it. The particular filter required can be selected by simple trial and error using a lamp which, outside the sphere, matches a comparison lamp when the two are compared in the photometer head usually employed with the sphere. When this lamp is placed inside the sphere, the colour match is disturbed and the filter which when placed over the sphere window, restores it most nearly is the filter required [70]. If none of the filters available gives a satisfactory colour match it may be necessary to use a liquid filter which is readily adjustable (see p. 301) or to use a filter which provides over-correction and to move this across the sphere window until a colour match is obtained in the photometer head. The arrangement of window, filter and photometer head is then left undisturbed and photometric measurements are made as if the sphere paint and window were perfectly non-selective. It will be clear that the use of a filter which does not entirely cover the window is inadmissible when the latter forms one of the comparison surfaces in the photometer head.

Laboratory Spheres—It will be seen from the foregoing paragraphs that the requirements which should be met in a satisfactory sphere are very exacting, and, as is so often the case, they are to a certain extent incompatible with ease of construction and convenience in use. It follows that the exact form of construction adopted for a sphere must depend on its size and the nature of the work for which it is intended [71]. Spheres more than 1 metre in diameter are frequently made to divide into two parts along a meridian, the halves being mounted on rollers so that they can be readily separated for repainting [72]. The lamps may be introduced into the sphere through an opening at the top, or a door may be provided at the side. The 10-foot sphere at the National Physical Laboratory is not divided but is of a solid wooden rib construction, lined internally with sheet zinc [73]. It has a large hinged door at one side, giving a clear opening of 6 ft. diameter, and an aperture of 5 ft. diameter at the top is closed with a series of annular sections so that an opening of any desired size can be obtained. Slots in the metal lining are provided at the bottom of the sphere to provide adequate ventilation when flame sources are being measured. There are two windows, each 4 ins. in diameter, one opposite the door and the other at 90° from this on the equator. The source to be measured is usually suspended by a rod or cable passing through a small hole in the top of the sphere and the screen is carried on fine wire supports stretched across the sphere at the correct distance from the centre (see p. 266).

For work in a laboratory where a large number of lamps have to be measured in rapid succession, it is essential to use a sphere designed in such a way that as little time as possible is lost in changing lamps. Since the size of the sphere used in such circumstances does not generally exceed about 1 metre in diameter, it may conveniently be constructed of sheet copper [74]. A convenient arrangement for changing the lamp is the double door device shown in plan in Fig. 155 [75]. When this door is swung anti-clockwise around its central vertical

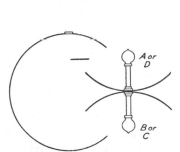

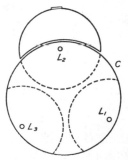

Fig. 155. Double Door Device for Rapid
Changing of Lamps in the Sphere.

Fig. 156. Lamp Changing Device
for an Integrator.

axis, so that lamp A is in the sphere and ready for measurement, lamp B can be removed from its socket and a fresh lamp C can be put in its place. As soon as the measurement on A is completed the double door is swung round clockwise so that C is now in the sphere. Another lamp D can then be substituted for A. A somewhat similar device is that shown in Fig. 156. The cylinder C, carrying three identical sphere segments, can be rotated about its axis so that while one lamp L_2 is being measured, the lamp just finished with, L_1, can be removed and a new lamp, L_3, can be inserted ready for measurement [76].

The luminance of the window may be measured visually, as described on p. 261. Instead of using the inverse square method of varying the illumination on the comparison lamp side of the photo-meter head, a second smaller integrator, either sphere or cube, with a window of adjustable area, has sometimes been employed as the comparison source. The measurements are then made by varying the area of this window [77].

When the measurements are made photo-electrically, the cell, with its sensitivity correction filter, is usually placed in a box attached to the sphere, the cell facing the window [78], and the measurement is made by one of the methods described in Chapter IV (see especially pp. 99 to 103). The provision of an adjustable diaphragm over the window, as recommended on p. 262 is very convenient for extending the range of the apparatus.

If a photo-emissive cell is employed with the form of circuit shown in Fig 57 on p. 100, the routine measurement of lamps may be facilitated by inserting a variable resistor in the potentiometer circuit (see p. 102). The current through the potentiometer windings can then be adjusted so that the luminous flux from a lamp in the sphere can be read directly on the potentiometer. With a sub-standard giving, say, 1192 lumens, the potentiometer is set to a reading of 1·192 and a balance is obtained by adjusting the variable resistor. This is then left unchanged during the subsequent measure-ments of test lamps, the balance being obtained in the ordinary way by means of the potentiometer. The luminous flux from any test lamp is then equal to the potentiometer reading multiplied by 1000. Sometimes it is convenient to use a simple factor such as 2 or 5 instead of unity to convert the potentiometer reading to the value of lumens.

The current in the potentiometer circuit provides a useful indication of the condition of the apparatus, for any reduction in the reflection factor of the integrator, or a drop in the sensitivity of the photocell, reduces the photo-current obtained for any given lamp and this is shown by a reduction in the potentiometer current. Routine measurements of this current with a milliammeter provide a continuous check on performance and, if the constancy of the photocell can be assumed, indicate when the integrator requires re-painting.

If a photo-voltaic cell is used, the Campbell-Freeth circuit shown in Fig 66 on p. 107 is generally the most convenient for then the voltmeter V may be shunted with a variable resistance so that, again, values of lumens are obtained either by direct reading or by the application of a simple factor.

Measurement of Flame Sources—When flame sources are meas-ured in a sphere, it is necessary to arrange efficient ventilation, and this can only be done by the provision of at least two openings, one near the bottom and another at the top of the sphere [79]. If very small openings are used, efficient air supply can only be ensured by means of a forced draught, and this is liable to create undesirable air currents, with consequent disturbance of the flame. Too large an opening leads to a serious departure from the theoretical conditions governing the distribution of the reflected light, since an opening must be regarded as an area of zero reflection factor. It is clear that if this area relative to the total sphere area is A, and if the average value of the direct illumination on this area is $E_d{}'$, while that on the remainder of the sphere wall is E_d, then the illumination of the window is reduced from $\{(1 - A(E_d + AE'_d)\rho/(1 - \rho)$ to $\{(1 - A)E_d\rho\}/\{1 - (1 - A)\rho\}$. If $E_d{}'/E_d = \theta$, the magnitude of the error is therefore

$$A\{\theta + \rho(1 - \theta)(1 - A)\}/\{1 - \rho(1 - A)\}\{1 - A(1 - \theta)\}.$$

If A is small ($<0\cdot01$, say) this is approximately equal to

$$A\{\theta + \rho(1 - \theta)\}/(1 - \rho),$$

which, when $\rho = 0\cdot8$, becomes $A(\theta + 4)$, so that if the error due to the apertures is not to exceed 1 per cent, their total area A must not be more than $0\cdot002$. This, in the case of a sphere of 1 metre diameter, allows two circular holes, each of about 6 cm. diameter, assuming that θ is not much greater than 1, i.e. that the directions of maximum luminous intensity of the source are not directed towards either aperture. It must be remembered that the actual error of a measurement made by either of the methods described on pp. 259-260 is much less than that just calculated so long as both test lamp and sub-standard are measured with the sphere in the same condition, i.e. so long as the apertures remain the same for the measurement of both B_S and B_T. The error may be diminished still further by placing a whitened screen over the aperture, but at a sufficient distance from it to allow adequate ventilation [80]. This screen should be of such a size and so placed as to prevent the aperture from receiving any direct light from the source. The whole of the lost flux is then reflected flux, and its amount being closely proportional to the illumination of the window, the error introduced into the measurements is very small.

Measurement of Flux emitted in the Lower Hemisphere—By a suitable modification of the methods described above for the measurement of total flux the sphere may also be used to measure the flux emitted by a source in the lower hemisphere. The source is inserted in an opening at the top of the sphere as shown in Fig. 157 [81]. The radius of this opening must be at least twice that of the smallest sphere which will contain the light source, but must not exceed about

$0.5R$, where R is the radius of the sphere. The screen S_1 placed over the sub-standard lamp must be sufficiently large to screen

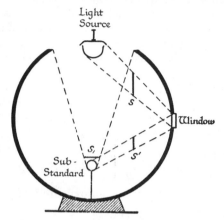

Fig. 157. The Measurement of Flux in the Lower Hemisphere.

the whole of the opening from the direct light from this lamp. The measurement is then made in the usual way.

A less accurate method, but one applicable to either hemisphere or to any zone, is that illustrated in Fig. 158 [82]. The source is

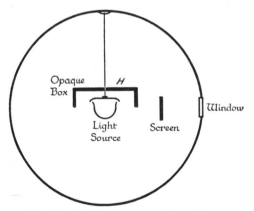

Fig. 158. The Measurement of Zonal Flux.

surrounded by a box screen H, which, being blackened on the inside, absorbs all the light from the source except that emitted in the hemisphere or zone for which measurements are desired. This screen must be whitened on the outside, but even so it disturbs the distribution of reflected flux in the sphere to a degree depending on its size, so that this method should only be used in the case of small sources.

A similar arrangement may be used in making measurements by the substitution method. The screen H used with the test lamp in the sphere is placed over the sub-standard so that the light from it is absorbed exactly over the same zonal areas as in the case of the test lamp. The flux emitted by the screened sub-standard is then found from the polar curve determined as described earlier in this chapter, and the value thus obtained is multiplied by the ratio B_T/B_S, where B_T and B_S are respectively the luminance of the sphere window when the test lamp and the sub-standard are placed in the sphere, each being shaded by the screen H.

It is clear that, with a source of finite dimensions, a sharp cut-off at the edge of a given zone can only be obtained when the screen is large compared with the dimensions of the light source. In the same way, accurate delimitation of the hemisphere can only be obtained by the method illustrated in Fig. 157 when the radius of the opening is large, and as this is limited by other considerations to a maximum of $0.5\,R$, it follows that the sphere used for measuring the flux emitted by a source in the lower hemisphere must have a diameter equal to at least eight times that of the source. Exact positioning of the source with reference to the edge of the opening is necessary, and an auxiliary photometer has been devised [83] for determining the photometric " centre of gravity " of a source of light. This piece of apparatus is shown in section in Fig. 159. The light from

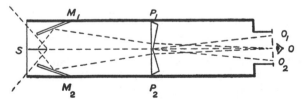

FIG. 159. The Photometric Centroid Finder.

the upper and lower parts of the lamp respectively illuminate the two sides of the Bunsen screen S, which is placed at a distance $r\sqrt{3}$ from the source, where r is the radius of the circular opening at the top of the sphere. The two sides of the screen are seen in juxtaposition at O by means of the mirrors M_1, M_2, and the prisms P_1, P_2. When a balance has been obtained the eye is shifted to O_1 or O_2, and then sees the source directly with the screen S as a horizontal black line dividing it into two parts. The position of the line on the source is noted, and the latter is then placed in the sphere so that this line lies in the plane of the edges of the sphere opening.

Non-Spherical Integrators—Certain disadvantages attendant on the spherical form, notably the difficulties of construction and the awkwardness of standing any object in a sphere, have led to suggestions for a modification of form. Of the regular polyhedra, the simplest to construct is the cube, and this form of integrator has, therefore, received considerable attention [84].

It is clear that, if a light source is placed in the centre of a cube, and if a window is provided at the centre of one of the sides, the line joining the source and the window forms an axis of symmetry of the apparatus and, by means of four imaginary planes passing through this axis, the cube can be divided into eight portions, each of which is similarly situated with respect to the source and the window (see Fig. 160). It follows that the flux reflected to the

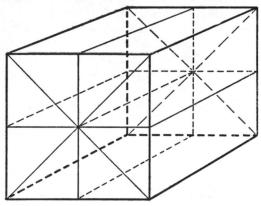

Fig. 160. Symmetrical Division of a Cubical Integrator.

window from any given area in one of these eight portions will be exactly equal to the flux reflected to the window from an equal and equally bright area similarly situated in any of the other seven portions. Thus if a light source had a flux distribution such that its luminous intensity was uniform (but not necessarily the same) in each of the eight angular regions defined by the four imaginary planes above mentioned, the reflected flux received at the window would be proportional to the total flux given by the source. It follows from this general consideration of the problem that the best position for a source in an integrating cube is at the centre of the cube, with its axis of symmetry perpendicular to the line joining the source and the window.

The amount of flux received at the window as a result of the incidence of a given amount of flux at each part of the cube surface has been determined empirically [85], and, using the results thus obtained, it is possible to calculate for any source of which the polar curve is approximately known the error which will be made in comparing it with a source of some other known flux distribution. The results of this calculation applied to typical light sources in common use are given in the table below :

TABLE SHOWING THE ERRORS OF MEASUREMENT DUE TO THE USE OF AN INTEGRATING CUBE FOR CERTAIN TYPICAL LIGHT SOURCES.

Light Source	Polar Curve Type (see Fig. 161)	Apparent Flux in Cube (Relative to Point Source)
Point source - - - - - -	—	1·00
Electric incandescent lamp (vacuum, squirrel-cage filament) - - - -	A	0·99
Electric lamp (gas-filled, ring filament) -	B	1·005
Tubular fluorescent lamp - - - -	A	0·99
Gas lamp (inverted mantle) - - -	C	1·05
Arc lamp - - - - - - -	D	0·955

N.B.—The above figures have been calculated on the assumption that (a) the source is placed at the centre of the cube, with its axis of symmetry vertical, and (b) the reflection factor of the cube surface is about 85 per cent.

As a compromise between the simple cube and the sphere, the proposal has frequently been made to use a cube in which the corners

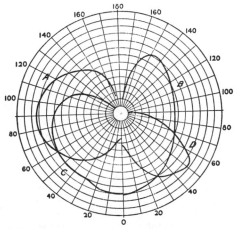

FIG. 161. Typical Polar Curves for the Sources referred to in the above Table.

are blocked out so as to form a fourteen-sided polyhedron [86]. Experiments have also been made with a rectangular box modified in this way [87], and on the regular icosahedron [88]. Another form of integrator which has been used is a hemisphere, either open, or closed with a plane cover [89]. A modified form of hemispherical integrator has been devised for the measurement of large sources [90] or for finding the total flux in the beam of light given by a projector (see Chapter XIV, p. 471).

The statement has been made that the form of the integrator is not of great importance, but this is incorrect, except when the light distribution of the test lamp is identical with that of the sub-standard. In all other cases no adequate theoretical treatment can be given, but from the general principles outlined in previous sections it may safely be concluded that the inaccuracy increases with (a) the difference in light distribution between test lamp and sub-standard, (b) the departure of the integrator from the true spherical form, and (c) the absorption factor of the inner surface of the integrator. The departure from the theoretical flux distribution due to the presence of objects in the integrator is also greater in the case of a non-spherical integrator, and it is probable that lack of perfect diffusion from the inner surface would be more important than in the case of a sphere [91].

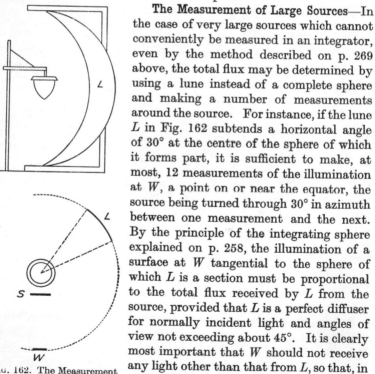

The Measurement of Large Sources—In the case of very large sources which cannot conveniently be measured in an integrator, even by the method described on p. 269 above, the total flux may be determined by using a lune instead of a complete sphere and making a number of measurements around the source. For instance, if the lune L in Fig. 162 subtends a horizontal angle of 30° at the centre of the sphere of which it forms part, it is sufficient to make, at most, 12 measurements of the illumination at W, a point on or near the equator, the source being turned through 30° in azimuth between one measurement and the next. By the principle of the integrating sphere explained on p. 258, the illumination of a surface at W tangential to the sphere of which L is a section must be proportional to the total flux received by L from the source, provided that L is a perfect diffuser for normally incident light and angles of view not exceeding about 45°. It is clearly most important that W should not receive any light other than that from L, so that, in addition to the usual screen at S, other

Fig. 162. The Measurement of Flux from Large Sources.

screening must be arranged to prevent any stray light from being reflected to W by the surroundings.

If the light distribution from the source is perfectly symmetrical about its vertical axis, only one measurement is necessary, while for sources which have two vertical planes of symmetry at right angles (e.g. trough-shaped fittings) sufficient measurements to cover 90° in azimuth must be made.

It is worth remarking that the total flux given by a large source can be determined without an integrator by a point to point method which is similar to that employed for finding a polar curve of light distribution, but without the restriction as to the distance at which the measurements are made [92]. If the source is surrounded with a sphere, clearly the total flux can be found by measuring the average illumination, by direct light, of the inside surface of this sphere. All that is required, therefore, is a sufficient number of measurements of illumination made at points equally distributed over the surface of an imaginary sphere containing the source. If, as is usually the case, the source has an axis of symmetry, it is sufficient to make a number of measurements in any convenient plane containing this axis and to plot the results in the form of a polar curve. The average illumination can then be found by constructing a Rousseau diagram from this polar curve, just as in the calculation of flux from a polar curve of luminous intensity (see p. 126). It is to be noted that the polar curve of illumination is not usually identical with the polar curve of light distribution of the source, owing to the fact that the measurements are generally made on a comparatively short radius. Further, the centre about which the illumination measurements are made need not be the light centre of the source so long as it is on the axis of symmetry.

General Conclusions regarding the Practical Use of a Sphere— While it is difficult to lay down any definite rules regarding the employment of an integrator for the practical measurement of the total flux given by a source, the following general principles may be regarded as of fairly wide application to such problems as are met with in ordinary photometric practice where an accuracy of 1 to 2 per cent is aimed at :

(1) The integrator should preferably be spherical in form, and the closer the approximation to the spherical form the more certainly is it possible to calculate the magnitude of the error likely to be made in measurements under any given set of conditions.

(2) The integrator must be coated internally with a paint which dries with a surface which has a reflection factor of about 80 per cent and is as matt and as non-selective as possible. The surface must be renewed at frequent intervals, a year being the maximum period allowed to elapse between re-painting.

(3) The true substitution method of measurement is preferable to the simultaneous method, but it demands a larger integrator. When the true substitution method is used the ratio of the surface area of the integrator to that of the light source (including any surfaces, such as shades or reflectors, which affect the light distribution of the source under normal working conditions) should be not less than 100 times the ratio of the absorption factor of these surfaces to the absorption factor of the sphere surface. When the simultaneous method of measurement is used, the ratio of the surface area of the integrator used to that of the test source and its auxiliary apparatus may be as low as 40.

(4) Any auxiliary parts of the light source which it is necessary to have in the sphere (excluding the surfaces which affect the light distribution of the source under working conditions) should be painted white or covered with a white material.

(5) The window should behave as nearly as possible as a perfect diffuser for transmitted light, it should be non-selective, and its inner surface should be matt and flush with the inner surface of the sphere. Its diameter should not exceed one-tenth of the diameter of the sphere, and may with advantage be smaller than this.

(6) Each screen should be just large enough to shield the window from the direct light coming from any part of a source (either test lamp or sub-standard) which contributes to the total flux from that source under ordinary working conditions, e.g. light from a reflector, frosted globe, etc., must be prevented from reaching the window directly by interposing a screen. Screens should be painted on the side facing the window with the same material as that used for the sphere surface, and on the other side with a paint of the highest attainable reflection factor. They should not be larger than is necessary to shade the window completely, and they should preferably be placed at a distance from the source equal to about one-third of the distance between the source and the window.

(7) The sub-standard used should, if possible, have a light distribution which is similar to that of the test source. If this can be arranged, the true substitution method can be used and the errors due to non-compliance with recommendations (1), (2), (5) and (6) are much reduced. Where this is impossible, as in the measurement of sources giving a concentration of light in certain directions, the test source should be so oriented that the regions of maximum illumination of the sphere are visible from the window, and the simultaneous method of measurement is generally preferable.

(8) When the true substitution method is employed, the source should be placed as nearly as possible at the centre of the sphere. When the simultaneous method is used, the two sources should be

placed symmetrically with respect to the sphere window, and not too close either to each other or to the surface of the sphere.

(9) When the cube or fourteen-sided polyhedron is used instead of the sphere, the light source should be placed in the centre and should have its axis of symmetry perpendicular to the line joining the window of the integrator and the source. The window should be in the centre of one side, and not at an edge or corner.

Too much emphasis cannot be placed on the fact that the above rules are only generalisations, and any attempt to apply them universally without an intelligent appreciation of the theory of the sphere is certain to lead to large errors in particular cases. The integrating photometer is an instrument of the utmost value when properly used, but its unintelligent application may easily be attended by unsuspected errors quite outside the limits of accuracy of ordinary photometric measurement.

For the measurement of sources showing rapid variation of luminous flux, one of the methods described in Chapter VII for the measurement of the intensity of variable sources (see p. 235) must be used in conjunction with an integrating sphere [93].

The sphere has been applied to several problems in photometry other than the measurement of luminous flux. Some of these applications will be described in Chapter XIII, pp. 419 and 433. It can be used, in conjunction with a lamp, as a comparison source of adjustable luminous intensity, since the flux emitted from a window in the sphere is strictly proportional to the area of the window [94].

BIBLIOGRAPHY

E. Liebenthal. Articles " Lichtstärken-Mittelwerte " and " Lichtstrommesser " in *Physikalisches Handwörterbuch*. (Springer, Berlin, *1924*.)

R. Ulbricht. *Das Kugelphotometer*. (Oldenbourg, Munich and Berlin, *1920*.)

E. B. Rosa and A. H. Taylor. Bureau of Standards, Bull., 18, *1922*, p. 281.

" The Measurement of Mean Spherical Candle-Power." Illumination Research Technical Paper No. 5. (H.M. Stationery Office, *1927*.)

R. G. Weigel and O. Knoll. Licht u. Lampe, 17, *1928*, pp. 753, 794, 837 and 875.

REFERENCES

1. See, e.g., L. Bell, Astrophys. J., 45, *1917*, p. 1 ; J. Teichmüller, Licht u. Lampe, 2, *1913*, pp. 802 *et seq.*

2. See also Report of Frank. Inst. Committee, J., 90, *1885* (supplement) ; C. Heim., E.T.Z., 7, *1886*, p. 384 ; P. H. Ledeboer, Lum. El., 26, *1887*, p. 58 ; Soc. Belge d'Opt., Rev. d'Opt., 11, *1932*, p. 74.

3. It has been found that the candle-power of a gas-filled tungsten filament lamp is higher when the lamp is mounted " tip-up " than when it is pendent. See G. W. Middlekauff and J. F. Skogland, Bureau of Standards, Bull., 12, *1915*, p. 587.

4. F. W. Hartley. J. of Gas Lighting, 41, *1883*, p. 1008.
W. J. Dibdin. Soc. Chem. Ind., J., 3, *1884*, p. 277.
E. Liebenthal. *Prakt. Phot.*, p. 287.

5. The mirror must be large enough to enable the whole of the test-lamp to be seen in it from the position of the photometer head.
E. Voit and H. Krüss. Lum. El., 7, *1882*, p. 402.

6. See p. 187 and F. Uppenborn, *Lehrbuch d. Phot.*, p. 253.
On the determination of the reflection factor of a mirror, see Chap. XIII, p. 424.

7. F. von Hefner-Alteneck. E.T.Z., 4, *1883*, p. 445.
A. P. Trotter. Inst. El. Eng., J., 21, *1892*, p. 360.
A. Blondel. Ecl. El., 2, *1895*. p. 385.

8. F. Laporte. Ecl. El., 20, *1899*, p. 302.
C. P. Matthews. El. World, 35, *1900*, p. 824.
L. W. Wild. Illum. Eng., 2, *1909*, p. 193.

9. See, e.g., H. Krüss, J.G.W., 41, *1898*, p. 253 ; M. Herschkowitsch, *ibid.*, 44, *1901*, p. 650 ; E. Brodhun and F. F. Martens (see H. Korte, *Handbuch d. Lichttechnik*, p. 318) ; W. H. McMillan, Colliery Guardian, 147, *1933*, p. 1115.

10. E. Brodhun. See E. Liebenthal, *Prakt. Phot.*, pp. 227 and 292.
A. Vernon-Harcourt. Electrician, 21, *1888*, pp. 412 and 474.
M. Schanzer (K. Satori). E.u.M., 31, *1913*, p. 443.
C. C. Colby and C. M. Doolittle. Illüm. Eng. Soc. N.Y., Trans., 18, *1923*, p. 273.

11. H. Krüss. J.G.W., 41, *1898*, p. 253 and 50, *1907*, p. 1017.
Van R. Lansingh. Am. Gas Light J., 85, *1906*, p. 92.
Electrician. 107, *1931*, p. 669.
A. R. McGibbon and P. C. Sugg. Light and Ltg., 29, *1936*, p. 169.

12. H. Krüss. Der Gastechniker, 7, *1887*, p. 241.
R. B. Williamson and J. H. Klinck. Frank. Inst., J., 149, *1900*, p. 66.
G. H. Stickney and S. L. E. Rose. Illum. Eng. Soc. N.Y., Trans., 6, *1911*, p. 641 and 8, *1913*, p. 379.

13. Alternatively a simple linkage may be used to ensure that L remains upright as it moves round M.

14. This formula assumes that distances are in mm., and that the values of d_c have been based on a standard illumination of ten lux at the photometer surface.

15. Since the light is incident on the glass at an angle of about 45°, the true correction for mirror thickness is $2t(\sec \theta)/n$ where $\sin \theta = (\sin 45°)/n$. This equals $2t/\sqrt{n^2 - 0.5}$ which, for $n = 1.5$, reduces to $1.51t$.

16. Though the flux is not 4π times the mean of the values of luminous intensity thus measured (see p. 126, and J. Abady, J. of Gas Lighting, 87, *1904*, p. 108).
C. Hering. Illum. Eng. Soc. N.Y., Trans., 4, *1909*, p. 354.

17. E. Brodhun. Z.f.I., 15, *1895*, p. 337.
J. S. Dow and V. H. Mackinney. Opt. Convention, Proc., *1912*, p. 70.
C. H. Sharp. Illum. Eng., 5, *1912*, p. 264.
For a photographic method, see G. I. Pokrowski, Z.f.I., 47, *1927*, p. 520.
See also H. Pécheux, Rev. Gén. de l'El., 18, *1925*, p. 776.

18. J. Ondracek. E.u.M., 37, *1919*, p. 537.
See also K. Franck, Illum. Engng., 45, *1950*, p. 763.

19. C. B. Platt. Colliery Guardian, 147, *1933*, p. 241.
World Power, 22, *1934*, p. 181.
C. L. Dows and G. R. Baumgartner. Illum. Eng. Soc. N.Y., Trans., 30, *1935*, p. 476.
G. R. Baumgartner. *Ibid.*, 36, *1941*, p. 1340.
S. C. Gladden. Am. J. Phys., 9, *1941*, p. 283.
K. Kirsch. Licht u. Lampe, 31, *1942*, pp. 123 and 131.
G. A. Horton. Illum. Engng., 45, *1950*, p. 458.
K. Franck and R. L. Smith. Illum. Engng., 49, *1954*, p. 287.
See also Illum. Eng. Soc. N.Y., Trans., 38, *1943*, p. 509 for a description of apparatus incorporating a photo-emissive cell.

20. K. Edgcumbe. Light and Ltg., 29, *1936*, p. 167.
G. A. Horton. Illum. Engng., 63, *1948*, p. 989 (see also p. 1270).

21. See, e.g., R. Maxted, Light and Ltg., 29, *1936*, p. 378.

22. W. F. Little and H. J. Eckweiler. Illum. Eng. Soc. N.Y., Trans., 26, *1931*, p. 810.
    R. Sewig. Licht, 1, *1931*, p. 215.
    G. Weber. *Ibid.*, 2, *1932*, p. 77 and 8, *1938*, p. 145.
    R. Sewig and W. Vaillant. Z.f.I., 53, *1933*, p. 388.
    A. Gouffé. J. des Usines à Gaz, 57, *1933*, pp. 446 and 59, *1935*, p. 134 ;
Rev. Gén. de l'El., 38, *1935*, p. 355.
    G. H. Wilson and W. Weir. J. Sci. Inst., 11, *1934*, p. 114.
    P. Grundfest. Licht, 5, *1935*, p. 123.
    For a description of apparatus for use with large fittings see G. R. Baumgartner, Illum. Engng., 45, *1950*, p. 253.
    For earlier work, mostly with other physical receptors, see the refs. in note (90) on pp. 339 and 340 of *Photometry (1926)*.
    Apparatus for obtaining a curve of light distribution in the horizontal plane has been described by E. Spiller (Z. f. techn. Phys., 8, *1927*, p. 15).

23. C. Müller. Z. f. techn. Phys., 9, *1928*, p. 154.

24. M. Horioka *et al.* Electrotech. Lab., Tokyo, Researches No. 213 (*1927*) (In Japanese) Nos. 268 (*1929*) and 296 (*1930*) (In English) ; World Eng. Congress, Tokyo, *1929*, Vol. 24, p. 169.
    K. Abe and T. Takegami. Int. Illum. Congress, *1931*, Proc., Vol. I, p. 510.
    V. J. Tyler and R. H. Brown. J. Sci. Inst., 12, *1935*, p. 253.

25. E. Rousseau. L'Ingenieur Conseil, 6, *1884*, p. 251 ; Comptes rendus des travaux du Comité international des essais electriques de l'Exposition d'Anvers, *1885*, p. 85 ; L'Eclairage à l'Exposition d'Anvers, p. 233 ; Lum. El., 26, *1887*, p. 60.
    H. Krüss. E.T.Z., 8, *1887*, p. 356.

26. J. A. Fleming. Inst. El. Eng., J., 32, *1902*, p. 119.
    See also F. W. Carter, El. Rev., 47, *1900*, p. 197.

27. A. Crova. Congrès des Electriciens, Paris, *1889*, C.r., p. 205.
    C. P. Matthews. Phys. Rev., 6, *1898*, p. 55.
    A gas-filled tungsten filament lamp shows marked changes of luminous intensity when rotated (see G. W. Middlekauff and J. F. Skogland, Bureau of Standards, Bull., 12, *1915*, p. 587). On the rotation of discharge lamps see L. E. Barbrow, Illum. Eng. Soc. N.Y., Trans., 32, *1937*, p. 662.

28. E. P. Hyde and F. E. Cady. Bureau of Standards, Bull., 3, *1907*, p. 357.
    C. Paulus. Z. f. Bel., 14, *1908*, pp. 195 and 206.

29. J. of Gas Lighting, 104, *1908*, p. 33. (See also the description on pp. 202–3 of *Photometry, 1926*.)
    E. P. Hyde and F. E. Cady. El. Rev. and West. Elect., 61, *1912*, p. 942.

30. E. P. Hyde and F. E. Cady. Bureau of Standards, Bull., 4, *1907*, p. 91.
    Société Belge d'Opt., Rev. d'Opt., 11, *1932*, p. 74.

31. C. H. Sharp. Phys. Rev., 11, *1900*, p. 181.

32. E. Liebenthal. *Prakt. Phot.*, p. 332. (See also Z.f.I., 19, *1899*, pp. 193 and 225.)
    A. Krüss. Z. f. Bel., 18, *1912*, p. 421.
    See also E. P. Hyde and F. E. Cady, Bureau of Standards, Bull., 2, *1906*, p. 415.

33. F. Uppenborn. E.T.Z., 28, *1907*, pp. 139 and 168.

34. See the refs. in note (29) on p. 231 of *Photometry (1926)*.

35. H. J. Helwig. Licht, 3, *1933*, p. 243 (see also *ibid.*, 4, *1934*, p. 80).
    See also H. Pécheux, L'Electricien, 65, *1934*, p. 151.

36. See, e.g., A. Blondel, C.R., 120, *1895*, p. 550 and Soc. Int. des Elect., Bull., 4, *1904*, p. 39 ; C. P. Matthews, Am. I.E.E., Trans., 18, *1901*, p. 677 and 20, *1902*, p. 59 ; C. Léonard, Ecl. El., 40, *1904*, p. 128 and 45, *1905*, p. 329 ; E. P. Hyde, Bureau of Standards, Bull., 1, *1905*, p. 255 ; H. Krüss, J.G.W., 51, *1908*, p. 597 ; J. Sahulka, E.T.Z., 39, *1918*, p. 253.
    See also A. Blondel, C.R., 206, *1938*, p. 1231.

37. P. M. Tikhodéev. Annales (Vremennik) Chambre Centrale des Poids et Mesures, Leningrad, Liv. 4 (16), *1930*, p. 56.
    See also E. D. Déviatkova, Travaux de l'Inst. de Métrologie, U.R.S.S., No. 133, *1934*, p. 3 ; Rev. Gén. de l'El., 36, *1934*, p. 780 ; Bureau Int. des Poids et Mesures, Procés-verbaux, 16, *1933*, p. 333.

38. W. E. Sumpner. Phys. Soc. Proc. 12, *1892*, p. 10.

39. This may also be shown thus :

The total flux emitted by the source must be equal to that absorbed by the walls of the sphere, i.e. to the total flux reaching the walls, multiplied by the absorption factor. Hence $F = (1 - \rho)(F + 4\pi r^2 \Phi)$ where Φ is the flux reaching unit area of the sphere by reflection. Hence $\Phi = \rho F / 4\pi r^2 (1 - \rho)$. (R. Ulbricht, *Das Kugelphotometer*, p. 15.) See also E. Mascart, Lum. El., 28, *1888*, p. 180.

40. R. Ulbricht. E.T.Z., 21, *1900*, p. 595.

41. See, e.g., L. Bloch, E.T.Z., 26, *1905*, pp. 1047 and 1074, and 27, *1906*, p. 63 , E. Dyhr, *ibid.*, 31, *1910*, p. 1295 ; E. B. Rosa and A. H. Taylor, Bureau of Standards; Bull., 18, *1922*, p. 281 ; H. Hartinger, Licht u. Lampe, 15, *1926*, p. 393 ; H. Korte and M. Schmidt. Lichttechnik, 6, *1954*, p. 88.

See also the papers referred to in the notes which follow.

42. B. P. Dudding and G. T. Winch. J. Sci. Inst., 5, *1928*, p. 312.

43. See, e.g., W. Arndt, Licht u. Lampe, 15, *1926*, p. 431.

44. N. A. Halbertsma. Z. f. Bel., 22, *1916*, p. 43.

45. N. K. Chaney and E. L. Clark. Illum. Eng. Soc. N.Y., Trans., 10, *1915*, p. 1.

46. R. Ulbricht. *Das Kugelphotometer*, p. 93 ; E.T.Z., 26, *1905*, p. 512.

N. K. Chaney and E. L. Clark. Illum. Eng. Soc. N.Y., Trans., 10, *1915*, p. 1. (See also R. B. Chillas, *ibid.*, p. 34.)

47. Further, in the case of a small source the two screened areas (*ac* and *bd* in Fig. 154) are equal if the distance between source and screen is one-third of the sphere radius. Equality of these areas clearly tends towards equality of δ and δ_s in the general case where the lamps may have any distribution whatever.

48. Ulbricht has proposed (E.T.Z., 28, *1907*, p. 777) to correct for the presence of the screens by adding the percentage $(20s - 25s')$ to the measured value of L_T, s and s' being respectively the (single side) areas of the screens S and S'.

49. R. Ulbricht. E.T.Z., 21, *1900*, p. 595.

C. H. Sharp and P. S. Millar. Illum. Eng. Soc. N.Y., Trans., 3, *1908*, p. 502.

50. N. K. Chaney and E. L. Clark. Illum. Eng. Soc. N.Y., Trans., 10, *1915*, p. 1.

51. F. A. Benford. Illum. Eng. Soc. N.Y., Trans., 11, *1916*, p. 997.

52. The surface is here assumed to be either convex or flat everywhere. The area of a concavity is to be reckoned as that of the plane surface defined by its edges. In other words, A is the area of a piece of paper which just covers the object when stretched tightly over it.

53. R. Ulbricht. *Das Kugelphotometer*, p. 24.

54. E. B. Rosa and A. H. Taylor. Illum. Eng. Soc. N.Y., Trans., 11, *1916*, p. 453.

55. See, e.g., H. J. Helwig, Licht, 8, *1938*, p. 147.

56. J. W. T. Walsh. Illum. Eng., 18, *1925*, pp. 12 and 42.

57. R. Ulbricht. *Das Kugelphotometer*, p. 33.

E. B. Rosa and A. H. Taylor. Bureau of Standards, Bull., 18, *1922*, p 281.

58. H. J. Helwig. Licht, 3, *1933*, p. 143 and 4, *1934*, pp. 115, 135, and 156. Illum. Eng., 28, *1935*, p. 296.

K. Edgcumbe. Light and Ltg., 29, *1936*, p. 167.

See also W. Arndt and H. J. Helwig, Licht, 5, *1935*, p. 257.

59. R. G. Weigel and O. H. Knoll. Licht, 10, *1940*, p. 208.

See also W. Voege, *ibid.*, 14, *1944*, p. 32.

60. F. E. Cady. El. World, 77, *1921*, p. 368.

61. The difficulty of maintaining a surface of high reflection factor has, however, led to the suggestion that a grey surface should be adopted (E. Presser, Elektrot. Anzeiger, 23, *1906*, pp. 885 and 912). This is not advisable for the reason stated on p. 266.

62. See the refs. in notes (62) to (66) on p. 233 of *Photometry (1926)* and the following :

S. Seki, T. Ogawa and K. Tsurui. Electrotech. Lab., Tokyo, Researches No. 424, *1938* (In Japanese).

R. G. Weigel and O. H. Knoll. Licht, 10, *1940*, p. 208.

British Standard No. 354, *Photometric Integrators*.

W. E. K. Middleton and C. L. Sanders. Illum. Engng., 48, *1953*, p. 254.

J. Terrien. Soc. Franç. Elect., Bull., 6, *1956*, p. 307 ; Comité Int. des Poids et Mesures, Procès-verbaux, 25, *1957*, p. 33.

63. A. Utzinger. E.T.Z., 36, *1915*, p. 137.
64. H. Hartinger. Licht u. Lampe, 15, *1926*, p. 393.
H. Buckley. Illum. Eng. Soc. Lond., Trans., 11, *1946*, p. 167.
65. H. Buckley and W. Barnett. J. Sci. Inst., 12, *1935*, p. 258.
L. B. Johnson. Illum. Eng. Soc. N.Y., Trans., 32, *1937*, p. 646.
66. M. Corsepius. Gesell. deut. Naturforscher u. Aerzte, Verh., 80, *1908* (2, i), p. 66.
67. See, e.g., A. Adderley and M. O. Pelton, Textile Inst., J., 20, *1929*, p. T203.
68. W. Dziobek. Licht u. Lampe, 15, *1926*, p. 395.
69. J. W. T. Walsh and W. Barnett. Opt. Soc., Trans., 28, *1926*, p. 21.
F. Benford. Opt. Soc. Am., J., 25, *1935*, p. 332.
H. Buckley. Phil. Mag., 20, *1935*, p. 745.
W. E. Forsythe. Illum. Eng. Soc. N.Y., Trans., 31, *1936*, p. 181.
R. G. Weigel and O. H. Knoll. Licht, 10, *1940*, p. 208.
A. Dresler. *Ibid.*, 11, *1941*, p. 180.
70. R. C. Fox. Opt. Convention, Proc., *1926*, Vol. I, p. 289.
71. There is a British Standard for Photometric Integrators, No. 354.
See also E. T. Price *et al.*, South African Institute of El. Engineers, Trans., 25, *1934*, p. 187.
72. M. Corsepius. E.T.Z., 27, *1906*, p. 468.
E. W. Marchant. Illum. Eng., 4, *1911*, p. 37.
G. H. Sechrist. Illum. Engng., 49, *1954*, p. 345.
See also E. B. Rosa and A. H. Taylor, Illum. Eng. Soc. N.Y., Trans., 11, *1916*, p. 453.
73. National Physical Lab., Ann. Report, *1925*, p. 155.
For a description of larger spheres see Bureau of Standards, Techn. News Bulletin, 32, *1948*, p. 65, and Light and Ltg., 42, *1949*, p. 86.
74. K. Schmidt. Helios, 25, *1919*, p. F313.
A. J. Small. Electrician, 120, *1938*, p. 375.
N. M. Mohler. Am. J. Phys., 9, *1941*, p. 229.
75. This device is used in the Sharp-Millar spheres made by the Foote, Pierson Company of New York.
76. Used at Philips' Glow Lamp Works, Eindhoven, Holland.
77. R. von Voss. E.T.Z., 38, *1917*, pp. 188 and 605.
E. Zopf. Licht u. Lampe, 8, *1919*, p. 94.
A. H. Taylor. Frank. Inst., J., 194, *1922*, p. 543.
78. C. Deshler and H. Schroeder. Illum. Eng. Soc. N.Y., Trans., 23, *1928*, p. 391.
W. F. Little and C. E. Horn. *Ibid.*, p. 419.
W. W. Loebe and C. Samson. E.T.Z., 52, *1931*, p. 861.
J. W. T. Walsh. Illum. Eng., 26, *1933*, p. 64.
P. Selényi. E.u.M., 52, *1934*, Lichttech., p. 19.
P. D. Oakley. Illum. Eng., 28, *1935*, p. 181.
See also F. K. Moss, Gen. El. Rev., 27, *1924*, p. 592.
79. H. Lux. Licht u. Lampe, 15, *1926*, p. 430.
80. E. B. Rosa and A. H. Taylor. Bureau of Standards, Bull., 18, *1922*, p. 281.
81. R. Ulbricht. E.T.Z., 26, *1905*, p. 512 and 27, *1906*, p. 50.
82. M. Corsepius. Illum. Eng., 1, *1908*, pp. 801 and 895.
83. R. Ulbricht. E.T.Z., 28, *1907*, p. 777 and 30, *1909*, pp. 322 and 507.
84. W. E. Sumpner. Illum. Eng., 3, *1910*, p. 323 (see also pp. 387–93).
L. W. Wild. Illum. Eng., 3, *1910*, p. 549.
R. Ulbricht. Z. f. Bel., 28, *1922*, p. 43.
W. Voege. Licht u. Lampe, 29, *1940*, pp. 377, 397 and 417 and 31, *1942*, p. 139.
H. J. Helwig. Licht, 12, *1942*, p. 85.
85. H. Buckley. Inst. El. Eng., J., 59, *1921*, p. 143.
86. G. W. O. Howe. Illum. Eng., 3, *1910*, p. 391.
G. Gehlhoff. Licht u. Lampe, 15, *1926*, p. 428.
See also Illum. Eng., 18, *1925*, p. 49 ; J. T. MacGregor-Morris and A. H. Mumford, J. Sci. Inst., 2, *1925*, pp. 353 and 385.
87. L. O. Grondahl. Illum. Eng. Soc. N.Y., Trans., 11, *1916*, p. 152.
For a description of a cylindrical integrator for measuring miners' lamps see R. Burgholz, Glückauf, 77, *1941*, p. 281.

88. K. S. Weaver and B. E. Shackleford. Illum. Eng. Soc. N.Y., Trans., 18, *1923*, p. 290.

89. B. Monasch. E.T.Z., 27, *1906*, pp. 669, 695 and 803.

90. F. A. Benford. Illum. Eng. Soc. N.Y., Trans., 13, *1918*, p. 323 and 15, *1920*, p. 19 ; Opt. Soc. Am., J., 6, *1922*, p. 1040.

91. See, e.g., A. Buchbinder, Z. f. techn. Phys., 12, *1931*, p. 164 ; Nat. Phys. Lab., Ann. Report, *1927*, p. 131 ; K. Fränz, Licht, 4, *1934*, p. 17.

92. R. G. Weigel. Lichttechnik, 5, *1953*, p. 296.
See also H. D. Einhorn and J. D. Sauermann, Inst. El. Eng., J., 95 (Part II), *1948*, p. 319.

93. T. H. Projector and L. E. Barbrow. Rev. Sci. Inst., 16, *1945*, p. 51.
D. L. Munden. Light and Ltg., 42, *1949*, p. 313.

94. See, e.g., J. of Gas Lighting, 104, *1908*, p. 33 ; L. Bloch, J.G.W., 62, *1919*, p. 355 ; E. Karrer and A. Poritsky, Opt. Soc. Am., J., 8, *1924*, p. 355.
See also p. 274 above.

CHAPTER IX

HETEROCHROMATIC PHOTOMETRY

In the descriptions of visual methods of photometry given in previous chapters it has been tacitly assumed that the lights being compared are either alike, or nearly alike, in colour, so that while the eye of the observer is endeavouring to make a judgment of equality of brightness of the comparison surfaces it is not embarrassed [1] by a difference of hue. In other words, it is assumed that measurement of *quantity* is not interfered with by a difference in *quality* of the things compared.

Unfortunately this condition, which until now it has been necessary to assume fulfilled in order to simplify the treatment of the subject, is completely satisfied in but few of the problems met with in practical photometry. It has already been said (p. 182) that the primary standard gives a light which is very much yellower than that given by modern light sources under working conditions. It follows that the measurement of such sources by comparison with the standard must, fundamentally, involve a considerable colour difference. It is true that steps are taken to ensure that this colour difference is very much reduced, if not eliminated, in everyday photometry, but the difficulty is thereby only transferred to another link in the chain of measurements by which the source under test is compared with the primary standard, and nothing can remove the necessity for heterochromatic photometry at one stage or another in the series of comparisons.

An observer faced with the problem of making a photometric measurement by the comparison of two surfaces differing markedly in colour is tempted at once to condemn the operation as senseless, and the result obtained as almost without meaning [2], and he is to a certain extent justified by the physical principle that things which differ in kind cannot be compared in degree except by some quality which is common to both. Thus, in the case of two lights of different colours, while there is no theoretical difficulty in comparing their relative energies expressed in watts, this quantity being common to all forms of radiation, there is very considerable difficulty in comparing their relative effects on the retina, since these effects are different in kind as well as in degree. This argument, however, if pushed to its logical conclusion, would almost deny the possibility of photometry at all. The position has been well expressed by C. Fabry [3], as follows :

" Confining oneself to the region of pure theory, one would therefore be tempted simply to condemn the problem as, by its very nature, contrary to reason. But it is not only from the theoretical point of view that the problem of heterochromatic photometry must be faced ; its interest is pre-eminently practical and even commercial ; the problem *demands* solution, even if it be partly by means of a convention."

As a matter of common experience, although it may be difficult, if not impossible, to say with certainty when two contiguous red and green luminous surfaces have the same brightness, yet if one or the other is varied there is certainly a point on one side of equality at which the red is definitely brighter than the green, while there is similarly a point on the other side of equality at which the green is certainly the brighter, always assuming that the observer is normal as regards colour vision. The methods used in visual heterochromatic photometry have been devised with the object of reducing, as much as possible, the gap between the points at which definite inequality just appears on each side. The same degree of precision as in the case of homochromatic photometry is not attainable [4], and, unfortunately, the physiological phenomenon of spatial induction (see p. 63) causes the difference between the colours of two adjacent bright fields to appear even greater than it really is [5]. The various methods which have been used by different workers at different times will be described in this chapter, and the particular advantages and difficulties inherent in each of them will then be appreciated. It is essential that the principal phenomena of colour vision, described in outline in Chapter III, should be borne in mind when any problem of visual heterochromatic photometry is under consideration.

It is self-evidently essential that the results obtained by any method of photometry should be in accordance with the ordinary laws of physical quantities, i.e. that two luminances found to be each equal to a third should also be equal to each other, and that the luminance which results from superposing two illuminations should be equal to the sum of the luminances due to each illumination separately [6]. With lights of the same colour and spectral energy distribution these laws are rigorously obeyed whatever the method of photometry adopted, at any rate under photopic conditions, but the same is not true when lights of different colours have to be compared [7]. In heterochromatic photometry, therefore, it is necessary to ensure that the method used obeys these laws and, further, that it gives the same result as would be obtained by an observer (or a physical receptor) for whom the relative response to radiation at every wave-length is identical with the agreed values of relative luminous efficiency (see p. 72) [8].

One source of error which must be avoided in all photometry involving colour difference is the reduction of the luminance of the comparison surfaces to below the limit at which the Purkinje effect begins to be noticeable (see p. 73). Thus, unless colour difference has been completely eliminated, the illumination of the photometer field should not fall below 10 lux, for otherwise the variation of sensation with change of luminance will be different on the two sides, e.g. a balance made at 10 lux will no longer be a balance to the eye if the illumination of both comparison surfaces be reduced to 1 lux and, moreover, the amount of the difference will depend on the size of the comparison field [9]. This consideration at once rules out one of the early methods of heterochromatic photometry, viz. that in which acuteness of vision was used as a measure of luminance [10]. A test chart, such as a number of lines of small type printed in black on white paper, or some geometrical pattern, was illuminated in turn by the lights to be compared, and the illumination was gradually altered in each case until a given line of type or a pattern of a certain fineness became just distinguishable. The illuminations under these conditions were assumed to be equal, and the luminous intensities of the sources were calculated accordingly [11].

The same objection applies also to the elimination of the colour difference by reducing the brightness of the comparison surfaces to within the photochromatic interval of the eye [12] (see p. 78). The sensitivity of both these methods is, moreover, very low.

Compensation or Mixture Methods—In these methods of heterochromatic photometry an ordinary direct-comparison photometer head is used, but the colour difference is reduced by illuminating one or both of the comparison surfaces with light from both the sources which are being compared. [13]. While the ease with which a setting of the photometer head can be made is much improved by the reduction of the colour difference thus achieved, the sensitivity is correspondingly reduced by reason of the very fact that the photometer surfaces do not each receive light from one source alone (see p. 198).

A similar objection applies to methods in which the light from two lamps operating at different colour temperatures is mixed in such a proportion as to give, in the photometer head, a colour match with a lamp of intermediate colour temperature [14].

A mixture method in which this difficulty is largely overcome depends on the fact that a light of comparatively low colour temperature, such as that of the primary standard, can be brought to a very close colour match with a light of much higher colour temperature, such as that of a gas-filled lamp, by the addition of only a small percentage of blue light from the region of the spectrum in the neighbourhood of 0.48μ [15]. Fig. 163 shows the arrangement used. P is the photometer head, illuminated on the right by the system D, F, C, in which D is a white diffusing surface illuminated by the

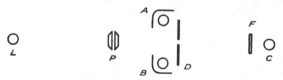

FIG. 163. The Pirani-Dziobek Method of Heterochromatic Photometry.

lamps A and B, shielded so that no direct light from them reaches P, while C is an auxiliary lamp and F a blue filter transmitting only light in the spectral region mentioned above. Light from C, transmitted through F, passes through a small aperture in D, so that the right-hand side of P is illuminated by a mixture of this light with that received by reflection from D.

The lamp of lower colour temperature is placed at L and the voltage on A and B is adjusted so that, with C extinguished, a colour-match is obtained in the photometer head. The distance of L from the photometer, d_1 say, at which a brightness match is obtained is carefully determined. The lamp of higher colour temperature is then placed at L and C is switched on and adjusted to a known colour temperature and luminous intensity. The spectral transmission curve of F is known and so the illumination at P due to the light from C can be determined for any distance CP. The distances CP and LP are adjusted to values, c and d_2 say, which give both a colour match and a brightness match in the photometer, the system P, A, B, D remaining exactly as before. If I_1 and I_2 are the respective luminous intensities of the two lamps, it will be clear that

$$I_2/d_2{}^2 = I_1/d_1{}^2 + E_c,$$

where E_c is the illumination from the combination of C and F when $CP = c$.

The great advantages of the method are its flexibility and the fact that for even the large colour difference between the primary standard and a gas-filled lamp only a comparatively small amount, of the order of 20 to 25 per cent, of blue light is required to give a colour match, so that a small uncertainty in the luminous intensity of the lamp and filter combination does not materially affect the accuracy of the measurements. The chief objection to the method is that the lights compared, although of the same colour, have different spectral energy distributions so that the results obtained are not independent of the sensitivity curve of the observer's eye (see p. 298 infra.).

The method may be extended to the photometry of sources giving light of any colour whatsoever by using a mixture of three monochromatic radiations[16] but as the spectral distributions of the lights being compared are then altogether different, the results obtained are likely to vary considerably with the observer's visual characteristics.

Direct Comparison with Small Colour Differences—The direct comparison of sources giving lights of markedly different colours is, as stated at the beginning of this chapter, inaccurate and unsatisfying to the observer, but if the colour difference is comparatively slight a measurement may be made, with a suitable form of photometer head [17], to an accuracy of about the same order as that obtainable by either of the methods already described in Chapter VII, so long as the luminance of the comparison surfaces is considerably in excess of the value at which the Purkinje effect begins to operate. If this precaution is not observed very large errors may be introduced (see p. 75). If the two fields of a Lummer-Brodhun contrast photometer, for example are illuminated by lights differing slightly in colour, a position of the photometer head can be found at which the contrast on both sides of the field appears to be equal. This may be taken as the position of balance. When the colour difference is about the same as that between two sources giving full radiation with a difference of temperature of about 100° K, it is found that an observer, following the procedure described on pp. 210 to 214, will repeat his measurements from day to day to an accuracy of about 1 per cent, while two normal-sighted observers will generally agree with each other to about the same accuracy. When, however, the colour difference is increased beyond this limit, not only do different observers disagree markedly, but the same observer becomes inconsistent from day to day [18]. It is a somewhat curious psychological effect that, with a considerable colour difference, a single observer may obtain very consistent readings during the course of a single set of observations, but on another occasion his readings, although again consistent among themselves, are quite different from his previous set [19]. There is apparently an unconscious adoption of a certain criterion of equality which, although remembered throughout a single set of measurements, is forgotten if a considerable period elapses between one set and the next.

One method of overcoming the uncertainty of a measurement involving a large colour difference is to divide this difference into a number of steps, using sets of lamps operating at intermediate efficiencies. Each set of lamps is then measured by comparison with the set next to it.

Although, when many readings are taken, the results obtained with this " cascade " method by any one observer are not more consistent with the average of a number of observers than when a comparison entailing the whole colour difference is made, it appears that the day-to-day consistency of a single observer is better [20].

Attempts have been made to eliminate, or at least reduce the consistent differences between observers by causing them to make two or more sets of measurements with the comparison fields differently arranged in the field of view. This may be achieved by inserting in the eyepiece of the photometer head a prism of the form shown in Fig 164 (a), or an arrangement of mirrors as shown in

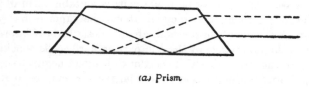

(a) Prism

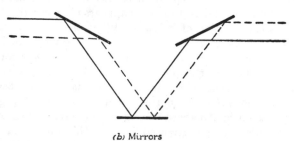

(b) Mirrors

FIG. 164. Inversion Systems.

Fig. 164 (b). If either of these systems is rotated through an angle of 90°, the image seen through it is rotated through 180°. If the photometer field is symmetrically divided into two parts, as in the case of the Lummer-Brodhun contrast photometer, measurements may be made with the prism in each of four positions 45° apart. A simple left-to-right reversal of field may be obtained by rotating the photometer through 180° about its horizontal axis, and then turning it through 180° about its vertical axis, the observer being now on the opposite side of the bench [21].

Use of Characteristic Equations—For many purposes it has been found convenient to use the characteristic equation connecting the luminous intensity of a vacuum electric lamp with its current or potential so as to enable a large range of efficiencies to be covered by a single standard. For this purpose the characteristic equation of a lamp may be taken as $\log I = A (\log x)^2 + B \log x + C$ [22], and measurements of I at three or more values of x suffice to determine the constants A, B and C. The method may clearly be extended by treating a combination of a lamp with a blue glass as a single unit and finding the values of the constants for the combination. It will be seen that, as in the cascade method, colour difference is not avoided, but with a comparatively small number of standardisations by several observers a standard is available for homochromatic comparisons over a wide range of efficiencies.

Homochromatic Methods—The most fundamental method of making a photometric comparison between two lights which differ in colour is to resolve each into components which are visually monochromatic and to compare the intensities of these components pair by pair. If I_λ and $x_\lambda I_\lambda$ be the respective intensities of any one pair of similar components whose wave-length range is $\delta\lambda$, and whose mean wave-length is λ, then the ratio of the two original intensities is $\Sigma x_\lambda I_\lambda \delta\lambda / \Sigma I_\lambda \delta\lambda$, where Σ denotes summation throughout the visible spectrum. In this way a single heterochromatic comparison is converted into a large number of homochromatic comparisons. These comparisons are carried out in a special form of instrument, known as a spectrophotometer, in which a composite light is resolved into its spectral components and photometric measurements are then made on as many of these components as may be necessary [23]. This method is, clearly, of universal application, and it will be described more fully in Chapter XI. It is, however, exceedingly tedious, and is liable to large errors unless numerous precautions are taken. For many purposes, therefore, some fundamentally less accurate method is preferable for ordinary work. The methods now to be described are of this kind, and, although based ultimately on spectrophotometric determinations, they enable such determinations to be relegated to the standardising laboratory, where they can be performed most conveniently and accurately.

The Crova Wave-length Method—One of the earliest of these

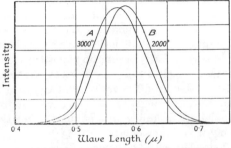

FIG. 165. The Principle of the Crova Method.

methods is that of A. Crova [24], which may best be explained by reference to Fig. 165. Curves A and B represent, respectively, the relative luminous intensities throughout the visible spectrum of the light given by two sources. These curves are obtained with a spectro-photometer. The ordinate scale is so arranged, for each curve separately, that the areas of the two curves are equal, i.e. the luminous intensity is the same for each source. If these curves intersect at wave-length λ it is clear that equality at this wave-length is a criterion for equality of the integral light. It follows, therefore, that for sources having respectively the spectral distributions exhibited in curves A and B, comparison at wave-length λ gives the same result as a comparison of the integral lights. Hence, by placing in front of the eyepiece of the photometer a medium which only transmits a narrow portion of the spectrum on either side of λ, practically homochromatic observations may be made, and the results obtained will be valid for the integral light given by the two sources. Instead of using a filter the measurement may be made with a spectrophotometer [25].

The curves of Fig. 166 show the Crova wave-lengths for the comparison of two sources giving full (black-body) radiation at

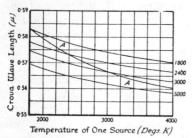

FIG. 166. The Crova Wave-length for Pairs of Full Radiators.

the temperatures shown respectively (a) on the curve, and (b) on the axis of abscissae [26]. For full radiators at temperatures between 2000° and 3000° K, the Crova wave-length is seen to be about $0\cdot57$ to $0\cdot58\mu$. A suitable solution having, at a thickness of 25 mm., a well-defined transmission band in this region consists of $CuCl_2$, 86 gm.; $K_2Cr_2O_7$, 60 gm.; HNO_3 (sp. gr. $1\cdot05$), 40 c.c. with water to 1 litre at 20° C. [27]. Curve A of Fig. 166 is the line of limiting Crova wave-lengths, i.e. the line which gives the Crova wave-length for two full radiators at the temperatures $T \pm \delta T$, when δT is vanishingly small. To a fair approximation, the Crova wave-length for two such sources may be found by taking the arithmetic mean of the limiting Crova wave-lengths for the respective temperatures of those sources. It will be clear that if two sources give radiation which is exactly similar to that of a full radiator at two accurately known temperatures, a measurement of the relative intensities at *any* convenient wave-length is sufficient to enable the relative intensities of the integral lights to be calculated [28].

A method somewhat similar to that of Crova was developed by

Macé de Lépinay and Nicati [29], who assumed that for bodies giving approximately full radiation $I/I_R = f(I_G/I_R)$, where I is the integral luminous intensity for all frequencies, and I_R and I_G are the luminous intensities in regions of the spectrum confined to the red and the green respectively. Further, they found that

$$f(I_G/I_R) = [1 + 0 \cdot 208 (1 - I_G/I_R)]^{-1}$$

represented the results for a number of ordinary sources, so that the ratio of the integral luminous intensities of two sources could be obtained from the results of two comparisons made (a) with a red transmitting medium, and (b) with a green medium in front of the eyepiece. Both of these methods of heterochromatic photometry depend on the energy distribution in the spectrum of the sources to be compared. They have been used with some success for sources giving a continuous spectrum with approximately the same energy distribution as a full radiator at some temperature. For sources with a discontinuous spectrum, however, they are quite useless, except that Crova's method may be used for approximate work when once the Crova wave-length has been determined by spectrophotometry. These methods make no claim to be fundamental in any sense of the word, and both suffer from the disadvantage that, since the transmission factors of the coloured media used are necessarily small, the brightness of the photometric field is reduced to an undesirable extent if any ordinary form of photometer head is used with sources of normal luminous intensity.

Colour Filter Methods—It is clear that if, when two sources giving lights of different colours are being compared, there be placed between the photometer and one of the sources a coloured transparent medium of such a tint as to cause the light from this source to match that from the other, the difficulty due to colour difference disappears, except that it now becomes necessary to determine the transmission factor of this colour filter. This may be done by direct visual comparison, using a source of light with the same spectral distribution as that with which the filter is intended to be used. The luminous intensity of this source is measured first without the filter, and then with the filter placed between the source and the photometer, any of the more accurate methods of heterochromatic photometry being used for the second comparison [30].

It will be seen that one of these measurements involves a colour difference as great as that which the filter is designed to eliminate, so that no gain would seem to result, but in fact there is an important practical gain, since the transmission factor may be determined once for all by a large number of observers working on several different occasions, and the mean value thus obtained may then be used in conjunction with the results of one or two observers working with the filter. Since these observers have now no colour difference to contend with, the mean of a comparatively few results of theirs will be equal in accuracy to the mean of the results which would be obtained by the larger number of observers working on every occasion on which the filter is employed. The gain of time in this procedure, when many similar sources have to be compared with a standard of a different colour, may be very great.

An alternative and much more fundamental method of measuring the transmission factor of the filter is to determine its spectral transmission curve by spectrophotometry (see Chapter XI) and then to calculate the transmission factor for light having the spectral distribution of the source with which the filter is to be used (see pp. 162 and 372) [31]. This method, besides being independent of the visual characteristics of individual observers, has the great advantage that the spectral distribution curve of the transmitted light can be compared with that of the light to be measured. It will be clear that, unless these curves are similar, a good colour match in the photometer is no guarantee that the results obtained by different observers will be identical, for the ratio of the integral lights is

$$\int V_\lambda E_\lambda \, d\lambda / \int V_\lambda E_\lambda' \, d\lambda,$$

where E_λ and E_λ' are the respective energies at wave-length λ, and this expression is not independent of V_λ unless $E_\lambda = k E_\lambda'$ where k is the same for all values of λ [32].

It is to be noted that if two or more filters are used in combination, the overall spectral transmission curve cannot be obtained from the curves for the individual filters by simple multiplication, owing to the effect of inter-reflections (see p. 230).

Types of Colour Filters—A colour filter may be either a glass, a stained gelatine film, or a cell with parallel glass walls containing a chemical solution. The glass has the advantage of greater permanence and of convenience in use and cobalt glasses of special composition are used for bridging the colour step between the primary standard and sub-standards at higher colour temperatures [33]. A yellow glass for bridging the colour step in the opposite direction has also been described [34].

The gelatine film has the advantage of much greater flexibility as far as the spectral transmission is concerned and such films mounted between glass are extensively used [35] although they are generally less permanent than glass. Special sets of filters, known as " photometric filters " are made [36] for use with tungsten filament lamps to give an approximate colour match between lamps operating at different colour temperatures [37].

By far the most flexible form of filter is a solution of carefully specified chemical composition and filters of this kind will be described more fully in later sections of this chapter.

Whatever the form of filter used, it is essential that there should be complete absence of any curvature or unevenness in the surfaces, otherwise the lens effect introduced causes a change in transmission factor as the distance between the filter and either the source or the photometer surface is altered (see p. 231) [38]. Any trace of scatter within the filter is also to be avoided (see p. 228).

If the spectral transmission curve of a colour filter is such that full radiation at one temperature T_1 becomes, after transmission through the filter, identical with full radiation at some other temperature T_2, then it can be shown that $(1/T_2 - 1/T_1)$ is a constant of the filter, i.e. that full radiation at another temperature, T_3, becomes, after transmission, identical with full radiation at temperature T_4, where $1/T_4 - 1/T_3 = 1/T_2 - 1/T_1$, all the temperatures being expressed in degrees absolute [39]. This follows at once from Wien's expression for the spectral distribution of full radiation at any temperature T, viz. $c_1 \lambda^{-5} e^{-c_2/\lambda T}$ (see p. 40), for clearly the transmission factor of the filter at wave-length λ is given by $e^{-c_2/\lambda T_2} = \tau_\lambda e^{-c_2/\lambda T_1}$, so that $\log_e \tau_\lambda = -(c_2/\lambda)\{1/T_2 - 1/T_1\}$ [40]. Thus for any such filter the spectral transmission curve is defined by $\tau_\lambda = e^{-k/\lambda}$. The constant k expresses the colour of the filter in terms of the difference between the reciprocals of the two temperatures which respectively identify the radiation before and after transmission through the filter. This difference is often stated in terms of the " mired ", derived from " micro-reciprocal-degree " [41]. For example, the temperatures 2042·1° and 2354° are, in " reciprocal-degrees ", 0·0004897 and 0·0004248 respectively and the difference is therefore 64·9 mireds. This way of expressing the colour of a filter used to bridge the step from one colour temperature to another is often convenient even when the spectral distribution of the transmitted light is not strictly identical with full radiation. In the case of a homogeneous medium such as a coloured glass or a liquid, the change of colour-temperature produced by a filter, expressed in mireds, is proportional to the thickness. In the case of a liquid it is not proportional to the concentration unless Beer's law is obeyed (see p. 160).

It is to be noted that, on account of inter-reflections, the transmission factor at any given wave-length for a composite filter consisting of two or more filters which are not in optical contact is not exactly the same as the product of the respective transmission factors of the components. It follows that the colour difference, in mireds, produced by the combination is not exactly equal to the sum of the differences produced by the component filters and, further, it has been shown that the value is affected slightly by the order in which the components are traversed by the light [42].

Variable Tint Filters—A variable tint filter can be designed to give a colour match with a tungsten lamp operating at any colour temperature within a given range [43]. The comparison lamp is placed in an enclosure with a translucent glass window, over which moves a metal slide containing two smaller windows, Y and B

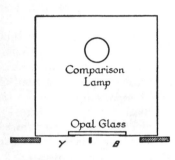

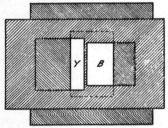

Fig. 167. A Variable Tint Filter with Constant Transmission.

(see Fig. 167). These are covered, one with a yellow and the other with a blue filter (e.g. Wratten 86 and 78). The heights of the windows are inversely as the transmission factors of the two filters for the light from the comparison lamp. It follows that as the slide is moved across the front of the window the luminous intensity is not altered, while the colour of the light changes from yellow to blue. The method may be extended and, in fact, a 3-filter combination of this kind can be used to obtain a colour match with a source of any colour whatever [44]. It is, in fact, in some respects equivalent to a trichromatic colorimeter (see p. 333).

A different form of variable tint filter may be obtained by making use of the rotatory dispersion of quartz. When plane polarised light passes through a plate of quartz cut with its surfaces perpendicular to the optic axis, the plane of polarisation is rotated by an amount which varies with the wave-length of the light [45]. The result is that, if the incident polarised light is composite, the plane of polarisation of the transmitted light will be different for each monochromatic component, i.e. the plane of polarisation of the component of wave-length λ is rotated through an angle α_λ, where α_λ is a function of λ. If, therefore, a Nicol prism or similar analyser be placed in the path of the light transmitted by the quartz, the intensity of the component λ in the light transmitted by this Nicol will be proportional to $\sin^2(\phi - \alpha_\lambda)$, where ϕ is the angle of rotation of the second Nicol measured from the position of extinction with the quartz plate removed.

Thus it follows that the spectral transmission curve of a system consisting of a quartz plate between two Nicol prisms may be altered in a manner which is calculable theoretically, since the value of α_λ, is known for all values of λ, and is proportional to the thickness of the quartz plate. By using plates of different thicknesses the flexibility of the combination may be much increased. A still greater range may be obtained by using two quartz plates sandwiched between three Nicol prisms, two of which are capable of independent rotation.

It has been found that by the use of such a system, the light from a source at one colour temperature can be matched, not only in colour but also approximately in spectral distribution, with the light from a source at a different colour temperature [46]. For instance, the single quartz plate system can be used in combination with a gas-filled lamp having a colour temperature of 2,830° K. to obtain a colour match with the light from a full radiator at any temperature between 3,100° and 4,000° K. For the range 4,000° to 7,000° K. the two-plate system must be used.

Liquid Filters—The use of a filter consisting of a chemical solution in a glass cell was first suggested by Ch. Fabry [47] for eliminating the colour difference involved in the photometric comparison of sources giving approximately full radiation. Such solutions have the advantage of ready reproducibility from specification and easy adjustment by alteration of concentration. Their chief disadvantage is, generally, a marked change of transmission with change of temperature.

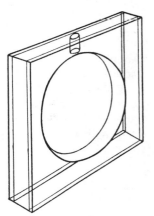

A very convenient form of cell is that shown in Fig. 168. The central section of solid glass is accurately ground to a specified thickness, frequently 1 cm., and the two faces are plane parallel sheets of an optical glass resistant to chemical attack, such as borosilicate crown. The components may be cemented together or, after thorough cleaning with nitric acid and distilled water, they may be

FIG. 168. Glass Cell for Colour Filter Solution.

pressed together and held by a seal of paraffin wax run round the edge with a hot metal point [48].

To obtain an approximate colour match between sources having different colour temperatures, a yellow solution is used with the source of higher colour temperature, or a blue solution with the source of lower colour temperature. Suitable solutions are as follows :

Yellow Solution		*Blue Solution*	
$CoSO_4(NH_4)_2SO_4.6H_2O$	100 gm.	$NiSO_4(NH_4)_2SO_4$	50 gm.
$K_2Cr_2O_7$	0·733 gm.	$(NH_4)_2SO_4$	10 gm.
Nitric Acid (1·05 sp. gr.) 10 c.c.		Ammonia (0·92 sp. gr.) 55 c.c.	
Water to 1 litre of solution		Water to 1 litre of solution	

The colour change produced by an aqueous solution containing n per cent of the above solutions is about $(4·3)n$ mireds (see p. 299) for the yellow and $(1·9)n$ mireds for the blue, although Beer's law is not strictly obeyed. The spectral distribution of the transmitted

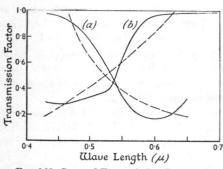

light differs appreciably from that given by a full radiator, as will be seen from Fig. 169 which shows the spectral transmission curves of (a) the blue solution at 100 per cent concentration and (b) the yellow solution diluted to 35 per cent concentration. The broken lines show the spectral transmission curves over the central part of the visible spectrum for

FIG. 169. Spectral Transmission Curves of Colour Filter Solutions.

ideal filters giving the same colour changes, viz. 190 and 150 mireds respectively.

A blue filter giving a much closer approximation to the spectral distribution required can be obtained by using two solutions in a double cell made of two glass containing elements sandwiched between three sheets of glass. The formulae for the two solutions are as follows :

Solution A		*Solution B*	
Copper sulphate		Cobalt ammonium sulphate	
($CuSO_4.5H_2O$)	a gm.	($CoSO_4(NH_4)_2SO_4.6H_2O$) b gm.	
Mannite ($C_6H_8(OH)_6$)	a gm.	Copper sulphate	
		($CuSO_4.5H_2O$)	c gm.
Pyridine (C_5H_5N)	30 c.c.	Sulphuric acid	
		(sp. gr. 1·835)	10 c.c.
Distilled water to make 1 litre		Distilled water to make 1 litre	

Filters of this type are generally known as Davis-Gibson filters [49]. The values of a, b and c are adjusted to give the change of colour temperature desired. For example, a change of 122·5 mireds is produced by a filter in which $a = 2·071$ gm., $b = 18·045$ gm. and

$c = 14 \cdot 000$ gm. both solutions being used in a thickness of exactly one cm. [50]. The close approximation of this filter to the ideal is shown in Fig. 170 in which the full line is the actual spectral transmission curve and the broken line and circles indicate the calculated curve for this particular colour step.

A filter of the Davis-Gibson type can be used to obtain a close approximation to sunlight from a tungsten lamp at a defined colour temperature and filters for which a, b and c

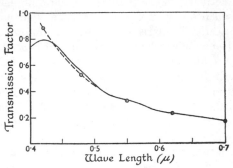

FIG. 170. Spectral Transmission Curve of a Davis-Gibson Filter.

have specified values are used in combination with a tungsten lamp at a colour temperature of 2854° K to provide the standard illuminants used in colorimetry (see p. 330). The permanence is satisfactory but there is an appreciable temperature coefficient, so that the value of transmission of a given filter must be determined at the temperature at which it is to be used. This, in fact, is the case with all colour filters, gelatine and glass [51] as well as liquid, especially when the spectral transmission curve shows a sharp rise or fall at any part of the spectrum.

The Flicker Photometer—In this instrument the criterion of the equality of luminance of two surfaces is the disappearance of the flicker produced by presenting them alternately to the eye at a certain minimum frequency. This minimum is defined as the lowest frequency which will just cause flicker to disappear over the smallest possible range of variation of either luminance alone. The extent of this range over which no flicker is discernible determines the sensitivity of the photometer under the conditions prevailing when the experiment is made. The actual method of working of this form of photometer, and the precautions to be observed when using it, must be described in some detail, since when the colour difference between the lights to be compared is large it has been found that the errors of measurement, especially in the case of inexperienced photometric observers, are considerably less with a flicker photometer than with a steady comparison instrument.

The underlying principle of the flicker photometer is that the frequency at which flicker disappears is a minimum for the condition of equality of luminance, and this whatever the difference of colour. When there is no colour difference the minimum frequency occurs when the two parts of the field are equally bright as judged by the steady comparison (often termed the " equality of brightness ") method. When there is a colour difference, the minimum may occur when the comparison fields are slightly unequal as judged by the steady comparison method, the difference depending on the conditions under which the instrument is used, particularly as regards the size and brightness of the comparison field.

The matter has been extensively studied, especially by H. E. Ives [52], who concluded that, for the comparison of lights of different colours, the flicker method of photometry gave the greatest sensitivity and the most reproducible results and that these results were in agreement with those obtained by the steady comparison method when the conditions of observation were suitably chosen.

Further, by a series of careful experiments he proved that luminances which measured equal to the same luminance by this method also measured equal to one another, and the sum of the parts was equal to the whole [53]. He suggested [54] the following as satisfactory conditions for the use of the flicker photometer :

(i) An illumination of the comparison surfaces of at least 25 lux (of the order of 120 trolands with a natural pupil), and

(ii) A photometric field of 2° diameter, surrounded by a bright field of about 25° diameter, maintained at approximately the same luminance as the photometric field.

In addition to the above conditions, the following have been laid down by A. H. Taylor [55] as essential for accurate work in flicker photometry :

(iii) There should be no dark ring between the photometric field and the surrounding bright field referred to in (ii).

(iv) When the moving parts of the flicker head are rotated slowly no shadows or unequally illuminated spots should be apparent in the field.

(v) The two halves of the flicker field should be visible for equal lengths of time during a complete cycle [56].

(vi) The photometer head should remain stationary, and the balance should be obtained by moving one of the lamps. This lamp should move with little effort on the part of the observer.

(vii) In order to give smooth and steady running, it is recommended that a direct-current series-wound motor be run at or near its rated speed, a fly-wheel being used to give additional steadiness and a reduction of eight or ten to one being used between the motor and the moving parts in the head.

(viii) The flicker photometer is not suitable for continuous work on account of its fatiguing effect. It should be used only for periods not exceeding about an hour.

Practical Forms of the Flicker Photometer—The older flicker photometers, designed before Ives published the results of his investigation, naturally did not comply with the conditions set out in the last section[57]. In particular, the field of view was usually large and there was no attempt to work at any stated level of retinal illumination. The aim, generally, was to provide as smooth a transition as possible from one comparison surface to the other. For instance, in the Bechstein flicker photometer as originally designed [58], a two-part prism of the form shown in the upper right-hand part of Fig. 171 was caused to rotate in front of a Ritchie

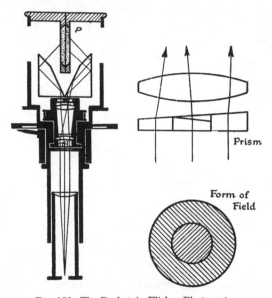

Fig. 171. The Bechstein Flicker Photometer.

wedge. The refracting surfaces of the outer annular portion of the prism and its central part were inclined in opposite directions with the result that, as the prism rotated in front of the wedge, each side was seen alternately in the centre of the field of view and in the outer annulus. When the two sides of the wedge were equally bright the flicker between annulus and centre disappeared. In a later form of the instrument, shown on the left-hand side of Fig. 171, the wedge was replaced by a plate P and two totally reflecting prisms were added, as shown, so that now the rotation of the two-part prism alternated the two sides of P in the central and annular portions of the field of view.

In modern instruments the conditions laid down by Ives and by Taylor are carefully observed. In the Ives-Brady flicker photometer [59], shown in Fig. 172, the test lamp or sub-standard illumin-

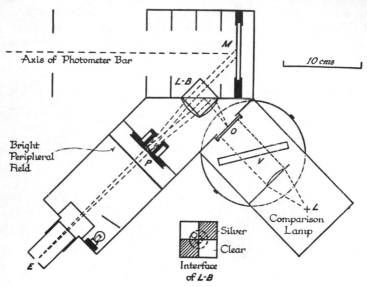

FIG. 172. The Ives-Brady Flicker Photometer.

ates the diffusing surface M, while a comparison lamp L illuminates an opal glass screen O. The brightnesses of these two surfaces are compared by means of a prism L-B, which is constructed on the Lummer-Brodhun principle, with a field of the form shown in detail at the bottom of the diagram. The field of view visible from E is made to travel over the interface of the prism by rotation of a small $10°$ prism P, the speed of rotation being under the control of the observer. V is a variable neutral filter of the form described at the top of p. 228.

Ives has also described a polarisation instrument, two forms of which are shown in Fig. 173 [60]. Two images of each half of the photometric field are formed by the double-image prism W, and the dimensions of the apparatus are so chosen that the horizontally polarised image of one half is superposed on the vertically polarised image of the other half. The Nicol prism N is rotated, with the result that the total brightness of the field seen at E is equal to $B_1 \sin^2 \theta + B_2 \cos^2 \theta$, where B_1 and B_2 are the brightnesses of the two individual fields. This expression is equal to

$$\tfrac{1}{2}\{(B_1 + B_2) - (B_1 - B_2)\cos 2\theta\}$$

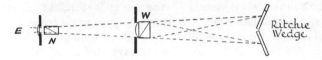

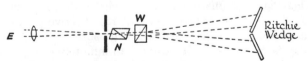

FIG. 173. Ives Polarisation Flicker Photometers.

so that the transition from one field to the other is not sudden, but follows a sine curve.

An altogether different type of instrument is that shown in plan in Fig. 174 [61]. S is a white surface of magnesium oxide illuminated, by way of the total reflection prism P, by the light from one of the sources to be compared. W is a whitened sector disc, which can be

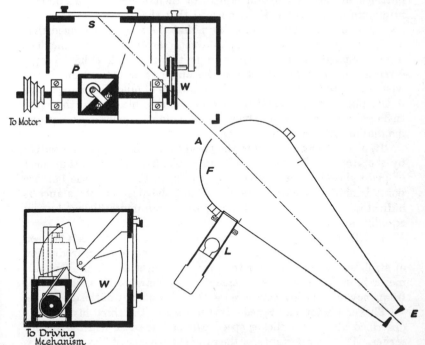

FIG. 174. Guild's Flicker Photometer.

rotated at any desired speed about a horizontal axis. Its surface is covered with magnesium oxide and is illuminated by the other source of light so that, when viewed by the eye at E, the field of view seen through the small aperture A is alternately occupied by W and by S. A is of such a size as to subtend an angle of $2°$ at E. It is cut with a sharp (back-bevelled) edge in a concave surface F, which is also covered with magnesium oxide and is evenly illuminated by the small lamp L, the light from which is transmitted through a piece of opal glass and is diffusely reflected from the white internal surface F. If P, S and W are so arranged that the effective position of the front surface of S coincides with the white surface of W, this latter plane may be taken as the position of an infinitely thin photometer screen, so that no correction for thickness is necessary. L is adjusted to give F a luminance of about 8 candelas per square metre, and the distances of the sources to be compared are then arranged so that the luminance of the field at A has approximately the same value. The test lamp and photometer are then fixed and measurements are made by moving the comparison lamp, the speed of rotation of W being reduced until flicker can be brought almost to disappear. Settings of the comparison lamp are then made to the point of minimum flicker. It is to be noticed that the surfaces of S and W are made of the same material, and that they are so arranged that a slight angular twist of the photometer head causes the incident light to change inclination (relative to the line of view) in the same direction in both cases. Hence the angle error noticed on p. 209 with regard to the Lummer-Brodhun head is of much less importance in this photometer. S and W are easily removable, so that the white surfaces can be readily renewed by holding them over burning magnesium ribbon.

If, in a flicker photometer, the two beams are reduced alternately by the same small amount as, for instance, by inserting a thin sheet of plain glass first in one beam and then in the other, the balance point is shifted slightly to and fro and the position of balance is indicated, not by absence of flicker or by minimum flicker, but by equality of flicker under the two conditions.

It will be clear that, in general, no form of sector disc can be used in combination with a flicker photometer owing to the introduction of stroboscopic effects. For the same reason, if this form of photometer is used for the measurement of discharge lamps, the flicker frequency must be low compared with the frequency of the discharge.

Flicker Photometer Speed—In the case of the three instruments described above, the flicker speed can be varied at will by the observer. This is important, for the range of absence of flicker increases with the speed [62], so that it is clearly desirable to work at the minimum speed at which flicker just disappears. This minimum depends both on the extent of the colour difference and on the field brightness [63] for the eye is more sensitive to flicker at high values of brightness than at low, so that higher speeds are necessary to cause disappearance of flicker when the illumination is increased. This is illustrated by the curves of Fig. 175, which show, for light of three colours compared with white light, the frequencies necessary to

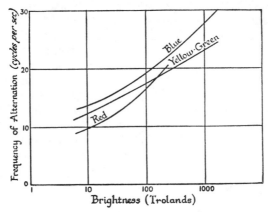

FIG. 175. The Effect of Field Luminance on Flicker Frequency.

cause disappearance of flicker at various values of retinal illumination [64]. Ives found [65] that flicker sensitivity was noticeably increased by enlarging the field of view from 1·86° diameter to 8·6° × 5·16°. By averted vision, when the image of the centre of the smaller field was 8° from the fovea, the sensitivity was again decreased. Although this result appears to be contrary to the known fact that the peripheral part of the retina is more sensitive to flicker than the fovea (see p. 71), the explanation of the discrepancy is found to be that this extra sensitivity by averted vision is quite transitory, and is very quickly reduced to a negative value when this part of the retina is used continuously. Binocular vision has been found to give a slight increase of sensitivity to flicker in the case of some observers [66].

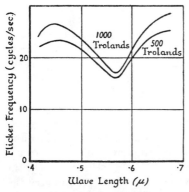

FIG. 176. The Effect of Colour Difference on Flicker Speed.

As regards the effect of the difference of colour between the lights being compared, Fig. 176 shows the frequency required for the elimination of flicker when the light from a tungsten lamp is compared with lights at different parts of the spectrum, while Fig. 177 shows the variation of sensitivity with speed at three different values of field brightness, the curves in this case showing the range over which flicker is absent at various speeds when a green and a white light are compared.

In general it may be said that the minimum speed increases with (i) field brightness, (ii) separation on the chromaticity diagram (see p. 327) and (iii) irregularity of the periods of exposure of the two comparison surfaces [67].

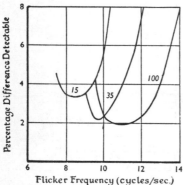

Fig. 177. The Variation of Sensitivity with Flicker Speed.

Errors and Reproducibility—Ives found that for a normal value of retinal illumination by the photometer field (abt. 80 trolands) the error of measurement in comparing different parts of the spectrum with white light was, on the average, four to five times as great with the steady comparison as with the flicker method, although in the case of experienced observers it was only about twice as great [68]. The error by both methods was, naturally, larger at the ends of the spectrum than in the middle. In the case of a lower level of retinal illumination (3 trolands) the difference between the errors obtained by the two methods was not nearly as great, being, in fact, negligible in the case of experienced observers. The reproducibility of the measurements by a single observer after an interval of two months was found to be rather higher in the case of the flicker photometer. Apparently the criterion of equality is more liable to alter from day to day in the steady comparison than in the flicker method. The reproducibility for both methods diminishes as the retinal illumination is decreased below about 6 trolands.

The Choice of Observers—It has been mentioned already that, unless there is a close similarity between the spectral energy distributions of the lights being compared in a photometer, the results obtained by different observers, all of whom have normal colour vision, are generally not identical owing to small differences in the sensitivity curves of individual eyes. This applies to both the flicker and the steady comparison methods of visual photometry [69].

It is clearly impracticable for every observer to make a complete determination of the sensitivity curve of his own eye and a more rapid method of testing for departure from the standard curve was devised by Ives in connection with his work on the flicker photometer [70]. Each observer is required to determine the transmission factors of two specified aqueous solutions, one yellow and the other blue, when used in a thickness of 1 cm. with a lamp operating at a colour temperature of 2073° K. The solutions contain, respectively, 72 gm. of potassium bichromate ($K_2Cr_2O_7$) and 57 gm. of copper sulphate ($CuSO_4.5H_2O$) in one litre of solution. The calculated transmissions for an observer having the standard sensitivity curve (see p. 73) are in the ratio $Y/B = 0.98$ but the average value of this ratio for normal sighted observers is possibly nearer unity [71]. Only observers, or groups of observers, who find for these solutions a ratio of transmission factors, the " Y/B ratio ", which is close to unity (at any rate to within about 5 per cent) should make observations in heterochromatic photometry [72]. The use of a coloured medium for correcting an observer to normal has been proposed [73] but has never found practical application.

General Conclusions regarding Visual Heterochromatic Photometry—There seems to be no doubt that, while the steady comparison method is satisfactory for comparing lights which do not differ greatly in colour, it should not be used when the colour difference is considerable. Although the requirements laid down in the first section of this chapter may still be met [74], the day-to-day uncertainty and the individual differences between observers make it necessary to take the mean of a large number of measurements, made by a group of at least five or six observers working on several different occasions. For a direct comparison with a considerable colour difference the flicker photometer is more satisfactory, especially with unpractised observers, when the above conditions as to illumination and field size are observed [75]. One fact which cannot be too much emphasized is that in all heterochromatic photometry, whether by the steady comparison method or by the flicker method, the brightness of the photometer field should always be well above the limit of the Purkinje effect. In addition it is most desirable that the size of field should be specified.

In most cases the best procedure is to avoid the colour difference, either entirely or to a considerable extent, by the use of a suitable colour filter in all day-to-day photometry. If this filter is used with a lamp of known, or at least constant spectral distribution, its transmission factor may be found once and for all, either by spectrophotometry or, where this is not possible, by one of the methods described above, measurements being made by a number of skilled observers working on several occasions under the most favourable conditions as regards accuracy [76]. Further, this method can be used for the photometry of sources, such as discharge tubes, which show periodic variations in light emission and for which, therefore, measurements made with the flicker photometer are liable to error due to a stroboscopic effect [77].

Photo-electric Methods—It will be clear that the various difficulties met with in visual heterochromatic photometry can be entirely overcome by the use of a photocell, or other physical receptor, provided it is possible to compensate, by the use of a colour filter or otherwise, for the difference between the sensitivity curve of the receptor and the standard curve of relative luminous efficiency [78].

In the case of photo-emissive cells of the thin film potassium type (see p. 98) a liquid filter consisting, of an aqueous solution of cupric chloride ($CuCl_2.2H_2O$), cobaltous ammonium sulphate ($CoSO_4.(NH_4)_2SO_4.6H_2O$) and potassium dichromate ($K_2Cr_2O_7$) has been used [79]. The relative amounts of the three components in the solution are adjusted so that the transmission factor of the filter at each wave-length λ is, as nearly as possible, equal to nV_λ/P_λ, where V_λ is the relative luminous efficiency and P_λ the relative response of the receptor, both at wave-length λ, and n is a constant. In the case of the photo-voltaic cell, an approximate correction can be made by means of a coloured glass or combination of glasses having suitable spectral transmission curves [80].

As might be expected *a priori*, perfect correction of the sensitivity curve of a given receptor cannot be obtained by the use of a colour filter consisting of only a few components. Unfortunately, if more than a few are used in series, the amount of light transmitted by the combination is very small and the method becomes unworkable on this account. This dilemma may be avoided by making a number of measurements, each with a single filter or a simple combination, and then taking a weighted mean of the results [81]. The value so found is the same as that which would be obtained by using a filter consisting of a combination, in parallel, of the various filters used for the individual measurements. For instance, if three filters are used and these have spectral transmission curves represented by $F_1(\lambda)$, $F_2(\lambda)$ and $F_3(\lambda)$ respectively, the mean of the results obtained with these filters, weighted respectively by the factors a, b and c, is the same as the value which would be obtained by using a filter with a spectral transmission curve represented by $aF_1(\lambda) + bF_2(\lambda) + cF_3(\lambda)$. It is clear that by using a sufficient number of filters any given spectral transmission curve can, at least theoretically, be imitated to any assigned degree of accuracy. Further it will be seen that the system is not restricted to its use for correcting the sensitivity curve of a given receptor ; it can equally well be used instead of a filter which changes full radiation from one temperature to another (see p. 299).

The Template Method—Instead of using a colour filter to weight the spectrum in accordance with the sensitivity curve of the receptor used, the light from the source may be dispersed by means of a spectrometer system and each wave-length may then be appropriately weighted by placing a template with an aperture of suitable form in the spectral image plane. The light passing through the template is recombined on the surface of the receptor and the response is therefore proportional to $\int E_\lambda h_\lambda \, d\lambda$, where E_λ is the energy at wave-length λ and h_λ the height of the template aperture at that position in the spectral image where the light is of wave-length λ.

This device was first suggested for use with a thermopile [82], the form of template in this case being the " photopic " curve of Fig. 44, modified to allow for the dispersion of the prism system employed. When a photocell is used as the receptor, the value of h_λ is proportional to the ratio V_λ/P_λ where P_λ is the relative sensitivity of the photocell at wave-length λ.

Fig. 178 shows how the components may be arranged [83]. S is the source and L_1 the first collimator lens, concentrating the light

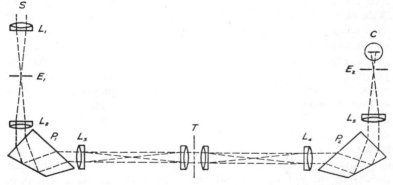

Fig. 178. The Dispersion-Template Method of Photo-electric Heterochromatic Photometry.

on E_1, the curved entrance slit. An enlarged spectral image of E_1 is formed on the template T by means of the two lenses L_2 and L_3 and the constant deviation prism P_1. Two field lenses, one on each side of T, form an image of lens L_3 at the plane of L_4, the collimator lens of the recombining system which consists of this lens, another constant deviation prism and the lens L_5. The recombined light passes through the curved exit slit E_2 and then reaches the sensitive surface of the photocell C.

The principal difficulty attending the use of apparatus of this kind is the necessity for a very high degree of accuracy both in the shape of the template and in registering its position with respect to wave-length in the spectral image. Stray light scattered from lens and prism faces must be prevented from reaching the photocell.

This is achieved in the instrument shown in Fig. 178 by bringing the recombined light to a sharp image in the plane of the exit slit, so that practically all out-of-focus light is cut off.

Trouble due to stray light may be reduced by using, in front of the photocell, a filter which gives an approximate correction to the standard curve for V_λ. It is then only necessary for the template to provide the residual correction, so that the aperture is much more uniform in height and the error due to stray light correspondingly small [84].

It will be clear that an instrument of the type described above may be used to measure the light given by a source in any specified region of the spectrum. For this purpose all that is necessary is to cover those portions of the template aperture which correspond to the unwanted wave-lengths (see p. 373).

Heterochromatic Photometry at Low Values of Brightness: Equivalent Luminance—All ordinary heterochromatic photometry is carried out by a method which is based, ultimately, on the standard table of values of V_λ, i.e. the sensitivity curve of the photopic, or light-adapted eye [85]. Sometimes, however, the conditions are such that a measurement made in this way gives a result which is in serious disagreement with ordinary observation and is therefore useless for practical purposes. For example, the brightness of a coloured luminescent surface may be compared visually with that of a white surface illuminated by the light from a tungsten lamp after transmission through a filter which gives a colour match. If this is done for, say, a red and a green surface which appear equally bright, it will be found that there is a considerable difference between the values of luminance found for the two surfaces by using the transmission factors of the appropriate red and green filters as calculated from their spectral transmission curves and the photopic curve of relative luminous efficiency. Further, the amount of the difference will depend on the level of brightness at which the comparisons are made.

The reason for the apparent discrepancy referred to in the last paragraph is the fact, already noted in Chapter III (p. 74), that at low levels of brightness the visual sensation due to a given physical stimulus varies with the colour, not only in kind but also in degree. In other words, the subjective brightness (or luminosity) corresponding to any given value of luminance (see p. 136) is not the same for all colours when the brightness is low. As stated in Chapter III, it has been agreed that, under these conditions, the subjective brightness of a surface shall be measured by visual comparison with a surface emitting or reflecting light having the same spectral distribution as that of a full radiator at a temperature of 2042° K.

The value of brightness obtained by visual comparison as just described may be called the *equivalent luminance* of the surface [86]. This quantity is, therefore, defined as the luminance of a surface which appears to have the same subjective brightness as the coloured surface when its spectral energy distribution is that of a full radiator at 2042° K. Subjective brightness, or luminosity, being a sensation, cannot be expressed in physical units, but the luminance of a surface under photopic conditions, or the equivalent luminance in the Purkinje and scotopic ranges, can be used as the quantitative expression of subjective brightness, so long as there is no risk of confusion of thought [87].

The equivalent luminance of a surface can be calculated from its luminance at any level of brightness for which the sensitivity curve of the eye is defined, provided the spectral distribution of the light from the surface is known [88]. If S_λ is the relative sensitivity at wave-length λ, the equivalent luminance is proportional to $\int S_\lambda E_\lambda \, d\lambda$ and the luminance to $\int V_\lambda E_\lambda \, d\lambda$ where E_λ is the energy per unit wave-length interval at wave-length λ; thus the ratio of the equivalent luminance to the luminance is equal to $\kappa \int S_\lambda E_\lambda \, d\lambda / \int V_\lambda E_\lambda \, d\lambda$ where κ is a constant. This ratio is, by definition, equal to unity when $E_\lambda = \lambda^{-5} e^{-c_2/2042\lambda}$ (using Wien's radiation formula), so that κ can be calculated if S_λ is known at all wave-lengths. In particular, under scotopic conditions $\kappa = 2 \cdot 568$ so that the scotopic equivalent luminance of a surface is equal to its (photopic) luminance multiplied by $2 \cdot 568 \int S_\lambda E_\lambda \, d\lambda / \int V_\lambda E_\lambda \, d\lambda$ where S_λ represents the scotopic sensitivity of the eye. The value of this ratio for full radiation over a range of temperatures is shown in Fig. 179 [89]. The maximum luminous efficiency of radiation for scotopic vision, K_m', is κK_m, i.e. 1745 scotopic lumens per watt.

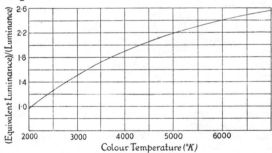

FIG. 179. The Equivalent Luminance for Full Radiation at Different Colour Temperatures.

It should be remarked that for any visual comparison of brightness carried out under non-photopic conditions the field of view should normally be large, viz. 10° or more in diameter, and symmetrically divided.

BIBLIOGRAPHY

C. Fabry. C.I.E., Proc., 6, *1924*, p. 184 ; 7, *1928*, p. 1155 ; 8, *1931*, p. 537.

H. König. Archiv f. techn. Messen, *1935*, T 6.

REFERENCES

1. Bouguer, writing in his *Traité d'Optique* (p. 50), characterises as " *embarrassante* " the comparison of two lights of different colours. Lambert, too (Photometria, 309), says : " Ægre comparantur claritates, quæ colore plus minusve differunt."

2. S. Kikkawa. Central Bureau of Weights and Measures, Tokyo, Researches, 6, *1916*.

3. C.I.E., Proc., 5, *1921*, p. 107.

4. The discrimination threshold is, in fact, about five times as great when red is compared with green as when there is no colour difference. See L. T. Troland, Frank. Inst., J., 182, *1916*, p. 112 ; Psychol. Rev. (N.Y.), 25, *1918*, pp. 305 and 359.

5. See, e.g., L. Bell, El. World, 59, *1912*, p. 201 ; R. Pauli, Naturwissenschaften, 1, *1913*, p. 976.

6. P. Lauriol. C.I.E., Proc., 2, *1907*, p. 147 ; J. of Gas Lighting, 99, *1907*, p. 243. R. G. Weigel. Licht, 3, *1933*, p. 17.
H. König. Licht, 7, *1937*, p. 261 ; Helv. Phys. Acta, 15, *1942*, p. 85 ; Rev. d'Opt., 27, *1948*, p. 551.

7. A. Dresler. Licht, 7, *1937*, p. 203.

8. Comité Int. des Poids et Mesures, Procès-verbaux, 18, *1937*, p. 223.
See also H. König, Helv. Phys. Acta, 7, *1934*, p. 427 and 15, *1942*, p. 85 and Licht, 7, *1937*, p. 261 ; Illum. Eng. Soc. N.Y., Trans., 27, *1932*, p. 738 ; A. Dresler, Z. f. techn. Phys., 19, *1938*, p. 369.

9. See, e.g., F. Laporte, Electrician, 57, *1906*, p. 549 ; W. Dziobek and O. Reeb, Phys. Z., 35, *1934*, p. 545.
On the effect of size of field see, e.g., J. S. Dow, Phys. Soc. Proc., 20, *1906*, p. 245 and 22, *1910*, p. 80.

10. J. Macé de Lépinay and W. Nicati. C.R., 90, *1880*, p. 1275 ; Ann. Chim. Phys., 24, *1881*, p. 289 and 30, *1883*, p. 145.
See also G. Holst. Physica, 13, *1933*, p. 33.

11. F. W. Carter. El. Rev., 47, *1900*, pp. 120 and 128.
H. E. Ives. El. World, 55, *1910*, p. 939.
See also the refs. in note (11) on p. 264 of *Photometry (1926)*.

12. See, e.g., J. B. Spurge, Phys. Soc., Proc., 12, *1894*, p. 522.

13. See the refs. given in notes (13) to (16) on p. 265 of *Photometry (1926)* ; also R. A. Houstoun, Nature, 135, *1935*, p. 1000.

14. C. Fabry. C.I.E., Proc., 8, *1931*, p. 546.
It is impossible, by the mixture method, to avoid heterochromatic comparison altogether. See a paper by P. M. Tikhodéev (Comité Int. des Poids et Mesures, Procès-verbaux, 14, *1931*, p. 301 ; Congrès Int. d'Electricité, Paris, *1932*, C.r., Vol. VIII, p. 29) and a discussion of it by H. König (Helv. Phys. Acta, 8, *1935*, p. 82). A photo-electric method based on this principle has been described by J. Vorobeitchik (C.R., 205, *1937*, p. 1222).

15. M. Pirani and W. Dziobek. World Engineering Congress, Tokyo, *1929*, Proc., Vol. 24, p. 207 ; Licht u. Lampe, 20, *1931*, p. 102.
S. Suzuki. Electrotech. Lab. Tokyo, Researches No. 276, *1930*.
C. Fabry. C.I.E., Proc., 8, *1931*, p. 544.
Z. Yamauti. Int. Illum. Congress, *1931*, Proc., Vol. I, p. 188.
See also F. Blottiau and M. Françon, Rev. d'Opt., 21, *1942*, p. 121.

16. E. Ferencz and J. Urbanek. C.I.E., Proc., 9, *1935*, p. 219.

17. O. Lummer. El. World, 50, *1907*, p. 570.

18. See, e.g., R. K. Kövesligethy and P. Selényi, Int. Illum. Congress, *1931*, Proc., Vol. I, p. 164 ; B. P. Dudding, G. T. Winch and B. S. Cooper, *ibid.*, p. 178.

19. H. E. Ives. Phys. Rev., 34, *1912*, p. 387.

20. C. C. Paterson and B. P. Dudding. Phys. Soc., Proc., 27, *1915*, p. 263.

21. See also K. Schaum, Z. phys. Chem., 131, *1928*, p. 226.

22. L. E. Barbrow and J. F. Meyer. Bureau of Standards, J. of Research, 9. *1932*, p. 721.
See also Appendix X, p. 532.

23. L. S. Ornstein, J. G. Eymers and D. Vermeulen. Rev. d'Opt., 12, *1933*, p. 390.
J. Terrien. C.R., 230, *1950*, p. 531.

24. C.R., 93, *1881*, p. 512, 95, *1882*, p. 1271 and 99, *1884*, p. 1067.
Trotter has pointed out (*Illumination, etc.*, p. 171) that apparently Crova developed this method empirically, but the problem is treated fundamentally in C.R., 95, *loc. cit. supra.*
M. Vuillaume and A. Boutaric. Rev. d'Opt., 2, *1923*, p. 41.
H. E. Ives. Phys. Rev., 32, *1911*, p. 316.
M. Pirani. Z. f. Bel., 19, *1913*, p. 333.

25. G. Ribaud. Rev. d'Opt., 12, *1933*, p. 193.
G. Ribaud and H. Djoudat. *Ibid.*, 16, *1937*, p. 297.

26. W. E. Forsythe. Frank. Inst., J., 197, *1924*, p. 517.

27. H. E. Ives and E. F. Kingsbury. Illum. Eng. Soc. N.Y., Trans., 10, *1915*, p. 716.
The transmission band of the solution originally suggested by Crova is far too broad to give accurate results. (See R. Jouaust and P. Waguet, Rev. Gén. de l'El., 22, *1927*, p. 371.) A solution with a very narrow transmission band at 0·56 has been described by K. S. Gibson (Opt. Soc. Am., J., 25, *1935*, p. 131).

28. G. Ribaud. C.R., 196, *1933*, pp. 687 and 852.
See also H. Buckley and F. J. C. Brookes, J. Sci. Inst., 10, *1933*, p. 351.

29. C.R., 97, *1883*, p. 1428.

30. See remark on p. 228 concerning the position of the filter.

31. M. Pirani. Z. f. Bel., 21, *1915*, p. 41.
See also E. C. Crittenden and A. H. Taylor, Illum. Eng. Soc. N.Y., Trans., 24, *1929*, p. 153 ; R. Jouaust, Soc. Franç. des Elect., Bull., 9, *1929*, p. 720.
For the application of this method to the photometry of discharge lamps, see C. Fabry, L. Roux and E. Perrin, Rev. d'Opt., 8, *1929*, p. 1 and Z. Yamauti, Int. Illum. Congress, *1931*, Proc., Vol. I, p. 188 (neon) ; W. Dziobek and O. Reeb, Z. f. techn. Phys., 14, *1933*, p. 350 (sodium) ; H. Buckley, Illum. Eng., 27, *1934*, pp. 118 and 148 (general) ; F. Benford, Gen. El. Rev., 37, *1934*, p. 342 (sodium) ; G. T. Winch, E. H. Palmer, C. F. Machin and B. P. Dudding, G.E.C. Journ., 5, *1934*, p. 125 (general) ; P. Clausing, Physica, 2, *1935*, p. 731 (general) ; W. F. Little and R. S. Estey, Illum. Eng. Soc. N.Y., Trans., 32, *1937*, p. 628 (general) ; H. König, Helv. Phys. Acta, 12, *1939*, p. 229 (sodium) and p. 519 (theory of the general case) ; W. E. Forsythe, B. T. Barnes and A. L. Shrider, Opt. Soc. Am., J., 28, *1938*, p. 241 (mercury); H. G. W. Harding, Illum. Eng. Soc. Lond., Trans., 9, *1944*, p. 89 (sodium).
See also W. E. Forsythe, Illum. Eng. Soc. N.Y., Trans., 31, *1936*, p. 181 and L. B. Johnson, *ibid.*, 32, *1937*, p. 646.

32. R. Jouaust. C.R., 192, *1931*, p. 616.
See also G. T. Winch and E. H. Palmer, Illum. Eng., 27, *1934*, p. 223 ; H. König, Helv. Phys. Acta, 8, *1935*, p. 637.

33. Comité Int. des Poids et Mesures, Procès-verbaux, 16, *1933*, pp. 296, 304, 307 and 323.
J. S. Preston and F. W. Cuckow. Phys. Soc., Proc., 48, *1936*, p. 869.
H. Buckley. Phil. Mag., 24, *1937*, p. 1059.
H. G. W. Harding. J. Sci. Inst., 25, *1948*, p. 333.
W. E. K. Middleton. Opt. Soc. Am., J., 44, *1954*, p. 499.

34. H. G. W. Harding. Phys. Soc., Proc., 56, *1944*, p. 21.

35. A. Biot. Soc. Sci. de Bruxelles, Ann., 61 (Sér. I), *1947*, p. 242.

36. By Messrs. Kodak, Ltd., (Wratten Division), Kingsway, London, W.C. 2.
See also D. L. MacAdam, Opt. Soc. Am., J., 35, *1945*, p. 670.

37. C. E. K. Mees. Illum. Eng. Soc. N.Y., Trans., 9, *1914*, p. 990.

38. The filter should preferably be placed close to the photometer head and glass surfaces should be optically worked.

39. H. P. Gage. Opt. Soc. Am., J., 23, *1933*, p. 46.

40. K. S. Weaver. Opt. Soc. Am., J., 26, *1936*, p. 339

41. I. G. Priest. Opt. Soc. Am., J., 23, *1933*, p. 41.
R. S. Estey. *Ibid.*, 26, *1936*, p. 293.

42. F. Benford. Opt. Soc. Am., J., 25, *1935*, p. 136.

43. R. von Voss. Z. f. Bel., 25, *1919*, p. 53.

44. H. E. Ives. Opt. Soc. Am., J., 7, *1923*, p. 243.
See also E. Ferencz and J. Urbanek, C.I.E., Proc., 9, *1935*, p. 219.

45. T. Preston, *Theory of Light*, § 257 ; Glazebrook's *Dict. Appl. Physics*, vol. 4, p. 509.

46. I. G. Priest. Phys. Rev., 6, *1915*, p. 64 ; 9, *1917*, pp. 341 and 580 ; 10, *1917*, p. 208 ; Opt. Soc. Am., J., 7, *1923*, p. 1175.
K. S. Gibson. Opt. Soc. Am., J., 11, *1925*, p. 75.
F. F. Blottiau and H. Royer. Rev. d'Opt., 32, *1953*, p. 91.
See also I. G. Priest, Opt. Soc. Am., J., 5, *1921*, p. 178 and 6, *1922*, p. 27 ; P. Proisy and J. Gauzit, Rev. d'Opt., 26, *1947*, p. 1.

47. C.R., 137, *1903*, p. 743 ; Illum. Eng. Soc. N.Y., Trans., 8, *1913*, p. 302.

48. See also W. Pinfold, J. Sci. Inst., 9, *1932*, p. 331 ; National Phys. Lab., Annual Report, *1933*, p. 65.

49. R. Davis and K. S. Gibson. Bureau of Standards, Miscellaneous Publication No. 114, *1931*.
See also Opt. Soc. Am., J., 21, *1931*, p. 654.

50. This is the filter to which chart 37 in the above publication refers.

51. E. C. Crittenden and A. H. Taylor. Illum. Eng. Soc. N.Y., Trans., 24, *1929*, p. 153.
H. Lütge. Glastechn. Ber., 10, *1932*, p. 374.
K. Weber. Z. wiss. Photog., 35, *1936*, p. 193.
J. Escher-Desrivières and Y. Godron. C.R., 210, *1940*, p. 215.
A. J. Holland. Soc. of Glass Technol., J., 25, *1941*, p. 164.
See also D. B. Judd, Bureau of Standards, J. of Research, 1, *1928*, p. 859.

52. Phil. Mag., 24, *1912*, pp. 149, 352, 744 and 845 ; Opt. Soc. Am., J., 7, *1923*, p. 363.
See also J. S. Dow, Phys. Soc., Proc., 20, *1906*, p. 245 and 22, *1910*, p. 80 and Electrician, 58, *1907*, pp. 609 and 647 ; M. Luckiesh, El. World, 61, *1913*, pp. 620 and 835 (see also p. 734).
On the theory of the flicker photometer, see, e.g., H. E. Ives and E. F. Kingsbury, Phil. Mag., 28, *1914*, p. 708 and 31, *1916*, p. 290 ; H. E. Ives, *ibid.*, 33, *1917*, p. 18, and the other references in note (78) on p. 267 of *Photometry* (*1926*). See also S. O. Maisel, Akad. Nauk, U.S.S.R., Doklady, 59, *1948*, p. 49 (In Russian) ; Y. Galifret and H. Piéron, Rev. d'Opt., 36, *1957*, p. 157.

53. Phys. Rev., 34, *1912*, p. 389.
See also C. Schaefer, Phys. Z., 26, *1925*, p. 58 ; G. Blet, C.R., 216, *1943*, p. 531 and 226, *1948*, p. 712 and Mesures, 10, *1945*, p. 327 ; F. Blottiau, C.R., 218, *1944*, p. 933.

54. Phil. Mag., 24, *1912*, p. 854 ; Illum. Eng. Soc. N.Y., Trans., 7, *1912*, p. 376.

55. Illum. Eng. Soc. N.Y., Trans., 16, *1921*, p. 585.

56. See also H. E. Ives and E. F. Kingsbury, Phys. Rev., 7, *1916*, p. 149. J. S. Dow found that unequal periods of exposure for the two surfaces in the photometer did not materially affect the accuracy of the measurement (Electrician, 58, *1907*, p. 647).

57. See the refs. in notes (51) to (53) and (55) to (61) on pp. 266–7 of *Photometry* (*1926*). L. Piatti devised a flicker form of the Joly block photometer described on p. 4 (Nuovo Cimento, 7, *1930*, p. 117 ; Z. f. Phys., 72, *1931*, p. 803) while J. Jaumann used the stereoscopic photometer mentioned on p. 232 (Z. f. Phys., 69, *1931*, p. 153)

58. W. Bechstein. Z.f.I., 25, *1905*, p. 45, 26, *1906*, p. 249 and 27, *1907*, p. 178.

59. Phys. Rev., 4, *1914*, p. 222.
See also E. F. Kingsbury, Frank. Inst., J., 180, *1915*, p. 215.

60. Phil. Mag., 33, *1917*, p. 360.
Other forms of polarisation flicker photometer have been described by S. Maisel

(Russkoe Fisiko-Khimicheskoe Obschestvo, Jurnal (First Section), 39, *1907*, p. 193 (In Russian with French abs.) ; J. de Phys., 7, *1908*, p. 739) and by G. Yvon (Rev. d'Opt., 1, *1922*, p. 499).

61. J. Guild. J. Sci. Inst., 1, *1924*, p. 182.
See also E. Gambetta, Rev. d'Opt., 18, *1939*, p. 41 ; G. Blet, C.R., 216, *1943*, p. 531 and Mesures, 10, *1945*, p. 298.

62. J. S. Dow. Electrician, 59, *1907*, p. 255.

63. L. T. Troland. Illum. Eng. Soc. N.Y., Trans., 11, *1916*, p. 947.
H. E. Ives. Phil. Mag., 34, *1917*, p. 99 ; Opt. Soc. Am., J., 7, *1923*, p. 363.

64. L. T. Troland. Frank. Inst., J., 182, *1916*, p. 261.

65. Phil. Mag., 24, *1912*, pp. 149, 352, 744 and 845.

66. C. S. Sherrington. Brit. J. of Psychol., 1, *1904*, p. 26.

67. M. Luckiesh. Phys. Rev., 4, *1914*, p. 1.
H. E. Ives. Opt. Soc. Am., J., 6, *1922*, p. 254.

68. Phil. Mag., 24, *1912*, p. 149.
See also S. W. Ashe, El. World, 56, *1910*, p. 734.

69. On the use of a filter in comparisons made with the flicker photometer, see J. Voogd, Philips Techn. Rev., 5, *1940*, p. 270.

70. H. E. Ives and E. F. Kingsbury. Illum. Eng. Soc. N.Y., Trans., 10, *1915*, p. 203.
E. C. Crittenden and F. K. Richtmyer. Bureau of Standards, Bull., 14, *1918*, p. 87.
K. S. Gibson. Opt. Soc. Am., J., 9, *1924*, p. 113.
See also P. Devaux, Soc. Franç. des Elect., Bull., 3, *1943*, p. 112 ; G. Blet, Mesures, 10, *1945*, p. 327 ; C.I.E., Proc., 11, *1948*, p. 183.

71. J. S. Preston. Phys. Soc., Proc., 51, *1939*, p. 757.

72. A. H. Taylor. Illum. Eng. Soc. N.Y., Trans., 23, *1928*, p. 361.

73. H. E. Ives and E. F. Kingsbury. Illum. Eng. Soc. N.Y., Trans., 10, *1915*, p. 259.
M. Richter. Licht, 8, *1938*, p. 127.
See also W. S. Stiles, Phil. Mag., 17, *1934*, p. 660.

74. W. de W. Abney and E. R. Festing. Phil. Tran., 177, *1886*, p. 423 and 179, *1888*, p. 547.
C. Schaefer. Phys. Z., 26, *1925*, p. 58.

75. E. C. Crittenden and F. K. Richtmyer. Bureau of Standards, Bull., 14, *1918*, p. 87.
F. K. Richtmyer and E. C. Crittenden. Opt. Soc. Am., J., 4, *1920*, p. 371.
See also A. H. Taylor, Opt. Soc. Am., J., 13, *1926*, p. 193 and Illum. Eng. Soc. N.Y., Trans., 21, *1926*, p. 804 ; W. Dziobek, Z.f.I., 46, *1926*, pp. 476 and 586 ; C.I.E., Proc., 7, *1928*, p. 1155 ; E. C. Crittenden and A. H. Taylor, Illum. Eng. Soc. N.Y., Trans., 24, *1929*, p. 153 ; R. G. Weigel, Licht, 1, *1931*, pp. 291, 315, 339 and 364 ; J. Terrien, Rev. d'Opt., 30, *1951*, p. 415 ; J. Schiess, Z. f. angewandte Phys., 4, *1952*, p. 374, Optik, 9, *1952*, pp. 274 and 312, Lichttechnik, 3, *1951*, pp. 57, 146 and 276 and 4, *1952*, p. 133.

76. H. E. Ives and E. F. Kingsbury. Phys. Rev., 5, *1915*, p. 230.
G. W. Middlekauff and J. F. Skogland. Bureau of Standards, Bull., 13, *1916*, p. 287.

77. See, however, G. Heller, Philips Techn. Rev., 1, *1936*, p. 120.

78. On the use of a filter with a thermopile as receptor see, e.g., C. Féry, J. de Phys., 7, *1908*, p. 632 ; E. Karrer, Phys. Rev., 5, *1915*, p. 189 ; H. E. Ives and E. F. Kingsbury, Phys. Rev., 6, *1915*, p. 319 ; M. Pirani, Licht, 3, *1933*, p. 161 ; R. P. Teele, Bureau of Standards, J. of Research, 27, *1941*, p. 217 ; B. A. Stevens. Opt. Soc. Am., J., 45, *1955*, p. 995.

79. J. S. Preston and L. H. McDermott. J. Sci. Inst., 11, *1934*, p. 150.
J. S. Preston. *Ibid.*, 23, *1946*, p. 211.

80. A. Dresler. Licht, 3, *1933*, p. 41 ; Z. d. Vereines deut. Ing., 80, *1936*, p. 1405.
E. Ferencz *et al.* C.I.E., Proc., 9, *1935*, p. 229.
J. Rieck. Licht, 5, *1935*, p. 131 and 7, *1937*, pp. 115, 137, 157 and 213.
M. E. Fogle. Illum. Eng. Soc. N.Y., Trans., 31, *1936*, p. 773.
H. P. Gage. Opt. Soc. Am., J., 27, *1937*, p. 159.
L. A. Wentman. Jurnal technicheskoi Fisiki, 7, *1937*, p. 1898. (In Russian).
O. H. Knoll and R. G. Weigel. Licht, 8, *1938*, pp. 39 and 65.

M. S. Kapnik and S. G. Yurov. Jurnal technicheskoi Fisiki, 18, *1948*, p. 573. (In Russian.)

81. H. König. Helv. Phys. Acta, 7, *1934*, p. 433, 8, *1935*, p. 211, 10, *1937*, p. 165, 11, *1938*, p. 432, 12, *1939*, p. 313 and 16, *1943*, p. 421 ; Assn. Suisse des Elect. Bull., 28, *1937*, p. 385 ; Rev. d'Opt., 27, *1948*, p. 547.

82. C. Féry. J. de Phys., 7, *1908*, p. 632.
H. Strache. C.I.E., Proc., 3, *1911*, p. 107.
H. E. Ives. Phys. Rev., 6, *1915*, p. 334.
A. Blondel. C.R., 169, *1919*, p. 830.
J. Thovert. Soc. Franç. de Phys., Procès-verbaux, *1929*, p. 948 ; J. de Phys., 1, *1930*, p. 121.
H. Bertling. Licht, 2, *1932*, pp. 181 and 201.
M. Laporte and F. Gans. C.R., 203, *1936*, p. 62 ; Rev. d'Opt., 15, *1936*, p. 321 ; Rev. Gén. de l'El., 41, *1937*, p. 483.
See also R. Jouaust, Rev. Gén. de l'El., 38, *1935*, p. 419.

83. G. T. Winch and C. F. Machin. Illum. Eng. Soc. Lond., Trans., 5, *1940*, p. 93.
F. Mäder. Helv. Phys. Acta, 18, *1945*, p. 125.
G. T. Winch. Illum. Eng. Soc. Lond., Trans., 11, *1946*, p. 107 ; Instrument Practice, 5, *1951*, p. 137.
See also J. Terrien, C.R., 230, *1950*, p. 1462 ; H. Korte and M. Schmidt, Lichttechnik, 6, *1954*, p. 355.

84. H. König. Helv. Phys. Acta, 7, *1934*, p. 433.
J. Voogd. Philips Techn. Rev., 4, *1939*, p. 260.
J. Terrien. C.I.E., Proc., 12, *1951* (Vol. II), Paper Ii.

85. Comité Int. des Poids et Mesures, Procès-verbaux, 18, *1937*, p. 223.
C. M. Garelli. N. Cimento, 3, *1946*, p. 152.

86. British Standard for Fluorescent and Phosphorescent Materials, No. 1316, *1946*.
A. A. Gershun. Acad. Sci. U.R.S.S., C.r.(Doklady), 37, *1942*, p. 125.

87. See, on this subject, F. Blottiau, Rev. d'Opt., 26, *1947*, p. 370 ; J. Terrien, *ibid.*, p. 411 ; W. de Groot. Philips Techn. Rev., 15, *1953*, p. 182.

88. P. J. Bouma. Physica, 8, *1941*, p. 413 ; Philips Techn. Rev., 6, *1941*, p. 161.
K. S. Weaver. Opt. Soc. Am., J., 39, *1949*, p. 278 (see also p. 888 and *ibid.*, 40, *1950*, p. 60).
See also W. S. Plymale and G. T. Hicks. Opt. Soc. Am., J., 42, *1952*, p. 344.

89. Y. Le Grand and E. Geblewicz. Année psychologique, 38, *1937*, p. 1.
Y. Le Grand. Rev. d'Opt., 21, *1942*, p. 71.
The values in Fig. 179 are calculated on the basis of the scotopic curve shown in Fig. 44 on p. 73.

CHAPTER X

COLORIMETRY

Colorimetry was at first developed solely for measuring the colour qualities of a light, but it also provides a method of heterochromatic photometry which is applicable to light of any colour whatever [1] and which is therefore more flexible than any of the methods described in the last chapter except, possibly, the photo-electric method using a dispersion system and a template (see p. 312).

The subject is treated here from the point of view of photometric measurement. The trichromatic theory is described only as a necessary introduction to the description of the instruments and methods which are suitable for photometry, and of which this theory is the basis. Other methods of colorimetry, most of them concerned solely with providing a quantitative description of colour apart from luminance, are briefly mentioned for the sake of completeness, but for a thorough treatment of the whole subject, one of the books mentioned in the Bibliography should be consulted [2].

It may be remarked, in passing, that the methods of colorimetry to be described are suitable only for use with extended fields and cannot be applied without modification to point sources of light as such [3].

The Basis of the Trichromatic System—Trichromatic colorimetry is based on the experimental fact that any light whatsoever can be matched, both in luminance and in chromaticity (i.e. colour characteristics as distinct from luminance), by a mixture of suitable, including negative, quantities of three lights of dissimilar colours [4]. Such a match is purely subjective and does not indicate equivalence of the two sets of physical stimuli in any other respect than that of the impression produced on the observer [5]. It is therefore not surprising that observers with different colour vision characteristics in general obtain slightly different results [6].

In order to establish a colorimetric system it is necessary to adopt three specified lights as *reference stimuli* [7] and the quantities of these three stimuli which, when mixed, give a sensation match with any light then form a specification of that light as regards both colour and luminance. These quantities are known as the *tristimulus values* of the light. To complete the system a " standard observer ", with colour vision characteristics representative of the average observer, has been defined.

A specification for colour only is provided by the relative amounts of the three reference stimuli used for the match, irrespective of their absolute values. It is usual to express this by means of three numbers, viz. the quantities of the stimuli which, when mixed, match unit quantity of the light to be specified. These numbers are known as the *chromaticity co-ordinates* of the colour. It is convenient to express the specification of a colour by means of a point on a " chromaticity diagram " and, since the three chromaticity co-ordinates are not independent but sum to unity, two of them can be used to fix, on a cartesian co-ordinate system (usually rectangular), the position of the point representing the colour. It will be seen that the chromaticity co-ordinates of the three reference stimuli are respectively (1,0,0), (0,1,0) and (0,0,1).

It might be assumed that the three reference stimuli would be measured in units of the same magnitude but in fact it is more convenient to adopt a different basis and to use as units the amounts of the three stimuli in a mixture which, for the standard observer, gives a match both in colour and luminance with three units of white light. The particular white light generally adopted is " equi-energy white ", i.e. light having a spectral distribution such that the amount of energy within any given wave-length interval is proportional to that interval [8].

The Choice of Reference Stimuli—So long as the addition law can be assumed to hold [9], i.e. under photopic conditions [10], if two lights C_1 and C_2 are represented respectively by the co-ordinates (x_1, y_1) and (x_2, y_2), a mixture of the two, or any light matching this mixture, will be represented by the co-ordinates $(x_1 + nx_2)/(1 + n)$, $(y_1 + ny_2)/(1 + n)$. It follows from this that the point representing the mixture lies on the line joining the points representing C_1 and C_2 on the chromaticity diagram.

Since all real lights are additive mixtures of two or more monochromatic radiations, the line on the chromaticity diagram which represents pure spectral radiation is of great importance. It is known as the spectrum locus and is shown in Fig. 180 on a diagram for which the three reference stimuli are the monochromatic radiations having the wave-lengths 0·7000, 0·5461 and 0·4358μ respectively.

It will be seen that the spectrum locus is everywhere convex, except over the long-wave range where it is sensibly rectilinear. This clearly indicates that, while all the points representing real lights lie within the spectrum locus and the straight line joining its extremities, they cannot all lie within any triangle which can be drawn with three pure spectral radiations as the reference stimuli. It follows, therefore, that if these stimuli are physically realisable radiations, certain colours must lie outside the chromaticity diagram.

This means that they can only be matched with a mixture which contains a negative quantity of one of the reference stimuli. In other words, when the right amount of this stimulus is mixed with the spectral light, a match can be obtained with a correctly proportioned mixture of the other two reference stimuli. Clearly this is the case for all lights which are represented by points lying outside the triangle but within the spectrum locus.

The C.I.E. System—Although the need for negative values in the specification of certain colours cannot be avoided so long as the reference stimuli are real, there is, in fact, no reason why this should be the case and in the universally adopted C.I.E. system of colour specification [11] the reference stimuli are hypothetical stimuli represented by points such that they form a triangle which lies wholly outside the spectrum locus. These are the points marked X, Y and Z in Fig. 180. Although these reference stimuli are unrealisable

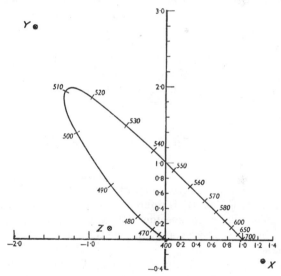

FIG. 180. The C.I.E. Reference Stimuli on the R,G,B, System.

in practice, they can be defined by their positions on the diagram of Fig. 180, i.e. in terms of the three real stimuli used in the construction of that diagram. These real stimuli can be defined with a high degree of precision since (a) in the region of 0.700μ the position of a point on the spectrum locus is very insensitive to small changes of wave-length and (b) the other two wave-lengths used are those of prominent lines in the mercury spectrum so that these radiations can be realised very accurately and conveniently.

Changing from One Set of Reference Stimuli to Another—If the specification of a colour is known in terms of any set of reference stimuli, R, G, B, its specification on the C.I.E. system can be calculated so long as (a) the reference stimuli of the R, G, B system are specified on the C.I.E. system and (b) the specification for some standard colour is known on both systems.

Let the co-ordinates of the standard colour on the R, G, B system be (f, g, h). This means that unit quantity of light of that colour can be matched by a mixture of f, g and h units respectively of the three reference stimuli on this system, where $f+g+h=1$. Further, let the co-ordinates of the R, G, B reference stimuli on the C.I.E. system be respectively (x_1, y_1, z_1), (x_2, y_2, z_2) and (x_3, y_3, z_3) so that these stimuli can be matched by mixtures containing the reference stimuli of the C.I.E. system in the proportions $x_1 : y_1 : z_1$, $x_2 : y_2 : z_2$ and $x_3 : y_3 : z_3$ where, again, $x_1+y_1+z_1=1$, etc. Unit quantities of these stimuli on the R, G, B system can therefore be matched by mixtures whose composition may be written (lx_1, ly_1, lz_1), (mx_2, my_2, mz_2) and (nx_3, ny_3, nz_3) respectively, l, m and n being constants as yet undetermined.

If, now, the co-ordinates of the standard colour on the C.I.E. system are (u, v, w) so that unit quantity of this colour can be matched by a mixture containing respectively u, v and w units of the C.I.E. reference stimuli, it follows that

$$u = flx_1 + gmx_2 + hnx_3$$
$$v = fly_1 + gmy_2 + hny_3 \quad \dots\dots\dots\dots\dots\dots(i)$$
$$w = flz_1 + gmz_2 + hnz_3$$

and since all the quantities in these equations are known except l, m and n, the values of these constants can be found and the expressions for units of the R, G, B reference stimuli on the C.I.E. system follow at once. Thus the specification of any light on the R, G, B system can be directly converted to give the corresponding specification on the C.I.E. system.

For example, if the tristimulus values of a light on the R, G, B system are r, g, b, it can be matched by a mixture whose three components may be written respectively as follows :

red component	rlx_1,	rly_1,	rlz_1
green component	gmx_2,	gmy_2,	gmz_2
blue component	bnx_3,	bny_3,	bnz_3

so that the tristimulus values on the C.I.E. system are seen to be

$$rlx_1 + gmx_2 + bnx_3$$
$$rly_1 + gmy_2 + bny_3 \quad \dots\dots\dots\dots\dots\dots(ii)$$
$$rlz_1 + gmz_2 + bnz_3$$

Since the sum of the three tristimulus values is $(rl + gm + bn)$, the chromaticity co-ordinates of the colour on the C.I.E. system are respectively :

$$(rlx_1 + gmx_2 + bnx_3)/(rl + gm + bn)$$
$$(rly_1 + gmy_2 + bny_3)/(rl + gm + bn)$$

and $$(rlz_1 + gmz_2 + bnz_3)/(rl + gm + bn)$$

It will be clear that the method just described is perfectly general and can be used for converting the specification of any colour on one system of reference stimuli to that on any other system, so long as the reference stimuli of the first system are known in terms of the second and the specification of some colour in both systems is also known [12].

It is of interest to apply the above method to find the chromaticity co-ordinates of the C.I.E. reference stimuli on the R, G, B system of Fig. 180 using the C.I.E. specification for the three reference stimuli of the R, G, B system, viz. :

Stimulus	x	y	z	
$0 \cdot 7000\mu$	$0 \cdot 73467$	$0 \cdot 26533$	$0 \cdot 00000$	
$0 \cdot 5461\mu$	$0 \cdot 27376$	$0 \cdot 71741$	$0 \cdot 00883$	(iii)
$0 \cdot 4358\mu$	$0 \cdot 16658$	$0 \cdot 00886$	$0 \cdot 82456$	

The standard colour is equi-energy white which is represented on both systems by the chromaticity co-ordinates $(\frac{1}{3}, \frac{1}{3}, \frac{1}{3})$. Thus $f = g = h = u = v = w = 0 \cdot 33333$ and it follows from the equations (i) above that

$$lx_1 + mx_2 + nx_3 = 1$$
$$ly_1 + my_2 + ny_3 = 1$$
$$lz_1 + mz_2 + nz_3 = 1$$

where x_1, etc., are the values tabulated in (iii) above. The values of l, m and n are respectively given by

$$l\triangle = \begin{vmatrix} x_2 & x_3 & 1 \\ y_2 & y_3 & 1 \\ z_2 & z_3 & 1 \end{vmatrix} \qquad m\triangle = - \begin{vmatrix} x_1 & x_3 & 1 \\ y_1 & y_3 & 1 \\ z_1 & z_3 & 1 \end{vmatrix} \qquad n\triangle = \begin{vmatrix} x_1 & x_2 & 1 \\ y_1 & y_2 & 1 \\ z_1 & z_2 & 1 \end{vmatrix}$$

$$\text{where } \triangle \equiv \begin{vmatrix} x_1 & x_2 & x_3 \\ y_1 & y_2 & y_3 \\ z_1 & z_2 & z_3 \end{vmatrix}$$

If the tristimulus values of one unit of the C.I.E. reference stimulus (1, 0, 0) are r, g, b on the R, G, B system, then, since they are 1, 0, 0 on the C.I.E. system, it follows from (ii) above that

$$rlx_1 + gmx_2 + bnx_3 = 1$$
$$rly_1 + gmy_2 + bny_3 = 0$$
$$rlz_1 + gmz_2 + bnz_3 = 0$$

The value of r is

$$
\begin{vmatrix} mx_2 & nx_3 & 1 \\ my_2 & ny_3 & 0 \\ mz_2 & nz_3 & 0 \end{vmatrix} \div \begin{vmatrix} lx_1 & mx_2 & nx_3 \\ ly_1 & my_2 & ny_3 \\ lz_1 & mz_2 & nz_3 \end{vmatrix} = \begin{vmatrix} x_2 & x_3 & 1 \\ y_2 & y_3 & 0 \\ z_2 & z_3 & 0 \end{vmatrix} \div l\Delta
$$

$$
= \begin{vmatrix} x_2 & x_3 & 1 \\ y_2 & y_3 & 0 \\ z_2 & z_3 & 0 \end{vmatrix} \div \begin{vmatrix} x_2 & x_3 & 1 \\ y_2 & y_3 & 1 \\ z_2 & z_3 & 1 \end{vmatrix}
$$

On substituting the values of x_1, etc., from the table (iii) r is found to be 2·36393 and similarly the values of g and b are respectively $-0·51516$ and 0·005303. Dividing each of these figures in turn by the sum of the three gives the chromaticity co-ordinates of the C.I.E. reference stimulus (1, 0, 0) on the R, G, B system. Similarly, the co-ordinates for the other two stimuli can be found. The results are :

Stimulus	r	g	b
(1, 0, 0)	1·2750	$-0·2779$	0·0029
(0, 1, 0)	$-1·7395$	2·7675	$-0·0280$
(0, 0, 1)	$-0·7431$	0·1409	1·6022

Calculation of Colour Coefficients from Spectral Energy: The Distribution Curves—Since all light is compounded of monochromatic radiations of various wave-lengths, it follows that if the chromaticity co-ordinates on the C.I.E. system are known for every wave-length in the visible spectrum, the tristimulus values for any light of specified spectral energy distribution should be calculable by applying the laws of colour mixture.

These co-ordinates for monochromatic light at convenient wave-length intervals have been determined experimentally [13] for a large number of observers, using real stimuli defined on the R, G, B system described above. Agreed mean values have been tabulated [14] and form the specification of the " standard observer " on the C.I.E. colour system. From these figures the chromaticity co-ordinates on the C.I.E. system have been calculated by the method described above. The values have been tabulated [15] and from them the spectrum locus shown in Fig. 181 can be drawn.

The chromaticity co-ordinates of spectral radiation cannot be used directly for the determination of the co-ordinates of a composite light since, as they stand, they represent different amounts of energy at different wave-lengths. It is necessary to weight them so as to obtain the tristimulus values at every wave-length for an equi-energy spectrum. The necessary multiplying factors can be found by measuring experimentally the relative intensities of unit amounts of each of the three reference stimuli, i.e. not equal amounts of energy but amounts which, when added, produce a match with equi-energy white. This cannot be done directly for the C.I.E. reference stimuli since these are not real but it has been done for the

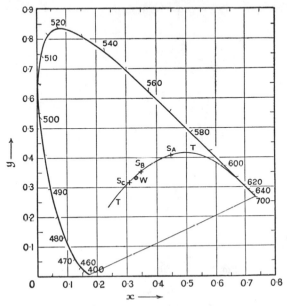

FIG. 181. The C.I.E. Chromaticity Diagram.

R, G, B reference stimuli 0.7000, 0.5461 and 0.4358μ and the mean values adopted for the standard observer are $1 : 4.5907 : 0.0601$. By means of the co-ordinates for the C.I.E. reference stimuli on the R, G, B system (see above), the relative intensities of these stimuli may readily be calculated and are found to be $0 : 10.96 : 0$.

The fact that the intensities of the $(1, 0, 0)$ and $(0, 0, 1)$ reference stimuli are zero is not accidental [16]; these stimuli were selected for the C.I.E. system so that the luminance of any light expressed on this system would be proportional to the tristimulus value for $(0, 1, 0)$. It follows that if this tristimulus value at each wave-length is made equal (or proportional) to the relative luminous efficiency at that wave-length, the resulting tristimulus values refer to equal amounts of energy. They have been tabulated (see Appendix VI) and are denoted by the symbols $\bar{x}$, $\bar{y}$ and $\bar{z}$ [17]. It will be seen that at each wave-length the ratio of these coefficients to the corresponding chromaticity co-ordinates, i.e. $\bar{x}/x$, $\bar{y}/y$ and $\bar{z}/z$, is equal to $2V_\lambda/y$, where V_λ is the relative luminous efficiency of radiation.

$\bar{x}$, $\bar{y}$ and $\bar{z}$ are usually referred to as the " distribution coefficients " since when plotted, as in Fig. 182, they show the distribution of the three C.I.E. reference stimuli throughout the equi-energy spectrum.

It will be clear that the tristimulus values for any light of given spectral distribution may now be found by multiplying the relative

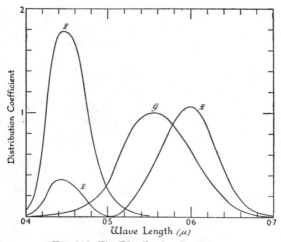

FIG. 182. The Distribution Coefficients.

value of the energy E_λ at each wave-length λ by the corresponding three distribution coefficients $\bar{x}_\lambda$, $\bar{y}_\lambda$ and $\bar{z}_\lambda$ and finding the relative areas under the three curves obtained by plotting $E_\lambda\bar{x}_\lambda$, $E_\lambda\bar{y}_\lambda$ and $E_\lambda\bar{z}_\lambda$ as ordinates with values of λ as abscissae. Alternatively, if λ is taken at equal intervals throughout, the tristimulus values are proportional to $\Sigma E_\lambda\bar{x}_\lambda$, $\Sigma E_\lambda\bar{y}_\lambda$ and $\Sigma E_\lambda\bar{z}_\lambda$. The chromaticity coordinates for the light under consideration are then x_c, y_c and z_c, respectively equal to the three sums written above, divided by the sum of the three. For example, in the special case of equi-energy white E_λ is constant, so that $x_c = \Sigma \bar{x}_\lambda/\{\Sigma \bar{x}_\lambda + \Sigma \bar{y}_\lambda + \Sigma \bar{z}_\lambda\}$ and it will be found that the three sums are all equal so that $x_c = y_c = z_c = \frac{1}{3}$ as expected. This is the point marked W in Fig. 181. The line marked T is described later in this chapter (see p. 340).

The points at which any line through W intersects the spectrum locus indicate a pair of wave-lengths which are often known as " complementaries " since lights of these two wave-lengths, if mixed in the correct ratio, produce the sensation of white [18].

It should be noted that the chromaticity diagram shown in Fig. 181 has the disadvantage that just noticeable differences of colour are represented by lines of very different lengths in different regions [19]. This had led to proposals for other forms of the diagram, known as

" uniform chromaticity charts " in which this difficulty is overcome, at least to some extent, although at the price of a certain loss of simplicity [20].

Colours of Mixtures—The colour of the light obtained by mixing specified amounts of two or more lights of known colour can be readily calculated [21]. If the intensity of any one light be I and its chromaticity co-ordinates x, y, z the tristimulus values for this light are clearly $(I/y)x$, I, and $(I/y)z$. Thus if the mixture consists of I_1, I_2, etc. of lights whose co-ordinates are (x_1, y_1, z_1), (x_2, y_2, z_2), etc., the chromaticity co-ordinates of the resulting light are $k(\Sigma I_1 x_1/y_1)$, $k(\Sigma I_1)$ and $k(\Sigma I_1 z_1/y_1)$ where $1/k$ is the sum of all the tristimulus values, and is therefore equal to $\Sigma I_1/y_1$. Thus the chromaticity co-ordinates of the mixed light are $(\Sigma I_1 x_1/y_1)/(\Sigma I_1/y_1)$, $(\Sigma I_1)/(\Sigma I_1/y_1)$ and $(\Sigma I_1 z_1/y_1)/(\Sigma I_1/y_1)$.

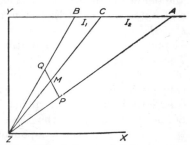

A geometrical construction for finding x_m and y_m is that shown in Fig. 183 for the simple case of two lights represented respectively by the points P and Q whose co-ordinates are x_1, y_1 and x_2, y_2. ZP and ZQ cut the line $y = 1$ at A and B and AB is divided at C in the ratio $AC : BC = I_2 : I_1$. The point M at which ZC intersects PQ

FIG. 183. A Geometrical Construction for finding the Chromaticity Co-ordinates of a Mixture.

represents the mixture, as it will be found that the co-ordinates of this point are

$$(I_1 x_1/y_1 + I_2 x_2/y_2)/(I_1/y_1 + I_2/y_2) \quad \text{and} \quad (I_1 + I_2)/(I_1/y_1 + I_2/y_2).$$

Reflection and Transmission—It will be seen that the work involved in calculating the colour of a mixture of lights of specified intensities is much simplified by the fact that on the C.I.E. system the y tristimulus value is proportional to the intensity, while the other two are independent of it. This is equally advantageous when considering the reflection characteristics of surfaces and the transmission of light through coloured media. As explained in Chapter V (p. 162), these two phenomena may be regarded as exactly analogous, so that it is sufficient here to deal in detail with one only, viz. that of reflection.

If the spectral reflection curve of a surface is known and if this surface is illuminated with light of known spectral energy distribution, the energy distribution of the reflected light can be found as explained on p. 155 and so the tristimulus values for the reflected light can be calculated as explained above [22]. It will be clear, however, that these values depend solely on the products $\rho_\lambda E_\lambda \bar{x}_\lambda$, etc., and these products may be formed in any convenient order. Thus if the values of $E_\lambda \bar{x}_\lambda$, $E_\lambda \bar{y}_\lambda$ and $E_\lambda \bar{z}_\lambda$ are already known for any given illuminant, the tristimulus values of the reflected light can be found by multiplying each of these quantities by the appropriate value of ρ_λ and then finding the relative areas under the three curves obtained by plotting $E_\lambda \bar{x}_\lambda \rho_\lambda$, etc., against λ [23]. Alternatively, if λ is taken at equal intervals, the values are proportional to $\Sigma E_\lambda \bar{x}_\lambda \rho_\lambda$, etc.

The Standard Illuminants—The values of $E_\lambda \bar{x}_\lambda$, etc., at equal intervals of λ have been tabulated for three specified lights, viz. those denoted on the diagram of Fig. 181 by the points S_A, S_B and S_C and defined both as to spectral energy distribution and as to practical realisation in the C.I.E. system of colorimetry [24]. The light represented by S_A and known as Standard Illuminant A is a tungsten filament gas-filled lamp operating at a colour temperature of 2854° K. The spectral energy distribution is taken to be identical with that of a full radiator at this temperature, the value of c_2 used for the calculation of the spectral energy distribution being 1·4380 cm. deg. Standard Illuminant B (point S_B) is the same lamp used with a double liquid filter of the Davis-Gibson type (see p. 302) in which the quantities of the components are $a = 2·452$ gm., $b = 21·71$ gm. and $c = 16·11$ gm. Standard Illuminant C (point S_c) is similar, but the quantities are $a = 3·412$ gm., $b = 30·580$ gm. and $c = 22·520$ gm. The chromaticity co-ordinates of the three illuminants are :

	x	y	z
S_A	0·44757	0·40745	0·14498
S_B	0·34842	0·35161	0·29997
S_C	0·31006	0·31616	0·37378

A filter of the same type has been designed to give approximately equi-energy white when used in conjunction with a source having a colour temperature of 2854° K. The values of a, b and c in the formulae given on p. 302 are 2·954, 28·440 and 17·840 respectively [25]. This combination is known as " standard illuminant E ".

The Calculation of Reflection Factor—Since the Y tristimulus value for a light is proportional to the intensity, it follows that the reflection factor of a surface is equal to the ratio of the y tristimulus values for the reflected light and for the illuminant respectively, i.e. when the values of λ are equally spaced it is equal to $\Sigma E_\lambda \bar{y}_\lambda \rho_\lambda / \Sigma E_\lambda \bar{y}_\lambda$. This, indeed, follows directly from the fact that $\bar{y}$ is proportional to the relative luminous efficiency V_λ (see p. 327).

The calculation of reflection factor can be simplified if, instead of tabulating the simple products $E_\lambda \bar{x}_\lambda$, $E_\lambda \bar{y}_\lambda$ and $E_\lambda \bar{z}_\lambda$ for each illuminant, the values are multiplied by a constant k such that $k\Sigma E_\lambda \bar{y}_\lambda = 100$. The relative values are clearly unaffected, while the value of $\Sigma k E_\lambda \bar{y}_\lambda \rho_\lambda$ is now equal to the reflection factor of the surface expressed as a percentage. Tables constructed on this basis [26] will be found in Appendix VI (pp. 525 to 527).

Tables of the values of $E_\lambda \bar{x}_\lambda$, $E_\lambda \bar{y}_\lambda$ and $E_\lambda \bar{z}_\lambda$ for standard illuminant E [27] and for full radiations at different temperatures have also been prepared [28].

The Selected Ordinate Method—The calculation of the products $E_\lambda \bar{x}_\lambda \rho_\lambda$, etc., at a large number of equally spaced values of λ is very laborious and a much shorter process is to determine ρ_λ for values of λ spaced at unequal intervals such that $E_\lambda \bar{x}_\lambda \delta\lambda$ is a constant. The value of $\Sigma E_\lambda \bar{x}_\lambda \rho_\lambda$ is then proportional to the sum of these values of ρ_λ. The values of λ to be used are different for the three stimuli and tables of 30 and of 100 such " selected ordinates " have been prepared for each coefficient with each of the three illuminants S_A, S_B and S_C [29]. Similar tables for $\bar{x}_\lambda \delta\lambda = \text{const.}$ have been prepared for facilitating the calculation of the tristimulus values of the light given by a source [30]. Selected tables are given in Appendix VI (pp. 524 to 527).

The " Monochromatic-plus-White " System of Colour Specification—Since all real colours are represented by points on that part of the chromaticity diagram which lies within the spectrum locus and the straight line joining its extremities, it will be clear that any colour can be matched by a mixture of radiation of any convenient colour, represented by a point at or near the centre of the diagram, and a monochromatic radiation in suitable proportions [31]. The wave-length of the monochromatic radiation is that of the point at which the spectrum locus is intersected by the line which joins the selected reference point and the point representing the colour under consideration. For instance, if the selected reference point corresponds to equi-energy white, the point P in Fig. 184 represents a colour which can be matched with a suitable mixture of white and monochromatic light of wave-length 0.53μ. In the case of a colour represented by a point such as P', monochromatic radiation of wave-length 0.505μ when mixed in the correct proportions with the light under consideration, gives a colour match with equi-energy white.

On this method of specification the wave-length of the monochromatic radiation is usually known as the dominant wave-length. The proportions of the mixture can be specified in two ways. The first is by the ratio of PW to LW or $P'W$ to $L'W$ on the C.I.E. chromaticity diagram. This ratio is known as the " excitation purity " and is represented by either

$$(x - x_w)/(x_d - x_w) \quad \text{or} \quad (y - y_w)/(y_d - y_w),$$

whichever is more convenient. The second method of expression is by the ratio of the luminance of the monochromatic radiation to the total luminance of the mixture. To obtain the value of this ratio,

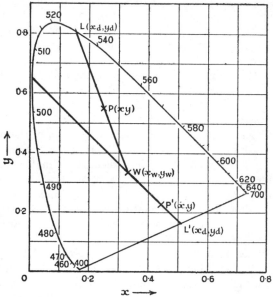

Fig. 184. The Monochromatic-plus-White System of Colour Specification.

the numerator and denominator of either fraction expressing the excitation purity must be multiplied respectively by y_d, the luminance value of a unit of the monochromatic radiation, and by y, the luminance value of a unit of the mixture. The colorimetric purity is therefore $y_d(x - x_w)/y(x_d - x_w)$ or $y_d(y - y_w)/y(y_d - y_w)$. It will be seen that in both cases, the purity of the standard white is zero and that of the monochromatic radiation unity.

It is sometimes convenient to describe a colour, specified on the trichromatic system, in terms of dominant wave-length and excitation purity, as this may give a better mental picture of the colour under consideration. The two quantities may be found graphically by means of the chromaticity diagram [32] or they may be calculated [33]. The rigorous method is somewhat laborious [34] and in practice it is often more convenient to obtain first an approximate graphical solution and then to determine the accurate values by calculation. Putting $x_w = y_w = \tfrac{1}{3}$, the dominant wave-length is given by the intersection of the line $y(3x_1 - 1) - x(3y_1 - 1) = x_1 - y_1$ with the spectrum locus, where x_1 and y_1 are the chromaticity co-ordinates of the colour. Trial solutions, using the values of x and y for the two wave-lengths in the tables which are nearest to the estimated wave-length, will usually by interpolation give a sufficiently accurate value of the dominant wave-length and the excitation purity may then be readily calculated from one of the two expressions given above.

Trichromatic Colorimeters—A trichromatic colorimeter is, in essence, a device for enabling the chromaticity and luminance of a light to be determined by matching it with a measurable mixture of three accurately specified reference lights. These may be spectral radiations [35] or lights obtained from any convenient standard source by the use of suitable colour filters. When the measurement is made visually, the angular diameter of the field of view should not exceed about 2 degrees ; otherwise the field may appear uneven because the two halves differ in spectral distribution and the colour vision of the central part of the retina, the macula (see p. 72), differs somewhat from that of the surrounding areas [36].

In the Wright colorimeter, the reference lights are three monochromatic radiations from different parts of the spectrum [37]. The optical system is shown in Fig. 185. Light from the standard lamp S

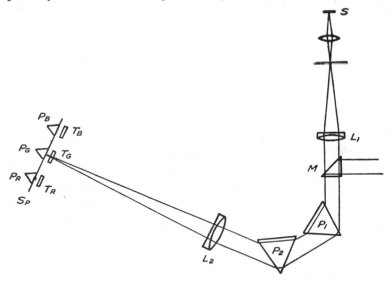

Fig. 185. The Wright Trichromatic Colorimeter.

is focused on a slit and a beam, collimated by the lens L_1 passes through the upper half of two dispersing prisms, P_1 and P_2, to the lens L_2 which focuses a spectrum in the plane Sp. In this plane are three small roof-prisms, P_R, P_G and P_B, which reflect the light they receive so that it returns almost on its original path, but tilted very slightly downwards. The three elementary reflected beams are

re-united on their return path through P_1 and P_2 so that what
emerges is a mixture of the light from three small portions of the
spectrum formed by the original beam from the slit. This mixture

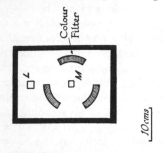

is reflected to a photometer prism
and eyepiece (not shown), by means
of a right-angled prism placed just
below the incident beam at some
point such as M. T_R, T_G and T_B are
three neutral wedges by means of
which the relative intensities of the
elementary beams from P_R, P_G and
P_B can be independently varied until
the colour of the mixture, as viewed
in the eyepiece, matches that of the
light under examination.

A number of colorimeters have
been designed using colour filters to
provide the reference lights [38]. In
the earlier instruments the lights
were mixed by persistence of vision,
rotating lenses or prisms being used
to bring the three lights in rapid succession into the field of view [39]. A
typical instrument of this kind is the
Guild colorimeter [40] shown in Fig.
186. A standard lamp and condensing lens provide a beam of nearly
parallel light which illuminates the
left-hand face of the colour-mixing
apparatus. This face is shown separately at the right of the figure. In it
are cut three 60° sectorial openings
(shown shaded), each backed by a
sheet of ground glass and a coloured
gelatine filter. These filters are respectively a highly saturated red,
green and blue, i.e. the light given by
each of them can be matched with

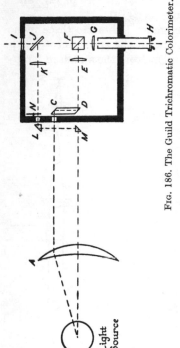

Fig. 186. The Guild Trichromatic Colorimeter.

monochromatic radiation from the appropriate part of the spectrum
when diluted with a very small amount of white light.

Inside the colour-mixing box a prism CD of shape shown is
mounted in such a way that it is capable of rapid rotation about an
axis DE. During rotation the end C passes each of the sectorial
openings in turn. When C is opposite an opening, light enters the

prism and, after two internal reflections at the inclined faces of the
prism, emerges along *DE*. A lens *E* is placed so that the effective
stop (a circular hole in the mount of the prism *CD*) is at its focus.
F is a Lummer-Brodhun photometric prism giving a triple rectangular
field. *G* is a lens with its focus at *H*. An observer with his eye at *H*
sees the reflected section of the photometer field illuminated by light
from the particular sector which the end of the rotating prism is
opposite. Thus the colours red, green and blue alternate in the field
as the prism rotates. If the speed is sufficiently rapid the sensations
mingle and a mixed colour is observed. Each sector opening is
fitted with a sectoral shutter, not shown in the diagram, by which the
relative durations of the red, green and blue stimuli may be varied,
thus varying the proportions of these colours in the mixture. The
colour to be matched is situated outside the aperture *I*. Light from
this aperture fills the transmitted portion of the photometer field.
J is a plain glass plate ; its purpose, in conjunction with the lens *K*
and prisms *L* and *M*, is to make it possible to add a little white light
to the coloured light to be matched. This is sometimes necessary
when matching very saturated colours in certain regions of the spectrum. The amount of this white light is regulated by a neutral
annular wedge *N*, of varying density.

An instrument in which an integrating sphere is used to mix

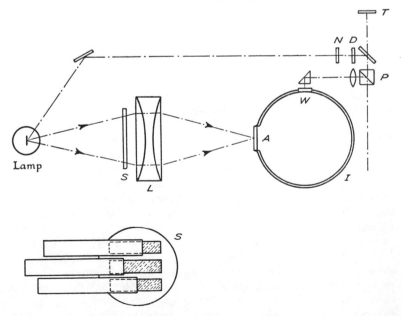

FIG. 187. The Donaldson Trichromatic Colorimeter.

the reference lights is the Donaldson colorimeter [41] shown in Fig. 187. Light from the standard lamp passes through three windows in a screen S to a condensing lens L which forms an image of the source at an opening, A, in the integrating sphere I. The three windows in S are covered with the three coloured filters, red, green and blue, which provide the reference lights. As will be seen from the separate drawing at the bottom of the figure, movable shutters are used to vary the relative areas of the three windows and thus to control the relative amounts of the three colours in the light which reaches the clear glass window at A. The surface of the sphere, except that immediately opposite A, is diffusely illuminated with a homogeneous mixture of the light entering this window, and that portion of the surface which is opposite the clear glass window W forms one part of the matching field seen in the photometer cube P. The other part is occupied by the white surface T, usually of magnesium oxide, which is illuminated by the light to be measured. If this light is highly saturated it is often necessary, in order to obtain a colour match, to add a small amount of light from the colorimeter lamp and the optical system shown, consisting of a mirror, a neutral wedge N, a diffusing plate D and a transparent plate at $45°$, is provided for this purpose. The light so added is measured on the colorimeter in the usual way and the unknown light is then found by subtraction.

Instruments have also been designed for the measurement of colour on the monochromatic-plus-white system (see p. 331) [42].

Colour Measurement with a Colorimeter—By means of an instrument such as those described above, the chromaticity co-ordinates of a light may be obtained in terms of the instrumental reference stimuli. In order to obtain the co-ordinates on the C.I.E. system it is necessary to know the co-ordinates of these instrumental stimuli on this system and the readings obtained on the instrument for some standard colour which can be conveniently realised in practice and for which the co-ordinates on the C.I.E. system are known.

The most direct method of finding the chromaticity co-ordinates of the instrumental stimuli is by calculation from their spectral distribution curves [43], using the distribution coefficients as explained above. The reference colour may be one of the standard illuminants described on p. 330. Frequently illuminant B is selected for the purpose and each observer determines the instrumental readings which, for his eye, give a colour match with this illuminant. In subsequent work, this observer's readings are divided by factors proportional to his readings on illuminant B so that, in effect, his three values are expressed in units of such relative magnitudes that a mixture of equal numbers of each of them matches standard illuminant B. Thus, if the observer's readings for illuminant B are r_B, g_B and b_B and his readings for any other colour are r, g and b, the tristimulus values for that colour, in terms of the instrumental stimuli measured in these new units, are r, $g(r_B/g_B)$ and $b(r_B/b_B)$.

The values obtained as just described have now to be transformed to the C.I.E. system by finding the X, Y, Z tristimulus values of the instrumental stimuli. These are obtained from the corresponding chromaticity co-ordinates by multiplying them by appropriate factors, and these factors are determined by the condition that equal numbers of units of the instrumental stimuli, when mixed, match illuminant B for which the chromaticity co-ordinates on the C.I.E. system are 0·348, 0·352 and 0·300 (see p. 330).

For example, if the chromaticity co-ordinates of the instrumental stimuli are as follows :

	x	y	z
Red stimulus	0·727	0·273	0·000
Green stimulus	0·197	0·749	0·154
Blue stimulus	0·150	0·029	0·821

the required multipliers, l, m and n, are given by the three equations

$$0·727l + 0·197m + 0·150n = 0·348 \times 3$$
$$0·273l + 0·749m + 0·029n = 0·352 \times 3$$
$$0·000l + 0·054m + 0·821n = 0·300 \times 3$$

and are found to be 0·948, 1·022 and 1·030 respectively, so that the tristimulus values for the three instrumental stimuli are

	X	Y	Z
Red stimulus	0·689	0·259	0·000
Green stimulus	0·201	0·766	0·055
Blue stimulus	0·155	0·030	0·845

The tristimulus values for the measured light are therefore as follows :

$$X = 0·689r + 0·201g\,(r_B/g_B) + 0·155b\,(r_B/b_B)$$
$$Y = 0·259r + 0·766g\,(r_B/g_B) + 0·030b\,(r_B/b_B)$$
$$Z = \qquad\quad\; 0·055g\,(r_B/g_B) + 0·845b\,(r_B/b_B)$$

and the chromaticity co-ordinates can be immediately obtained. The C.I.E. tristimulus values of the instrumental stimuli in any particular instrument are usually supplied with the instrument by the makers.

Photometry with a Colorimeter—Since, with a colorimeter, it is possible to determine the tristimulus values of a light, it will be clear that the instrument may also be used for comparing two given lights, not only as regards colour, but also as regards luminance [44].

If the readings obtained for the two lights are respectively r, g, b and r', g', b' ; the corresponding tristimulus values on the C.I.E. system can be found as described in the last section and the relative intensities are then given by the ratio of the two values of Y. Thus, if the X, Y, Z values for the instrumental stimuli are respectively

Red stimulus	X_1	Y_1	Z_1
Green stimulus	X_2	Y_2	Z_2
Blue stimulus	X_3	Y_3	Z_3

the relative intensities of the lights are

$$\{Y_1 r + Y_2 g\,(r_B/g_B) + Y_3 b\,(r_B/b_B)\}$$
and
$$\{Y_1 r' + Y_2 g'\,(r_B/g_B) + Y_3 b'\,(r_B/b_B)\}.$$

Colour and Reflection Factor of a Surface—It will be clear that the colour of a surface viewed under any given light can be found at once by means of a colorimeter. In the case of the instrument shown in Fig. 187, for instance, the illuminated surface is substituted for the white surface T and the work proceeds as described above. In general, the surface should be illuminated by light incident at 45° and should be viewed normally ; if the measurements are made under any other conditions, these should be specified [45].

The reflection factor of a surface under any given illuminant can be found by determining its tristimulus values and then substituting for it a white surface of known reflection factor, such as magnesium oxide [46], without changing the illumination in any way. The ratio of the values of Y for the two surfaces is equal to the ratio of their reflection factors.

Exactly similar methods are used for measuring the colour and the transmission factor of a transparent medium.

Energy Differences: Colorimetry with more than Three Matching Stimuli—There is one serious source of error in the measurement of a light with trichromatic colorimeters such as those described above, viz. the fact that the lights which are matched in colour are very different in spectral distribution. For example, when a match is obtained with a white light such as one of the standard illuminants, the spectral distribution curve of this light is quite smooth, whereas the corresponding curve for the matching mixture has three pronounced peaks, separated by regions in which there is very little energy at all. In these circumstances the results obtained are naturally not independent of the observer's colour vision [47]. It is therefore essential to use an observer or, more generally, a group of observers whose colour vision resembles as closely as possible that of the C.I.E. standard observer.

One way of avoiding this difficulty, or at least of reducing the error, is to increase the number of instrumental stimuli [48]. If these are suitably selected, it should be possible to obtain a mixture which shows some degree of similarity to the light to be measured, as far as spectral distribution is concerned. Then by making comparatively small further adjustments of three of the stimuli, a colour match can be obtained in which the matching lights are sufficiently similar in spectral distribution to avoid errors due to small differences between the observer's colour vision and that of the C.I.E. standard observer.

A Donaldson colorimeter has been designed on this principle [49]. It is similar to the instrument described on p. 335 but the number of filters is increased to six, viz. red, orange, yellow-green, green, blue-green and blue. It is clear that the chromaticity co-ordinates of the six matching stimuli can be found by spectrophotometry and calculation as before, but the factors by which these have to be multiplied in order to obtain the six tristimulus values cannot be determined by means of a match with a standard illuminant since there are six multipliers and only three equations available. This naturally arises from the fact that, while a match with three stimuli is unique, that obtained by the use of more than three is not. The multipliers are therefore found by means of a series of luminance measurements on light of known spectral distribution transmitted in turn through each of six colour filters which are identical with those used in the colorimeter and for which therefore, the transmission factors for the light used may readily be calculated.

Since there are now no large differences between the spectral distributions of the lights being compared, it is possible to improve the accuracy of the instrument by using a larger field of view, e.g. 15° instead of the 2° necessary with the three-stimulus instrument.

In using the instrument it is necessary first to adjust the positions of the shutters over the six filters so that the best approximation to a spectral energy match is obtained. This is done by placing over the eyepiece a filter similar to one of those used in the instrument and adjusting the corresponding shutter until a brightness match is obtained. This is done for each of the six shutters in turn and the process is then repeated in order to compensate for the small effect which the setting of each shutter has on the best setting for its immediate neighbours in the spectrum. When all the necessary adjustments have been made and there is a brightness match as viewed through each one of the six filters in turn, there is normally also an approximate but not an exact colour match when the field is viewed directly. To obtain an exact match only three of the shutters are adjusted, viz. those for the red (or orange), the green and the blue, and the amount of the adjustment is usually so small that the energy match is not appreciably affected. From the six readings obtained as a result of this final adjustment, the X, Y, Z values of the measured light are obtained by using the tristimulus values of the six instrumental stimuli in the normal way.

Photo-electric Colorimeters—Instruments have been designed for determining the colour of a light photo-electrically. In some cases one or more photocells are used with a series of filters, the cell-filter combinations forming the instrumental stimuli [50]. If these stimuli can be made identical with the C.I.E. reference stimuli, the values of X, Y and Z are indicated directly by the instrument. This condition is, however, difficult to fulfil accurately by means of available colour filters and several instruments have been designed, using the dispersion system and templates, as described in Chapter IX, p. 312 [51]. Three templates are used, one for each stimulus. The template for finding X is so shaped that the response of the instrument to a given amount of energy at any wave-length is proportional to the distribution coefficient $\bar{x}$ at that wave-length, and so for the other two templates. That used for finding Y is necessarily identical with the template used in the instrument for ordinary photometry as described in Chapter IX.

The Vector Colorimeter—An alternative method of locating the point which represents any particular light on the chromaticity diagram depends on matching the light with two mixtures in succession [52]. In the first, radiation of some wave-length near the red end of the spectrum is mixed with radiation from some other part of the spectrum and the wave-length and intensity of this component are varied until a match is obtained. The wave-length is then noted, and the point required lies on the line joining this wave-length to that of the red radiation on the chromaticity diagram. The second mixture contains, as one component, radiation from the blue end of the spectrum and the matching process is carried out as before. The point required lies at the intersection of the two lines thus established.

Colour Temperature—A very convenient method of describing the colour of a light which matches the radiation from a full radiator at some temperature is the value of that temperature, which can be referred to as the " colour temperature " of the light [53]. This form of description has already been used in earlier chapters, especially Chapter IX. The line marked T in Fig. 181 is the locus of a point representing full radiation at different temperatures and is often called the " black-body locus " [54]. This part of the chromaticity diagram is shown on an enlarged scale in Fig. 188, which also shows the points S_A, S_B and S_C, representing the standard illuminants, and W representing equi-energy white. It will be noticed that W

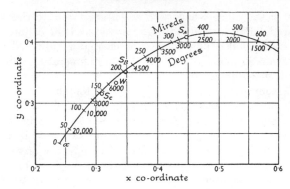

FIG. 188. The " Black Body Locus " on the C.I.E. Chromaticity Diagram.

does not quite lie on the line since at no temperature does full radiation exactly match equi-energy radiation.

Unless the point representing a light on the chromaticity diagram lies on or very close to the black-body locus, the use of colour temperature as a description of the colour of the light is open to serious objection. In the first place there is no means of indicating the distance of the point from the locus and in the second place there is considerable uncertainty as to the best method of determining which point on the locus most closely represents the colour of the light [55].

The colour temperature of the light given by a source may be measured by direct visual comparison in a photometer head with a calibrated tungsten filament lamp [56]. The curve relating the colour temperature of this lamp with the voltage or current supplied to the filament is determined by a similar direct visual comparison with a full radiator, the temperature of which is measured with an optical pyrometer [57].

If a sensitive photometer such as the Lummer-Brodhun contrast head is used, a visual comparison may be made in this way with a precision of about 2 to 3 degrees at the colour temperature of an ordinary tungsten lamp [58]. An exact brightness match in the photometer is essential and the substitution method should always be used.

Attempts have been made to obtain greater precision in the visual estimation of colour temperature by using colour filters placed between the eye and the comparison field [59] but the improvement has generally been found negligible. On the other hand, by using two photocells with very different spectral sensitivity curves or a single cell with two widely different colour filters a much higher precision is attainable [60].

When two cells are used, the response of one is exactly balanced with that of the other when both are illuminated by the source to be measured. This source is then removed and the calibrated lamp is substituted for it. The voltage or current is adjusted until the cells are again in balance and the colour temperature can then be found from the calibration curve.

It is essential that the balance point for the cells should be independent of small changes in the position of either source, or of the light distribution. This is usually secured by placing the lamps at the centre of an integrating sphere, the two cells being placed side by side facing the sphere window. The effect of any selectivity of the sphere or of the window can usually be neglected since at the balance point both sources have the same spectral distribution, at least to a very close approximation.

The lamp used in a colorimeter must give light of a definite spectral distribution. It is generally a gas-filled tungsten lamp which has been carefully aged (see p. 179) and adjusted to a specified colour temperature, frequently 2854° K [61].

Subtractive Colorimetry—In the colorimeters described above, the light to be measured is matched with an additive mixture of three or more lights, viz. the matching stimuli, but it is also possible to match a coloured light with a white from which has been subtracted, by absorption in transparent colour filters, suitable amounts of light from three different parts of the spectrum. This is the basis of subtractive colorimetry and the filters employed [62] are usually referred to as yellow, magenta and cyan (or blue-green) although, as they absorb chiefly in the blue, green and red parts of the spectrum respectively, they may also be described as minus-blue, minus-green and minus-red.

In the Lovibond Tintometer [63] there is, for each of the three colours, a series of glasses of graded density and these are numbered on an additive scale so that all combinations which show the same total are equivalent. The light to be measured illuminates a white surface and this is compared with a similar surface viewed through a combination of slides selected so as to give a colour match. The relative brightnesses of the two surfaces can be varied independently of the colour by the use of neutral slides or otherwise, so that a brightness match can be maintained in the field of view while the colour match is being made. A method has been devised for obtaining the chromaticity co-ordinates on the C.I.E. system from the readings on the Tintometer scales [64].

Arrays of Colour Samples—Many so-called colour " atlases ", consisting of arrays of shade cards or patterns, have been produced at different times for the description of surface colours [65]. The most complete and systematic is that based on the Munsell system [66] in which the patterns are graded by their position in three scales, one of hue, one of saturation, termed the " chroma " scale, and one of luminance, which is related to the reflection factor of the pattern and is called the " value " scale.

The chief advantage of an array of this kind is its simplicity and the ease with which a colour description of a surface can be given as the result of direct visual comparison with the patterns in the array or the appropriate portion of it. The chief disadvantages are (a) the very large number of patterns required if more than a strictly limited range of colours is to be covered [67] and (b) the difficulty of preparing patterns which are uniform and sufficiently evenly graded and at the same time satisfactorily permanent [68]. A check on uniformity and permanence is provided if, as in the case of the Munsell system, the colours of all the patterns are defined on the C.I.E. system [69]. It is clearly of importance that the nature of the illuminant under which a surface is compared with the patterns should be specified [70].

The steps between the individual patterns in a colour atlas may be sub divided by making visual estimates, or a disc colorimeter may be used, especially if the chief requirement is accurate interpolation over a very limited range of the patterns. This form of colorimeter is, in principle, the Maxwell colour disc used for early experiments in additive mixture. The disc has four sectors which are respectively black, white and coloured to match the two patterns nearest to the specimen with respect to hue. The disc is spun rapidly so that there is complete merging of the sectors and their relative areas are altered until a match with the specimen is obtained [71]. Alternatively, the disc may be stationary and viewed through a rotating prism [72].

BIBLIOGRAPHY

A. C. Hardy (ed.). *Handbook of Colorimetry*. (Massachusetts Institute of Technology, *1936*.)

P. J. Bouma. *Physical Aspects of Colour*. (Cleaver Hume Press, London, *1948*.)

F. Blottiau. *Colorimétrie*. (Rev. d'Optique Press, Paris, *1951*.)

H. D. Murray, editor. *Colour in Theory and Practice*. (Chapman and Hall, *1952*.)

D. B. Judd. *Colour in Business, Science and Industry*. (Wiley, New York, *1952*.)

Optical Society of America. *The Science of Colour*. (T. Y. Crowell, New York, *1953*.)

W. D. Wright. *The Measurement of Colour*. (Hilger & Watts, *1958*.)

J. Guild. Optical Convention, *1926*, Proc., Vol. I, p. 61.

H. Schober. Phys. Z., 38, *1937*, p. 514.

P. Moon and D. B. Judd. Illum. Eng. Soc. N.Y., Trans., 36, *1941*, pp. 313 and 336. (Two separate papers.)

REFERENCES

1. See, e.g., J. Dourgnon, Soc. Franç. des Elect., Bull., 8, *1938*, p. 887 and 9, *1939*, p. 929 ; H. König, Helv. Phys. Acta, 14, *1941*, p. 559 ; M. Richter, Licht, 12, *1942*, p. 126.

2. On the subject of terminology see Appendix II, especially pp. 513 and 517. Earlier papers are : Opt. Soc. Am., J., 13, *1926*, p. 43 ; J. Guild, Opt. Soc., Trans., 27, *1926*, p. 295 ; H. D. Murray, Oil and Colour Chem. Assn., J., 24, *1941*, p. 205.

3. J. Escher-Desrivières. Rev. d'Opt., 10, *1931*, p. 389 and 15, *1936*, p. 182.
A. Blondel. C.R., 204, *1937*, p. 1695.
See also J. G. Holmes, Illum. Eng. Soc. Lond., Trans., 6, *1941*, p. 71.

4. J. C. Maxwell. Roy. Soc. Edin., Trans., 21, *1855*, p. 275 ; Phil. Trans., 150, *1860*, p. 57.
J. H. Parsons. Opt. Soc., Trans., 32, *1931*, p. 165.
See also H. von Helmholtz, Ann. d. Phys., 87, *1852*, p. 45.

5. T. Smith. Opt. Soc., Trans., 33, *1932*, p. 214.
P. J. Bouma. Physica, 12, *1946*, p. 189.

6. W. F. Hamilton and E. Freeman. Opt. Soc. Am., J., 22, *1932*, p. 369.

7. These have frequently been termed " primaries " in the past.

8. On the choice of an energy distribution to represent white, see I. G. Priest, Bureau of Standards, Bull., 17, *1921*, p. 231.

9. H. Grassman. Ann. d. Phys., 89, *1853*, p. 69 ; Phil. Mag., 7, *1854*, p. 254.
E. Schrödinger. Ann. d. Phys., 63, *1920*, pp. 397, 427 and 481.
P. J. Bouma. Physica, 12, *1946*, p. 545.
P. W. Trezona. Phys. Soc., Proc. (B), 66, *1953*, p. 548 and 67, *1954*, p. 513.
On departures from the additivity law (see p. 290), see, e.g., H. Piéron, C.R., 212, *1941*, p. 284 ; F. Blottiau, Rev. d'Opt., 26, *1947*, p. 193.

10. For an extension of colour theory to scotopic conditions, see P. J. Bouma, Amsterdam Acad., Proc., 38, *1935*, pp. 35, 148 and 258.

11. C.I.E., Proc., 8, *1931*, pp. 19 and 647.
T. Smith and J. Guild. Opt. Soc., Trans., 33, *1932*, p. 73.
D. B. Judd. Opt. Soc. Am., J., 23, *1933*, p. 359.
G. Ribaud. Rev. d'Opt., 15, *1936*, p. 161.
P. Fleury. *Ibid.*, 17, *1938*, p. 337.
M. Richter. Licht, 4, *1934*, pp. 205 and 231. (See also pp. 101 and 125.)
W. S. Stiles. Optica Acta, 2, *1955*, p. 168.

12. H. E. Ives. Frank. Inst., J., 180, *1915*, p. 673 and 195, *1923*, p. 23.
J. Guild. Opt. Soc., Trans., 26, *1924*, p. 95.
C. L. Froelich. Opt. Soc. Am., J., 9, *1924*, p. 31.
W. Dziobek . Z.f.I., 46, *1926*, p. 81.
I. Runge. *Ibid.*, 48, *1928*, p. 387.
J. G. Holmes. Phys. Soc., Proc., 47, *1936*, p. 400.
D. L. MacAdam. Opt. Soc. Am., J., 27, *1937*, p. 294.
F. J. Bingley. Opt. Soc. Am., J., 44, *1954*, p. 109.
See also C. C. Paterson. G.E.C. Journ., 10, *1939*, p. 172.

13. W. D. Wright. Opt. Soc., Trans., 30, *1929*, p. 141 and 31, *1930*, p. 201.
J. Guild. Phil. Trans. (A), 230, *1932*, p. 149.
See also J. C. Maxwell, Phil. Trans., 150, *1860*, p. 57 ; A. König and C. Dieterici, Z. f. Psychol. u. Physiol. d. Sinnesorgane, 4, *1893*, p. 241 ; W. de W. Abney, Phil. Trans. (A), 205, *1906*, p. 333 ; D. B. Judd, Opt. Soc. Am., J., 10, *1925*, p. 635 and 21, *1931*, p. 699.

14. C.I.E., Proc., 8, *1931*, pp. 20 and 21.

15. C.I.E., Proc., 8, *1931*, pp. 25 and 26.
T. Smith and J. Guild. Opt. Soc., Trans., 33, *1932*, p. 98.

16. D. B. Judd. Bureau of Standards, J. of Research, 9, *1930*, p. 515.
J. Guild. Opt. Soc., Trans., 32, *1930*, p. 1.
See also R. Luther, Z. f. techn. Phys., 8, *1927*, p. 544.
On the conception of stimuli with zero intensity, W. D. Wright (*Measurement of Colour*, 1st ed., p. 86) has said that " in so far as it helps to the understanding of the system to attempt to picture what kind of stimuli X and Z must be, they may be described as having colour but no luminosity. This is not, in fact, very helpful and it is far better to recognise that X and Z are simply mathematical abstractions, whose

employment as stimuli is of no little convenience in colorimetry." Comprehension may, perhaps be assisted by considering the readily observable fact that if a small amount of blue light is added to white the resulting colour change is far greater than that produced by adding the same amount of green light ; for equal intensities the blue is much more " colourful ".

17. C.I.E., Proc., 8, *1931*, pp. 25 and 26.
Analytical expressions for $\bar{x}$, $\bar{y}$ and $\bar{z}$ have been given by P. Moon and D. E. Spencer, Opt. Soc. Am., J., 35, *1945*, p. 399 (see also J. of Maths. and Phys., 25, *1946*, p. 111).

18. I. G. Priest. Opt. Soc. Am., J., 4, *1920*, p. 402 and 5, *1921*, p. 513.
I. H. Godlove. *Ibid.*, 20, *1930*, p. 411 and 24, *1934*, p. 264.
E. Genberg. Phys. Soc., Proc., 45, *1933*, p. 836.
D. L. MacAdam. Opt. Soc. Am., J., 28, *1938*, p. 103.
See also R. H. Sinden, Opt. Soc. Am., J., 7, *1923*, p. 1123.

19. W. D. Wright. Phys. Soc., Proc., 53, *1941*, p. 93.
D. L. MacAdam. Opt. Soc. Am., J., 32, *1942*, p. 247.
See also D. B. Judd, Opt. Soc. Am., J., 22, *1932*, p. 72 ; R. H. Sinden, *ibid.*, 35, *1945*, p. 737 ; A. A. Wundheiler, *ibid.*, p. 767.

20. D. B. Judd. Opt. Soc. Am., J., 25, *1935*, p. 24.
D. L. MacAdam. *Ibid.*, 27, *1937*, p. 294.
F. C. Breckenridge and W. R. Schaub. *Ibid.*, 29, *1939*, p. 370.
J. G. Holmes. Phys. Soc., Proc., 52, *1940*, p. 359.
J. W. Perry. *Ibid.*, 53, *1941*, p. 272.
See also E. Q. Adams, Opt. Soc. Am., J., 32, *1942*, p. 168 ; L. Silberstein, *ibid.*, p. 552 ; Various authors, *ibid.*, 33, *1943*, pp. 1, 18, 260, 270, 632 and 675 ; D. E. Spencer, Frank. Inst., J., 236, *1943*, p. 293 ; D. L. MacAdam, *ibid.*, 238, *1944*, p. 195 ; J. L. Saunderson and B. I. Milner, Opt. Soc. Am., J., 36, *1946*, p. 36 ; R. W. Burnham. *ibid.*, 39, *1949*, p. 387.

21. J. Guild. Opt. Soc., Trans., 26, *1924*, p. 139.
M. M. Gourevich. Opt. Soc. Am., J., 35, *1945*, p. 196.
F. J. Bingley. Inst. Radio Engrs., N.Y., Proc., 36, *1948*, p. 709.
H. von Schelling. Opt. Soc. Am., J., 43, *1953*, p. 706.

22. See also J. Wouda, Amsterdam Acad., Proc., 38, *1935*, p. 585 ; M. Ravazzi, N. Cimento, 1, *1943*, p. 363.

23. The integration may also be performed mechanically. See A. C. Hardy, Opt. Soc. Am., J., 18, *1929*, p. 96 ; J. A. Van den Akker, *ibid.*, 29, *1939*, pp. 364 and 501 ; H. R. Davidson and L. W. Imm, *ibid.*, 39, *1949*, p. 942.
See also S. Rösch. Z. f. techn. Phys., 12, *1931*, p. 410.

24. C.I.E., Proc., 8, *1931*, p. 23.
T. Smith and J. Guild. Opt. Soc., Trans., 33, *1932*, p. 73.
Opt. Soc. Am., J., 34, *1944*, p. 643.
See also R. Davis and K. S. Gibson, Bureau of Stds., J. of Research, 7, 1931, p. 791 ; G. N. Rautian *et al*, Soviet Physics (Techn. Phys.), 1, *1956*, pp. 193 and 233 .
The colour temperature of standard illuminant A as defined by the C.I.E. was 2848° K on the temperature scale in use in 1931. The temperature for the same spectral distribution on the 1949 temperature scale is 2854° K (D. B. Judd, Bureau of Standards, J. of Research, 44, *1950*, p. 1).

25. R. Davis and K. S. Gibson. Bureau of Stds., J. of Research, 12, *1934*, p. 263.

26. T. Smith. Phys. Soc., Proc., 46, *1934*, p. 372.

27. C.I.E., Proc., 10, *1939*, Vol. I, pp. 155–7.

28. H. G. W. Harding and R. B. Sisson. Phys. Soc., Proc., 59, *1947*, p. 814.
S. A. E. Hird. *Ibid.*, 61, *1948*, p. 198.

29. A. C. Hardy. *Handbook of Colorimetry*, p. 49.
See also D. L. MacAdam, Opt. Soc. Am., J., 28, *1938*, p. 163 ; H. W. Swank and M. G. Mellon, *ibid.*, 27, *1937*, p. 414 ; F. W. Sears, *ibid.*, 29, *1939*, p. 77 ; M. Richter, Licht, 10, *1940*, p. 121 ; H. A. Robinson, Opt. Soc. Am., J., 36, *1946*, p. 270.

30. F. T. Bowditch and M. R. Null. Opt. Soc. Am., J., 28, *1938*, p. 500.
For the special case of a light consisting of a line spectrum superposed on a continuous spectrum see C. W. Jerome, Illum. Engng., 45, *1950*, p. 225.

31. J. Guild. Opt. Soc., Trans., 27, *1925*, p. 130.

32. H. E. Ives. Frank. Inst., J., 195, *1923*, p. 23.
A. C. Hardy (*Handbook of Colorimetry*) has given charts for finding dominant

wave-length and excitation purity to a high accuracy : these are based on the use of illuminant C instead of equi-energy white as the reference point on the chromaticity diagram.

33. H. E. Ives. Frank. Inst., J., 180, *1915*, p. 673.
I. G. Priest. Opt. Soc. Am., J., 9, *1924*, p. 503 and 13, *1926*, p. 123.
D. B. Judd. *Ibid.*, 13, *1926*, p. 133 ; Bureau of Standards, J. of Research, 7, *1931*, p. 827.

34. D. B. Judd. Opt. Soc. Am., J., 23, *1933*, p. 359.

35. J. C. Maxwell. Phil. Trans., 150, *1860*, p. 57.
H. von Helmholtz. *Physiol. Optik*, vol. 2, p. 334 (Eng. trans., p. 396).
W. de W. Abney. Phil. Trans. (A), 193, *1900*, p. 259.
J. Zernike. Opt. Soc. Am., J., 22, *1932*, p. 418.
H. P. J. Verbeek. Physica, 13, *1933*, p. 77 and 1, *1934*, p. 1082.
See also the other refs. in note (32) and the first in note (36) on p. 313 of *Photometry (1926)*.

36. W. D. Wright. *Measurement of Colour*, p. 67.
See also " D.L.T.G. Regeln," Licht, 5, *1935*, p. 37.
On the influence of a " surround " to the matching field see W. Schönfelder, Z. f. Sinnesphysiologie, 63, *1933*, p. 228.

37. W. D. Wright. Opt. Soc., Trans., 29, *1927*, p. 225 ; J. Sci. Inst., 16, *1939*, p. 10.
See also P. Fleury, J. de Phys., 10, *1939*, p. 35 S.

38. See the refs. in note (36) on pp. 313–14 of *Photometry (1926)* ; R. Luther, Z. f. techn. Phys., 8, *1927*, p. 540 ; M. Richter, Licht, 7, *1937*, p. 90 and Archiv f. techn. Messen, *1940*, T 99 ; R. W. G. Hunt, J. Sci. Inst., 31, *1954*, p. 122.

39. F. E. Ives. Frank. Inst., J., 164, *1907*, pp. 47 and 421.
A. Klughardt and M. Richter. Archiv f. techn. Messen, *1933*, T 64.
M. Richter. *Ibid.*, *1940*, T 99.

40. J. Guild. Opt. Soc., Trans., 27, *1925*, p. 106.
See also E. Lax and M. Pirani, Int. Illum. Congress, *1931*, Vol. I, p. 324.

41. R. Donaldson. Phys. Soc., Proc., 47, *1935*, p. 1068.
See also Adam Hilger, Ltd., J. Sci. Inst., 13, *1936*, p. 199 ; M. Richter, Z. f. techn. Phys., 19, *1938*, p. 98 ; F. Blottiau, Rev. d'Opt., 25, *1946*, p. 209.
On the use of a sphere for mixing lights see P. Moon and D. P. Severance, Opt. Soc. Am., J., 29, *1939*, p. 20.

42. P. G. Nutting. Bureau of Standards, Bull., 9, *1913*, p. 1.
L. A. Jones. Phys. Rev., 4, *1914*, p. 454.
I. G. Priest. Opt. Soc. Am., J., 8, *1924*, p. 173

43. T. Smith. Opt. Soc., Trans., 33, *1932*, p. 228 (see also p. 231).

44. See, e.g., J. Guild, Illum. Eng. Soc. Lond., Trans., 2, *1937*, p. 128.
The method described in Chapter IX, p. 293 is identical in principle with the use of a colorimeter in which the primaries are three monochromatic radiations.

45. C.I.E., Proc., 8, *1931*, p. 23.
L. C. Martin. Roy. Soc. Arts, J., 73, *1924*, p. 249.
J. Guild. Opt. Soc., Trans., 27, *1926*, p. 106.
See, however, A. C. Hardy, Opt. Soc. Am., J., 35, *1945*, p. 289.

46. See p. 372 and note (3) on p. 448.

47. See, e.g., J. Guild, Phil. Trans. (A), 230, *1931*, p. 149 ; W. D. Wright, Opt. Soc., Trans., 30, *1928*, p. 141.

48. See also M. Richter, Z. f. techn. Phys., 19, *1938*, p. 98.

49. R. Donaldson. Phys. Soc., Proc., 59, *1947*, p. 554.

50. J. Guild. J. Sci. Inst., 11, *1934*, p. 69.
K. S. Gibson. Instruments, 9, *1936*, pp. 309 and 355.
G. T. Winch and E. H. Palmer. Illum. Eng. Soc. Lond., Trans., 2, *1937*, p. 137.
J. A. Van den Akker. Opt. Soc. Am., J., 27, *1937*, p. 401.
J. W. Perry. J. Sci. Inst., 15, *1938*, p. 270.
A. Dresler and H. G. Frühling. Licht, 8, *1938*, p. 238.
A. Dresler. Licht u. Lampe, 27, *1938*, pp. 625 and 638.
B. T. Barnes. Opt. Soc. Am., J., 29, *1939*, p. 448 ; Rev. Sci. Inst., 16, *1945*, p. 337.
R. S. Hunter. Opt. Soc. Am., J., 32, *1942*, p. 509.

R. C. Hanselman. Am. J. Clinical Pathology, 13, *1943*, p. 108.
H. König. Helv. Phys. Acta, 17, *1944*, p. 571.
G. C. Sziklai. Opt. Soc. Am., J., 41, *1951*, p. 321.
B. Buchmann-Olsen. *Objective Measurements of Colour and Colour Changes.*
(Copenhagen, *1950.*)
D. A. Shklover and R. S. Ioffe. Akad. Nauk, U.S.S.R., Izvestya (Otdel.
Tekhn.), 15, *1951*, p. 667 (In Russian).
See also H. E. Ives and E. F. Kingsbury, Opt. Soc. Am., J., 21, *1931*, p. 541.

51. G. F. G. Knipe and J. B. Reid. Phys. Soc., Proc., 55, *1943*, p. 81.
H. König and F. Mäder. Helv. Phys. Acta, 16, *1943*, p. 419.
G. T. Winch. Illum. Eng. Soc. Lond., Trans., 11, *1946*, p. 107.
J. Cohen. Illum. Engng., 49, *1954*, p. 50.
H. Korte and M. Schmidt. Lichttechnik, 6, *1954*, p. 355.
See also A. C. Hardy, Opt. Soc. Am., J., 18, *1929*, p. 96 ; H. Bertling, Licht u.
Lampe, 24, *1935*, p. 320 ; H. König, Helv. Phys. Acta, 17, *1944*, p. 571.

52. J. Guild. Opt. Soc., Trans., 27, *1925*, p. 139.
See also R. A. Houstoun *et al.*, Phil. Mag., 16, *1933*, p. 945 ; 17, *1934*, p. 1047 ;
19, *1935*, p. 1107 ; 20, *1935*, p. 1055 ; 21, *1936*, p. 505 ; 23, *1937*, p. 49.

53. I. G. Priest. Opt. Soc. Am., J., 23, *1933*, p. 41.

54. H. G. W. Harding. Phys. Soc., Proc., 56, *1944*, p. 305 and 58, *1946*, p. 1.

55. E. P. Hyde and W. E. Forsythe. Frank. Inst., J., 183, *1917*, p. 353.
R. Davis. Bureau of Standards, J. of Research, 7, *1931*, p. 659.
D. B. Judd. *Ibid.*, 17, *1936*, p. 771.
D. L. MacAdam. Opt. Soc. Am., J., 33, *1943*, p. 18.
H. G. W. Harding. Phys. Soc., Proc., 57, *1945*, pp. 222 and 63, *1950*, p. 685.
F. Tarnay. Soc. Franç. des Elect., Bull., 6, *1946*, p. 468.
O. Reeb and M. Richter. Lichttechnik, 2, *1950*, pp. 186 and 205.

56. J. T. Morris, F. Stroude and R. M. Ellis. Electrician, 59, *1907*, p. 584.
E. P. Hyde. Phys. Rev., 27, *1908*, p. 521 ; Frank. Inst., J., 169, *1910*, p. 439
and 170, *1910*, p. 26.
C. C. Paterson and B. P. Dudding. Phys. Soc., Proc., 27, *1915*, p. 230.
W. E. Forsythe. Opt. Soc. Am., J., 16, *1928*, p. 307.
W. Dziobek. Z. wiss. Photog., 25, *1928*, p. 287 (gives c.t. of Mg flame).
H. Djoudat. Rev. d'Opt., 16, *1937*, p. 401.
See also N. Macbeth, Illum. Eng. Soc. N.Y., Trans., 23, *1928*, p. 302.

57. H. Buckley, L. J. Collier and F. J. C. Brookes. C.I.E., Proc., 6, *1924*, p. 203.
H. T. Wensel, D. B. Judd and W. F. Roeser. Bureau of Standards, J. of
Research, 12, *1934*, p. 527.
W. Northdurft and H. Willenberg. Phys. Z., 43, *1942*, p. 138.
See also Chapter IX, p. 301.

58. W. E. Forsythe. Opt. Soc. Am., J., 6, *1922*, p. 476.
H. G. W. Harding. Phys. Soc., Proc., 56, *1944*, p. 21.
See also D. B. Judd, Bureau of Standards, J. of Research, 5, *1930*, p. 1161 ;
Opt. Soc. Am., J., 23, *1933*, p. 7.

59. See also E. M. Lowry and K. S. Weaver, Photog. J., 79, *1939*, p. 413 ; G.
Naeser, Z. f. techn. Phys., 10, *1929*, p. 160 ; "Pyrowerk," J. Sci. Inst., 15, *1938*, p. 415.

60. F. A. Lindemann and T. C. Keeley. Phys. Soc., Proc., 38, *1925*, p. 69.
N. R. Campbell *et al.* J. Sci. Inst., 2, *1925*, p. 177 ; 3, *1925*, pp. 2, 38 and 77 ;
4, *1926*, p. 38.
T. H. Harrison. Opt. Convention, *1926*, Proc., Part I, p. 245 ; Opt. Soc.,
Trans., 28, *1927*, p. 195.
G. T. Winch. J. Sci. Inst., 6, *1929*, p. 374.
C. H. Sharp. Opt. Soc. Am., J., 20, *1930*, p. 62.
J. S. Preston. Phys. Soc., Proc., 47, *1935*, p. 1012.
M. Roulleau and L. Heymann. C.I.E., Proc., 11, *1939*, Vol. II, p. 193.
M. H. Sweet. Opt. Soc. Am., J., 30, *1940*, p. 568.
H. G. W. Harding. Phys. Soc., Proc., 63, *1950*, p. 685 ; J. Sci. Inst., 29, *1952*,
p. 145.
E. J. King, A. E. Snider and F. Hamburger. Opt. Soc. Am., J., 42, *1952*,
p. 178.
W. J. Brown. J. Sci. Inst., 31, *1954*, p. 469.
See also W. Richter, Electronics, 10, *1937*, Mar., p. 28.

61. D. B. Judd. Bureau of Standards, J. of Research, 17, *1936*, p. 679.

62. See, e.g., L. A. Jones, Opt. Soc. Am., J., 4, *1920*, p. 420 ; R. A. Houstoun, Opt. Soc., Trans., 33, *1932*, p. 199.

63. F. E. Lovibond. Opt Convention, *1926*, Proc., Part I, p. 211.
See also K. S. Gibson and F. K. Harris, Bureau of Standards, Sci. Papers, 22, *1927*, p. 1 ; I. G. Priest, D. B. Judd, K. S. Gibson and G. K. Walker, Bureau of Standards, J. of Research, 2, *1929*, p. 793 ; G. K. Walker, *ibid.*, 12, *1934*, p. 269 ; K. S. Gibson and G. W. Haupt, *ibid.*, 13, *1934*, p. 433 ; R. K. Schofield, J. Sci. Inst., 16, *1939*, p. 74 ; G. W. Haupt and F. L. Douglas, Opt. Soc. Am., J., 37, *1947*, p. 698.

64. R. K. Schofield. J. Sci. Inst., 16, *1939*, p. 74.

65. Société Française des Chrysanthémistes. *Répertoire des Couleurs, 1905.*
R. Ridgway. *Colour Standards and Colour Nomenclature* (Baltimore, *1912*).
W. Ostwald. *Farbnormen-Atlas* (Leipzig, Unesma, *1926*) ; *Farbkunde.* (English trans. by J. Scott Taylor, *Colour Science*, Winsor and Newton, *1931–3 Ostwald Colour Album*, Winsor and Newton, *1933*).
P. Baumann. *Neue Farbtonkarte, System Prase* (Aue i. Sa., *1927*).
A. Maerz and M. R. Paul. *Dictionary of Colour* (McGraw-Hill, *1950*). (See also D. Nickerson, Paper Trade J., 125, *1947*, Nov. 6, p. 153 (Tappi Sect., p. 219).)
M. R. Paul. Opt. Soc. Am., J., 21, *1931*, p. 358.
British Colour Council. *Dictionary of Colour Standards* (London, *1934*).
E. Séguy. *Code Universel des Couleurs* (Paris, Lechevalier, *1936*).
G. Reimann, D. B. Judd and H. J. Keegan. Opt. Soc., Am., J., 36, *1946*, p. 128.
C. L. Boltz. Nature, 166, *1950*, p. 129.
H. Hönl. Naturwissenschaften, 41, *1954*, pp. 487 and 520.
M. Richter. Opt. Soc. Am., J., 45, *1955*, p. 223.
On the Ostwald system see, e.g., M. E. Bond and D. Nickerson, Opt. Soc. Am., J., 32, *1942*, p. 709 and various authors, *ibid.*, 34, *1944*, pp. 353, 355, 361 and 382. See also H. Arens, Phys. Z., 43, *1942*, p. 43.
An interim report on Colour Systems was issued by the Colour Group of the Physical Society (London) in Nov., *1957*.

66. A. H. Munsell. *A Colour Notation* (Baltimore, *1941*).
The Munsell Book of Colour (Munsell Colour Coy., *1942*).
D. Nickerson. Opt. Soc. Am., J., 30, *1940*, p. 575 ; Illum. Eng. Soc. N.Y., Trans., 41, *1946*, p. 549.
See also the refs. in note (69) *infra* and B. R. Bellamy and S. M. Newhall, Opt. Soc. Am., J., 32, *1942*, p. 465.

67. D. B. Judd and K. L. Kelly. Bureau of Standards, J. of Research, 23, *1939*, p. 355.
D. Nickerson. Opt. Soc. Am., J., 33, *1943*, p. 419.
A. Riot. Soc. Scientifique de Bruxelles, Ann. (Sér. I), 60, *1946*, p. 149.
D. L. MacAdam. Opt. Soc. Am., J., 37, *1947*, p. 308.

68. See, e.g., F. A. O. Krüger, Z. Verein Deut. Ing., 73, *1929*, p. 465.

69. J. E. Tyler and A. C. Hardy. Opt. Soc. Am., J., 30, *1940*, p. 587.
K. S. Gibson and D. Nickerson. *Ibid.*, p. 591.
J. J. Glenn and J. T. Killian. *Ibid.*, p. 609.
K. L. Kelly, K. S. Gibson and D. Nickerson. *Ibid.*, 33, *1943*, p. 355.
W. C. Granville, D. Nickerson and C. E. Foss. *Ibid.*, p. 376.
D. Nickerson. Illum. Eng. Soc. N.Y., Trans., 40, *1945*, p. 159 (also p. 373).
See also I. G. Priest, K. S. Gibson and H. J. McNicholas, Bureau of Standards, Technol. Paper No. 167, *1920* ; A. E. O. Munsell, L. L. Sloan and I. H. Godlove, Opt. Soc. Am., J., 23, *1933*, pp. 394 and 419 ; I. H. Godlove and A. E. O. Munsell, *ibid.*, 24, *1934*, p. 267 ; D. Nickerson, *ibid.*, 30, *1940*, p. 575 ; S. M. Newhall, *ibid.*, p. 617 ; S. M. Newhall, D. Nickerson and D. B. Judd, *ibid.*, 33, *1943*, p. 385 ; J. L. Saunderson and B. I. Milner, *ibid.*, 34, *1944*, p. 167 ; N. Macbeth, Illum. Engng., 44, *1949*, p. 106.

70. C.I.E., Proc., 8, *1931*, p. 24.
D. B. Judd. Bureau of Standards, J. of Research, 23, *1939*, p. 355.
See also D. Nickerson, Illum. Eng. Soc. N.Y., Trans., 36, *1941*, p. 373.

71. D. Nickerson. Opt. Soc. Am., J., 25, *1935*, p. 253.
See also J. M. McGinnis and D. S. Piston, *ibid.*, 15, *1927*, p. 117.

72. D. Nickerson. Opt. Soc. Am., J., 21, *1931*, p. 640.

CHAPTER XI

SPECTROPHOTOMETRY

In ordinary photometry the light emitted by a source is measured as a whole, and quite irrespective of its spectral distribution, i.e. of the relative intensities of the components of different wave-lengths. For many purposes, however, including heterochromatic photometry by certain methods (see p. 298), it is necessary to know in what manner the integral light is made up of its spectral components. In order to obtain this information it is necessary first to disperse the composite light by some device, such as a prism or grating (see p. 25), and then to measure the intensity of each component, or, in practice, the small group of components lying within a certain narrowly-restricted region of the spectrum. It is to be noted that, in general, spectrophotometry is used solely for determining spectral distribution, so that the intensities measured at the different parts of the spectrum are only relative and are expressed in quite arbitrary units.

Originally, the light emitted by a source within a given range of wave-lengths was measured by comparison with the *total* light given by the same or any other convenient source [1], or by using some "absolute" criterion for estimating its intensity, such as visual acuity [2] or the reduction necessary for extinction. In all modern spectrophotometry, however, the light emitted by the source under examination is compared with that given by a standard source in the same spectral region. If the spectral distribution of the light given by the standard source is known, a comparison of this kind at every part of the spectrum gives at once the spectral distribution of the light from the test source.

Another very important application of spectrophotometry is one which has been referred to in previous chapters, viz. the determination of the spectral transmission curve of a colour filter. No standard of spectral distribution is required in this case or in the analogous process of finding the spectral reflection curve of a surface.

The Standard of Spectral Distribution—The most fundamental form of source giving light of a known spectral distribution is the full radiator (see p. 35) but the use of this as a standard of distribution is attended with considerable experimental difficulties and is therefore generally confined to the standardising laboratory, some more convenient, though less fundamental, radiator being used in ordinary work. The acetylene flame in various forms has been employed for the purpose and its spectral distribution has been very carefully determined [3]. The most commonly used form of standard is, however, the tungsten filament lamp [4] and it is convenient here to describe in some detail the reasons for this.

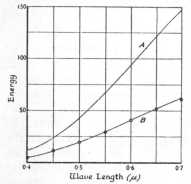

FIG. 189. The Relation between True Temperature and Colour Temperature.

Although the emissivity of tungsten is far from being the same at all wave-lengths, yet within the limits of the visible spectrum the change is not very great [5]. It is, moreover, fairly regular so that although the spectral distribution differs from that of a full radiator at the same temperature, even in the visible spectrum, it matches very closely that of a full radiator at a slightly higher temperature. This will be seen from Fig. 189 in which curve A represents the spectral distribution of full radiation at the temperature 2800° K, while the circles represent that of the radiation from tungsten at the same temperature, assuming the emissivity at 0.45μ to be 0.45 and that at 0.65μ to be 0.43. Curve B represents the spectral distribution of full radiation at the temperature 2840° K, the scale of ordinates having been so chosen that the curve passes through the centre of the circle at 0.60μ. It will be seen that the circles lie everywhere so close to the curve that the spectral distribution of the tungsten may be regarded as identical, for most practical purposes, with that of a full radiator at 2840° K, its colour temperature [6].

The colour temperature of a body is to be carefully distinguished from its " luminance temperature " (also " brightness temperature " or " black-body temperature ") which is the temperature of the full radiator which has the same luminance as the body at some specified wave-length or narrow band of wave-lengths, frequently in the neighbourhood of 0.65μ. Since the emissivity of a body cannot exceed unity at any wave-length it follows that the luminance temperature cannot be greater than the true temperature and for most bodies radiating under open conditions it is considerably less ; in the case of

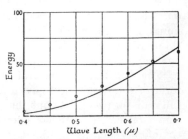

FIG. 190. The Relation between True Temperature and Luminance Temperature.

tungsten at 2800° K for example, the luminance temperature measured at 0·665μ is about 2515° K [7]. This is illustrated in Fig. 190 in which the circles again show the radiation from tungsten at 2800° K but the full line now represents, on the same scale, the radiation from a full radiator at 2515° K. The colour temperature of a body may be either higher or lower than its true temperature, depending on the way in which the emissivity varies within the visible spectrum. In the special case of a non-selective, or grey body the colour temperature and the true temperature are necessarily identical.

The Tungsten Lamp as Radiation Standard—The colour temperature of a vacuum lamp can be related fairly closely to its efficiency in lumens per watt and the curve of Fig. 191 shows this relationship for a tungsten filament [8]. For an actual lamp, owing to conduction

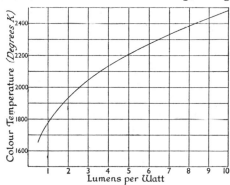

FIG. 191. Colour Temperature and Efficiency of a Tungsten Filament.

and other losses the efficiency is some 10 to 20 per cent less, depending on the lamp rating and on the filament temperature. For a gas-filled lamp the relationship is much more indefinite. Values of colour temperature for some different types of tungsten lamps are given in Appendix VIII but if a lamp is to be used as a standard of spectral distribution its colour temperature must be accurately determined by comparing it with a full radiator, either directly or, more often, indirectly by means of other lamps which have themselves been directly calibrated (see p. 341).

The Spectrometer—In the foregoing sections a description has been given of the manner in which a standard of spectral distribution may be obtained. The remainder of this chapter will be devoted to a description of the methods which may be employed for comparing the spectral distribution of the unknown light with that from the standard. Every such method necessarily involves the production of a spectrum, either by a glass prism or a grating, and an essential part of every spectrophotometer is a device by means of which any part of the spectrum may be isolated and observed. All such devices are based on the instrument known as a spectrometer, the principle of which will be clear from Fig. 192, where a section in the plane defined by the path of the light rays is shown. C is known as the

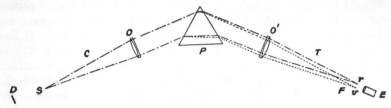

FIG. 192. The Principle of the Spectrometer.

collimator, and has, at the end nearest the source of light, a narrow slit S, which is at the focus of O, a converging lens system. S receives light from a diffusing surface (or a lens) D, which is large enough to enable the light passing through S to fill the aperture of the collimator completely. The light admitted by S is converted by O into a parallel beam with the wave front perpendicular to the direction of propagation (see p. 23). It then traverses the dispersion prism P, and thereby undergoes a deviation which varies in amount according to the refractive index of the prism material for light of different wave-lengths (see p. 25). All the light of any given wave-length remains, however, in a parallel beam and, traversing a second converging lens O' at one end of the telescope T, it is brought to a focus at F, where, in fact, an image of S in light of that particular wave-length is formed. It is clear that if the light admitted at S is not homogeneous a series of images of S will be formed at F, one corresponding to each wave-length present in the original light. Further, the images formed by the less deviated (red) light will be on the right (r), while the images formed by the more powerfully deviated (violet) light will be on the left (v). These images are viewed by means of an ordinary Ramsden eyepiece E.

Calibration of the Spectrometer—In instruments provided with an ordinary 60° prism the telescope is movable about the vertical axis of the instrument in order to allow the different images to be viewed in the eyepiece. In most modern instruments the form of prism shown in Fig. 17 is used [9], and the telescope is fixed with its axis perpendicular to that of the collimator. The image of S formed in light of any particular wave-length is brought into the field of view of E by rotating the prism about the vertical line in which the plane bisecting the 90° angle of the prism intersects its reflecting surface [10]. Before using the instrument it is necessary to calibrate it carefully throughout the visible spectrum, i.e. to draw the curve connecting wave-length with angular reading. For this purpose vacuum tubes containing helium, hydrogen, etc., are convenient. The angles at which the prominent lines in the spectra of these elements [11] appear in the centre of the field at E are plotted against the wave-lengths of those lines and the points joined by a smooth curve. The whole of the visible spectrum should be calibrated in this way, at least thirty points on the curve being taken.

It should be noticed that the breadth of the image of S formed by light of any given wave-length is proportional to the width of S, and that if S is displaced so is the image. Hence, it follows that a symmetrically opening slit should always be used at S, for otherwise the centre of the image shifts as the width of the slit is altered, and so the mean wave-length corresponding to any angle of the telescope or prism is changed.

In some spectrometers, particularly those of the constant-deviation (movable prism) type, the prism table is rotated by means of a screw provided with a drum head marked in wave-lengths. The calibration of this drum head can clearly be true only for one position of the prism. Calibration, in this case, consists in determining the errors in the scale with the instrument adjusted as it is to be used. An angular calibration is still necessary if reduction to a normal spectrum is desired (see next section).

When the light to be examined consists of a limited number of homogeneous components a corresponding number of images of S is seen in E, but in any other case the number of images is infinite, or at any rate so great that they overlap, and what is actually observed is a long band of light of every spectrum colour from red, at one end to violet at the other. Reduction of the breadth of S produces two results, viz. (i) the breadth of each image, and therefore, in the case of a continuous spectrum, the luminance of the band of light, is everywhere reduced in the same ratio as the slit width, and (ii) the reduction of the image breadth decreases the range of wave-length present at any given point of the spectrum, so that the " purity " of the spectrum is increased.

If the distance between the centres of the images corresponding to wave-lengths λ and $\lambda + d\lambda$ is dx, and if the image breadth at this wave-length is b, it follows that at any given point in the spectrum one edge of the image formed in light of wave-length λ will coincide with the other edge of the image formed in light of wave-length $(\lambda + b \cdot d\lambda/dx)$. Hence at any point of the spectrum the luminance is due, not to light of wave-length λ alone but to light of all wave-lengths lying between λ and $(\lambda + b \cdot d\lambda/dx)$ and this range is directly proportional to b (and therefore to the slit-width) and to $d\lambda/dx$. Owing to diffraction there is a theoretical limit to the degree of purity that can be obtained in the continuous spectrum given by a spectrometer. Although this limit can only be reached by the use of an infinitely narrow slit, yet a purity only 6 per cent less than the maximum can be obtained with a slit width equal to $f\lambda/2D$, where f and D are respectively the focal length and diameter of the collimator lens [12]. For most spectrometers f/D is about 16. The use of such a narrow slit as that indicated by this formula is generally impossible, except when dealing with the middle part of the spectrum of a very bright source.

Prismatic Dispersion—It was pointed out in Chapter II (p. 27) that the wave-lengths in the spectrum formed by a grating were so distributed that $d\lambda/dx$ was constant throughout the spectrum (to the accuracy with which $\tan\theta = \sin\theta$). In the case of a prismatic spectrum, however, no such simple relation between wave-length and separation can be found, for the refractive index of glass is not a linear function of the wave-length of the light, so that the spacing in the spectrum is uneven and is, moreover, different for different kinds of glass. It follows that, owing to the overlapping of the images of the slit, the total light reaching any given point of the spectrum is greater at the parts where the crowding of the images is denser, i.e. where the dispersion is less, and vice versa.

Although this effect has not generally to be allowed for in visual spectrophotometry where, as will be seen later, both the spectra compared are equally affected, it does enter into the slit-width correction to be described at the end of this chapter. Moreover, in the determination of spectral energy distribution by any absolute method as, for example, by means of a thermopile (see p. 47), the correction for dispersion must always be made, for what is required is the energy within a given wave-length interval, and the interval included within a given breadth is different for different parts of the spectrum. In fact, if the calibration curve of the spectrometer is plotted, its differential gives the multiplying factor to be applied at each wave-length to convert prismatic intensity to the intensity in a normal spectrum. If $\delta\lambda$ is the effective slit width at wave-length λ, while I_p and I_λ are respectively the prismatic and the normal spectrum intensities, then $I_\lambda/\delta\lambda = I_p$. A typical dispersion curve is shown in Fig. 193.

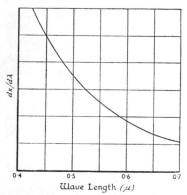

Ulaue Length (μ)

FIG. 193. A Typical Dispersion Curve for a Glass Prism.

The Spectrophotometer—From what has been said above it will be clear that every spectrophotometer consists of the following two principal parts :

(i) Apparatus for analysing the light given by the two sources to be compared, and for presenting to the eye, in a manner suitable for photometric comparison, a limited region of the spectrum from each source.

(ii) Means for readily altering the luminance of one or both parts of the spectral field in a continuous and known manner.

The first part consists of an optical device similar in action to a spectrometer, the light from the two sources compared being admitted either into two separate collimators or, by two slits (or different parts of a single slit), into a single collimator.

There are two principal types of spectrophotometer field. In one of these the lights to be compared are presented to the eye in the form of two spectral bands placed one above the other, shutters being provided for isolating the particular portion of the spectrum being studied. In the other form of field the Maxwellian view is employed (see p. 152), so that the field appears homochromatic, although the light entering the eye is not strictly homogeneous. These two types of field will be referred to as the juxtaposed spectra type and the homochromatic field type respectively. The latter type generally gives a more satisfactory form of field as regards accuracy of equality match. The precautions to be observed as regards size of image when the Maxwellian view is used have already been mentioned (see p. 153). The purity of the field is naturally governed by the breadth of the ocular aperture or of the natural pupil, whichever is the smaller. The juxtaposed spectra type of field possesses the advantage that any rapid changes in intensity of either spectrum can be at once seen, and the degree of uncertainty arising from this cause (see p. 367, *infra*) can be estimated.

The necessity for a fine and sharp line of demarcation between the comparison surfaces as seen by the eye is just as important in spectrophotometry as in ordinary photometry [13], and many of the older forms of spectrophotometer fail in this respect.

The means used for luminance control in ordinary photometry may also be employed in spectrophotometry, but the inverse square method is not generally suitable, since it is important to have as high an illumination of the slit as possible, especially when working at the ends of the spectrum where the luminosity is low [14].

Early Spectrophotometers—The first instrument (after those mentioned on p. 349) was that of Vierordt [15], in which the diaphragm method of luminance control was employed. This instrument consisted simply of a spectrometer in which the collimator was provided with a divided slit.   Each half of the slit was illuminated by one of the sources to be compared, and the widths of the two halves were separately adjusted until the portions of the two spectra seen in the eyepiece were equally bright.

The method of equality adjustment by alteration of slit width even when symmetrically opening slits are used, is unsatisfactory [16], both from a practical and a theoretical point of view.   It is necessary, in order to obtain the requisite range at different parts of the spectrum, to use a slit width varying from at least 1 mm. to a few hundredths of a millimetre.   In the former case the spectrum is very impure (see p. 353), and in the latter case an error of 1 per cent is produced by an inaccuracy of less than 0·001 mm., and diffraction effects introduce considerable uncertainty into the measurements. The results are further complicated by the fact that the correction to be applied on account of slit width varies according to the width employed.   It is therefore desirable in spectrophotometry always to work with a fixed slit, so that the correction for slit width may be applied with certainty (see p. 367).

A variety of other methods of controlling the luminance of one part of the comparison field has been adopted in later instruments. The Brodhun variable sector disc described on p. 224 was used in the Lummer-Brodhun spectrophotometer described below and the special form of disc illustrated in Fig. 134 on p. 225 was designed particularly for spectrophotometry.   A neutral wedge may be moved across one slit or a polarisation system of control may be inserted in one of the beams.

Spectrophotometers with Two Collimators—The Lummer-Brodhun spectrophotometer [17] consisted of an ordinary spectrometer with the addition of a second collimator at right angles to the usual one and a special form of Lummer-Brodhun cube, with horizontal dividing lines [18], placed at the intersection of the two collimated beams.   The light from this cube passed through the dispersing prism to the telescope, which was focused on the interface of the cube.   An instrument which is somewhat similar in principle, but in which a constant deviation spectrometer is used, is that shown diagrammatically in Fig. 194 [19].   The second collimator is mounted above and parallel to that of the spectrometer by means of two supports A and B, one of which is provided with adjustments for securing exact parallelism of the collimators.   The slits of these two collimators are illuminated by focusing upon them images of the two sources to be compared or, if the spectral transmission of a filter is to be measured, the arrangement illustrated in the figure is used.   An image of the filament of a strip filament lamp is focused on the slit of each collimator by means of lenses C and D and

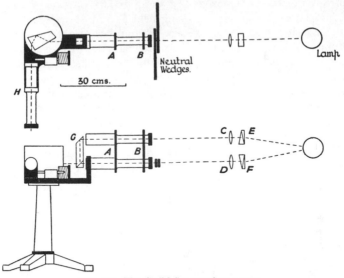

Fig. 194. The Guild Spectrophotometer.

achromatic prisms E and F. The photometric prism G is built of
two parts, a parallelepiped and an isosceles prism. A central strip
of the hypotenuse face of the latter is ground away, and the remainder put in optical contact with one of the short faces of the parallelepiped to form a composite prism of the shape indicated in the figure.
Light from the lower collimator passes straight through this prism
except at the part of the interface where there is no optical contact.
Light from the upper collimator is totally reflected down the prism
by the first inclined face. At the part of the interface where there is
no optical contact it is totally reflected in a direction parallel to the
beam from the lower collimator, whereas at the regions of optical
contact it passes straight down and is lost. After passing through the
dispersing system of the spectrometer the two beams are focused as
superposed continuous spectra in the focal plane of the telescope H.
The eyepiece of the latter is replaced by a slit, and an eye placed
there sees the interface of the prism G as a photometric field of three
horizontal strips, the central one of which is illuminated by light
from the upper collimator, and the outer ones by light from the
lower collimator. The brightness match is obtained by means of a
series of sector discs of the type described on p. 225, the interval
between successive discs being bridged by means of a double neutral
wedge placed in front of the lower slit.

In both the instruments described above the homochromatic
type of field is used. The interface of the prism G in the Guild

spectrophotometer was originally designed to provide a contrast field instead of the simple matching field described above.

Polarisation Spectrophotometers—A number of different spectro-photometers depend on the polarisation method of intensity varia-tion [20]. In some of these a single collimator is used, and an image of one part of the slit formed by light polarised in one plane is com-pared with an image of the other half, either unpolarised, or polarised in the perpendicular plane. A Nicol prism placed in the path of the light is used for producing the photometric balance, as in the Martens polarisation photometer (see p. 219). A spectrophotometer typical of this class is that designed by König and modified by Martens [21]. Fig. 195 shows diagrammatically a section through

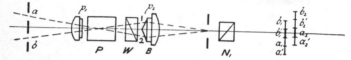

FIG. 195. The König-Martens Spectrophotometer.

the instrument perpendicular to the plane of the light rays, the bend of the rays at P being ignored for the sake of clearness. The light from each of the two halves of the slit, a and b, after passing through the dispersion prism P, enters the Wollaston prism W and, after separation into two parts polarised in mutually perpendicular planes, passes through the biprism B and forms, therefore, four series of images of both a and b. Of these four series of images of a, two, viz. a_1 and a_2, are polarised in one plane and are formed respectively by the two parts of the biprism, while the other two, a'_1 and a'_2, are polarised in the perpendicular plane. One series of images of a, viz. a_2, is caused to coincide with one series of images of b, viz. b'_1, and the remaining images are stopped off so that an eye placed at any point along the line formed by the two series of images sees the part 2 of the biprism bright by reason of light from a which is polar-ised in one plane, and the part 1 of the biprism bright by reason of light from b which is polarised in the perpendicular plane. A Nicol prism placed in the path of the light at N_1, and capable of rotation about an axis lying along the direction of the light rays, gives a means of determining the ratio of the intensities of the two images just as in the ordinary Martens photometer. The position of the eye along the line of images (perpendicular to the paper) determines the wave-length of the light for which the comparison is made. In practice the eye is not moved in order to make comparisons at dif-ferent wave-lengths, but the prism P is rotated about an axis per-pendicular to the plane containing the collimator and telescope axes until the image formed by light of the desired wave-length is formed at the position of the eyepiece. The plane of the light rays through the spectrometer is generally vertical in the König-Martens instrument, and horizontal in most other forms. Two prisms of small angle, p_1 and p_2, are introduced for the purpose of diverting light reflected from the surfaces of the various optical elements.

Instruments for use with Spectrometers—A number of instruments have been designed for use in combination with any form of accurate spectrometer [22]. Some of these are of the homochromatic and some are of the juxtaposed spectra type. The Nutting-Hilger spectrophotometer [23], which is of the latter type, is shown diagrammatically in Fig. 196. The two parallel beams of light to be compared

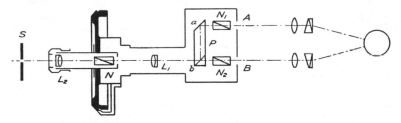

Fig. 196. The Nutting-Hilger Spectrophotometer.

enter the apertures A and B of the photometer and are respectively polarised in two mutually perpendicular planes by the fixed polarising prisms N_1 and N_2. The beam entering at A is totally reflected at the face a of the prism P and again at the silvered upper half of the face b. The light entering at B is transmitted directly through the lower clear part of the face b and thus the beam leaving b consists of two parts polarised in mutually perpendicular planes. This double beam then passes through a third polarising prism N which can be rotated about its axis by means of a head with a divided scale. In this way the intensities of the two parts are respectively reduced by the factors $\sin^2 \theta$ and $\cos^2 \theta$, so that the ratio of the two is altered by the factor $\tan^2 \theta$ as measured from the position of extinction for one part [24]. The dividing line in the surface b is sharply focused on the slit S of a spectrometer by means of the lenses L_1 and L_2, so that the spectrum seen in the spectrometer eyepiece is divided horizontally into two parts, the relative intensities of which can be varied by rotating N. The brightness and purity of the spectrum are governed by the width of the slit S and the spectral range seen is adjusted by means of two sliding shutters in the telescope which can be closed in from the sides in the plane in which the spectrum is formed. These isolate a field of any desired breadth on either side of a pointer which indicates the exact region corresponding to the wave-length shown on the scale of the spectrometer.

In addition to the angular scale giving θ directly in degrees, the head by which N is rotated may be provided with a second scale giving values of $\log_{10} \tan^2 \theta$ [25]. This is convenient when the instrument is being used, not for comparing two different sources of light but for measuring the transmission factor of a filter for light of various wave-lengths. The two beams of light entering the instrument are then both derived from the same light source and two settings are made, one of them with the filter inserted in the path of one of the beams and the other with the filter removed. It is clear that the density of the filter (see p. 161) is equal to the difference between the two readings obtained.

The Nutting-Hilger instrument possesses the double advantage that it can be used in combination with any good spectrometer and that the wide separation of the apertures A and B permits a measurement of the transmission factor of a filter of ordinary size to be made at any part of its surface and not only near the edge.

A source of error which has to be carefully considered in the design of polarisation spectrophotometers is the partial polarisation introduced by passage through glass surfaces, such as those of the dispersion prism. According to Fresnel's equation (see p. 156), if unpolarised light falls on a reflecting surface (such as a glass surface) at an angle of incidence θ, and if θ' be the angle of refraction, the reflection factor for light which is polarised in the plane of incidence is $\rho_I = \sin^2(\theta' - \theta)/\sin^2(\theta' + \theta)$, while for that polarised in the perpendicular plane it is $\rho_P = \tan^2(\theta' - \theta)/\tan^2(\theta' + \theta)$. The corresponding transmission factors will be $\tau_I = 1 - \rho_I$ and $\tau_P = 1 - \rho_P$. Since in a prism at the angle of minimum deviation (the usual arrangement in a spectrometer) the angle of incidence on entering the prism is equal to the angle of refraction on leaving it [26], the transmission factor of the whole prism for light polarised in the plane of incidence is $(1 - \rho_I)^2$, while for light polarised in the perpendicular plane it is $(1 - \rho_P)^2$ (neglecting absorption in both cases). The values of these factors for a $60°$ prism for which $n = 1.65$ are respectively 0.660 and 0.997. If, therefore, the spectrum produced by such a prism is observed through a polarising prism, and the latter is rotated, the beam varies in intensity from $(1 - \rho_P)^2$ to $(1 - \rho_I)^2$ [27].

The difficulty may be avoided in either of two ways, viz., (i) the light, *after* traversing the dispersing prism, may pass through a *fixed* polariser before reaching the movable polarising prism (as in the König-Martens instrument), or (ii) the polarising device for changing the relative intensities of the beams may be arranged so that both beams are always polarised in the same plane when passing through the dispersing prism (as in the Nutting-Hilger instrument).

It will be clear that all polarisation photometers must be liable to error if either of the incident beams contains any polarised light [28] and some other type of instrument must then be used [29].

Flicker Instruments—The use of the flicker principle is unnecessary in ordinary spectrophotometry, since colour difference is entirely eliminated. Instruments of the flicker type have, however, been designed [30] in connection with the determination of the relative luminous efficiency of radiation (see p. 73), since for this purpose it is necessary to make a photometric comparison between the brightnesses of two fields which are respectively illuminated by light from two different parts of the spectrum.

Photometric Procedure—As mentioned at the beginning of this chapter, the measurements made in spectrophotometry are nearly always relative, i.e. it is the form of the spectral distribution curve that is required and not the absolute intensity at any given wavelength. If absolute values are needed the non-spectral luminous intensity of the test source must be measured separately by ordinary photometric methods. The ratio of this to the value obtained by finding the area under the spectral light distribution curve gives the factor by which the measured intensity at any given wave-length must be multiplied in order to obtain the luminous intensity per unit wave-length interval at that wave-length.

The accuracy attainable in visual spectrophotometry is usually less than that generally expected in ordinary photometric measurements under good conditions [31]. One of the chief difficulties is lack of light, especially at the ends of the spectrum, so that it is impossible to obtain a sufficiently bright comparison field without unduly widening the entrance slit of the spectrometer [32]. The images formed on this slit should be larger than the largest slit used and should be of uniform illumination. The lenses used for forming these images should be large enough to ensure that they do not act as stops in the optical system.

Another source of error is stray light, i.e. light from other parts of the spectrum than that at which the measurements are being made. This may be due to reflections from the sides of the collimator or telescope if the diaphragm system is not perfect ; more often it is the result of reflection from the various glass surfaces or of scattering by dust or scratches on these surfaces [33]. The trouble may be avoided by the use of suitable colour filters over the eyepiece. Each such filter has a band of high transmission in one region of the spectrum and a low transmission elsewhere and a set of filters is required for making measurements throughout the spectrum [34].

Stray light may be entirely eliminated by the use of a double monochromator which, as its name implies, consists of two, generally similar, dispersing systems in tandem. The exit slit of the first system is also the entrance slit of the second. Both systems are set to the same wave-length and the light emerging from the exit slit of the second system is entirely free from admixture with light of any other wave-length [35].

Photo-electric Spectrophotometery—Photo-electric methods have largely superseded visual methods of spectrophotometry, partly because of the higher sensitivity available [36] but even more on account of their much greater speed and convenience [37]. It will be clear that, since the lights compared are sensibly homogeneous and of the same wave-length, the spectral sensitivity curve of the cell is unimportant so long as it adequately covers the whole of the visible spectrum. The chief requirement is linearity of response of the cell at all wave-lengths (see p. 95). The principal difference between the photo-electric and the visual methods is that in the former the lights are compared by successive exposure and not simultaneously.

It will be clear that an instrument of this type may take many different forms but in general the light to be measured illuminates the entrance slit of a spectrometer and an exit slit is fitted in the telescope so as to isolate the portion of the spectrum to be measured. Both slits should have symmetrical width adjustment. An enlarged image of the exit slit is formed on the cathode surface of a sensitive photocell.

A typical arrangement [38] is that shown diagrammatically in Fig. 197 where F_1 is the collimator (entrance) slit and F_2 the exit slit referred to above. The lens L forms an enlarged image of F_2 on the photocell C which is connected in a measuring circuit such as that described on p. 100. A filter G for absorbing stray light is inserted between L and C. It is usually slightly inclined so as to avoid inter-reflections. F_2, C and all the intermediate components are enclosed in a light-tight box with light-absorbing walls.

When the spectral distribution of a source is being measured this source and a standard are placed at S and S' respectively and a total reflection prism is mounted so that it can be readily inserted at P; an opaque screen between S and P is inserted or removed with P. Readings are taken alternately (a) on the standard, P being in position as shown, and (b) on the test source, P being removed. The necessity for exact linearity of the cell over a very wide range can be avoided by using sector discs of known transmission in front of one of the sources, so long as the photocell can be assumed to obey Talbot's law (see p. 98). Alternatively, a nominally neutral filter may be used but in this case its spectral transmission curve must be determined separately, as the transmission factor of such a filter is not perfectly independent of wave-length (see p. 228).

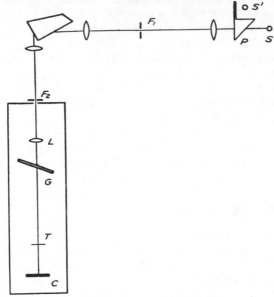

Fig. 197. A Photo-electric Spectrophotometer.

An alternative arrangement is to use a photocell which is known to obey Talbot's law accurately and to place over the entrance slit of the spectrometer a variable sector disc of the kind described on p. 225. The position of the sector disc is then adjusted at each wavelength until the photocurrent has some convenient fixed value.

If the luminance of the source is low, a multiplier photocell may be used with advantage [39].

A photo-electric spectrophotometer may be used to obtain an automatic record of a spectral distribution curve. The mechanism used to rotate the dispersing prism is geared to the recorder drum through a cam so designed as to give a uniform scale of wavelengths. Between the exit slit of the spectrometer and the photocell there is a diaphragm or shutter, the aperture of which is controlled by mechanism linked with the movement of the prism and in this way the change of dispersion of the prism and the variation of sensitivity of the photocell throughout the spectrum can be compensated. The response of the cell at any wave-length is then proportional to the amount of light of that wave-length entering the spectrometer. The light is interrupted on its way to the photocell so that the photocurrent is intermittent and can be amplified sufficiently to actuate a pen which traces on the recorder drum the spectral distribution curve required [40].

The spectral transmission curve of a colour filter can be determined quite as easily with a photo-electric as with a visual spectrophotometer [41]. In this case only one source of light is used and its
spectral distribution need not be known ; the chief requirements
are high intensity and constancy. Provision is made for inserting
the filter somewhere in the light path and removing it rapidly and
easily. In the case of the instrument shown in Fig. 197 the filter is
inserted at T and is very slightly tilted to avoid trouble due to inter-
reflections. Measurements are made alternately with and without
the filter in place and means are provided for inserting and removing
it without opening the light-tight box [42]. The insertion of the filter
may cause a slight shift of the patch of light on the photocell cathode.
This patch should cover a considerable area ; otherwise errors may
be introduced by small irregularities in the sensitivity of the cathode
surface (see p. 97). An analogous arrangement may be used for
determining the spectral reflection curve of a surface [43].

It will be clear that any photo-electric spectrophotometer may
be used for determining the spectral sensitivity curve of a photocell [44]. The most accurate method is to take readings throughout
the spectrum of (a) the current from the photocell and (b) the energy
as measured by a receptor such as a linear thermopile (see p. 47)
placed in the same position as the photocell. Alternatively, a source
of light of accurately known spectral distribution may be used,
allowance being made for the dispersion in the prism so that the relative energy received by the photocell from the exit slit of the spectrometer is known for all wave-lengths.

A modification of the Hardy recording spectrophotometer, to be
described later, has been used for a rapid determination of the
spectral sensitivity curve of a photocell [45].

Photographic Methods—For certain kinds of photometric measurements, particularly the spectrophotometry of transient or fluctuating sources or of sources giving line spectra, the photographic
plate possesses certain advantages since it may be used to obtain a
record of relative intensities at different parts of the spectrum at
some particular time. Although the spectral sensitivity curve of a
photographic plate varies greatly with the type of emulsion used, for
spectrophotometry, which involves only sensibly monochromatic
comparisons, this is not a serious disadvantage.

For light of any given spectral composition, the density D of the
image developed on an exposed plate, varies with the illumination E
and with the time of exposure t, approximately according to the
relationship $D = \gamma (\log Et^p - \log i)$ where γ is a constant, the
" gamma " of the plate, p is Schwarzchild's·constant [46], usually
somewhat less than unity and i is another constant of the plate, the

" inertia " [47]. This relationship only holds over a limited, though usually fairly wide range of the variables. Fig. 198 shows the shape of the curve connecting D with log Et^p and it will be seen that the equation given above applies over the straight-line portion of the curve, but not at either end.

The constants γ and i are liable to change, not only according to the type of sensitive emulsion used on the plate but also, though to a less extent, between plates of the same type or even from one part to another of a single plate [48]. Further, the density of the image obtained under any given set of conditions is affected by the process of development [49]. It follows that, for accurate measurement, the photographic plate is subject to the same limitations as the eye in that it can only be used as a detector of equality [50]. Unfortunately it is inferior to the eye in that Talbot's law is not strictly obeyed, an intermittent exposure giving, generally, less effect than the same amount of light (energy) acting continuously [51] unless the flashes are exceedingly brief [52]. A sector disc cannot, therefore, be used to vary the intensity of one of the comparison lights in a known manner and some other device must be employed. This is sometimes a neutral filter or a piece of netting [53], but more often a neutral wedge is used as described below [54].

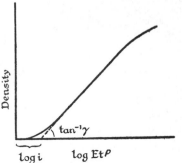

FIG. 198. Exposure-Density Curve for a Photographic Plate.

The instrument generally used for photographic spectrophotometry is, in essence, a spectrometer with a fixed prism, the telescope being replaced by a camera with the photographic plate in the plane of the focused spectrum. A neutral wedge is placed over the slit of the spectrometer or, preferably, over the photographic plate [55], he density gradient being in the direction of the length of slit in either case, so that the image on the plate changes uniformly in density from top to bottom. Two exposures of equal duration are made, one for the source to be measured and the other for a standard of known spectral distribution, the same wedge being used and all the conditions being the same for both exposures. The wedge has a horizontal fiducial line and after the plate has been developed, the vertical distances from the trace of this line to the position at which the density has some selected value is measured on both images along the line corresponding to a given wave-length λ. If the difference between these distances is d and the distance on the image which corresponds to unit change of density in the wedge is k, it follows that the ratio of the intensities of the two sources at wave-length λ is $10^{d/k}$. This ratio can be found for as many points in the spectrum as may be desired and so the spectral distribution of the test source can be determined.

The method by which the density of the image at any given point can be measured will be described in Chapter XIII. There is some advantage in selecting a density not far from 0·5 to define the points to which distances from the fiducial line are measured [56].

It cannot be assumed that the length of wedge corresponding to a given change of density is the same at all wave-lengths and for this and other reasons the wedge should be calibrated under the conditions of use. This can be done quite readily by making a second exposure of the standard source, of the same duration as the other two exposures but with a neutral filter of a density not far from unity placed over the slit. The spectral transmission curve of this filter is separately determined, and if, at any wave-length λ, the transmission of the neutral filter is τ and the distances from the fiducial mark to a fixed density in the two images of the standard spectrum are respectively d_1 and d_2, it follows that the distance $(d_2 - d_1)$ on the wedge image corresponds to a density change of $\log_{10}(1/\tau)$ at wave-length λ.

It will be seen that in the procedure described above, since all the exposures are made on the same plate and the exposure times are equal, equal densities must result from equal values of the various constants. The only assumptions made are (a) that the area of plate used is uniform in its characteristics and in development and (b) that an image of the slit is uniformly illuminated throughout its length, or at least over the maximum distance measured.

Other methods of photographic spectrophotometry have been used, most of them based on the relationship between D, E and t given above [57]. In particular, the relation between t and E for a given value of D has frequently been used [58] but whenever possible the use of this or of any other relationship depending on the value of a more or less empirically determined constant should be avoided.

There are certain problems of light measurement, other than spectrophotometry, in which photography finds an application, notably in stellar photometry and in determining the luminance distribution in a non-uniform field of view. The methods usually found most suitable in such work differ from the procedure described above and some sacrifice of accuracy has generally to be made for the sake of greater simplicity (see pp. 478 and 402). Photographic methods are frequently used when no direct visual comparison is possible as in the measurement of ultra-violet light. Such work is, however, outside the scope of this book.

Slit-width Correction—It has been pointed out already that, owing to the finite width of the slit of a spectrometer, the light reaching any point of the spectrum is not homogeneous, but consists of a mixture composed of a given range of wave-lengths. This lack of purity of the spectrum does not introduce any serious error into a spectrophotometric comparison so long as the spectra compared are continuous and not very different in energy distribution. When, however, an irregularly distributed spectrum, such as that given by a Welsbach mantle, is compared with a black-body spectrum, or when two black-body spectra corresponding to widely different temperatures are compared, the correction for the finite width of the slit cannot be neglected [59]. The mathematical treatment of the problem is somewhat lengthy, and for it the original papers should be consulted [60]. The method of applying the correction will best be understood from an example. Let the energy distribution curve of the standard source be represented by $f(\lambda)$, and that of the test source by $\phi(\lambda)$. Further, let the intensity curve of the impure spectrum of the standard source as seen in the spectrophotometer be represented by $F(\lambda)$, and let the ratio of the intensities at any wavelength λ be $p(\lambda)$. In Fig. 199 let the curve ABC represent the function $p(\lambda)F(\lambda)$, and let OP represent a given wave-length λ. Let PM and PN each represent a wave-length interval equal to $\frac{1}{2}(a+b)$, where $2a$ and $2b$ are respectively the breadths of the collimator and telescope slits in terms of the wave-length scale

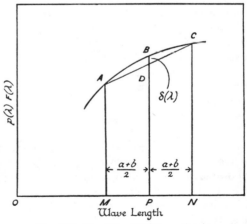

FIG. 199. The Slit-width Correction in Spectrophotometry.

of the spectrometer. Let $BD = \delta(\lambda)$. Then it may be shown that if $n \equiv b/a$,

$$\frac{\phi(\lambda)}{f(\lambda)} = \frac{\{p(\lambda)F(\lambda) - l\delta(\lambda) + m\delta'(\lambda) - \ldots\}}{\{F(\lambda) - l\delta_0(\lambda) + m\delta_0'(\lambda) - \ldots\}},$$

where $l = (1+n^2)/6(1+n)^2$,

and $m = (6 + 5n + 10n^2 + 5n^3 + 6n^4)/180(1+n)^4$.

$\delta_0(\lambda)$ is found in the same manner as $\delta(\lambda)$ from the curve for $F(\lambda)$, and $\delta'(\lambda)$ and $\delta_0'(\lambda)$ are found in an exactly similar manner from the curves for $\delta(\lambda)$ and $\delta_0(\lambda)$. It should be noticed that $\delta(\lambda)$ is positive when the curve is convex towards the λ-axis (*i.e.* it is negative in Fig. 199). When $a = b$ the expression reduces to

$$\frac{\phi(\lambda)}{f(\lambda)} = \frac{\{p(\lambda) F(\lambda) - \delta(\lambda)/12 + \delta'(\lambda)/90 - \ldots\}}{\{F(\lambda) - \delta_0(\lambda)/12 + \delta_0'(\lambda)/90 - \ldots\}}.$$

$F(\lambda)$ may be calculated from $f(\lambda)$ if the dispersion curve of the spectrometer prism is known, for $F(\lambda) \propto V_\lambda f(\lambda)/\varDelta(\lambda)$, where $\varDelta(\lambda)$ represents the dispersion (see p. 354) and V_λ the relative luminous efficiency of radiation.

It is to be remarked that in the case of an instrument in which the spectrum is viewed by means of an eyepiece, $2b$ represents the width of the aperture limiting the spectral region viewed by the eye. In the case of an instrument in which the Maxwellian view is employed, $2b$ represents the width of the pupil in the eyepiece, or the natural pupil, whichever is the smaller.

The Use of Colour Filters for Approximate Work—Rough spectrophotometric determinations may be carried out with any ordinary form of photometer by placing over the eyepiece coloured media having comparatively narrow transmission bands in the different parts of the visible spectrum [61]. The relative intensities of the two lights compared are thus obtained for the regions of the transmission bands of the media. Special glasses or gelatine filters suitable for this purpose have been prepared [62]. By using a modified form of direct-vision spectroscope in the eyepiece of an ordinary photometer it is possible to obtain photometric comparisons at different parts of the spectrum [63].

Unsteady Sources—In the visual spectrophotometry of unsteady sources, such as the arc, it is generally necessary to use an ordinary photometer as a control instrument, readings on the spectrophotometer being made only when an auxiliary observer at the ordinary photometer signals that the arc is of normal intensity and sufficiently steady for observation [64].

Determination of Spectral Transmission Curves—It has already been mentioned that a very important application of spectrophotometry is to the measurement of the transmission factor of a colour filter throughout the visible spectrum and the way in which such measurements may be made has been indicated [65]. In the case of a visual instrument the substitution method should be used, the transmission factor at any given wave-length being the ratio of the intensities measured at that wave-length for *the same part* of the comparison field (*a*) with and (*b*) without the filter interposed. It is sometimes convenient to use a dummy filter of high transmission permanently in that beam of light which traverses the filter under measurement, partly to avoid any possibility of the intensity on that side being greater than the intensity on the comparison side and partly to bring the balance point to a convenient part of the scale.

The spectral transmission curves of liquids and of solutions are often of considerable importance in chemical analysis [66]. Measurements are made as in the case of a colour filter, the liquid being contained in a cylindrical or trough-shaped glass vessel which may be of any length up to 100 mm. so that the particular form of spectrophotometer chosen for the work must be capable of accommodating such a vessel in the path of one of the incident beams.

The containing vessel generally consists of an accurately known length of glass or quartz tube against the ends of which are pressed plane parallel plates of colourless glass or of quartz. One convenient form is shown in Fig. 200. Sometimes the whole vessel is immersed in water contained in a larger outer vessel, so that the temperature may be kept constant and accurately measured by means of thermocouples immersed in the water.

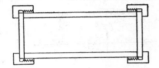

FIG. 200. Cell for Spectral Transmission Measurements.

If absolute values of transmission are required, it is necessary to compensate for (a) the shortening of the effective light path, due to refraction in the liquid (see p. 24), and (b) the loss of light by reflection from the end faces of the containing vessel [67]. This may be done by inserting in the comparison beam of light a vessel similar to that containing the liquid being measured. This " dummy " vessel is filled with the solvent (in the case of a solution) or with some colourless liquid of a refractive index close to that of the liquid being measured [68].

Photo-electric instruments have been designed to enable the spectral transmission curve of a colour filter or of a transparent liquid to be traced out automatically [69]. For instance the Hardy recording spectrophotometer described below may be used to determine spectral transmission curves as well as curves of spectral reflection factor.

Spectral Reflection Curves—The most direct way of determining the spectral reflection curve of a diffusing surface is to illuminate both the test surface and a surface of magnesium oxide by the same source of light and then to compare the light reflected by these two surfaces, using one of the spectrophotometers described earlier in this chapter [70]. The conditions of both illumination and reflection should be stated (see p. 338). The chief disadvantage of this method is lack of light and it is necessary to use very high values of illumination, e.g.

by forming images of a bright source of light on the surfaces [71]. In many cases this is undesirable, if only because of the risk of damage to the specimen, and it is better to disperse the light first and then illuminate the surface with nearly monochromatic light [72].

A very convenient instrument in which this is done is the Wright photo-electric spectrophotometer [73] which may be regarded as a modification of the colorimeter shown in Fig. 189 (p. 333). Instead of the three roof-prisms, a single strip of mirror reflects a narrow band of wave-lengths to the prism M and this light, after traversing a simple optical system, illuminates in turn a magnesium oxide surface and the test surface. The light reflected by these surfaces is then measured by means of a photocell.

In the Hardy recording spectrophotometer [74], which is shown diagrammatically in Fig. 201, the light leaving the exit slit of a

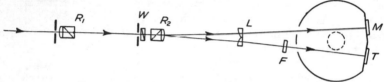

Fɪɢ. 201. The Hardy Recording Spectrophotometer.

spectrometer (in this case a double monochromator) passes through a polarising prism R_1 which can be rotated about the axis of the optical system and then through a fixed Wollaston prism W (see p. 32) where it is split into two beams polarised in mutually perpendicular planes. Both these beams pass through a second polarising prism R_2 which is mounted inside the hollow shaft of a synchronous motor. After further separation by means of a pair of decentred lenses the two beams enter an integrating sphere and respectively illuminate M, a surface of magnesium oxide, and T the surface to be measured. It will be seen that as R_2 is rotated each beam fluctuates in intensity from zero to a maximum, the fluctuations being 180° out of phase. The relative intensities of the two maxima can be varied by rotating R_1 with respect to W, the position of equality being that in which the plane of polarisation of the light from R_1 bisects the angle between the two planes of polarisation of the light leaving W. As R_1 is rotated from this position one maximum increases and the other diminishes, the ratio of the maxima being $\tan^2 \alpha$ for an angle of rotation α. Thus, if the ratio of the reflection factor of T to that of M is ρ, the ratio of the maxima in the light reflected from the two surfaces is $\rho \tan^2 \alpha$ and these maxima may therefore be brought to equality by making $\tan^2 \alpha = 1/\rho$. At this value of α there is no fluctuation in the total light reflected from M and T taken together, but if α is greater or less than this a fluctuation occurs in the total light ; this is the basis upon which the instrument operates.

The surfaces M and T are placed in an integrating sphere so that the light reaching a window in the side of this sphere is proportional to the total light reflected from M and T together and fluctuations in this total light are reproduced in the output of a photocell placed behind the window. These fluctuations are amplified and applied to the grids of two thyratrons connected, as shown in Fig. 202, through the field coils of a balance motor by which R_1 is slowly rotated in one direction or the other. The transformer at the right of Fig. 202 is supplied with a.c. of a frequency double that of the rotation of R_2. Depending on whether the light from M or that from T is the greater, the amplified signal from the photocell is in phase or

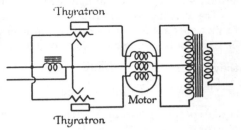

FIG. 202. Driving Mechanism for the Hardy Spectrophotometer.

180° out of phase with the a.c. through the transformer. Consequently current passes through one or other of the two thyratrons and the motor rotates in the corresponding direction. This movement is so arranged that the resulting rotation of R_1 tends to equalise the light reflected from M and from T and when this condition is reached, the signal from the photocell is reduced to zero and the motor stops. The position of R_1 is then a measure of ρ for the wavelength of the light entering the sphere.

The mechanism for changing the wave-length is driven by a motor and is geared to a recording drum, while the rotation of R_1 moves a stylus which traces a line on this drum. It follows that, when the wave-length mechanism is set in motion and R_1 automatically takes up the balance position at each point on the spectrum, the stylus traces out the spectral reflection curve on graph paper wrapped round the recording drum.

This instrument, which has recently been redesigned [75], may be used to find the spectral transmission curve of a filter by substituting for T a surface identical with M and inserting the filter at F.

It will be clear that a non-recording instrument can be designed on similar principles, R_1 being rotated by hand and some sensitive detector, either audible or visible, being used to establish the point at which the fluctuations in the amplified signal from the photocell are reduced to zero.

It will be noticed that the reflection factors obtained by the methods described above are not absolute but are relative to magnesium oxide. If a layer of oxide at least one millimetre in thickness is deposited on clean silver, the surface has a reflection factor of between 98 and 99·5 per cent, depending on the wave-length (see Appendix VII) and the observed values can be corrected accordingly if absolute values are required [76].

The spectral reflection curve of a polished surface may be found by arranging that a suitable source of light and an image of this source, formed by reflection in the polished surface, respectively provide the two beams of light compared in a spectrophotometer [77].

The Plotting of Spectrophotometric Data—It is often convenient to plot spectral reflection or transmission curves in such a way that, in addition to giving the values of ρ_λ or τ_λ throughout the spectrum, they also show graphically, by their areas, the values of $\int V_\lambda \rho_\lambda \, d\lambda$ or $\int V_\lambda \tau_\lambda \, d\lambda$, i.e. the integral reflection or transmission factors for an equal energy spectrum. This can be done by plotting the values of ρ_λ or τ_λ on specially prepared co-ordinate paper on which the scale of abscissae is such that $x_\lambda = a \int_0^\lambda V_\lambda \, d\lambda$ [78]. The principle may clearly be extended so as to exhibit the values of ρ and τ for light of any given spectral distribution by making $x_\lambda = a \int_0^\lambda V_\lambda E_\lambda \, d\lambda$ where E_λ is the energy per unit wave-length interval at wave-length λ (see p. 154) for the light adopted. An example of this method of plotting is given in Fig. 203, where the curve represents the spectral transmission of a certain blue-green medium. The ordinate at any value of λ gives the value of τ_λ, while the total area gives the value of τ for light having an equal energy spectrum.

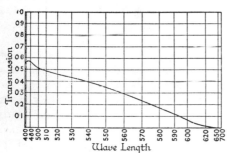

FIG. 203. Spectrophotometric Plot on Scale of Abscissae Proportional to V_λ.

Tables have been prepared to enable the integral transmission or reflection factor of a coloured medium to be calculated readily for lights of certain defined spectral distributions of practical importance [79].

Abridged Spectrophotometry—For certain purposes a complete spectral distribution curve is not required or may even be undesirable (see below) ; it is sufficient to measure the flux in certain broad bands of wave-length distributed through the visible spectrum. The most satisfactory method of making such measurements is to use the dispersion and template (or mask) system described in Chapter IX (see p. 312). Any spectral band may be isolated by means of a suitable template and in this way the whole spectrum may be divided into any desired number of bands and the flux in each may be determined [80]. Approximate values of the same kind may be obtained without a dispersion system, colour filters with narrow transmission bands being used to isolate the various wave-length regions. Both visual [81] and photo-electric [82] instruments have been designed on this principle, generally for the approximate determination of the spectral reflection or transmission curves of coloured materials [83].

Line Spectra—The measurement of the relative intensities of spectral lines is a special problem in spectrophotometry. A photographic method, such as that described earlier in this chapter, is generally employed [84] but allowance has to be made for the fact that, whereas in the case of a continuous spectrum the luminance at any wave-length is not only proportional to the energy per unit wave-length interval but is also inversely proportional to the dispersion of the prism, in the case of a line spectrum the luminance of the lines is independent of the dispersion.

Instead of using a continuous spectrum as a basis of comparison, the energy in each line may be measured directly by means of a very sensitive receptor such as a photo-multiplier cell (see p. 93) [85].

Since the luminance of a continuous spectrum seen in a spectrometer is approximately proportional to the width of the entrance slit, whereas in the case of a line spectrum the only effect of widening the slit is to broaden the lines without affecting their luminance, it is clear that the ordinary form of spectral distribution curve has no meaning in the case of light consisting of both a continuous spectrum and a line spectrum. This also follows from the fact that the ordinary spectral distribution curve shows the relative value of the energy or the light per unit wave-length interval and the wave-length interval covered by a spectral line is very much smaller than this [86]. A useful convention is to show the energy from the line as though it were spread uniformly over a band $10m\mu$ in width centred on the wave-length of the line.

The matter is of considerable practical importance especially in the case of light sources depending on an electric discharge through a gas, and for such sources the spectral distribution is usually indicated by means of a diagram such as that shown in Fig. 204. The spectrum is divided into a comparatively small number of sections, not necessarily covering equal intervals of wave-length, and the area of the

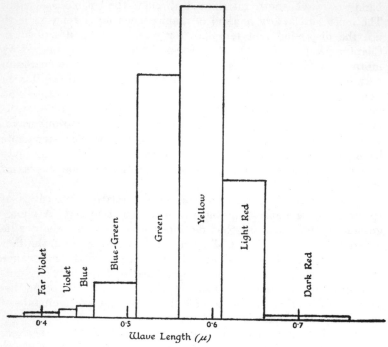

FIG. 204. A Block Diagram of Spectral Distribution obtained by
Abridged Spectrophotometry.

rectangle drawn on any section is proportional to the energy, or the
luminous flux emitted by the source within the corresponding wave-
length interval [87].

The measurement of energy, or flux within each wave-length
interval may conveniently be made as described in the previous
section.

BIBLIOGRAPHY

VISUAL METHODS

Report of Committee on Spectrophotometry. Opt. Soc. Am., J., 10, *1925*,
p. 169. (Contains an extensive bibliography.)

K. S. Gibson. Opt. Soc. Am., J., 24, *1934*, p. 234; *Spectrophotometry*
(Bureau of Standards Circ. No. 484, *1949*).

PHYSICAL METHODS

(a) Photographic

G. M. B. Dobson, I. O. Griffith and D. N. Harrison. *Photographic Photometry.* (Oxford Univ. Press, *1926*.)

G. R. Harrison. Opt. Soc. Am., J., 19, *1929*, p. 267 and 24, *1934*, p. 59.
(Contain extensive bibliographies.)

(b) General

L. S. Ornstein, W. J. H. Moll and H. C. Burger. *Objective Spektralphotometrie.* (Vieweg, Brunswick, *1932*.)

REFERENCES

1. J. Fraunhofer. Munich Denkschriften, 5, *1814*, p. 193 ; Gilbert's Ann., 56, *1817*, p. 297.
2. A. Crova and H. Lagarde. C.R., 93, *1881*, p. 959.
   S. P. Langley. Am. J. Sci., 36, *1888*, p. 359.
3. W. W. Coblentz. Bureau of Standards, Bull., 13, *1916*, p. 355 ; Frank. Inst., J., 188, *1919*, p. 399.
   E. P. Hyde, W. E. Forsythe and F. E. Cady. Frank. Inst., J., 188, *1919*, p. 129.
4. See, e.g., L. S. Ornstein, D. Vermeulen and E. F. M. van der Held, Opt. Soc. Am., J., 20, *1930*, p. 573.
5. A. G. Worthing. Phys. Rev., 10, *1917*, p. 377 ; Z. f. Phys., 22, *1924*, p. 9.
   L. S. Ornstein. Physica, 3, *1936*, p. 561. J. C. de Vos. *Ibid.*, 20, *1954*, p. 691.
6. E. P. Hyde. Phys. Rev., 27, *1908*, p. 521 ; Frank. Inst., J., 169, *1910*, p. 439 and 170, *1910*, p. 26 ; Gen. El. Rev., 20, *1917*, p. 819.
   E. P. Hyde and W. E. Forsythe. Frank. Inst., J., 189, *1920*, p. 663.
   W. E. Forsythe. Opt. Soc. Am., J., 7, *1923*, p. 1115.
   See also I. G. Priest, Bureau of Standards, Bull., 18, *1922*, p. 221.
7. A. G. Worthing. Phys. Rev., 10, *1917*, p. 377.
8. H. Buckley, L. J. Collier and F. J. C. Brookes. C.I.E., Proc., 6, *1924*, p. 203.
   W. E. Forsythe and A. G. Worthing. *Ibid.*, p. 100.
   See also the other refs. in note (11) on p. 290 of *Photometry* (*1926*).
9. P. Pellin and A. Broca. J. de Phys., 8, *1899*, p. 314.
   See also G. Guadet, Rev. d'Opt., 4, *1925*, p. 493 ; S. Makishima, Z. Koana and K. Oshima, Opt. Soc. Am., J., 41, *1951*, p. 249.
10. W. E. Forsythe. Astrophys. J., 45, *1917*, p. 278.   [p. 145.
    See also S. Uhler, Phys. Rev., 29, *1909*, p. 37 ; E. Bloch, J. de Phys., 7, *1917*,
11. Tables of the wave-lengths are to be found in such books as *Physical and Chemical Constants*, by G. W. C. Kaye and T. H. Laby ; also in " Report on Spectrophotometry " (Opt. Soc. Am., J., 10, *1925*, p. 185).
    See also J. A. Van den Akker, Opt. Soc. Am., J., 33, *1943*, p. 257.
12. A. Schuster. Astrophys. J., 21, *1905*, p. 197.
    A. Schuster and J. W. Nicholson. *Theory of Optics*, § 84.
13. See, e.g., J. R. Milne, Optical Convention, *1905*, Proc., p. 178.
14. Instruments have, however, been designed for use on the photometer bench in the same manner as an ordinary head. See, e.g., J. Thovert, C.R., 148, *1909*, p. 625 and C.I.E., Proc., 3, *1911*, p. 101 ; H. Krüss, Z.f.I., 18, *1898*, p. 12, 24, *1904*, p. 201 and 32, *1912*, p. 6 ; P. Eitner, Z. f. techn. Phys., 6, *1925*, p. 201.
15. C. Vierordt. Ann. d. Phys., 140, *1870*, p. 172 and 3, *1878*, p. 357.
    See also G. A. Shook, Astrophys. J., 46, *1917*, p. 305 ; A. J. Bull, Opt. Soc., Trans., 23, *1922*, p. 197.
16. W. Dieterich. Fortschritte d. Phys., 37, *1881*, p. 472.
    H. Krüss. Repertorium f. exp. Phys., 18, *1882*, p. 217.
    For a description of a symmetrical slit, see R. S. Whipple, Opt. Soc., Trans., 22, *1920*, p. 35.
17. O. Lummer and E. Brodhun. Z.f.I., 12, *1892*, 132.
    See also D. B. Brace, Phil. Mag., 48, *1899*, p. 420 and H. B. Lemon, Astrophys. J., 39, *1914*, p. 204.
18. E. Brodhun and O. Schrönrock. Z.f.I., 24, *1904*, p. 70.
    S. Czapski. *Ibid.*, 12, *1892*, p. 161.
    J. Terrien and F. Desvignes. J. de Phys., 10, *1949*, p. 6.
19. J. Guild. Opt. Soc., Trans., 26, *1924*, p. 74.
20. See the refs. given in notes (34), (36) to (40) and (43) on p. 293 of *Photometry* (*1926*) ; also K. Fischer, Z.f.I., 51, *1931*, p. 347.

21. A. König. Berlin phys. Gesell., Verh., 4, *1885*, p. 50 and 5, *1886*, p 49 ; Ann. d. Phys., 53, *1894*, p. 785.
F. F. Martens. Deut. phys. Gesell., Verh., 1, *1899*, p. 280.
F. F. Martens and F. Grunbaum, Ann. d. Phys., 12, *1900*, p. 984.
F. Herzfeld-Hoffmann. Z.f.I., 48, *1928*, p. 105.

22. See the refs. given in notes (44) to (48) on p. 292 of *Photometry (1926)*. See also p. 285 of that edition.
J. Terrien and F. Desvignes. Opt. Soc. Am., J., 40, *1950*, p. 845.

23. P. G. Nutting. Bureau of Standards, Bull., 7, *1911*, p. 239.
P. R. Ord. Illum. Eng., 16, *1923*, p. 167.

24. For a system in which the ratio is $\tan^4 \theta$ see J. H. Dowell, J. Sci. Inst., 8, *1931*, p. 382 and 10, *1933*, p. 153.

25. See also M. Richter, Z. f. techn. Phys., 13, *1932*, p. 493 ; L. Honty, Z.f.I., 58, *1938*, p. 212.

26. Both are equal to $\sin^{-1}$ ($n \sin A/2$) where A is the angle of the prism.

27. F. Twyman. Phys. Soc., Proc., 20, *1907*, p. 467.

28. A. Cornu. C.R., 103, *1886*, p. 1227.
See also R. D. Nutting, Opt. Soc. Am., J., 25, *1935*, p. 211.

29. See, e.g., H. Buckley and F. J. C. Brookes, J. Sci. Inst., 7, *1930*, p. 305 ; L. S. Ornstein, J. G. Eymers and D. Vermeulen, Amsterdam Acad., Proc., 35, *1932*, p. 278.

30. See, e.g., H. Bender, Ann. d. Phys., 45, *1914*, p. 105 ; J. R. Milne, Roy. Soc. Edin., Proc., 33, *1913*, p. 257.

31. I. G. Priest, H. J. McNicholas and M. K. Frehafer. Opt. Soc. Am., J., 8, *1924*, p. 201.
R. Weigel. Licht, 1, *1930–1*, pp. 25, 243 and 266.
See also P. Vaillant, C.R., 195, *1932*, p. 487.

32. J. Terrien and F. Desvignes. Rev. d'Opt., 27, *1948*, p. 451.

33. H. E. Ives. Phys. Rev., 30, *1910*, p. 446.
See also J. H. Dowell, J. Sci. Inst., 8, *1931*, p. 382 ; T. D. Gheorghiu, C.R., 194, *1932*, p. 1810.

34. *Ilford Colour Filters.* Ilford, Ltd., Ilford, London.
See also J. S. Preston, J. Sci. Inst., 13, *1936*, p. 368 ; K. S. Gibson, Opt. Soc. Am., J., 21, *1931*, p. 564.

35. See, e.g., C. F. Goodeve, Roy. Soc., Proc., 155, *1936*, p. 664 ; E. Strohbusch, Z.f.I., 59, *1939*, p. 417 ; G. Fraudet and B. Vodar, Rev., d'Opt., 19, *1940*, p. 49 (contains an extensive bibliography) ; G. A. Boutry and J. Gillod, C.R., 217, *1943*, p. 20. See also A. Baylo, Réunions de l'Inst. d'Opt., 6, *1935*, " La spectrophotométrie visuelle," p. 17.

36. L. Taylor. Opt. Soc. Am., J., 14, *1927*, p. 332.

37. K. S. Gibson. " Photo-electric Cells and their Applications," Phys. and Opt. Socs., *1930*, p. 157.
R. Stair. Bureau of Standards, J. of Research, 46, *1951*, p. 437.

38. J. S. Preston and F. W. Cuckow. Phys. Soc., Proc., 48, *1936*, p. 869 and 49, *1937*, p. 189.

39. S. F. Rodionov. Jurnal technicheskoi Fisiki, U.S.S.R., 9, *1939*, p. 1180 (In Russian).
F. J. Studer. Opt. Soc. Am., J., 37, *1947*, p. 288 and 38, *1948*, p. 467.
W. S. Plymale. *Ibid.*, 37, *1947*, p. 399.
S. J. Henderson and M. B. Halstead. Brit. J. Appl. Phys., 3, *1952*, p. 255.
See also L. Le Blan, C.R., 224, *1947*, p. 383.

40. V. K. Zworykin. Opt. Soc. Am., J., 29, *1939*, p. 84.
See also G. A. Boutry and J. Gillod, C.R., 213, *1941*, p. 255 and 217, *1943*, p. 20 ; J. Gillod, Mesures, 9, *1944*, pp. 34, 62 and 117 ; F. J. Studer and W. R. Jacobson, Gen. El. Rev., 52, *1949*, Oct., p. 34.

41. K. S. Gibson. Bureau of Standards, Bull., 15, *1919*, p. 325 ; Opt. Soc. Am., J., 7, *1923*, p. 693 and 21, *1931*, p. 564.
L. H. Tardy. Rev. d'Opt., 7, *1928*, p. 189.
D. S. Perfect. " Photo-electric Cells and their Applications," Phys. and Opt. Socs., *1930*, p. 174.
M. Barnard and P. McMichael. Opt. Soc. Am., J., 21, *1931*, p. 588.

M. Richter. Z. f. techn. Phys., 13, *1932*, p. 491.
C. H. Sharp and H. J. Eckweiler. Opt. Soc. Am., J., 23, *1933*, p. 246.
L. A. Woodward. Roy. Soc., Proc., 144, *1934*, p. 118.
M. v. Ardenne and E. Haas. Z. phys. Chem. (A), 174, *1935*, p. 115.
M. Kniazuk. Opt. Soc. Am., J., 29, *1939*, p. 223.
C. J. Barton and J. H. Yoe. Industrial and Engng. Chem. (Anal. Ed.), 12, *1940*, p. 166.
S. Jacobsohn et al. Rev. Sci. Inst., 11, *1940*, p. 220.
Z. Koana et al. Phys.-Math. Soc. Japan, Proc., 22, *1940*, p. 940.
H. H. Cary and A. O. Beckman. Opt. Soc. Am., J., 31, *1941*, p. 682.
K. S. Gibson and M. M. Balcolm. Ibid., 37, *1947*, p. 593.
W. C. Miller et al. Ibid., 39, *1949*, p. 377.
See also C. Müller, Z. f. Phys., 34, *1925*, p. 824 ; S. M. Seeley and E. I. Anderson, Rev. Sci. Inst., 12, *1941*, p. 392 ; H. G. W. Harding, Nature, 163, *1949*, p. 924.
An instrument in which a grating is used to disperse the light and the photocell is of the rectifier type has been described by C. Sheard and M. N. States (Opt. Soc. Am., J., 31, *1941*, p. 64).

42. S. Shlaer. Opt. Soc. Am., J., 28, *1938*, p. 18.

43. J. Bannon. J. Sci. Inst., 24, *1947*, p. 205.
See also H. J. Dutton and G. F. Bailey, Industrial and Engng. Chem. (Anal. Ed.), 15, *1943*, p. 275 ; G. E. Pride, Opt. Soc. Am., J., 36, *1946*, p. 510.

44. R. Sewig, L. Bähr and A. Zincke. Z.f.I., 51, *1931*, p. 479.

45. J. T. Tykociner and L. R. Bloom. Opt. Soc. Am., J., 31, *1941*, p. 689.
See also T. B. Perkins, ibid., 29, *1939*, p. 226.

46. K. Schwarzchild. Astrophys. J., 11, *1900*, p. 89.
J. K. Robertson. Opt. Soc. Am., J., 7, *1923*, p. 996.
L. A. Jones et al. Ibid., 7, *1923*, p. 1079 ; 11, *1925*, p. 319 ; 12, *1926*, p. 321 ; 13, *1926*, p. 443 and 14, *1927*, p. 223.
H. Kienle. Naturwissenschaften, 23, *1935*, p. 762.

47. See, e.g., C. E. K. Mees, *Theory of the Photographic Process*, (Macmillan Coy., New York, *1942*), Chap. V, and L. A. Jones, Soc. Motion Picture Engrs., 17, *1931*, pp. 491 and 695 and 18, *1932*, pp. 54 and 324.

48. J. Clavier. Bull. Astronomique (Part I), 3, *1923*, p. 341.
J. T. Lay and I. C. Cornog. Opt. Soc. Am., J., 24, *1934*, p. 149.
W. H. E. Bandermann. Z. f. Phys., 90, *1934*, p. 266.
G. de Vaucouleurs. Rev. d'Opt., 27, *1948*, p. 541.

49. C. Fabry and H. Buisson. J. de Phys., 5, *1924*, p. 97.

50. H. Buisson and C. Fabry. Rev. d'Opt., 3, *1924*, p. 1.
See also H. M. Kellner, Z. wiss. Photog., 24, *1926*, p. 79.

51. W. de W. Abney. Roy. Soc., Proc., 54, *1893*, p. 143.
K. Schwarzchild. Astrophys. J., 11, *1900*, p. 89.
H. M. Kellner. Z. wiss. Photog., 24, *1926*, p. 41.
E. A. Baker. Opt. Convention, *1926*, Proc., Vol. I, p. 238.
J. M. Blair and M. C. Hylan. Opt. Soc. Am., J., 23, *1933*, p. 353.
See also R. H. Davis, Bureau of Standards, Bull., 21, *1926*, p. 95.

52. J. H. Webb. Opt. Soc. Am., J., 23, *1933*, pp. 157 and 316.
See also L. Silberstein and J. H. Webb, Phil. Mag., 18, *1934*, p. 1.

53. R. Frerichs. Z. f. Phys., 35, *1926*, p. 524.
G. Landsberg. Ibid., 46, *1927*, p. 106.
G. R. Harrison. Opt. Soc. Am., J., 18, *1929*, p. 492.
See also A. Jobin and G. Yvon, Rev. d'Opt., 8, *1929*, p. 392 ; O. E. Miller, Rev. Sci. Inst., 3, *1932*, p. 30 ; M. Duffieux and L. Grillet, Rev. d'Opt., 12, *1933*, p. 425.

54. A " wedge " sector disc has been described by F. Twyman and F. Simeon (Opt. Soc., Trans., 31, *1930*, p. 169).
See also R. v. Hirsch and M. Schön, Z. f. Astrophys., 1, *1930*, p. 164 ; E. W. Müller, Z. f. Phys., 97, *1935*, p. 97 ; J. A. Van den Akker, Opt. Soc. Am., J., 36, *1946*, p. 561.

55. R. E. Slade and F. C. Toy. Roy. Soc., Proc., 97, *1920*, p. 181.
L. A. Jones. Opt. Soc. Am., J., 10, *1925*, p. 561.
G. E. Davis and J. W. Woodrow. Rev. Sci. Inst., 13, *1942*, p. 223.

56. G. M B. Dobson, I. O. Griffith and D. N. Harrison. *Photographic Photometry*, p. 66.

57. See, e.g., H. Ewest, Photog., J., 54, *1914*, p. 99 ; M. Abribat, Sci. et Indust. Photog., 2, *1931*, p. 321.

58. G. Holst and L. Hamburger. Amsterdam Acad., Proc., 20, *1918*, p. 1021.

59. See, e.g., P. Vaillant, C.R., 138, *1904*, p. 1088 ; G. L. Buc and E. I. Stearns, Opt. Soc. Am., J., 35, *1945*, p. 458.

60. C. Runge. Z. f. Math. u. Phys., 42, *1897*, p. 205.
F. Paschen. Ann. d. Phys., 60, *1897*, p. 712.
E. L. Nichols and E. Merritt. Phys. Rev., 30, *1910*, p. 328.
E. P. Hyde. Astrophys. J., 35, *1912*, p. 237.
F. Hoffmann. Z. f. Phys., 37, *1926*, p. 60.
G. Ribaud and I. Peychès. Rev. d'Opt., 11, *1932*, p. 241.
W. Meyer-Eppler. Z.f.I., 60, *1940*, p. 197.
T. Murakami. Phys.-Math. Soc. Japan, Proc., 23, *1941*, p. 227.
P. Boillet. Rev. d'Opt., 24, *1945*, p. 85.
A. Biot. Soc. Sci. de Bruxelles, Ann. (Sér. I), 61, *1947*, p. 127.
A. C. Hardy and F. M. Young. Opt. Soc. Am., J., 39, *1949*, p. 265.
W. Eberhardt. *Ibid.*, 40, *1950*, p. 172.

61. F. Gaud. C.R., 129, *1899*, p. 759.
W. Voege. Illum. Eng., 5, *1912*, p. 375.

62. K. S. Gibson, E. P. J. Tyndall and H. J. McNicholas. Bureau of Standards, Technol. Paper No. 148, *1920*.
Wratten Filters. (Eastman Kodak Co., Rochester, N.Y.)
See also L. A. Jones, Opt. Soc. Am., J., 16, *1928*, p. 259.

63. J. Thovert. J. de Phys., 8, *1909*, p. 834.

64. I. G. Priest, W. F. Meggers, H. J. McNicholas, K. S. Gibson and E. P. T. Tyndall. Bureau of Standards, Technol. Paper No. 168, *1920*.
P. R. Ord. Illum. Eng., 16, *1923*, p. 167.

65. See also J. Terrien and F. Desvignes, Opt. Soc. Am., J., 40, *1950*, p. 845. When the medium for which the transmission is required is thick and inhomogeneous some modifications of the optical system are required. See, e.g., T. H. Wang, Phil. Mag., 34, *1943*, p. 684 and J. Terrien and F. Desvignes, Rev. d'Opt., 28, *1949*, p. 3.

66. See, e.g., G. F. Lothian, *Absorption Spectrophotometry* (with Hilger instruments), (Hilger, *1949*).
See also H. v. Halvan *et al.*, Z. f. phys. Chem., 96, *1920*, p. 214, 100, *1922*, p. 208 and 170 (A), *1934*, p. 212 ; T. D. Gheorghiu, Ann. de Phys., 20, *1933*, p. 133 ; A. G. Winn, Faraday Soc., Trans., 29, *1933*, p. 689 ; M. G. Mellon, Industrial and Engng. Chem. (Anal. Ed.), 9, *1937*, p. 51 ; G. Kortüm, Z. f. angewandte Chem., 50, *1937*, p. 193.

67. See, e.g., J. Vallot, C.R., 161, *1915*, p. 127.

68. K. S. Gibson, H. J. McNicholas, E. P. T. Tyndall, M. K. Frehafer and W. E. Mathewson. Bureau of Standards, Bull., 18, *1922*, p. 121.
F. P. Zscheile, T. R. Hogness and T. F. Young. J. Phys. Chem., 38, *1934*, p. 1.
T. R. Hogness, F. P. Zscheile and A. E. Sidwell. *Ibid.*, 41, *1937*, p. 379.

69. G. R. Harrison and E. P. Bentley. Opt. Soc. Am., J., 30, *1940*, p. 290.
W. R. Brode and C. H. Jones. *Ibid.*, 31, *1941*, p. 743.
H. Himmelreich. Z. f. techn. Phys., 22, *1941*, p. 148.
T. Coor and D. C. Smith. Rev. Sci. Inst., 18, *1947*, p. 173.
See also C. Müller, Z. f. Phys., 34, *1925*, p. 824 ; G. A. Boutry and J. Gillod, C.R., 213, *1941*, p. 235.

70. K. S. Gibson, E. P. T. Tyndall and H. J. McNicholas. Bureau of Standards, Technol. Paper No. 148, *1920*.
K. S. Gibson. Article " Spectrophotometry " in Dict. Appl. Phys., vol. 4, p. 748.
C. W. Keuffel. Opt. Soc. Am., J., 11, *1925*, p. 403.
See also E. v. Angerer and J. O. Brand, Z. f. techn. Phys., 19, *1938*, p. 254.

71. K. S. Gibson. Bureau of Standards, Bull., 15, *1919*, p. 325.
See also H. J. McNicholas, Bureau of Standards, J. of Research, 1, *1928*, p. 793 ; K. S. Gibson, Opt. Soc. Am., J., 21, *1931*, p. 564 ; P. J. Mulder and J. Razek, *ibid.*, 20, *1930*, p. 155.

72. R. Donaldson. J. Sci. Inst., 16, *1939*, p. 114.
73. W. D. Wright. Optica Acta, 1, *1954*, p. 102.

74. A. C. Hardy. Opt. Soc. Am., J., 25, *1935*, p. 305 and 28, *1938*, p. 360 (see also *ibid.*, 18, *1929*, p. 96 and Gen. El. Rev., 31, *1928*, p. 684).

J. L. Michaelson and H. A. Liebhafsky. Gen. El. Rev., 39, *1936*, p. 445.

J. L. Michaelson. Opt. Soc. Am., J., 28, *1938*, p. 365.

K. S. Gibson and J. H. Keegan. *Ibid.*, p. 372.

See also O. W. Pineo, Opt. Soc. Am., J., 30, *1940*, p. 276.

75. B. S. Pritchard and W. A. Holmwood. Opt. Soc. Am., J., 45, *1955*, p. 690.

76. F. Benford, G. P. Lloyd and S. Schwarz. Opt. Soc. Am., J., 38, *1948*, p. 445. See also J. W. Gabel and E. I. Stearns, Opt. Soc. Am., J., 39, *1949*, p. 481.

77. E. Hagen and H. Rubens. Ann. d. Phys., 1, *1900*, p. 352.

J. T. Tate. Phys. Rev., 34, *1912*, p. 321.

78. F. Benford Illum. Eng. Soc. N.Y., Trans., 18, *1923*, p. 67.

79. H. Buckley and F. J. C. Brookes. Illum. Eng. 18, *1925*, p. 239.

Z. Yamauti. World Engng. Congress, Tokyo, *1929*, Proc. Vol. 24, p. 197.

Z. Yamauti and M. Okamatu. Electrotechn. Lab., Tokyo, Researches No. 420, *1937*.

D. L. MacAdam. Opt. Soc. Am., J., 28, *1938*, p. 163.

80. P. M. van Alphen. Philips Techn. Rev. 4, *1939*, p. 66; C.I.E., Proc., 10, *1939*, Vol. II, p. 45.

H. König and F. Mäder. Helv. Phys. Acta, 16, *1943*, p. 419.

G. T. Winch and H. Ruff. Illum. Eng. Soc. Lond., Trans., 16, *1951*, p. 13. See also note (83) to Chapter IX (p. 320).

81. Adam Hilger, Ltd. J. Sci. Inst., 18, *1941*, p. 10.

82. L. B. Desbleds. Cotton, 91, *1927*, p. 981 ; Electrician, 99, *1927*, p. 8.

R. Toussaint. Ing. Civils de France, Mém., *1932*, p. 743.

E. R. Bolton and K. A. Williams. Analyst, 60, *1935*, p. 447 and 62, *1937*, p. 3.

E. Rohner. Assoc. Suisse Elect., Bull., 46, *1955*, p. 567.

83. J. A. Van den Akker. Paper Trade J., 111, *1940*, Sept. 12, p. 28 (Tappi Sect., p. 142).

84. J. W. Nicholson and T. R. Merton. Phil. Trans., 216, *1916*, p. 459, 217, *1918*, p. 237 and 220, *1920*, p. 137.

J. K. Robertson. Opt. Soc. Am., J., 7, *1923*, p. 983.

H. B. Dorgelo. Phys. Z., 26, *1925*, p. 756.

An approximate method of finding the relative intensities of the lines in a spectrum photograph has been described by T. R. Merton (Roy. Soc., Proc., 99, *1921*, p. 78).

See also M. Laffineur, Rev. d'Opt., 25, *1946*, p. 219.

85. G. H. Dieke and H. M. Crosswhite. Opt. Soc. Am., J., 35, *1945*, p. 471.

86. See, e.g., F. Rössler, Z. f. Phys., 110, *1938*, p. 495, and 125, *1949*, p. 427, and Z. f. techn. Phys., 21, *1940*, p. 18 ; M. P. Lord, Phys. Soc., Proc., 58, *1946*, p. 477.

87. C.I.E., Proc., 11, *1948*, p. 5.

P. J. Bouma. C.I.E., Proc., 10, *1939*, Vol. II, p. 57.

G. T. Winch and H. Ruff. Illum. Eng. Soc. Lond., Trans., 16, *1951*, p. 13.

A. A. Kruithof. C.I.E., Proc., 12, *1951* (Vol. II), Paper V.

See also H. E. Ives, Opt. Soc. Am., J., 5, *1921*, p. 469 ; M. Richter, Licht, 6, *1936*, pp. 223 and 251 ; P. J. Bouma, Philips Techn. Rev., 2, *1937*, p. 1 ; A. Gouffé and P. Waguet, Rev. Gén. de l'El., 53, *1944*, p. 33 ; W. D. Wright, Illum. Eng. Soc. Lond., Trans., 12, *1947*, p. 1.

CHAPTER XII

ILLUMINATION AND LUMINANCE

The Measurement of Illumination—The instruments and methods described in Chapters VII and VIII are all designed primarily for the measurement of luminous intensity or luminous flux, and the illumination produced by the flux reaching a surface from a source is only considered in so far as it is a necessary intermediary in the process of intensity or flux measurement. For many purposes, however, the illumination of a surface at a point is of more interest than the sources of the light flux producing that illumination and most " lighting codes " contain tables giving the values of illumination considered suitable for various purposes [1].

There are several factors which have to be considered carefully in the design of instruments for illumination photometry. Chief of these are (a) the frequent necessity for making measurements in positions where bulky apparatus cannot be accommodated, or in which it is impossible to use delicate instruments or those requiring accurate positioning ; (b) the fact that the illumination at a point is generally derived from a number of sources, so that the flux reaching it comes from many different directions and must not be obstructed by the measuring apparatus itself or by the person of the observer. The first of these considerations may, for practical purposes, be summed up under the name of " portability ", and the aim of illumination photometer design is to obtain the maximum of sensitivity and accuracy with the minimum of size and weight [2]. The second consideration is extremely exacting and with many instruments it is impossible to obtain an accurate measurement of illumination when the flux reaches the surface from all directions.

For the everyday measurement of illumination in factories, streets, etc., some form of photo-electric photometer is generally employed [3] but for more accurate work, particularly with coloured light, a visual instrument is not infrequently more suitable [4]. Such an instrument depends on a comparison of the luminance of two surfaces, one a " test plate " of constant reflection factor placed at the position of measurement, the other a comparison surface within the photometer. The luminance of the latter surface is under the control of the observer and the action of adjusting it so that both surfaces appear equally bright, is caused to indicate, on a calibrated scale, the illumination of the test plate.

The Test Plate—From what has just been stated it will be clear that the accuracy of visual photometry depends on the constancy of the relation between the luminance of the test plate and its illumination [5]. This must be independent, not only of the colour of the light but also of the angle of incidence. The angle of view is under the control of the observer and needs less consideration. The diffusion characteristics of a number of surfaces have been studied to investigate their suitability for use as test plates [6]. Those generally employed are depolished pot opal glass or matt white celluloid and the behaviour of these two substances is shown in Fig. 205.

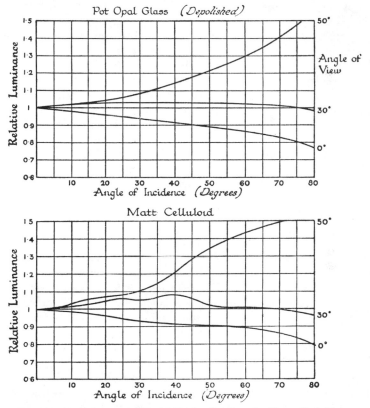

FIG. 205. The Characteristics of Diffusing Surfaces for Use as Test Plates.

The curves [7] show the departures exhibited by surfaces viewed normally and at 30° and 50° from the normal, the line of view being in the same plane with, but on the side opposite to, the incident light. The abscissae represent angles of incidence, and the ordinates the differences from the theoretical values, the value at 0° incidence being assumed correct. It will be seen that so long as the plate is viewed at an angle of 30° the errors in the case of the glass do not exceed about 3 per cent for angles of incidence up to 80°, while for matt celluloid the error may rise to 8 per cent.

These two surfaces have the very desirable quality of permanence, and both can readily be cleaned by simply wiping them with a damp cloth. In the case of celluloid, however, repeated wiping in this way results in a partial polish, and the surface should be occasionally renewed by rubbing it gently with a paste of fine pumice powder and water.

A very good matt white surface may be obtained by smoking a plate of metal or other material over burning magnesium ribbon [8]. Although the surface of magnesium oxide thus obtained is very easily damaged, and is therefore most suitable for use in enclosed apparatus, it is very readily renewed when it becomes dirty or scratched.

So-called " compensated " test plates have been designed to reduce the error of a measurement made when the light is incident very obliquely [9]. In these circumstances, however, it is better, whenever possible, to avoid the difficulty altogether by tilting the test plate until it is normal to the light [10]. The measured value of illumination is then multiplied by the cosine of the angle through which the plate has been tilted. This method is not always possible, however, particularly when a large number of sources contribute to the illumination at a point. Some error is then inevitable but as the more obliquely incident light is usually that derived from the more distant sources, the inverse square law combines with the cosine law of illumination to make this by far the least important part of the whole illumination, and the effect on the measured total is often small.

Illumination Photometers based on the Inverse Square Law— Illumination photometers, like photometers for measuring luminous intensity, may be classified according to the method adopted for altering the luminance of the comparison surface within the instrument. Among those in which the inverse square law is used the ordinary Weber photometer, already described on p. 218, must be included, since it is readily adapted to the measurement of illumination by the removal of the opal glass plate M_1 (Fig. 128, p. 218). The tube T_1 is then directed towards a test plate placed in the position at which it is desired to measure the illumination, and the luminance of this surface is compared with that of the surface M_2, photometric balance being obtained, as in the measurement of luminous intensity by moving M_2 backwards and forwards. The instrument is calibrated by illuminating the test plate with a standard lamp of luminous intensity I placed at a known distance d from it in the direction of the normal, so that the point of balance of M_2 under these conditions corresponds to an illumination of I/d^2.

Since brightness is independent of distance, the only restriction on the position of the photometer is that it must be sufficiently near the test surface for the latter to fill the field of the prism C completely. The general remarks on angle of view of the test surface (p. 381) apply to this photometer as to all others in which the angle of view is not fixed by the instrument itself. This angle may be made invariable by the provision of an arm rigidly attached to T_1 and carrying the test plate at its end.

Many other photometers depending on the inverse square law have been designed [11]. A very convenient one is the Macbeth illuminometer [12] the principle of which is shown in Fig. 206. The opal glass comparison surface S is illuminated by the lamp L, which, in its diaphragmed enclosure, is moved along the tube T by means of a rack and pinion R. An illumination scale is marked on the rod carrying the lamp enclosure. The lamp is supplied from a dry battery by means of leads plugged into the end of this rod. The battery is carried in a

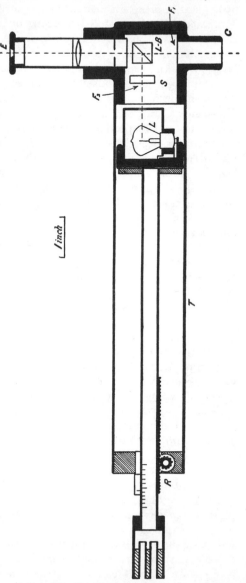

FIG. 206. The Macbeth Illuminometer.

separate control case, which also contains a rheostat and milliammeter by means of which the current through the lamp L is adjusted

to the value at which the illumination scale has been found, by
previous calibration to read correctly. The test plate is of depolished
opal glass and is detached from the instrument. Its luminance is
compared with that of S by means of the Lummer-Brodhun cube
$L\text{-}B$ viewed through the eyepiece E. A reflecting elbow-piece, to
fit on the end of C, is provided for use where convenient, particularly in making measurements in directions above the horizontal.
Neutral filters may be inserted either at F_1 or F_2 to extend in either
direction the normal scale of the instrument which is from 1 to 25
foot-candles (lm/ft^2). Two filters with nominal transmission factors
of 0·1 and 0·01 respectively are usually provided.

For work in which accuracy is more important than portability,
an instrument similar to the Macbeth illuminometer but on a rather
larger scale has been designed [13]. There are at least two advantages
to be gained by increasing the size. In the first place, it is possible
to accommodate a larger lamp, giving greater constancy and a
generally better performance. In the second place, errors due to
light reflected from the inside wall of the tube may be avoided by
inserting a series of small annular screens [14]. The source of supply
is a storage battery and the current through the lamp is controlled
by means of the special bridge circuit to be described later (see
p. 390).

Illumination Photometers based on other Principles—Apart from
instruments depending on visual acuity [15] the earliest form of illum-
ation photometer was probably that of W. H. Preece [16] who used
as his comparison source a glow lamp in circuit with a variable
resistance, so that a photometric balance could be obtained by varying the current through the lamp. The variation of luminous intensity with change of current was known by previous calibration
This principle was also employed in a number of later instruments [17].

Several illumination photometers were devised in which the variation of luminance of the comparison surface within the instrument
was achieved by tilting this surface so that the light from the comparison lamp reached it more or less obliquely. The first of these
instruments was designed by A. P. Trotter in 1891 [18] and subsequently modified to give greater portability [19]. The Harrison
photometer was a flicker instrument on the same principle [20].

The diaphragm method of control of the comparison brightness
has been the basis of several illumination photometers [21], notably
a very portable instrument called the Lumeter [22] in which the
comparison lamp is contained within a whitened enclosure with a
diffusing window which illuminates the comparison surface. The
exposed area of this window is varied by moving across it a disc with
a sectoral opening, and a scale attached to the handle controlling

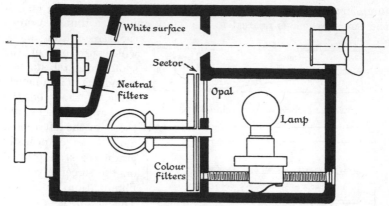

FIG. 207. The Holophane Lumeter.

this movement shows the illumination of the test plate (see Fig. 207). Colour filters, for use when measuring the illumination from sources such as discharge lamps, and neutral filters for extending the range of the instrument are provided.

In some types of portable illumination photometers a neutral wedge has been used to vary the luminance of the comparison surface [23] and an instrument depending on the use of polarising prisms has been described [24].

Field of View—The form of the field of view is not the same in all illumination photometers. Only in a comparatively large instrument, such as that described on p. 384, is it possible to use the Lummer-Brodhun contrast form of field ; in most instruments either the annular or the diametrally divided bipartite field is used. The latter is more satisfactory, especially when the brightness of the field of view is low, because under these conditions the colour sensitivity of the fovea differs from that of the surrounding areas of the retina (see p. 74) so that with the annular form of field a small colour difference between the two parts may lead to considerable errors [25].

Illumination Gauges—For certain purposes an instrument better described as an illumination gauge than as a photometer has been employed. The comparison surface has one or more fixed values of luminance corresponding to certain values of illumination of the test plate and comparison of the two surfaces indicates whether the illumination is greater or less than some selected value. Such an instrument is shown in Fig. 208 [26]. The lamp L illuminates the underside of a long screen S, partly by direct light and partly by reflection from a strip of mirror M, which is tilted as required when the instrument is re-adjusted from time to time. S consists of a strip of opaque white paper with a row of Bunsen spots in it. Since the luminance of these spots decreases progressively from the end of the screen which is nearest to the lamp, any given illumination of

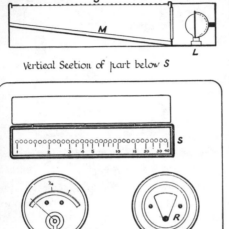

Vertical Section of part below S

FIG. 208. The Foot-candle Meter.

the screen from above will cause one of the spots to match its surroundings in luminance, while all those on the right appear bright, and those on the left appear dark. An empirically graduated scale printed on the screen gives the illumination directly. The lamp is supplied with current from a dry battery, the rheostat R being turned until the correct indication is given by the voltmeter V. To extend the range of the instrument downwards, R may be increased until the voltmeter needle indicates a division marked 1/10. The luminous intensity of the lamp is then one-tenth of its normal value, and the instrument therefore measures from 0·1 to 4 footcandles instead of from 1 to 40, as when the full current is passing through the lamp. An instrument of this kind can be used for making instantaneous measurements of a rapidly fluctuating illumination [27].

Precautions in the Use of Visual Illumination Photometers [28]— From the descriptions of illumination photometers which have been given in the preceding sections it will be noticed that almost without exception these instruments depend on a more or less arbitrary scale for indicating the value of the illumination which is being measured. Even in instruments which nominally depend solely on the inverse square law, the distance at disposal for the movement of the lamp is so restricted that, unless very great care is taken in the design and manufacture of such instruments, quite appreciable errors are likely to arise from the use of scales based absolutely on this law. It follows that an illumination photometer should be checked before every period of use, either to ensure that the instrumental constant is as near unity as may be necessary in the work which is to be undertaken, or, failing this, to determine the correct value of the constant so that a correction factor may be applied to the instrument readings. The latter scheme is inconvenient, and provision is made in most modern illumination photometers for easy adjustment to a constant of unity. Change of constant with lapse of time may be due to (a) reduction of reflection factor of the test surface due to dirt or discoloration ; (b) ageing of the lamp inside the instrument ; (c) change, due to dirt or other causes, in the transmission factor of glass plates or other devices through which any part of the light has to pass ; (d) change in the voltage of the battery supplying current if the standard source is an electric lamp. Of these four causes, the first three may be assumed to take place progressively and at a comparatively slow rate ; the fourth will be dealt with in detail later.

It is necessary, then, to provide a known standard illumination with which to check the photometer before commencing work with it. Quite the most accurate means of doing this in a photometric laboratory is to mount a standard lamp on the photometer bench in the usual way (see p. 190), and to place the test plate of the photometer in such a position on the axis of the bench that it is normal to the incident light, while its plane passes through the mark on the bench which indicates that the illumination has the value at which a check reading of the instrument is desired, e.g. 10 lux or 1 lm/ft.^{2} [(29)]. The instrument pointer is set to this reading, and the adjustment is altered until a photometric balance is obtained. It is important that the actual plate to be used in the subsequent work should be used for the checking.

The process of calibrating an instrument is carried out in a similar manner, except that the adjustment is arranged to give a minimum error over the greater part of the scale, or its more important part, and the actual magnitude of the error at every part of the scale is then determined. In photometers which include neutral filters or similar devices for extending the range of the instrument, the accurate determination of the transmission factors of these filters is included as part of the calibration of the instrument. This determination may be carried out by checking the instrument carefully at a convenient value of illumination E, say, with no filter in use. The filter (of nominal transmission factor τ) is then inserted and the illumination of the standard surface is raised to E/τ. The difference between the old and new readings of the instrument gives at once the error in τ. Sometimes the filters consist of pairs of wedges of neutral glass, so that the transmission factors can be adjusted accurately to the nominal values. In portable instruments errors of scale reading amounting to ± 2 to 3 per cent over the working parts of the scale are regarded as admissible, since this is within the accuracy aimed at in work carried out with these instruments [(30)].

In cases where a photometer bench and sub-standard are not

available for checking a portable photometer it is necessary to use some form of portable standard or " calibrator ". The apparatus designed for this purpose in connecton with the Macbeth illuminometer is shown in Fig. 209. The lamp M is supplied from the same

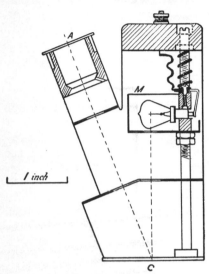

battery as that providing the current for the illuminometer lamp. A second rheostat is provided in the illuminometer control box for adjusting the current through M, and the ammeter is provided with a double-pole switch to enable it to be used on either the illuminometer or reference standard circuit. The calibrator is placed with its base C on the test plate, the illuminometer is sighted through the aperture A, and the current through M is adjusted to a stated value. The milliammeter is then put over to the illuminometer circuit and the current in the lamp is adjusted until the photometric balance point is attained at a

FIG. 209. The Portable Reference Standard for the Macbeth Illuminometer.

stated value of illumination corresponding to the stated value of the current through M.

It is now necessary to consider the fourth of the sources of error in illumination photometers which were enumerated above, viz. the alteration of battery voltage. An essential part of every visual illumination photometer (disregarding acuity instruments) is its comparison lamp supplied with current from a portable battery [31]. The requirement as to portability results in two practical difficulties of design and sources of error in use. The first of these, and the one more easily remedied, is the possibility of an imperfect contact somewhere in the electrical circuit. The great importance of this arises from the fact that a portable battery is essentially of a low voltage, one of 2 or 4 volts being employed in most cases. The remedy is extremely simple. All permanent contacts should be soldered, terminals making semi-permanent connection should have clean surfaces and should be screwed down as tightly as possible, and the lamp should have a screw cap and be firmly seated. A screw cap sometimes exhibits a tendency to become loose in its socket after a short period of use. Its firmness should be ascertained at frequent intervals. In many instruments, especially those of the most portable type, where the battery has to be as small as possible, a switch is provided in the lamp circuit so that the lamp is alight only while the measurement is actually being made. A press switch must be very firmly held during a reading and the contacts must be kept absolutely clean. A knife switch is much to be preferred. Since the lamp does not immediately take up its final value of luminous intensity, no reading of illumination should be made until the lamp has been switched on for at least 15 to 30 seconds. A switch of more robust type, such as an ordinary tumbler, may be put in parallel with the press switch, for use when a large number of readings have to be taken in a short period. A small ammeter in the lamp circuit is useful for giving an immediate indication of contact trouble, and in this respect it is preferable to a voltmeter. A faulty contact will frequently manifest itself unmistakably by a flicker in the photometer field, or by sudden changes of reading quite outside the ordinary experimental error.

The second source of trouble arising from the need for portability is the gradual diminution of voltage as the battery is discharged, especially when a dry battery is used. In the case of a lead accumulator of fairly large capacity and of suitable design, the voltage during discharge is very constant after the first half-hour, as shown by the discharge curve of Fig. 210. The capacity of the battery

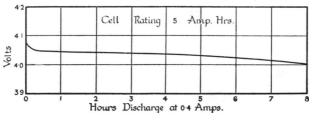

FIG. 210. Discharge Curve for a Lead Accumulator.

should, however, be such as to give a total period of discharge, with the current taken by the lamp, of at least twelve hours ; i.e. a 0·5 lamp requires a battery of at least 6 amp.-hours capacity, while it should not be used for more than half this period, i.e. the total time during which it is actually supplying current should not exceed six hours. The preliminary excess voltage after charging must be avoided by discharging the cell for at least half an hour at its normal rate before it is connected to the photometer. It should not be forgotten that accumulators become discharged gradually even when not used.

In accurate work an ammeter or voltmeter should always be used in the lamp circuit, so that the current may be regulated to the correct value [32]. In the case of small lamps, such as are generally used in portable photometers, the rate of change of luminous intensity with current or voltage is higher than in the case of normal tungsten filament lamps; a change of 1 per cent in current may cause a change of as much as 10 to 11 per cent in luminous intensity. For this reason the accuracy of setting is higher with a voltmeter than with an ammeter. When a voltmeter is used, it should be so connected that it is always in circuit when the lamp is alight.

Since the discharge curve of a dry battery is much less flat than that of an accumulator, its use necessitates frequent regulation of the lamp current. Its lighter weight and freedom from the unpleasant consequences arising from the accidental spilling of acid give it, however, a considerable practical advantage, at any rate for work outside the laboratory.

For accurate work, such as that for which the type of instrument described on p. 384 would be employed, a finer method of control than that provided by a miniature indicating instrument is required and the bridge circuit shown in Fig. 211 may be used [33]. If the illuminometer lamp takes 4 volts, R_1 should not exceed about one quarter of R so that the bridge may be run off a 6 volt battery. R_2 and R_3 may conveniently be some 5 times R_1 and R respectively; R_3 should be adjustable to suit the particular lamp used, but

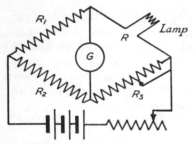

Fig. 211. Bridge Circuit for Illuminometer Lamp.

the connection should be soldered before the instrument is calibrated. G is a galvanometer of low resistance, e.g. 0·5 ohm. With this arrangement the current through the lamp can be regulated to a fraction of a milliampere.

There is one source of error in visual illumination photometry which so far has not been considered, viz. colour difference. The comparison lamp in the instrument is usually a tungsten filament vacuum lamp operating at or near its normal efficiency and to avoid a colour difference when measuring the illumination given by gas-filled lamps it is usual to insert a blue filter on the comparison lamp side and to calibrate the instrument with this filter in position. When daylight, or the illumination from sources such as discharge tubes is being measured, the colour differences encountered may often result in a serious reduction of accuracy unless a further compensating colour filter is inserted on the comparison lamp side of the photometer [34]. Allowance must be made for the transmission factor of this filter as determined in the laboratory for light of the colour of that given by the comparison lamp. The use of a colour filter on the test plate side is not usually to be recommended owing to the dependence of the transmission factor on the spectral distribution of the light passing through it.

The Method of Measuring Illumination—Whatever be the instrument employed, the general principles of the method of making a visual measurement of the illumination at a point are the same. Unless otherwise specified, it is usual to assume that the illumination measured is that of a horizontal surface at the point under consideration. The test plate must, therefore, be put as nearly as possible in the horizontal position. It generally happens that the greater part of the illumination is due to light which is incident at an angle of 45° or less, so that a tilt of 2° in any direction on the test surface does not introduce an error of more than $3\frac{1}{2}$ per cent in the value assigned to the most oblique component. When, however, this is not the case, and a considerable part of the light is incident obliquely, more care must be exercised in the exact positioning of the surface. With a little care it is usually possible to adjust the level of the surface to within 2° by eye. Self-levelling devices have been described [35]. Occasionally it is of more importance to know the illumination of a vertical or a sloping surface (e.g. the wall of a picture gallery, the desk in a library, etc.), and in such cases the position of the test plate should always be specified, i.e. its angle of slope and the direction of its normal.

Frequently the exact position of the plate is determined by the nature of the illumination problem under investigation. For example, the bed of a lathe, the plate of a sewing machine, the surface of a desk, etc., define the points where illumination is needed and where it must be measured. When this is not the case, however, and the illumination is treated generally, the test plate is placed at some definite height above floor level agreed upon as the height of the " working plane ". This has been defined as 85 cm. (approx. 2 ft. 9 ins.) [36]. Sometimes the floor level is taken when there is no obstruction from objects in the room. The *average* illumination is, clearly, the same whatever be the height of the plane (below the level of the lamps), except for the small amount of light absorbed by the extra strip of wall, but the *distribution* of the light may be very different, especially when the light sources are low.

When the test plate has been placed in position, the observer and photometer must be arranged so that (*a*) the surface fills the field of view of the instrument, (*b*) the angle at which the surface is viewed is not too oblique (see p. 382), and (*c*) no shadows are cast on the surface by either the observer or the instrument. The importance of the second requirement has been dealt with at length in an earlier part of this chapter. Generally speaking, the angle which the line of view makes with the normal to the test plate should not exceed 20° to 30°.

The third of the requirements mentioned above, viz. avoidance of shadow cast by observer or photometer, is difficult of fulfilment with most instruments, but it is nevertheless of considerable importance, especially in the case of illumination by diffused light, or when the number of sources contributing to the illumination is large, so that light reaches the test plate from all directions [37]. The best that can be done is to remove the observer to as great a distance as possible from the test plate while still fulfilling requirement (a) above. The solid angle obstructed is then as small as possible. Judicious choice of position, when some sources do not contribute much to the total illumination, will also materially assist in reducing errors arising from this cause.

There is one special problem in illumination measurement which is of sufficient importance to need separate notice. When the artificial illumination on a horizontal plane in a street is being measured the light is frequently incident very obliquely on the test plate, so that an error of as little as 1° in the level of the plate may produce a marked inaccuracy in the results, while lack of perfect diffusion also becomes very important [38]. For this reason the illumination of the horizontal plane is frequently obtained by calculation from measurements of direct illumination. The test plate is tilted so that the only light it receives is that which reaches it normally from one of the sources contributing to the illumination at the point in

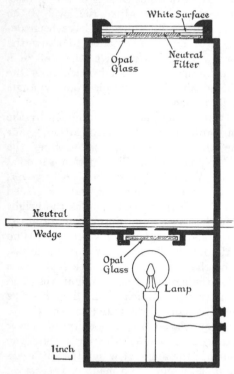

FIG. 212. A Photometer for measuring Low Illumination.

question. The direct illumination thus measured is multiplied by the cosine of the angle which the light makes with the vertical, and the illumination of the horizontal surface due to this single source is thus obtained. The total illumination is found by summing the components thus measured for each of the different sources contributing to the illumination at the point of observation [39].

The Measurement of Low Illumination—When very low values of illumination, such as the illumination from the night sky, are measured visually it is necessary to use a large field of view in order that the liminal increment of luminance for the eye may be as small as possible (see p. 61) [40]. It has been found that the greatest sensitivity is obtained by using a large comparison field viewed openly by both eyes, as in the case of the instrument shown in Fig. 212 [41].

Photo-electric Illumination Photometers—The photo-voltaic cell possesses many advantages as a portable illumination photometer [42]. It is light and compact and it needs no battery, though this gain is offset to a certain extent by the need for a sensitive instrument to measure the photocurrent. Its chief disadvantages are that the current generated for a given illumination falls off rapidly when the light is incident at an angle of more than about 50° to 60° from the normal (see p. 106) and that its spectral sensitivity curve differs from that of the eye (see p. 107) so that correction is needed if the colour of the light measured differs appreciably from that of the light by which the instrument was calibrated. Further, if a colour filter is used to give this correction the error due to obliquity of the light becomes even more pronounced.

In instruments designed to give an accuracy as good as that attainable with a visual photometer such as the Macbeth, the cell is usually mounted in a light-weight holder and is attached to the microammeter by a length of twin flexible wire [43]. This makes it possible to place the cell at any position at which a measurement of illumination is required, while the microammeter is placed on some convenient horizontal surface. If low values of illumination are to be measured two or more cells connected in parallel are mounted in a single holder [44]. In instruments designed for the maximum of portability, the same case usually houses both the cell and a very small milliammeter [45].

The total resistance in the photocell circuit should not be too high or the curve connecting the photocurrent and the illumination may depart very considerably from a straight line (see p. 105). Sometimes the resistance is made high deliberately so as to compress the scale at its upper end but this has the disadvantage that the photometer is then more liable to change its calibration with lapse of time [46]. The microammeter is generally scaled in illumination units and in most instruments shunts are used to give more than one illumination range.

Many devices have been proposed to correct the reduction of photocurrent with increase of obliquity of the incident light (see note (64) on p. 118) but none has proved sufficiently practical for general adoption [47]. Partial correction is sometimes achieved by giving the surface of the cell a matt finish [48]. It will be seen that this particular defect is shared by both photo-electric and visual photometers and the remarks in a previous section regarding the precautions needed on this account in the case of a visual illumino-meter apply with even greater force to a photo-electric instrument [49].

As mentioned in Chapter IV (p. 112), the effect of colour difference between the light measured and that used for calibration is usually allowed for by applying a correction factor and a table of the factors appropriate to various commonly used illuminants often accompanies the instrument. These factors are determined in the laboratory for the particular type of cell used. They vary somewhat from one type to another, but the following table shows the values found for two commonly used types and will serve to indicate the variation which may occur in practice.

TABLE OF CORRECTION FACTORS FOR VARIOUS ILLUMINANTS

Illuminant	Multiplying Factor	
	Cell I	Cell II
Tungsten (gas-filled) -	1	1
Fluorescent, daylight -	0·9	1·0
,, warm white	1·0	1·2
Mercury, high pressure -	1·15	1·2
,, low pressure -	0·85	1·1
Neon - - - -	0·6	0·95
Sodium - - - -	1·6	1·4

Instead of using multiplying factors, in some instruments the same result is achieved more conveniently for the user by providing a number of shunts to the microammeter, so that by switching in the appropriate shunt the corresponding correction factor is automatically included in the instrument reading. In some instruments a colour correction filter is mounted permanently over the photocell to make its spectral sensitivity curve closely the same as that of the eye [50]. This not only reduces the amount of light reaching the cell but, as mentioned above, it somewhat increases the obliquity error [51].

Fig. 213. Photo-electric Illumination Photometers
Above : The Holophane Street Lighting Photometer.
Below : The Edgcumbe Autophotometer.
(Photograph by courtesy of Messrs. Holophane, Ltd., and of Messrs. Everett, Edgcumbe and Co. Ltd.)

Other errors which may affect the readings obtained with a photo-electric illuminometer are those due to temperature and to fatigue. The former (see p. 106) is not serious except when extremes of temperature are experienced, e.g. sometimes in measurements of outdoor illumination. The latter is also not large compared with the other sources of error which have been mentioned, but recent exposure of the cell to a much higher illumination than that which is to be measured should always be avoided.

The calibration of a photo-electric illuminometer should be checked from time to time, either on a photometer bench in the laboratory, or by the use of some form of portable standard such as that described above as suitable for checking the calibration of a visual instrument [52].

For accurate work, or for measuring very low values of illumination, a less compact but still portable form of instrument, incorporating a photo-emissive cell and valve amplifiers, may be used [53].

Continuous Recording of Illumination—For obtaining continuous records of a variable illumination such as daylight, a photo-emissive cell is generally used, often with a colour filter to correct its spectral sensitivity [54]. A record of the photocurrent, either with or without amplification, is obtained by means of a reflecting galvanometer which gives a trace on sensitized paper mounted on a slowly rotating cylinder. The apparatus is calibrated from time to time while it is in operation by making visual measurements of the illumination and relating the values so obtained with the corresponding points on the photo-electric record.

If light reaches the photocell from a large solid angle, e.g. from

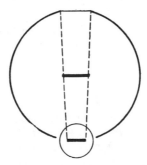

Fig. 214. Auxiliary Sphere for the Measurement of Oblique Illumination.

the whole or a considerable portion of the sky, the fact that much of it is incident very obliquely may give rise to errors which are far from negligible unless some device is used to overcome this difficulty. Several such devices have been used [55] but the most effective is that shown in Fig. 214 which consists of a hollow whitened sphere with an opening at the top, and the cell at the bottom. The latter is screened so that it receives no direct light from the opening but only light reflected from the walls of the sphere. The chief disadvantage of this device is the fact that the illumination of the cell is only a small fraction of that at the sphere opening unless the latter is so large compared with the size of the sphere that serious errors are introduced by the presence of the then necessarily large screen [56].

A time integration of a varying illumination may be obtained photo-electrically by means of the circuit described on p. 100 or in some similar way [57].

The Distribution of Illumination—The method of calculating the illumination at different points on a given plane (e.g. the working plane in a room or workshop, the road surface in a street, etc.) due to the direct light received from a number of sources of known light distribution, and placed in known positions with respect to the plane, has already been described (see p. 132).

The carrying out of such calculations and the corrections to be made to the results on account of light reflected from surrounding objects—particularly the walls and ceiling in the case of a room—or on account of the interposition of obstructions, is the function of the illuminating engineer, to whom belongs also the duty of designing installations on the data provided for him by the photometer. For a description of the details which have to be considered in the design of a lighting installation, such as the value of illumination required for a particular process, the use of shades and reflectors to avoid glare, the performance of the light sources commercially available, etc., reference must be made to some book dealing with illuminating engineering, a number of which are listed in Section II of Appendix I on p. 511.

In an actual installation the distribution of illumination can be determined experimentally by means of measurements with an illumination photometer at as many points as may be desired on the working plane [58]. These measurements include the effect of the reflected light above referred to, and if they are plotted on a plan of the area under investigation the points of equal illumination can be joined by curves, so that an isophot diagram is obtained (see Fig. 215) [59].

It is sometimes required to calculate the average illumination in lumens per square metre or per square foot, over the working plane in a room. For a direct lighting system in which the reflection from walls and ceiling can be neglected to the approximation desired, the average illumination in a large room is clearly equal to the total luminous flux emitted below the horizontal by all the sources, divided by the area of the room.   If the reflected flux is considerable, the total flux reaching the working plane must be related to the total flux emitted by the sources in all directions by means of a utilization factor (or coefficient of utilization) of the installation [60].   This is

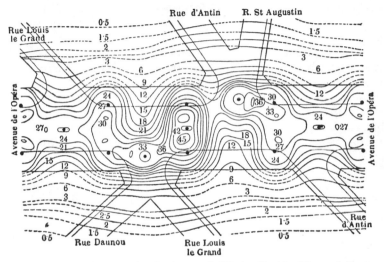

Fig. 215. Isophot Curves for the Avenue de l'Opéra (Paris).   Figures indicate lux (metre-candles).

the ratio of the first of these quantities to the second so that the average illumination is equal to uF/A where u is the utilization factor, F the total flux from the sources and A the area of the working plane.

The value of the utilization factor in any particular lighting installation depends on a number of conditions, particularly the dimensions of the room and the reflection factors of the walls and ceiling, the nature of the light distribution from the fittings and, except in the case of indirect lighting, the height of the fittings above the working plane [61].   Tables of values of u for a wide range of these conditions have been published and are given in several books on illuminating engineering [62].   Various functions have been used to express the degree of uniformity of the illumination over a given area [63].   The ratio of the maximum to the minimum has been termed the *diversity ratio* or the *variation range*.   The reciprocal of this has been called the *uniformity ratio*, though this term is more generally used to denote the ratio of the minimum to the average.

The Measurement of Diffusion and Shadow—It is sometimes of importance in practical lighting problems to know how much of the total light which reaches a certain point in a room is " direct ", i.e. received from the source without reflection from the walls or ceiling, and how much is " diffused ". This can be determined by placing a small opaque screen at a short distance from the point, and in such a position that the umbral part of its shadow, cast by the light source illuminating the point, completely covers the test plate or the photocell of an illumination photometer placed at the point. If E is the total illumination, and E' the illumination when the surface is screened from the direct light, the fraction $100(E - E')/E$ may be termed the percentage of " direct " illumination, and $100\ E'/E$ the percentage of " diffused " or " indirect " illumination [64]. The fraction $(E - E')/E$ is termed the " shadow factor " [65]. If more than one source contribute to the illumination at the point, a measurement must be made with each source screened in turn. The direct component is then $\Sigma(E - E')$, and the diffused component $E - \Sigma(E - E')$.

The values obtained in any given case clearly depend on the dimensions of the screen and its distance from the illuminometer

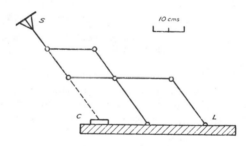

Fig. 216. The Measurement of the Shadow Factor.

test plate or photocell, especially when the illumination is diffused, and in order that the results obtained may be comparable, a standard form of " shadow-caster " such as that shown in Fig. 216 should be used [66]. C is a photocell and S a disc carried on a linkage system so that it can be moved in a semicircle about the centre of C. The whole linkage system can be moved about the axis CL so that, in effect, S can be moved to any position on a hemisphere with C as its centre.

The Visual Measurement of Luminance—Although, as already pointed out, all visual photometry depends on a comparison by the eye of the brightness of two juxtaposed surfaces, the object in view is generally to measure the illumination of one of these surfaces, or the luminous intensity of the source producing that illumination, and not to find the luminance of the surface. Since luminance is luminous intensity per unit area, it follows that the most direct method of measuring the luminance of a surface (supposed uniform) is to measure its luminous intensity in a given direction and divide this by the projected area of the surface in that direction.

In order to avoid edge effects it is often convenient to place an opaque diaphragm with an aperture of accurately known area, a, in front of the surface. The combination then becomes equivalent to a plane source of luminous intensity Ba, situated in the plane of the diaphragm (see p. 151). If this luminous intensity is measured, B can be found [67].

Except when the luminance is high, the inverse square law cannot be applied, for it has been shown that if the accuracy of measure-

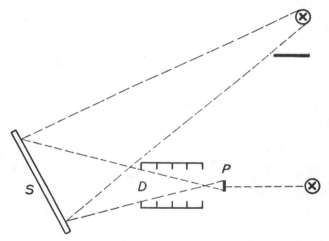

Fig. 217. The Direct Measurement of Luminance.

ment is to be better than 0·5 per cent the radius of a disc source should not exceed $0.07d$, where d is the distance from the photometer head. Hence if the luminance is B, the illumination of the photometer surface is $0.005B$, so that for a minimum illumination of 10 lux B must exceed 650 candelas per square metre. On the other hand, many matt surfaces behave as complete diffusers over a limited range of angles, so that in such cases the diaphragm can be placed comparatively near to the photometer surface as illustrated in Fig. 217. P

is the photometer surface and D the diaphragm so that the illumination of the central part of P is $\{r^2/(r^2+d^2)\}\pi B$ where B is the luminance of the surface S. It will be seen that if $r = 0\cdot2d$ (as shown) the illumination of P exceeds 10 lux so long as B is not less than about 83 candelas per square metre.

When the measurement cannot be carried out as described above, either because the luminance is too low or because the area is too small or not readily measureable, it must be made in some other way. In the former case, the most direct method is to cause the surface whose luminance is to be measured to occupy one part of the comparison field in a photometer [68]. As an example of this method the use of the ordinary Lummer-Brodhun head for the measurement of luminance may be described. A piece of mirror of known reflection factor (see p. 423) is placed over one surface of the plaster screen in the photometer so that, when this faces the surface to be measured, the image in the mirror is seen through the Lummer-Brodhun cube, and so fills one part of the comparison field in the photometer. A photometric balance is obtained in the usual way. The mirror is then removed and that side of the plaster screen is illuminated with a movable lamp of known luminous intensity. Photometric balance is obtained by moving this lamp and the illumination of the plaster screen, E, is calculated. If the luminance of the original surface is equal to B, it follows that $B\rho = E\rho'/\pi$ where ρ and ρ' are the reflection factors of the mirror and of the plaster screen respectively. Alternatively, if a surface of known and suitable luminance is available, a simple substitution method may be used and ρ and ρ' need not be determined [69].

For purposes where an accuracy of 2 to 3 per cent is sufficient, a portable illumination photometer with detached test plate may conveniently be employed [70] if its reflection factor, ρ_T, is known from previous laboratory measurement. The photometer is directed towards the surface to be measured and a photometric balance is obtained in the usual way, using this surface instead of the ordinary test surface. The luminance required is then equal to the reading given by the photometer multiplied by the factor ρ_T/π, for the photometer is calibrated to show the illumination of the test plate so that a reading E corresponds to a luminance $\rho_T E/\pi$. Alternatively the instrument may be separately calibrated and scaled in luminance units [71].

A coloured surface, or a white surface illuminated by coloured light, naturally introduces all the uncertainties of heterochromatic photometry. It is desirable to avoid these as far as possible by the use of colour filters, especially when, owing to the method of measurement used the luminance of the surface seen by the eye is much less than that of the original surface and may come within the Purkinje region. The spectral distribution of the light emitted or reflected from a surface may be measured as described in Chapter XI.

In certain cases, notably the measurement of the luminance of certain luminescent surfaces, it is impossible to avoid making a measurement within the Purkinje range, since by no optical means is it possible to increase the luminance of a surface. If the measurement is to be made on the photopic scale, the luminescent surface should be compared with a white surface illuminated by light of a known spectral distribution, this latter surface being viewed through a colour filter giving, as far as possible both a colour and an energy match with the surface to be measured [72]. The transmission factor of the colour filter for the light illuminating the white surface is calculated from its spectral transmission curve. If more convenient the filter may be placed between the light source and the surface which it illuminates.

If a measure of the equivalent luminance of the surface is required (see p. 74) it must be compared, either directly or indirectly with a white surface illuminated by light having a colour temperature of 2042° K and the results are expressed in one of the ordinary units of luminance described on pp. 136 and 138 [73]. It is important that nothing which might diminish the brightness should be interposed between the surface and the observer's eye [74].

In all cases in which the luminance to be measured is very low, the sensitivity of a visual comparison is greatly improved if the surfaces compared are large in extent and viewed openly at the normal distance from the eye for distinct vision [75].

The Photo-electric Measurement of Luminance—The luminance of an extended surface may be measured photo-electrically in several ways [76]. The luminous intensity of a known area of the surface may be found as described in the case of the visual measurement, but there is no necessity for the illumination on the photocell to be as high as 10 lux so that the distance between the diaphragm and the cell may be increased and the inverse square law can therefore be applied [77].

Another method, sometimes used when only an approximate result is required, depends on the fact that the illumination of a surface facing another surface of uniform luminance B and effectively infinite in extent is equal to πB. If, therefore, the photocell of an illuminometer is placed close to an extended surface, the luminance can be found from the value of illumination indicated. It is to be noted that this method is subject to error on account of the fact that the light from those parts of the surface remote from the photocell is not only incident very obliquely on the cell but is also emitted from the surface at considerable angles from the normal. The method is useful for making comparative measurements, e.g. of the fluorescence of solutions irradiated by ultra-violet light [78] or for measuring the luminance of a fluorescent screen excited by radioactive preparations [79].

Photo-electric methods have been used for measuring low values of luminance, either on the photopic or the scotopic scale, using a photo-multiplier cell with an appropriate filter [80]. Similarly a record of fluctuations of luminance can be obtained [81].

Luminance Distribution—The values of luminance of the different parts of an extended area such as a street scene are usually found most conveniently by photographing the scene under carefully controlled conditions and measuring the densities of the corresponding parts of the negative [82]. A series of surfaces having a convenient range of known values of luminance are included in the scene when the photograph is taken, in order to establish the scale relating density with luminance. Alternatively the scene may be explored visually with a telephotometer, or some simple form of photometer with a small external field may be used [83].

Apparatus has been designed for scanning a scene rapidly with photo-electric apparatus of high sensitivity and producing, on a cathode ray tube, a trace showing the luminance distribution along any given line [84].

Luminance of small Objects—When the extent of the surface to be measured is too small for any one of the methods described in the last section to be employed directly, some other arrangement must be used. This is generally based on the principle of the Maxwellian view (see p. 152), the system shown in Fig. 218 being typical [85].

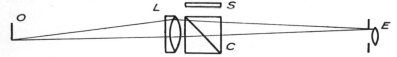

FIG. 218. The Measurement of Luminance of a Small Area.

The lens L forms an image, if necessary enlarged, of the object O at the pupil of the observer's eye, E. This image must be large enough to fill the pupil used, whether natural or artificial, so that L appears to have a luminance equal to τB where B is the luminance of O and τ the transmission factor of L. C is some form of comparison field, such as a Lummer-Brodhun cube, by means of which L can be compared with some other surface S, the luminance of which can be varied until a match with L is obtained. An extended surface of controllable luminance is then substituted for O and adjusted to give a match with S. The luminance of this extended surface is then equal to B and is measured by one of the methods previously described.

Various obvious modifications of the procedure just outlined can be made as may be convenient. For example, the extended surface substituted for O may have some known fixed value of luminance, B'. The ratio of B to B' is then determined by varying the luminance of S in a known manner.

An analogous method of measuring the brightness of a small area of a luminous object is to form an enlarged real image of the object by means of a convex lens as shown in Fig. 219 (a) and to

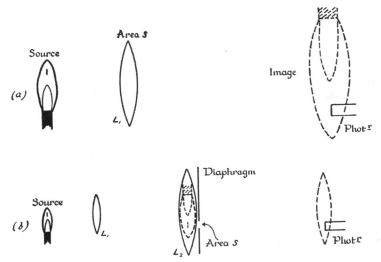

FIG. 219. The Measurement of Luminance of a Luminous Object.

measure the illumination at the corresponding part of the image by means of any ordinary photometer, either visual or photo-electric, with a small comparison surface [86]. If s is the area of the lens aperture, E the illumination of the photometer surface, and d the distance between this surface and the second focal point of the lens L_1, then the required luminance $B = E\,d^2/s\tau$ (see p. 152). An alternative scheme is shown in Fig 219 (b). L_2 is placed so as to coincide with the real image of the luminous object formed by L_1, and a diaphragm with an adjustable opening is placed close to L_2. If a photometer screen is placed in the position of the image of L_1 which is formed by L_2, then the illumination at the photometer gives the luminance of the luminous object by the same formula as before, but s is now the area of the opening in the diaphragm and d its distance from the photometer. Blondel's " nitometer " is designed on this principle [87].

A different method is sometimes used in the case of an object such as a glowing filament. If the luminance is not too great, the filament may be placed in front of an extended surface of adjustable luminance, such as a piece of matt glass illuminated from behind. The luminance of this surface is altered until the filament just disappears on its background, and is then measured by one of the means described in the last sections. If, however, the luminance of the filament is greater than about 10 candelas per square inch (the luminance of a gas-filled lamp with diffusing bulb), this method is not suitable, and an alternative in which the background is formed by the image of a tungsten strip or a Nernst filament may be used instead [88]. The apparatus is shown in Fig. 220. N is the standard

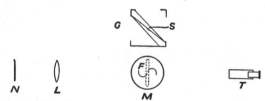

FIG. 220. The Measurement of Luminance of a Glowing Wire.

surface, of which an enlarged image is formed at M by means of the lens L. F is the filament to be measured, placed in the same plane as, and superposed on M. T is the observation telescope. The variation of luminance of M is achieved either (a) by altering the current through N when very bright filaments are measured, or (b) by inserting a pair of Nicol prisms between L and M.

If a tungsten strip is used at N the front surface of its enclosing bulb should be uniform in thickness and as nearly plane as possible, to avoid distortion in M. If a Nernst glower is used it should be enclosed in a box to avoid draughts. In either case the apparatus may be calibrated most conveniently by placing at F a tungsten filament lamp of standard pattern for which the luminance variation with change of current or voltage may be accurately found on the photometer bench. The absolute filament luminance of this lamp at a low efficiency may be found by causing its filament to " disappear " in front of a full radiator at a known temperature.

The luminance of a flame source may be measured with this apparatus by substituting for F the device shown at the top of the figure, G. This consists of a skeleton box containing a diagonal double wedge of clear glass in the centre of which is a very narrow strip of silver, S. The flame is placed so that a thin line of it, reflected in S, is seen by the eye at T to be superposed on the image M.

The average luminance of an array of small surfaces, e.g. the luminous markings on an instrument dial, may be measured by viewing it between two stencils of the same design as the array, these stencils being placed in front of extended surfaces of equal and controllable luminance. This luminance is altered until the array to be measured and the two stencils appear the same in brightness and the luminance of the array is then obtained by measuring that of the extended surfaces [89]. If the stencils are photographic, allowance must be made for the transmission factor of the clear portions.

The Measurement of Daylight—There is one important problem in light measurement which frequently involves both luminance and illumination. This is the quantitative assessment of the natural lighting in a room. While the artificial lighting of an area may be described quite definitely by measurements of the illumination at various positions within that area, since the sources of the illumination are, within practical limits, under control and constant from hour to hour, in the case of natural lighting the conditions are altogether different. Owing, no doubt, to the wonderful ease with which the eye can adapt itself to quite large changes of brightness without any conscious effort, it is seldom realised how large and how rapid are the fluctuations which occur under ordinary conditions of daylight illumination [90]. Large variations, such as those which have to be allowed for by the photographer, are perceived when the attention

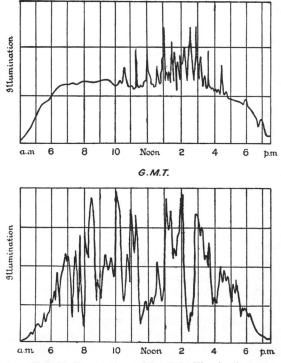

FIG. 221. Fluctuations of Daylight Illumination.

is specially directed to them, but in the majority of cases the degree of illumination is so much above the minimum required for comfortable vision that variations of 25 per cent or less are quite unnoticed. It is only at dusk, when the lower limit of comfort is approached, that differences of this order become apparent. Fig. 221 shows the daylight illumination of a horizontal surface in the open as actually measured on two typical spring days, direct sunlight being shielded from the test plate. It will be seen that in the upper curve variations of 25 per cent occurred within a period of five minutes, and yet to anyone relying solely upon the eye for measurement the illumination appeared to be quite constant.

It is clear that the daylight illumination at any point, indoors as well as out of doors, depends entirely on the luminance of that part of the sky from which the point in question receives its light. Hence it follows that a measurement of the daylight illumination in a room, taken at any particular instant, is quite destitute of any permanent value unless related to the luminance of the sky at the same instant.

Daylight Factor—The relation between the illumination at any point in a building and the luminance of the sky at the same instant is usually expressed by means of the " daylight factor ". This is the ratio (generally given as a percentage) of the illumination at the indoor point to that of a horizontal surface exposed to the whole hemisphere of sky [91]. It will be clear that for any given point this ratio depends upon the way in which the luminance of the sky varies from one part to another [92] and it is therefore necessary to make the proviso that the daylight factor is that value of the ratio which is found when the sky is uniform. Since the illumination of a surface exposed to a complete hemisphere of sky of uniform luminance B candelas per unit area is equal to πB lumens per unit area (see p. 148), the daylight factor is equal to $E/\pi B$ where E is the illumination at the indoor point when the sky has a uniform luminance B.

In practice the sky is scarcely ever uniform [93] but it has been found that, in general, overcast skies have a luminance distribution which can be represented approximately by $\frac{1}{3}B(1+2\sin\theta)$, where B is the zenith luminance and θ is the angle above the horizon. If, as is often the case, the greater part of the light reaching the indoor point comes from a comparatively small patch of sky, a good approximation to the daylight factor is $E/\pi B$ where E is the illumination when the luminance of this particular patch of sky is B. If most of the light reaching the indoor point is that reflected from neighbouring objects which are illuminated by different regions of the sky, this method cannot be used and the daylight factor can then only be measured on a day when the sky is fairly uniform. Even under these conditions, however, a direct measurement of the general sky luminance is often more convenient than a measurement of illumination in a completely open situation.

The illumination and the sky luminance may be measured by means of any ordinary visual illumination photometer with a detached test plate. If E is the reading at the indoor point and E_s the reading when the instrument is directed at the sky, the daylight factor is equal to $E/\rho E_s$ where ρ is the reflection factor of the test plate. If the sky measurement is made through a window, the daylight factor is $\tau E/\rho E_s$ where τ is the transmission factor of the window.

If a photo-electric illumination photometer is used, the sky luminance is most conveniently measured by means of a " daylight attach-

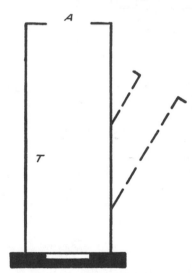

FIG. 222. The Daylight Attachment for an Illumination Photometer.

ment ", shown in Fig. 222 [94]. This consists of a cylinder T, blackened inside and covered with an opaque lid in which is a circular opening A. If the area of this opening is a and the height of the cylinder h, the illumination of a surface at the base of the cylinder is aB/h^2 when the opening is exposed to a portion of sky of luminance B. If the value of the fraction a/h^2 is $\pi/100$, the illumination of the surface is one per cent of that of a surface exposed to a complete hemisphere of sky of luminance B. If, therefore, two readings are taken with a photo-electric illuminometer, one indoors without the attachment, and one out-of-doors with the attachment placed over the photocell, the ratio of the readings is the daylight factor expressed as a percentage [95]. This attachment was originally designed for use with a visual photometer [96]. A side tube was then provided, as indicated by the broken line, so that the instrument could be directed at the test plate placed beneath the cylinder.

A photo-electric daylight-factor meter has been designed to give values of daylight factor directly [97]. Two photo-voltaic cells, one at the indoor point and the other, fitted with a daylight attachment, directed at the appropriate part of the sky, are connected alternately across a galvanometer. The second photocell is shunted with a variable resistor which is adjusted until the deflection of the galvanometer is the same for both cells. Previous calibration gives the day-light factor in terms of the reading on the variable resistor.

Several very conven-ient instruments called relative photometers [98] have been designed for measuring daylight fac-tors by making a direct comparison of the test plate with an image of a patch of sky viewed through a window. In the Thorner Illumination Tester shown in Fig. 223, the lens L forms at C an image of the portion of sky visible through the window towards which the mirror is directed. The luminance of this image is varied, by means of a diaphragm over L, until it matches the por-

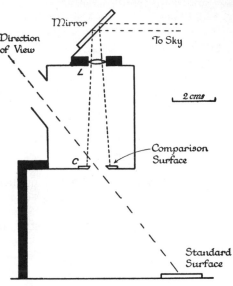

FIG. 223. Thorner's Illumination Tester.

tion of the standard surface seen through the aperture in C. Weber's relative photometer (Fig. 224) is similar in principle [99].

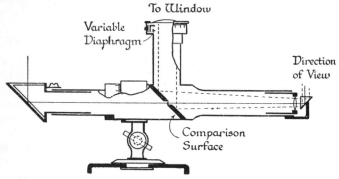

FIG. 224. Weber's Relative Photometer.

A simple instrument of this kind, the "hemera-photometer", is shown in Fig. 225 [100]. The light metal tube T is blackened inter-nally and fitted with diaphragms to eliminate stray light. When the instrument is in use the light from the sky passes through the aper-ture in the iris diaphragm I and illuminates the opaque matt white disc D. This disc has an aperture A, the edges of which are sharply bevelled, and the eye at F views a detached test surface through A. This detached test surface is placed at the point for which the daylight factor is to be measured, and photometric balance between the

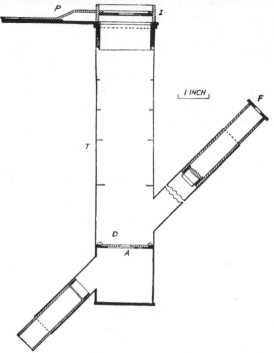

Fig. 225. The Hemeraphotometer.

luminance of this surface and that of the disc D seen surrounding it is achieved by varying the aperture of I. P is a lever for effecting this variation, and carries a pointer by means of which the daylight factor can be read directly on a previously calibrated scale. If D and the detached test plate are of the same material, there is no correction for the reflection factor of the surface, but the correction for transmission of the window must still be made.

The daylight factor is not restricted to the usual case, in which the illumination at the indoor point is that measured on a horizontal surface on the working plane, but if the indoor illumination is measured for some other plane that fact should always be stated.

Sky Factor—It will be clear that the illumination at a point in a building, due to the light received from a patch of sky of uniform luminance B and of defined size, shape and position relative to the point, can be calculated by the methods described in Chapter V (see especially pp. 146–147) since any portion of the sky may be regarded as a perfect diffuser. For example the illumination provided by a rectangular window with a completely unobstructed outlook is given by the formula for a rectangular diffusing surface (see p. 146) if the loss of light due to glazing and to window bars is either negligible or allowed for.

Such a calculation takes no account of the light received by reflection from the walls and ceiling of the room in which the point is situated and so the ratio of the illumination thus found to the value of πB differs somewhat from the daylight factor. It is known as the sky factor [101] and is chiefly of importance in the design of buildings, as it can be calculated in advance of construction.

Various charts and mechanical devices have been designed to facilitate the computation of the sky factor due to the light admitted by a rectangular window [102] and tables have been published showing for a range of sizes of windows, the shapes of the contours of constant sky factor on the working plane [103].

In many cases these devices are inapplicable because the shape of the patch of sky illuminating the point in question is irregular, owing to the presence of neighbouring buildings or other obstructions visible through the window. Recourse must then be had to some graphical method of solution [104]. The best known is that due to P. J. and J. M. Waldram [105]. The outline of the patch of sky visible from the point is traced on a network in which the scales are such that the area respresenting the patch is proportional to the contribution of that patch to the sky factor at the point. In Fig. 226, if P

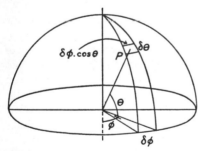

is an element of sky whose angles of azimuth and altitude are ϕ and θ respectively, the illumination of a horizontal surface at the centre of the hemisphere is

$$B\delta\phi \cos\theta . \delta\theta . \sin\theta$$
$$=\tfrac{1}{2}B \sin 2\theta . \delta\theta . \delta\phi.$$

If B is assumed constant, then the network must be drawn with a uniform scale of abscissae (ϕ) and a scale of ordinates such

FIG. 226. The Principle of the Graphical Determination of Sky Factor.

that θ is represented by $\int_0^\theta \sin 2\theta . d\theta = \sin^2\theta$ or $\tfrac{1}{2}(1 - \cos 2\theta)$. This was the original Waldram diagram. If, however, B is proportional to $(1 + 2\sin\theta)$ (see p. 406), the ordinate scale is given by

$$\int_0^\theta (1 + 2\sin\theta) \sin 2\theta . d\theta = \sin^2\theta + \tfrac{4}{3}\sin^3\theta,$$

and the network is as shown in Fig. 227 [106]. It will be seen that in both cases the area of the whole diagram, covering 180° in ϕ, represents a sky factor of 50 per cent. Similar networks may, clearly, be constructed for use when the window is horizontal instead of vertical and it is more convenient to measure ϕ from the normal to the illuminated surface, assumed horizontal.

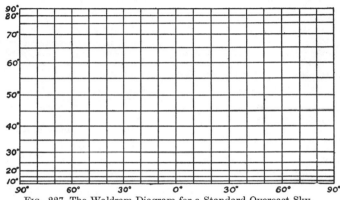

FIG. 227. The Waldram Diagram for a Standard Overcast Sky.

Other forms of diagram, mostly based on the solid angle projection method of calculation described in Chapter V (see p. 147), have also been devised [107].

In the original Waldram diagram and in that shown in Fig. 227 no allowance is made for loss of light due to window bars, absorption by dirt or reflection at the surfaces of the glass. An allowance of 20 per cent for dirt and for reflection losses combined is usual but the allowance to be made for window bars naturally depends on the type of window used. The reflection losses increase as the obliquity of the light increases and a form of Waldram diagram has been described in which this is allowed for by contracting the scale of ordinates at the top and the scale of abscissae at both ends [108]. The effect is, however, usually negligible except for unusually wide windows.

In the case of an existing building the flat projection of the windows, with any obstructions, can be obtained for any point in a room by using a suitably mounted camera or equivalent optical system. If the image or photograph is superimposed on a specially constructed network, the sky factor at the point can be obtained by counting the number of sections of the network covered by clear sky [109]. Alternatively, the sky factor can be obtained directly by means of a mechanical integrator so designed that, when the outline of a window has been traced out with a sighting device, the area of the corresponding projection on the Waldram diagram is indicated [110].

412   PHOTOMETRY

BIBLIOGRAPHY

A number of books dealing with illuminating engineering are listed in Section II of Appendix I on p. 511.

1. See, e.g., *I.E.S. Code for Lighting in Buildings* (Illum. Eng. Soc. London, *1955*).

2. See the British Standard Specification for Portable Photometers (Visual Type), No. 230.
See also L. Bloch, Licht u. Lampe, 26, *1937*, p. 76.

3. See, e.g., Illum. Eng. Soc. N.Y., Trans., 38, *1943*, p. 75.

4. For a comparison of the performance of visual and photo-electric instruments, see W. Voege, Licht u. Lampe, 23, *1934*, p. 519. This author has described (*ibid.*, 25, *1936*, p. 348) a combined visual and photo-electric illuminometer.

5. C.I.E. Proc., 7, *1928*, p. 454 and 8, *1931*, p. 325.

6. See the refs. cited in notes (2) to (9) on p. 372 of *Photometry* (*1926*) ; A. P. Trotter, Illum. Eng., 12, *1919*, p. 243 ; A. K. Taylor, Phys. Soc., Proc., 49, *1937*, p. 105.

7. A. K. Taylor. Opt. Convention, *1926*, Proc., Vol. I, p. 347.
C.I.E., Proc., 9, *1935*, p. 271 ; S. Pienkowski and I. Mrozowska, Acad. des Sciences Techniques, Warsaw, Ann., 2, *1935*, p. 15.
See also S. Seki, Int. Illum. Congress, *1931*, Vol. I, p. 234.

8. K. R. May. J. Sci. Inst., 17, *1940*, p. 231.
J. M. Dimitroff and D. W. Swanson. Opt. Soc. Am., J., 46, *1956*, p. 555.
On the reflection characteristics of this surface, see J. S. Preston, Opt. Soc., Trans., 31, *1930*, p. 15 ; W. W. Barkas, Phys. Soc., Proc., 51, *1938*, p. 274 ; V. G. W. Harrison, *ibid.*, 58, *1946*, p. 408.

9. C. H. Sharp and W. F. Little. Illum. Eng. Soc. N.Y., Trans., 10, *1915*, p. 727.

10. See, e.g., J. W. T. Walsh, Inst. El. Eng., J., 65, *1927*, p. 733.

11. See, e.g. the refs. cited in notes (14), (16) and (17) on pp. 372–3 of *Photometry* (*1926*) and the description of the Sharp-Millar photometer on pp. 348–9 of that edition.
See also Rev. d'Opt., 5, *1926*, p. 77 ; W. Voege, Licht u. Lampe, 16, *1927*, p. 700 ; J. W. T. Walsh, World Power, 13, *1930*, p. 134.

12. C. S. Redding. El. World, 65, *1915*, p. 85. This instrument is made by the Leeds and Northrup Co., Philadelphia, U.S.A.
See also W. E. K. Middleton and A. R. Ramsey, Canadian J. of Research (F), 26, *1948*, p. 59.

13. National Physical Laboratory, Ann. Report, *1928*, p. 146.

14. L. Djomkina. State Optical Inst. Leningrad, Trans. (Trudui), 4, *1928*, No. 42, p. 1. (In Russian.)

15. See the refs. in note (32) on p. 373 of *Photometry* (*1926*).

16. W. H. Preece. Roy. Soc., Proc., 36, *1884*, p. 270.
A. P. Trotter. Inst. Civil Eng., Proc., 110, *1892*, p. 69.

17. See the refs. in notes (24) to (27) and (29) on p. 373 of *Photometry* (*1926*) ; also O. Twerdy, Licht u. Lampe, 15, *1926*, p. 770.

18. A. P. Trotter. Inst. Civil Eng., Proc., 110, *1892*, p. 69.

19. See pp. 350 to 352 and the refs. in notes (19) to (21) and (28) on p. 373 of *Photometry* (*1926*) ; also J. Ockenden, Illum. Eng., 25, *1932*, p. 324.

20. H. T. Harrison. Electrician, 56, *1906*, p. 625.

21. See, e.g., A. Blondel, Illum. Eng., 3, *1910*, p. 314 and 18, *1925*, p. 237 ; Rev. Gén. de l'El., 22, *1927*, p. 7 ; W. Bechstein, Licht u. Lampe, 12, *1923*, p. 207 ; H. Frühling, *ibid.*, 15, *1926*, p. 895 ; H. Schober, E.u.M., 50, *1932*, Lichttech., p. 41 ; Licht u. Lampe, 21, *1932*, p. 183 ; National Phys. Lab., Ann. Report, *1929*, p. 156 and *1931*, p. 162.
See also the other refs. in note (33) on pp. 373–4 of *Photometry* (*1926*).

22. J. S. Dow and V. H. Mackinney. Opt. Soc., Trans., 12, *1910*, p. 66 ; Opt. Convention, *1912*, Proc., p. 70. Illum. Eng., 19, *1926*, p. 84 and 21, *1928*, p. 352.
S. English. Public Lighting, 13, *1948*, p. 15.
See also G. W. Rawcliffe, El. Rev., 127, *1940*, p. 325.

23. C. H. Williams. Illum. Eng. Soc. N.Y., Trans., 2, *1907*, p. 540.
G. A. Shook. Opt. Soc. Am., J., 8, *1924*, p. 803.
" Filmograph " (L. Lobel). Rev. d'Opt., 7, *1928*, p. 268.
P. Fleury. C.R., 192, *1931*, p. 1715.

24. J. M. Waldram. Illum. Eng., 26, *1933*, p. 288.

25. R. Pauli. Naturwissenschaften, 1, *1913*, p. 976.
A zig-zag dividing line for the bipartite field has been proposed (W. Voege, Licht u. Lampe, 18, *1929*, p. 183).

26. C. H. Sharp. El. World, 68, *1916*, p. 569.
C. F. Sackwitz. Illum. Eng. Soc. N.Y., Trans., 13, *1918*, p. 292.
H. Schober. E.u.M., 50, *1932*, Lichttech., p. 9.
See also H. T. Harrison, Illum. Eng., 3, *1910*, p. 373 and 21, *1928*, p. 354 ; A. Cunnington, *ibid.*, 9, *1916*, p. 89 ; J. S. Dow, *ibid.*, 9, *1916*, p. 98 ; Illum. Eng., 21, *1928*, p. 354 ; H. Pécheux, Rev. Gén. de l'El., 31, *1932*, p. 866 ; J. I. Graham, Colliery Guardian, 144, *1932*, p. 740 ; S. Maisel, Illum. Eng., 9, *1916*, p. 262.

27. Rev. d'Opt., 3, *1924*, p. 38.
Licht u. Lampe, 16, *1927*, p. 884.
See also A. P. Trotter, Illum. Eng., 11, *1918*, p. 253.

28. See also W. F. Little, Illum. Eng. Soc. N.Y., Trans., 10, *1915*, p. 766 ; J. W. T. Walsh, World Power, 13, *1930*, p. 134. See also Illum. Eng. Soc. Lond., Trans., 2, *1937*, p. 62.

29. See also L. Bloch, Licht u. Lampe, 14, *1925*, p. 229.

30. A. K. Taylor. Int. Illum. Congress, *1931*, Vol. I, p. 204.
W. E. K. Middleton and A. R. Ramsey. Canadian J. of Research, 26, (Sect. F), *1948*, p. 59.

31. Attempts have been made to substitute for the illuminated surface in the photometer a self-luminous (luminescent) surface (see the refs. in note (45) of *Photometry (1926)*) but such a device is only practicable when the values of illumination to be measured are very low. See G. E. V. Lambert, Light and Ltg., 32, *1939*, p. 252 and 34, *1941*, p. 3 ; H. Frieser, Licht, 13, *1943*, p. 16.

32. British Standard Specification for Visual Type Portable Photometers No. 230.

33. F. H. Schofield and D. C. Gall. J. Sci. Inst., 1, *1924*, p. 193.
A. K. Taylor. Opt. Convention, *1926*, Proc., Vol. I, p. 347.
R. Sewig. Z. f. techn. Phys., 15, *1934*, p. 384.
A method of regulation without an electrical measuring instrument has been described by C. H. Sharp and P. S. Millar (El. World, 60, *1912*, p. 266). See also J. S. Dow and V. H. Mackinney, Opt. Convention, *1912*, Proc., p. 70.

34. See, e.g., G. Trebbin, Licht u. Lampe, 17, *1928*, p. 880.

35. W. F. Little. Illum. Eng. Soc. N.Y., Trans., 10, *1915*, p. 766.
F. J. C. Brookes. J. Sci. Inst., 8, *1931*, p. 205.

36. C.I.E., Proc., 7, *1928*, p. 16.

37. J. W. T. Walsh. Illum. Eng., 18, *1925*, p. 36.

38. See, e.g., Light and Ltg., 29, *1936*, p. 111.

39. Illum. Eng. Soc. Lond., Trans., 2, *1937*, p. 62.

40. Light and Ltg., 33, *1940*, p. 22.
See also J. W. T. Walsh, Illum. Eng. Soc. Lond., Trans., 6, *1941*, p. 117 ; Light and Ltg., 32, *1939*, p. 250 ; J. Sci. Inst., 17, *1940*, p. 45 ; Electrotechniek, 18, *1940*, p. 163.

41. L. A. Jones and E. M. Lowry. Soc. Motion Picture Eng., Trans., 12, *1928* p. 1054.
See also A. H. Taylor, Opt. Soc. Am., J., 31, *1941*, p. 738 and 32, *1942*, p. 34 ; Illum. Eng. Soc. N.Y., Trans., 37, *1942*, pp. 19 and 424.

42. H. G. Frühling. Illum. Eng., 27, *1934*, p. 198.
P. Görlich. Licht u. Lampe, 24, *1935*, p. 579.
R. Doeckel. Lichttechnik, 6, *1954*, p. 360.
A. A. Butylev. Svetotechnika, 3, *1957*, No. 7, p. 12 (In Russian).
See also J. W. T. Walsh, El. Rev., 125, *1939*, p. 325.

43. A. H. Lamb. El. World, 99, *1932*, p. 692.
Holophane, Ltd. J. Sci. Inst., 12, *1935*, p. 398.
See also J. L. McCoy, Am. Inst. El. Eng., J., 49, *1930* p. 228

44. W. N. Goodwin. Illum. Eng. Soc. N.Y., Trans., 27, *1932*, p. 828.
J. Sci. Inst., 12, *1935*, p. 398 and 17, *1940*, p. 124.
Light and Ltg., 31, *1938*, p. 272.
Le Génie Civil, 109, *1936*, p. 229.
See also J. H. Jupe, Electrician, 123, *1939*, p. 70.

45. L. Bergmann. Phys. Z., 34, *1933*, p. 227.
H. C. Turner. El. Times, 86, *1934*, p. 393.
Illum. Eng., 27, *1934*, p. 138.
J. Sci. Inst., 11, *1934*, p. 331.
" Prolabo ". Rev. d'Opt., 13, *1934*, p. 413.
C. L. Dows and C. J. Allen. Illum. Eng. Soc. N.Y., Trans., 31, *1936*, p. 675.
Licht u. Lampe. 27, *1938*, p. 226.
C. L. Dows. Gen. El. Rev., 45, *1942*, p. 505.

46. J. S. Preston. Illum. Eng. Soc. Lond., Trans., 8, *1943*, p. 121.

47. See, however, G. B. Buck, Illum. Engng., 44, *1949*, p. 293. See also I. Good-bar, Illum. Eng. Soc. N.Y., Trans., 40, *1945*, p. 830 ; F. Hartig and H. J. Helwig, Lichttechnik, 7, *1955*, p. 181 ; O. Reeb and W. Tosberg, *Ibid.*, p. 275.
For a method of correction particularly applicable in measurements of street illumination, see F. Buchmüller and H. König, Assoc. Suisse des Elect., Bull., 31, *1940*, p. 122.

48. S. English. Illum. Eng., 28, *1935*, p. 94 (see also p. 48).

49. See also G. Mogford, El. Rev., 133, *1943*, p. 103 ; C. A. Morton, Light and Ltg., 38, *1945*, p. 157.

50. A. E. Parker. Illum. Eng. Soc. N.Y., Trans., 35, *1940*, p. 833.

51. See, however, C. L. Dows, Illum. Eng. Soc. N.Y., Trans., 37, *1942*, p. 103.

52. Illum. Eng. Soc. N.Y., Trans., 32, *1937*, p. 379.
See also El. World, 113, *1940*, p. 758.

53. J. S. Preston. J. Sci. Inst., 15, *1938*, p. 102.
See also G. Rougier, C.R., 194, *1932*, p. 1319 ; Illum. Engng., 38, *1943*, p. 612 ; J. Sci. Inst., 27, *1950*, p. 29 ; H. Schier, Lichttechnik, 4, *1952*, p. 91.

54. J. E. Ives. Illum. Eng. Soc. N.Y., Trans., 20, *1925*, p. 498.
L. R. Koller. Gen. El. Rev., 31, *1928*, p. 85.
W. R. G. Atkins and H. H. Poole. " Photo-electric Cells and their Applications," Phys. and Opt. Socs., *1930*, p. 128 ; Nature, 125, *1930*, p. 305.
T. H. Harrison. Nature, 125, *1930*, p. 704.
L. H. McDermott and C. J. MacManus. Illum. Eng., 24, *1932*, p. 41 ; Illum. Eng. Soc. Lond., Trans., 1, *1936*, p. 135.
W. R. G. Atkins and H. H. Poole. Phil. Trans., 235, *1936*, p. 245.
R. Grandmontagne. Rev. d'Opt., 19, *1940*, p. 78.
Light and Ltg., 34, *1941*, p. 176.
See also S. Strauss, E.u.M., 50, *1932*, Lichttech., p. 17 ; P. Toulon, Soc. Franç. des Elect., Bull., 5, *1935*, p. 465 ; C. T. Elvey and F. E. Roach, Astrophys. J., 85, *1937*, p. 213 ; M. Luckiesh and A. H. Taylor, Gen. El. Rev., 44, *1941*, p. 217.
The necessity for a colour correction filter, even in the case of a daylight recorder, arises from the fact that daylight is by no means invariable in its spectral distribution. See, e.g., P. W. Cunliffe, Textile Inst., J., 20, *1929*, p. T34 ; L. S. Ornstein *et al.*, Koninklijke Nederlandsche Akad. v. Wetenschappen, Amsterdam, Verh. (Sect. I), 16, *1936*, p. 1 ; A. H. Taylor and G. P. Kerr, Opt. Soc. Am., J., 31, *1941*, p. 3 ; A. H. Taylor, *ibid.*, p. 105.

55. M. G. Bennett. Phys. Soc., Proc., 40, *1928*, p. 316.
A. S. G. Hill. " Photo-electric Cells and their Applications," Phys. and Opt. Socs., *1930*, p. 138.
W. R. G. Atkins and H. H. Poole. Phil. Trans., 235, *1936*, p. 245.

56. Illum. Eng. Soc. N.Y., Trans., 32, *1937*, p. 379.
K. Larché and R. Schulze. Z. techn. Phys., 23, *1942*, p. 114.
K. Larché. Licht, 12, *1942*, p. 110.
P. L. Tea and H. D. Baker. Opt. Soc. Am., J., 46, *1956*, p. 875.
See also Illum. Eng., 21, *1928*, p. 198 ; J. Dourgnon, Rev. Gén. de l'El., 35, *1934*, p. 465 ; W. Dziobek, Article " Verfahren d. visuellen Photometrie " in *Handbuch d.*

Lichttechnik (Springer, *1938*), p. 276 ; E. Cooper and M. C. Probine, J. Sci. Inst. 26, *1949*, p. 348.

57. W. R. G. Atkins and H. H. Poole. Roy. Dublin Soc., Proc., 19, *1929*, p. 159.
R. H. Müller and G. E. Shriver. Rev. Sci. Inst., 6, *1935*, p. 16.
J. L. Michaelson. Gen. El. Rev., 42, *1939*, p. 92.
A. H. Taylor. Opt. Soc. Am., J., 31, *1941*, p. 105.

58. See, e.g., W. C. Clinton, Illum. Eng., 7, *1914*, p. 189 ; E. H. Rayner, J. W. T. Walsh and H. Buckley, *ibid.*, 15, *1922*, p. 107.
Photo-electric apparatus for recording the variation of illumination along a line has been described by H. H. Higbie and W. A. Bychinsky (Illum. Eng. Soc. N.Y., Trans., 29, *1934*, p. 206).

59. See, e.g., H. Laurain, C.I.E., Proc., 6, *1924*, p. 286 ; J. Mariage, *ibid.*, p. 301.

60. *International Lighting Vocabulary* (Commission Internationale de l'Eclairage, *1957*), p. 100.

61. W. Harrison and E. A. Anderson. Illum. Eng. Soc. N.Y., Trans., 11, *1916*, p. 67 and 15, *1920*, p. 97.
J. Wetzel. Rev. Gén. de l'El., 14, *1923*, pp. 1027 and 1073.
M. Cohu and J. Dourgnon. *Ibid.*, 21, *1927*, p. 531.
See also J. Dourgnon, Rev. Gén. de l'El., 23, *1928*, p. 271 and 33, *1933*, p. 579.

62. " Illumination Design for Interiors " (Lighting Service Bureau, 2 Savoy Hill, London, W.C.2).
W. E. Barrows. *Light, Photometry and Illuminating Engineering.*

63. C.I.E., Proc., 6, *1924*, p. 178.
British Standard No. 233.
International Lighting Vocabulary (C.I.E., *1957*), p. 100.
See also A. P. Trotter, *Illumination, etc.*, p. 58.
On a method of designing for uniform illumination, see H. R. S. M'Whirter, Inst. El. Eng., J., 68, *1930*, p. 1012 and Roy. Techn. Coll., Glasgow, J., 2, *1932*, p. 688.

64. K. Norden. E.T.Z., 32, *1911*, p. 607 ; Z. f. Bel., 25, 1919, p. 11 ; 26, *1920*, p. 73 and 27, *1921*, p. 109 ; Licht u. Lampe, 12, *1923*, p. 470 ; Int. Illum. Congress, *1931*, Vol. II, p. 1257 ; E.u.M., 55, *1937*, Lichttech., p. 17 ; *Shadow in Illuminating Engineering* (Pitman, *1948*) ; Illum. Engng., N.Y., 44, *1949*, p. 607.
W. Bechstein. Z. Vereines deut. Ing., 68, *1924*, p. 1271.
J. Ondracek. Licht, 7, *1937*, pp. 97 and 117.
H. Long. Illum. Eng. Soc. Lond., Trans., 2, *1937*, p. 52 ; El. Rev., 127, *1940*, p. 367.
See also L. Bloch, Licht u. Lampe, 12, *1923*, p. 491 ; H. Lingenfelser, *ibid.*, 17, *1928*, p. 313 ; H. Lux, Licht, 8, *1938*, p. 61.

65. C.I.E., Proc., 9, *1935*, pp. 20 and 567

66. K. Norden. *Shadow in Illuminating Engineering* (Pitman, *1948*), p. 113, and Illum. Engng., 44, *1949*, p. 607.

67. H. Lux. Z. f. Bel., 16, *1910*, p. 109.
See also J. Baille and C. Féry, Lum. El., 41, *1891*, p. 153 ; Various authors, Rev. Gén. de l'El., 36, *1934*, p. 780 ; E. A. Lindsay, Illum. Eng. Soc. N.Y., Trans., 39, *1944*, p. 23.

68. See, e.g., E. L. Nichols and E. Merritt, Phys. Rev., 23, *1906*, p. 37.

69. A. Blondel. Rev. Gén. de l'El., 24, *1923*, pp. 507 and 542.
M. V. Sokolov. Travaux de l'Inst. de Métrologie, U.R.S.S., No. 133, *1934*, p. 37 ; Rev. Gén. de l'El., 36, *1934*, p. 780.

70. H. E. Ives. Illum. Eng. Soc. N.Y., Trans., 9, *1914*, p. 183.
A. Blondel. Illum. Eng., 18, *1925*, p. 237 ; C.R., 181, *1925*, p. 310 and 186. *1928*, p. 1677.
H. G. Frühling. Licht u. Lampe, 19, *1930*, p. 79.
L. Bloch. *Ibid.*, p. 663.
B. H. Crawford. J. Sci. Inst., 11, *1934*, p. 14.
J. J. M. Reesinck. Physica, 12, *1946*, p. 296.
See also M. Luckiesh and F. K. Moss, Opt. Soc. Am., J., 27, *1937*, p. 292.

71. See, e.g., J. Peyre, Rev. d'Opt., 6, *1927*, p. 73 ; J. J. M. Reesinck, Physica, 12, *1946*, p. 296.
A separate scale is provided in the Lumeter described on p. 384.

72. C. C. Paterson, J. W. T. Walsh and W. F. Higgins. Phys. Soc., Proc., 29, *1917*, p. 215.

N. E. Dorsoy. Washington Acad. Sci., J., 7, *1917*, p. 1.

F. v. Hauer. Wien Ber. (IIa), 127, *1918*, p. 369.

L. Bloch. Licht u. Lampe, 16, *1927*, p. 395.

B. T. Squires and J. H. Jeffree. J. Sci. Inst., 5, *1928*, p. 273.

H. F. Meacock and G. E. V. Lambert. *Ibid.*, 8, *1931*, p. 214.

L. F. Curtiss. Bureau of Standards, J. of Research, 13, *1934*, p. 203 ; Rev. Sci. Inst., 11, *1940*, p. 428.

J. Clara. Rev. d'Opt., 21, *1942*, p. 128.

See also K. W. F. Kohlrausch, E.u.M., 44, *1926*, Lichttech., p. 37.

73. A special name, the " skot ", has been proposed for a luminance or equivalent luminance of 10^{-3} asb. On this system the illumination at which a perfect diffuser has a luminance or equivalent luminance of one skot is termed the " nox ". Thus at the colour temperature of the primary standard, 1 nox $= 10^{-3}$ lux and 1 skot $= 10^{-3}$ asb. (A. Dresler, Licht, 10, *1940*, pp. 37, 112, 118 and 145.)

74. M. Roulleau. Rev. d'Opt., 13, *1934*, p. 375.

J. W. T. Walsh. Illum. Eng. Soc. Lond., Trans., 6, *1941*, p. 117.

R. P. Teele. Bureau of Standards, J. of Research, 34, *1945*, p. 325.

W. E. K. Middleton. Opt. Soc. Am., J., 44, *1954*, p. 303.

British Standard No. 1316, for Fluorescent and Phosphorescent Materials, Appendix B.

See also W. G. White, J. Sci. Inst., 25, *1948*, p. 1.

On the errors which may occur in the photometry of a surface of diminishing luminance, see C. C. Trowbridge and W. B. Truesdell, Phys. Rev., 4, *1914*, p. 289.

75. J. Dufay and R. Schwégler. C.R., 189, *1929*, p. 1261 ; Rev. d'Opt., 9, *1930*, p. 263.

J. M. Waldram. Illum. Eng. Soc. Lond., Trans., 10, *1945*, p. 147.

See also P. H. Keck, Optik, 4, *1949*, p. 331.

76. E. E. Vezey. Illum. Engng., 50, *1955*, p. 543.

H. Buchbinder and G. Eckhardt. Lichttechnik, 9, *1957*, p. 550.

77. G. Weber. Licht, 3, *1933*, p. 65.

See also Y. G. Hurd, Illum. Engng., 44, *1949*, p. 555.

78. See, e.g., F. Kavanagh, Industrial and Engng. Chem. (Anal. Ed.), 13, *1941*, p. 108 ; G. F. Lothian, J. Sci. Inst., 18, *1941*, p. 200 ; R. P. Krebs and H. J. Kersten, Industrial and Engng. Chem. (Anal. Ed.), 15, *1943*, p. 132.

79. See, e.g., M. Blau and B. Dreyfus, Rev. Sci. Inst., 16, *1945*, p. 245.

80. J. R. De Vore. Opt. Soc. Am., J., 38, *1948*, p. 692.

81. F. Hamburger and E. J. King. Opt. Soc. Am., J., 38, *1948*, p. 875.

82. P. Toulon. Soc. Franç. des Elect., Bull., 5, *1935*, p. 465.

R. G. Hopkinson. Illum. Eng. Soc. Lond., Trans., 1, *1936*, p. 19 ; Light and Ltg., 29, *1936*, p. 270.

A. Bloch. J. Sci. Inst., 13, *1936*, p. 358.

J. M. Waldram. *Ibid.*, p. 352.

R. Maxted. Light and Ltg., 31, *1938*, p. 268.

J. Bergmans. *Ibid.*, 32, *1939*, p. 118.

G. J. Meyers and V. J. Mooney. Illum. Eng. Soc. N.Y., Trans., 36, *1941*, p. 643.

C. Marsh. Illum. Engng., 47, *1952*, p. 571.

See also F. Benford, Opt. Soc. Am., J., 27, *1937*, pp. 286 and 400 ; de Vilmorin, Soc. Franç. des Elect., Bull., 7, *1947*, p. 417.

An instrument for measuring relative luminance has been described by M. Luckiesh and F. K. Moss (Opt. Soc. Am., J., 27, *1937*, p. 292).

83. J. M. Waldram. Illum. Eng., 27, *1934*, pp. 305 and 339 ; 28, *1935*, pp. 56 and 420.

M. Luckiesh and A. H. Taylor. Opt. Soc. Am., J., 27, *1937*, p. 132.

J. F. Dunn and G. S. Plant. Photog. J., 85 (B), *1945*, p. 114 and 88 (A), *1948*, p. 230.

J. B. de Boer. Lichttechnik, 7, *1955*, pp. 273 and 307.

See also Light and Ltg., 31, *1938*, p. 268 and note (85) *infra*.

84. E. R. Thomas. J. Sci. Inst., 19, *1946*, p. 187.
See also F. E. Carlson and W. M. Potter, Illum. Engng., N.Y., 39, *1944*, p. 754 ;
D. Marlow and J. C. Pemberton, Rev. Sci. Inst., 20, *1949*, p. 724.

85. E. Karrer and A. Poritsky. Opt. Soc. Am., J., 8, *1924*, p. 355.
A. Blondel. Rev. Gén. de l'El., 24, *1928*, pp. 507 and 542.
J. S. Preston. J. Sci. Inst., 8, *1931*, p. 189.
C. C. Paterson. Phys. Soc., Proc., 50, *1938*, p. 119.
A. Jobin and G. Yvon. Rev. d'Opt., 19, *1940*, p. 135.

86. H. Hartinger. Licht u. Lampe, 13, *1924*, p. 651.
L. Bloch. *Ibid.*, 14, *1925*, p. 39.
K. Freund. Illum. Engng., 48, *1953*, p. 524.
F. F. Crandell and K. Freund. Illum. Engng., 52, *1957*, p. 319.

87. C.R., 156, *1913*, p. 1231.

88. H. E. Ives and M. Luckiesh. El. World, 57, *1911*, p. 438.
See also F. Born and H. Knauer, Licht, 3, *1933*, p. 247.

89. C. C. Paterson, J. W. T. Walsh and W. F. Higgins. Phys. Soc., Proc., 29,
1917, p. 215.
L. F. Curtiss. Bureau of Standards, J. of Research, 15, *1935*, p. 1.

90. See, e.g., P. J. Waldram, Illum. Eng., 7, *1914*, p. 15 ; J. E. Ives, Illum. Eng.
Soc. N.Y., Trans., 20, *1925*, p. 498 ; F. Benford, Gen. El. Rev., 31, *1928*, p. 87.

91. H. Cohn. Schlesische Gesell. f. vaterl. Cultur, Jahresber., 79, (Abt. Ib.),
1901, p. 2.
S. Ruzicka. Archiv f. Hygiene, 54, *1905*, p. 32.
A. P. Trotter. *Illumination, etc.*, p. 249.
Home Office Committee on Lighting in Factories and Workshops, First
Report (Cmd. 8000), *1915*, vols. 1 and 3, *passim*.
P. J. Waldram. Roy. Inst. British Architects, J., 32, *1925*, p. 405.
H. Frühling. Licht u. Lampe, 15, *1926*, p. 895.

92. F. L. Knowles and J. E. Ives. Illum. Eng. Soc. N.Y., Trans., 34, *1939*,
p. 523.

93. See, e.g., H. H. Kimball, Illum. Eng. Soc. N.Y., Trans., 16, *1921*, p. 255 and
18, *1923*, p. 434.
The empirical formula given on p. 406 is that proposed by P. Moon and D. E.
Spencer (Illum. Engng., 37, *1942*, p. 707) and subsequently recommended for general
adoption by the C.I.E. (Proc., 13, *1955*, Section 3.2). See also R. G. Hopkinson, Opt.
Soc. Am., J., 49, *1954*, p. 455.
An instrument has been designed for comparing the luminance of different parts
of the sky at the same instant. See F. Herxheimer, Z.f.I., 32, *1912*, p. 55.

94. See also Y. G. Hurd, Illum. Eng. Soc. N.Y., Trans., 41, *1946*, p. 306.

95. On the effect of polarization of the daylight reaching the indoor cell at oblique
incidence, see H. H. Hausner, Illum. Eng. Soc. N.Y., Trans., 38, *1943*, p. 382.
On the use of correction factors to allow for the effect of the obliquity of the light
reaching the cell at the indoor point, see W. E. Folsom and R. L. Biesele, Illum.
Engng., 43, *1948*, p. 355.

96. P. J. Waldram. Illum. Eng., 1, *1908*, p. 811 ; Soc. of Architects, J., 3, *1910*,
p. 131.
J. of Gas Lighting, 117, *1912*, p. 277.
H. G. Allpress. Illum. Eng., 19, *1926*, p. 348.

97. G. P. Barnard. J. Sci. Inst., 13, *1936*, p. 392 (see also 15, *1938*, p. 140).
See also W. R. G. Atkins and H. H. Poole, Roy. Dublin Soc., Proc., 19, *1929*,
p. 173 ; W. Koch and D. Kaplan, J. Sci. Inst., 29, *1952*, p. 179 ; J. Longmore and
R. G. Hopkinson, *Ibid.*, 31, *1954*, p. 214.

98. W. Thorner. Phys. Z., 9, *1908*, p. 855.
A. K. Taylor. J. Sci. Inst., 4, *1926*, p. 49.
S. English. Illum. Eng., 23, *1930*, p. 278.
A system of mirrors may be used to measure the illumination at any point in a
room in terms of the illumination at some arbitrarily selected point, so that the dis-
tribution of light in the room may be determined. See J. Classen, Naturwiss.
Rundschau, 16, *1901*, p. 589.

99. L. Weber. Naturwiss. Verein f. Schleswig-Holstein, Schriften, 15, *1911*,
p. 158 ; Z.f.Bel., 25, *1919*, p. 8.

100. A. K. Taylor. J. Sci. Inst., 1, *1924*, p. 214.

101. H. Schober. Licht, 8, *1938*, p. 217.
C.I.E., Proc., 10, *1939*, Vol. I, p. 498 and Vol. III, p. 12.

102. H. H. Higbie and W. Turner-Szymanowski. Illum. Eng. Soc. N.Y., Trans., 25, *1930*, p. 213.
H. H. Higbie and A. D. Moore. Int. Illum. Congress, *1931*, Proc., Vol. II, p. 1149.
P. J. Waldram. Builder, 153, *1937*, p. 598 and 162, *1942*, pp. 77, 106 and 129.
A. F. Dufton. J. Sci. Inst., 17, *1940*, p. 226.
W. Arndt. Licht, 10, *1940*, p. 13.
A. F. Dufton. Illum. Eng. Soc. Lond., Trans., 8, *1943*, p. 61.
Lighting of Buildings (H.M. Stationery Office, *1944*), pp. 77–89.
P. J. Waldram. Illum. Eng. Soc. Lond., Trans., 9, *1944*, p. 16.
W. Allen. Illum. Eng. Soc. Lond., Trans., 11, *1946*, p. 205.

103. T. Smith and E. D. Brown. *Natural Lighting of Houses and Flats with Graded Daylight Factor Tables.* (H.M. Stationery Office, *1944*.) Additions published *1947*.
T. Smith. Illum. Eng. Soc. Lond., Trans., 8, *1943*, p. 110.

104. Originally the solid angle subtended by the patch of sky visible at the indoor point was measured by optical or photographic apparatus (e.g. L. Weber's " Raumwinkelmesser ", Z.f.I., 4, *1884*, pp. 343 and 417) and this was multiplied by the sine of the angle of elevation of the centre of the patch to obtain a figure roughly corresponding to the sky factor at the point. See F. Pleier, Z. f. Schulgesundheits-pflege, 22, *1909*, p. 461.

105. P. J. and J. M. Waldram. Illum. Eng., 16, *1923*, p. 90.
" Penetration of Daylight and Sunlight into Buildings," Illum. Research Tech. Paper No. 7. (H.M. Stationery Office, *1932*.)

106. R. Vollmer. Lichttechnik, 9, *1957*, p. 407.
J. W. T. Walsh. Architects J. (*In the press*).

107. See, e.g., A. A. Gershun, State Optical Inst. Leningrad, Trans. (Trudui), 5, No. 44, *1929*, p. 25 (In Russian) ; A. C. Stevenson, Int. Illum. Congress, *1931*, Proc., Vol. II, p. 1167 ; A. Daniljuk, Licht, 4, *1934*, p. 241 and 5, *1935*, p. 16 ; P. Hartill, Illum. Eng. Soc. Lond., Trans., 11, *1946*, p. 253.

108. P. J. Waldram. Roy. Inst. British Architects, J., 43, *1936*, p. 1072.
F. L. Knowles and J. E. Ives. Illum. Eng. Soc. N.Y., Trans., 34, *1939*, p. 523.
See also A. C. Stevenson, J. Sci. Inst., 14, *1937*, p. 231.

109. P. J. Waldram. Illum. Eng., 24, *1931*, p. 313.
A. C. Stevenson. J. Sci. Inst., 9, *1932*, p. 96.
J. Swarbrick. *Easements of Light : A Synopsis* (Batsford, *1938*).
H. E. Beckett and A. F. Dufton. J. Sci. Inst., 9, *1932*, p. 158.
P. J. Waldram. Roy. Inst. British Architects, J., 40, *1933*, p. 614.
H. E. Beckett. Photog., J., 74, *1934*, p. 229.
P. J. Waldram. Junior Inst. Engrs., J., 54, *1943*, p. 65.
F. A. Benford. Opt. Soc. Am., J., 33, *1943*, p. 440.

110. H. C. H. Townend. J. Sci. Inst., 8, *1931*, p. 177.
V. H. Cherry, D. D. Davis and L. M. K. Boelter. Illum. Eng. Soc. N.Y., Trans., 34, *1939*, p. 1085.
See also L. Weber, Z.f.I., 28, *1908*, p. 129 ; E. Liustich, Acad. Sci. U.R.S.S.. C.r. (Doklady), 15, *1937*, p. 9.

CHAPTER XIII

MEASUREMENT OF REFLECTION, TRANSMISSION AND ABSORPTION FACTORS

The Measurement of Reflection Factor—The reflection factor of a surface was defined in Chapter V (p. 153) as the ratio of the luminous flux reflected by a surface to that incident upon it and it was explained that the reflection factor usually depended on the spectral composition of the incident light and on the angle of incidence. Further, the term " direct reflection factor " was used to denote the ratio of the luminous flux reflected directly (i.e. according to the laws of direct reflection) to the total incident flux while the term " diffuse reflection factor " referred to flux reflected in all directions other than that of regular reflection.

To measure the total flux reflected from a surface, irrespective of the way in which this flux is distributed, the principle of the integrating sphere (see p. 258) is generally used [1] and the test surface is arranged to form part of the surface of the sphere. For the case of direct light incident at some specified angle, the arrangement shown in Fig. 228 may be used. *A* is an aperture through which a powerful beam of light is directed on to the test surface *S*, the position of *S* being such that the angle of incidence of the light is that specified. Care is taken to ensure that the whole of the light in the beam falls on *S*, without any spill, and a screen is placed in the sphere so that no part of *S* is visible from the window *W*. The

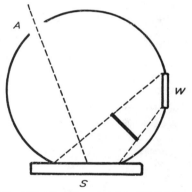

Fig. 228. The Measurement of Reflection Factor for Direct Incidence.

ratio of the illumination of *W* when the beam is directed on to *S* to the illumination when the same beam is directed on to some part of the sphere wall not screened from *W* is approximately equal to the reflection factor (ρ) of the test surface. This follows from the fact that if the total flux in the beam is *F*, when *S* is illuminated it is equivalent to a source of light giving ρF lumens placed in the sphere, while when the beam illuminates the sphere wall the conditions are nearly the same as those produced by a source of *F* lumens placed in the sphere.

A slight error may be introduced by the presence of the screen (see p. 265) and the aperture A, so that these should be as small as possible. Ignoring such departures from the ideal conditions, the result stated above can be proved by the following analysis.

If the reflection factor of the test surface is equal to ρ and the plane area it occupies, expressed as a fraction of the area of the sphere, is a', the total flux absorbed by the test surface when it is directly illuminated is $(1-\rho)F + a'(1-\rho)\rho_s E$, where E is the illumination of the sphere wall and ρ_s its reflection factor, for the test surface receives F lumens by direct illumination and $\rho_s E$ lumens per unit area by reflection from the sphere. The flux absorbed by the surface of the sphere is $(1-a)(1-\rho_s)E$ where a is the fraction of spherical surface occupied by the test surface. These two amounts of absorbed flux must together equal F, the total flux entering the sphere, so that

$$\{a'(1-\rho)\rho_s + (1-a)(1-\rho_s)\}E = \rho F.$$

While the illumination of most of the sphere surface is E, that of W is lower since it is screened from the test surface. The reduction is equal to the illumination due to direct light from the test surface, viz. $\rho F/(1-a)$ so that E_1, the illumination of W, is equal to $E = \rho F(1-a)$. It will be found that, since $a' = a(1-a)$,

$$E_1 = \frac{\rho\rho_s F\{1 - a(1-\rho)\}}{(1-a)\{(1-\rho_s) + a\rho_s(1-\rho)\}} \ .$$

When the flux F is incident on the wall of the sphere the amount reflected is $\rho_s F$ and of this $a\rho_s F$ reaches the test surface directly, while the remainder is distributed uniformly over the sphere wall. If the illumination of W is now E_2, the flux reaching the test surface from the sphere wall is $a(1-a)\rho_s E_2$. Since the flux absorbed by the sphere wall, together with that absorbed by the test surface is equal to $\rho_s F$, it follows that

$$(1-a)(1-\rho_s)E_2 + \{a\rho_s F + a(1-a)\rho_s E_2\}(1-\rho) = \rho_s F$$

or $\quad E_2(1-a)\{(1-\rho_s) + a\rho_s(1-\rho)\} = \rho_s F\{1 - a(1-\rho)\}$

It will be seen that $E_1/E_2 = \rho$.

A portable instrument designed on this principle and suitable for use on extended surfaces, with the light incident at 45°, is shown in Fig. 229 [2]. The tube T is movable so that the beam of light from L may be projected on to either the test surface at A or a portion of the sphere wall at B. Instead of the illumination of a window, the luminance of a portion of the sphere wall at C is measured. C is screened from A so that it cannot receive light directly from the test surface when the latter is illuminated by the beam of light. The ratio of the two values of luminance so obtained gives, as before, the value of ρ, the reflection factor of the test surface at A. It is, however, better to use the instrument purely as a comparator, the test

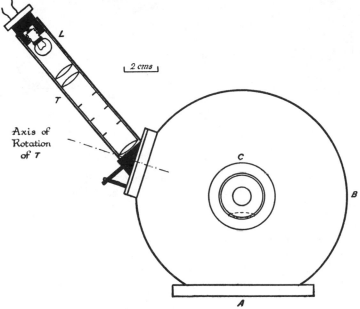

FIG. 229. The Portable Reflectometer.

surface and a standard surface of known reflection factor (e.g. magnesium oxide [3]) being placed in succession at A. It will be noticed that this method is used in the Hardy recording spectrophotometer for the determination of spectral reflection curves (see p. 370).

Reflection Factor for Diffuse Incident Light—The reflection factor of a surface for diffused light may be measured by a method analogous to that described above [4] but in this case the beam of light is always incident on the surface of the sphere and the value of a, the area of the sphere opening expressed as a fraction of the total area of the sphere, may conveniently be about 0·1. The arrangement is shown in Fig. 230 which gives an elevation in two perpendicular planes; B is the observing window.

From measurements of the illumination at B when (i) DE is uncovered (E_0), (ii) DE is covered with a surface of reflection factor ρ_s, the same as that of the sphere surface (E_s) and (iii) DE is covered with the test surface of reflection factor ρ (E_ρ), it is possible to find ρ. In the first case, the flux escaping through DE is made up of two parts viz. that directly reflected from the luminous patch at P, equal to

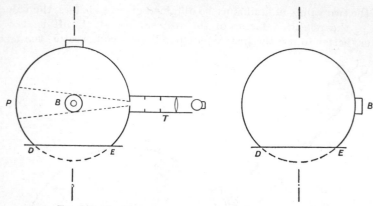

Fig. 230. The Measurements of Diffuse Reflection Factor.

$a\rho_s F$, and that reflected from the illuminated walls of the sphere, $a'\rho_s E_0$. This flux, added to that absorbed by the walls of the sphere, $(1-\rho_s)(1-a)E_0$ must be equal to the flux reflected from P viz. $\rho_s F$ so that

$$a\rho_s F + a'\rho_s E_0 + (1-a)(1-\rho_s)E_0 = \rho_s F \quad \dots\dots\dots\dots(i)$$

This equation gives E_0/F in terms of ρ_s, a and a'.

In the third measurement DE is covered with a surface of reflection factor ρ so that the flux lost is reduced in the ratio $(1-\rho):1$. Hence

$$(1-\rho)(a\rho_s F + a'\rho_s E_\rho) + (1-a)(1-\rho_s)E_\rho = \rho_s F \quad \dots\dots\dots\dots(ii)$$

and, substituting ρ_s for ρ, the equation for E_s becomes

$$(1-\rho_s)(a\rho_s F + a'\rho_s E_s) + (1-a)(1-\rho_s)E_s = \rho_s F \quad \dots\dots\dots(iii)$$

It will be clear that from equations (i) and (iii) ρ_s can be determined in terms of the ratio E_s/E_0 and then ρ can be found from equations (i) and (ii) in terms of E_ρ/E_0, or from (ii) and (iii) in terms of E_ρ/E_s.

There are two objections to this method. In the first place it will be seen that part of the light reaching the test surface, viz. that coming directly from P, is not diffused. The error introduced on this account can be reduced by making ρ_s as large as possible so that the ratio of diffused to direct light is high. In the second place it will be found that a large change in ρ produces only a comparatively small change in E_ρ/E_s or E_ρ/E_0, so that a high accuracy in the relative values of illumination under the three conditions is required. In this respect, too, an improvement can be effected by increasing ρ_s so that the use of a coating for the sphere such as magnesium oxide is to be recommended.

A method which is not open to the objection just mentioned

depends on illuminating the sample diffusely by a hemisphere of uniform luminance [5]. In Fig. 231 S is the test surface and H_1 a

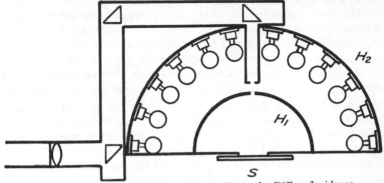

FIG. 231. The Measurement of Reflection Factor for Diffuse Incidence.

hemisphere of opal glass, the outer surface of which is illuminated as uniformly as possible by a large number of similar lamps more or less uniformly spaced over the inner surface of a whitened hemisphere H_2. Small holes are provided in H_1 and H_2 at selected intervals on a meridian so that the luminance of the test surface may be measured with a specially designed photometer. For most surfaces the luminance curve is the same in every meridian so that only one series of measurements is needed, but if necessary a series of luminance curves can be determined with the test surface turned through various angles about its normal as axis. A mean curve can be obtained directly by spinning the surface in its own plane at a sufficient speed to avoid flicker in the photometer. Provision is made for exploring the luminance distribution over H_1 so that the average value, B, may be found. The flux reaching the test surface is then πB lumens per unit area. The flux reflected per unit area can be found from the luminance curve, since it is equal to $\pi \int_0^{\pi/2} B_\theta \sin 2\theta \, . \, d\theta$, where B_θ is the luminance at angle θ (see p. 137). The ratio is the reflection factor of the surface for diffuse incident light.

The Measurement of Direct Reflection Factor—The definition of reflection factor given at the beginning of this chapter is unambiguous, no matter what the nature of the surface, but the same is true of the definition of direct reflection factor only when the surface is a perfect mirror. For all other actual surfaces the light is not directly reflected according to Snell's law but is scattered preferentially, so that more is concentrated in certain directions than in others [6]. Further, the preferential reflection is not necessarily confined to the angular region surrounding the direction of regular reflection. In these circumstances there is no obvious way of determining how much of the reflected flux should be regarded as directly reflected, and the direct reflection factor is, therefore, indefinite.

The direct reflection factor of a mirror is generally determined by the method indicated on p. 249. The luminous intensity of a source is measured (a) directly and (b) by reflection in the mirror, the distance of the source from the photometer being that actually traversed by the light. If the reflection factor is high, it is convenient to use several pieces so that the light suffers more than one reflection. The reflection factor is then $\sqrt[n]{I_M/I}$ where I_M is the apparent luminous intensity of the source after n reflections [7]. In the case of a silvered glass mirror the value of ρ thus found is that of the mirror as a whole, i.e. the light reflected from the front surface of the glass is included with that reflected by the metal. Since the reflection factor varies slightly with the angle of incidence of the light, this angle should always be stated with a value of reflection factor. For an angle of about 45° the arrangement shown in plan in Fig. 232 is convenient [8].

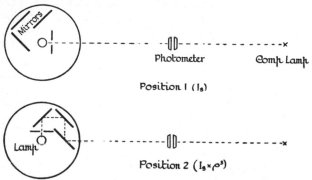

Fig. 232. The Measurement of Reflection Factor of a Mirror.

For most silvered mirrors of good quality the reflection factor is between 80 and 90 per cent and varies little with the colour of the light [9].

While, as has been said, the direct reflection factor is definite only in the case of a perfect mirror, it is nevertheless desirable for certain purposes to obtain a rough measure of the light reflected within a certain solid angle including the direction of direct reflection. Such a measurement may be made with an instrument of some specified design, often known as a " gloss-meter " [10] and the values obtained, although arbitrary, are comparable with one another so long as the same instrument is used. They are needed for such purposes as the control of the calendering process in paper manufacture, the description of the surface finish in paints or enamels, etc.

The Ingersoll Glarimeter [11], shown in Fig. 233, depends on the fact that directly reflected light is almost completely polarised in the

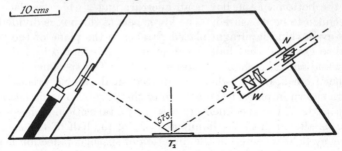

FIG. 233. The Glarimeter.

plane of incidence, while that diffusely reflected is unpolarised [12]. Light from a source subtending a certain small solid angle, approximately 0·038 steradian, illuminates the test surface at T_2, the light being incident at an angle of about 57·5°, the polarizing angle for paper. The Wollaston prism W (see p. 32) gives a double image of the slit S and is so set that the directly reflected light is completely extinguished in one image. The Nicol N is rotated until the two images are of equal luminance. In this case, if A is the angle of rotation of the Nicol, while D and S are the intensities of the diffuse and direct components within the angle of acceptance of the instrument,

$$\tfrac{1}{2}D/(\tfrac{1}{2}D+S)=\tan^2 A \quad \text{or} \quad S/(D+S)=\cos 2A,$$

i.e. of the light forming the images viewed in the eyepiece, the fraction which is directly reflected is equal to $\cos 2A$.

Instruments have been designed to measure the ratio of the luminance of the surface at the angle of direct reflection to that at some other angle (e.g. close to the direction of the incident light or along the normal) when the surface is illuminated by direct light at some definite angle of incidence, frequently 45°. Such is Trotter's

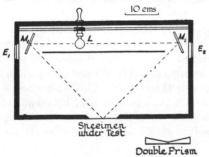

FIG. 234. Trotter's Gloss Tester.

Gloss Tester shown in Fig. 234. The lamp L can be moved, by means of a handle carrying a pointer, between the mirrors M_1, M_2. In the bottom of the box is an aperture under which is placed the specimen to be measured. The lower part of the box is divided into two by a thin diaphragm placed parallel to the plane of the paper, and so arranged that half the specimen is illuminated by light from M_1, and the other half by light from M_2. The specimen is viewed either from E_1 or E_2, where are placed small double prisms of the form shown in plan at the bottom of the figure. By this means the two parts of the specimen are seen in juxtaposition. The position of L is altered until the luminance (B_s) of the half of the specimen seen by light reflected in the direction of specular reflection is equal to the luminance (B_d) of the half seen from the direction of the incident light. The instrument is scaled to give directly, from the position of L, the value of $100B_s/(B_d + B_s)$ [13]. Jones's gloss meter is similar in principle but the surface is viewed normally instead of along the direction of incidence [14].

Reflection from Matt Surfaces—In the case of most surfaces, other than mirrors, the value of the reflection factor is, by itself, of little practical significance since it gives no information regarding the distribution of the reflected flux. What is frequently required is a knowledge of the luminance of the surface in one or more directions for specified conditions of illumination [15]. In the case of photographic papers, for example, the conditions usually specified are that the light should be incident at 45° and the surface viewed normally,* and special instruments, sometimes known as " reflection densitometers ", have been designed for making measurements of this kind [16]. Sometimes the area of the surface to be measured is very small and then the instrument used is an adaptation of a microphotometer (see p. 436, *infra*) [17].

The way in which the luminance of a surface varies, either with the conditions of illumination or, for constant illumination, with the direction of view, may be studied by an obvious adaptation of ordinary photometric procedure [18].

For illumination by direct light, the apparatus may be set up as shown in plan in Fig. 235 [19]. S is the test surface, mounted at one end of a photometer bench. It is illuminated by a lamp L_s which is carried on a radial arm capable of rotation through any desired angle about a vertical axis through S. The luminance of S is measured as described in Chapter XII (see p. 399) by means of a photometer P and comparison lamp L_c. The surface must be quite flat and the luminous intensity of L_s must be known if absolute values are required.

* These are also the conditions specified in colorimetry (see p. 338).

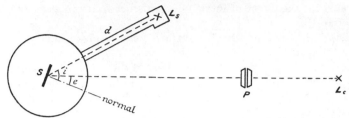

Fig. 235. The Measurement of Reflection Factor in a Single Direction.

The results are usually expressed in terms of the ratio of the luminance of the test surface to that of a perfect diffuser under the same conditions of illumination. This ratio is termed the " luminance factor " of the test surface for the specified conditions and for the particular angle of view (see p. 157) [20]. For the arrangement shown in Fig. 235, if i is the angle of incidence and I_s the luminous intensity of L_s, the illumination of S is $(I_s \cos i)/d^2$ and the luminance of a perfect diffuser substituted for S would be $(I_s \cos i)/\pi d^2$ candelas per unit area. If the measured luminance of S is B, the luminance factor $_i\beta_\epsilon$, for the angle of incidence i and angle of view ϵ on the same side of the normal, is equal to $B\pi d^2/(I_s \cos i)$. It is to be noted that in all cases, and especially if either ϵ or i is large, I_s must have a high value or the luminance to be measured will be too small (see p. 399).

The arrangement shown in Fig. 235 can be used for all conditions in which the direction of view is in the plane of incidence. For any other case it is necessary, either to raise or lower L_s, or to move L_s as before and to tilt S into such a position that the specified directions of incidence and of view are obtained.

A very convenient method of obtaining approximate values of β at various angles of view, both in the plane of incidence and in other planes, is that in which the reflecting surface is used as the test plate of a portable illumination photometer (see p. 400) [21]. Any convenient method may be used for positioning the instrument at known values of ϵ. The relative values thus obtained may be converted to absolute values by comparison with some standard surface for which β is known, or alternatively by a measurement of the absolute value of β is some *one* convenient position by means of the more accurate method first described.

The results obtained in this way for directions in a single plane may be expressed in the form of curves such as those of Fig. 205, p. 381. For directions in more than one plane a solid is necessary [22] or an isocandela diagram (see p. 126) may be used.

Sometimes, e.g. in the case of a powdered material, it is convenient to cover the surface with a sheet of glass. If this is done allowance must be made, not only for reflection losses at the glass surfaces, but also for the effect of inter-reflections between the glass and the material [23].

The luminance factor of a surface for any given angle of view when the incident light is perfectly diffused may be found by means of an ordinary integrating sphere. Part of the sphere wall is illuminated by means of a beam of light projected into the sphere and the test surface is placed against the wall in such a position that it can be viewed through the sphere window at the specified angle. A screen is placed so that no light can reach the test surface directly from the illuminated patch. The luminance of the surface as seen from the window is then measured, generally by means of a suitable visual illuminometer, and a similar measurement is made when a standard surface of known luminance factor, such as magnesium oxide, is substituted for the test surface [24].

The ratio of the luminance factors is approximately equal to the ratio of the two measured values of luminance, although a correction is necessary unless the test surface and the apertures in the sphere are very small or the luminance factor of the test surface does not greatly differ from that of the standard [25].

It is to be noted that the luminance factor thus measured is not the same as the reflection factor of the surface, unless the latter is a uniform diffuser or a perfect mirror ; for all other surfaces, even under diffuse illumination, the reflected light is not perfectly diffused and the luminance is not independent of the direction of view [26].

Nephelometry—When light passes through a slightly turbid or cloudy medium, part of it is obstructed by the particles causing the cloudiness. Some of this light is truly absorbed, while the remainder is scattered in all directions by reflection from the particles. It is this scattered light which renders visible the path of a beam of light traversing a dusty atmosphere. If the particles are small and their number not too great, so that the total cross-section of the beam is large compared with the total cross-section of the particles situated in its path, then the absorption factor of a given thickness of the medium bears a linear relation to the concentration of the particles. For a constant concentration the transmission factor varies with the length of path of the beam, according to the ordinary exponential law (see p. 160). When the dimensions of the particles are of the same order of magnitude as the wave-length of the light considered, $\tau = e^{-kt}$, where $k \equiv KN\lambda^{-n}$, N being the number of particles per unit volume, λ the wave-length [27], and n a constant whose value is 4 when the particles are small compared with λ. When, however, the particles are much larger, this law no longer holds and various empirical relations have been suggested [28]. These are useful for interpolating between the readings given by standard suspensions.

When the size of the particles and their concentration are both small, τ is very nearly equal to unity, and an accurate measure of concentration is therefore very difficult to obtain by this method. A much more convenient measure in this case is that of the light scattered in a direction making a definite angle (frequently 90°) with the direction of the beam [29]. This is the so-called Tyndall beam [30], and several instruments for making this measurement have been described [31] under the name of " Tyndall meters " or " nephelometers ".* That of Mecklenburg and Valentiner is shown in Fig. 236.

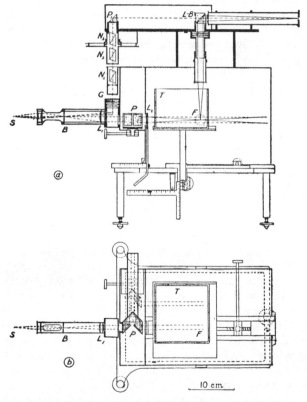

Fig. 236. The Nephelometer of Mecklenburg and Valentiner.

* The terminology appears to be somewhat confused at the present time. The name " nephelometer " has been used to designate an instrument for measuring the transmission factor (C. Chéneveau and R. Audubert, C.R., 170, *1920*, p. 728). This is more properly called an " opacimeter " (Lambert, F. Vlès and de Watteville, C.R., 168, *1919*, p. 797), although the name " turbidimeter " is sometimes used when the instrument is employed in connection with the study of suspensions, colloids, etc. (J. T. W. Marshall and H. W. Banks, Am. Phil. Soc., Proc., 54, *1915*, p. 176). Nephelometry proper, the measurement of the Tyndall beam, has also been called " Tyndallimetry " (S. E. Sheppard and F. A. Elliott, Am. Chem. Soc., J., 43, *1921*, p. 531).

The light from the source S is focused in the plane of B, a diaphragm with a small circular hole, which is completely filled with light. The beam from B is rendered parallel by the lens L_1 and is divided into two parts (Fig. 236 (a)), the lower of which, after suffering four total internal reflections in the prism system P (Fig. 236 (b)), traverses the lens L_2 and is brought to a focus at F, a point within the liquid under examination which is contained in the parallel-sided glass vessel T. The upper half of the beam from B illuminates a plaster screen G, which is seen through the three Nicols N_1, N_2 and N_3, the total reflection prism P_1, and the Lummer-Brodhun cube L-B. The other face of this cube is illuminated by the light scattered by the liquid at F in the vertical direction (i.e. at $90°$ to the original beam). Thus the luminance of the liquid at F is compared with that of the screen G, and photometric balance is obtained by rotating the Nicol N_2 about a vertical axis. The use of three Nicols avoids the possibility of error due to partial polarisation of the light transmitted at G. The vessel T is capable of an accurately measurable movement, both horizontal and vertical. By using the vertical movement it is possible to make measurements when F is at different depths below the surface of the liquid. The absorption of the Tyndall beam in the liquid itself can thus be allowed for by extrapolation. A small piece of auxiliary apparatus is provided for finding the height of F above the bottom of the vessel T. Measurements are also made with F at different distances from the " entrance " side of the vessel, and the results are again extrapolated to allow for absorption of the incident beam in the liquid.

An instrument for making measurements of the light scattered in various directions by atmospheric haze has been described [32].

Measurement of Transmission Factor of a Transparent Medium— A somewhat similar problem to that of measuring the reflection factor of a surface is the determination of the transmission factor of any substance, generally in the form of a plate. The transmission factor of a transparent plate is easily found by measuring the luminous intensity of a source with and without the plate between it and the photometer [33]. The value of τ thus found is that of the plate regarded as a unit, and not that of a certain thickness of the medium. The reflection factor per surface may usually be calculated with sufficient accuracy from the refractive index (see p. 156). If this is ρ, while τ is the actual transmission factor of the medium in a thickness equal to that of the plate, the light transmitted is easily seen to be $(1 - \rho)^2 \tau / (1 - \tau^2 \rho^2)$ (see p. 161). If $\rho = 0.04$, while $\tau = 0.5$, it will be seen that this value differs by a quite negligible quantity from $(1 - 2\rho)\tau$ [34]. It has to be remembered, in applying this method, that slight departures from planeness of the surfaces of the plate may produce large errors in the determination of the transmission factor owing to lens effects, unless the plate is placed quite near to the photometer (see p. 299). Allowance must be made for the effective shortening of the distance between the source and the photometer, due to refraction in the plate (see p. 24).

An alternative procedure is to measure the luminance of a uniform diffusing surface with and without the plate interposed. In this case, if the plate is near the diffusing surface allowance must be made for the inter-reflection of light between the two (see p. 229). Allowance for inter-reflections must also be made in determining the transmission factor of a system of two or more plates, etc., placed close to one another (see p. 230) [35].

Another method which, like the last, is independent of lens effects is shown diagrammatically in Fig. 237. The lens L forms an image

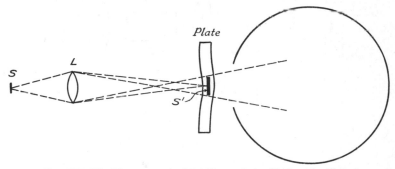

FIG. 237. The Measurement of the Transmission Factor of a Plate.

S' of a small, very bright source S and the whole of the flux from L enters an integrating sphere. The plate to be measured is then placed as shown, so that the image S' is formed within it. The spatial distribution of the flux after its passage through the plate is very little altered and the opening in the sphere is sufficiently large to allow all of it to enter the sphere. The ratio of the two values of flux, with and without the plate in position is the transmission factor of the plate [36].

The transmission factor of a body, like the reflection factor, naturally depends upon the spectral distribution of the incident light unless the body is neutral, i.e. has the same transmission factor at all wavelengths. The methods used for determining the spectral transmission curves of coloured media have been described in Chapter XI.

Many convenient self-contained instruments have been designed for measuring the transmission factor of a transparent medium. The underlying principle is, generally, to compare the intensities of two beams of light derived from the same source, after one of the beams has traversed the medium to be measured. A device is included, by means of which the intensity of one or both of the beams can be conveniently varied in a known manner. The comparison may be made either visually [37] or photo-electrically [38]. The use of a single source to provide both beams makes the measurement independent of the intensity of the source [39].

Such instruments are used in chemical analysis for measuring the concentrations of substances in solution. The transmission factor is then generally measured for light of a given colour, obtained by means of a colour filter with a fairly narrow transmission band [40]. For this reason, instruments used for this type of measurement are often erroneously referred to as " colorimeters " [41]. A typical photo-electric instrument is that shown in Fig. 238 [42]. L is the light

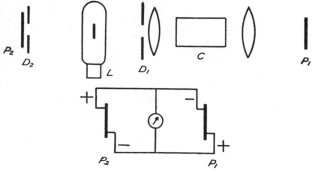

FIG. 238. The Measurement of the Transmission Factor of a Chemical Solution.

source, e.g. a 100-watt projector lamp, and C is the cell containing the solution to be measured. An approximately parallel beam, produced by the first convex lens, passes through C and is then ocused by means of the second convex lens on the surface of the photo-voltaic cell P_1. A second beam of light from L falls on another photocell P_2 in front of which is a variable diaphragm D_2. The two photocells are connected as in the lower part of the diagram and a sensitive galvanometer indicates the condition of balance. With C in place and the iris diaphragm D_1 opened to its full extent, D_2 is varied until the condition of balance is obtained. C is then removed and the aperture of D_1 is reduced until the balance is restored, D_2 remaining unaltered. The transmission factor of C is then equal to the ratio of the intensities of the collimated beam at the two positions of D_1. The scale associated with the movement controlling D_1 may be calibrated by means of plates of known transmission factors ; for many purposes a scale of densities is more convenient than one of transmission factors. It will be seen that the illumination of both photocells remains constant throughout a determination, apart from variations in the intensity of L, so that similarity of the response characteristics of the cells is required only over the small range covered by such variations [43]. When it is desired to make the measurements for light of a given colour, the appropriate portion of the spectrum is selected by means of a suitable colour filter placed in the path of the beam traversing the solution, an exactly similar filter being placed in the path of the beam reaching P_2 [44].

Measurement of the Transmission Factor of a Diffusing Medium— When the medium itself, or either bounding surface is even slightly diffusing, the above methods can no longer be applied, and some procedure similar to that described for the measurement of diffuse reflection factor must be used [45]. In the case of direct light incident at some specified angle, the medium is placed over an aperture in the side of an integrating sphere, as shown in Fig. 239 [46]. The beam of light used for illuminating the medium must be of a high intensity, and its cross-section must be considerably smaller than the aperture in the sphere. The illumination of a window in the side of the sphere, or the luminance of a portion of the sphere surface not directly illuminated, is measured with and without the medium in place [47]. The ratio of these two values is the

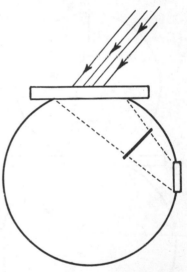

FIG. 239. The Measurement of the Transmission Factor of a Diffusing Plate.

transmission factor of the medium, to an approximation which depends both on the ratio of the size of the aperture to that of the whole surface of the sphere and on the reflection factor of the medium. The difference is due to the fact that the average reflection factor of the sphere is slightly higher when the aperture is covered than when it is open. This can be allowed for by making a subsidiary pair of measurements of the luminance of the sphere window when a portion of the sphere wall is illuminated, e.g. from a side tube, as shown in Fig. 230. The ratio of the value with the aperture open to that when it is covered with the medium is the correction factor to be applied to the approximate value of transmission factor obtained as described above.

For many purposes, the distribution of the light transmitted through a diffusing medium is important [48] and, by an obvious modification of the methods used for determining the luminance factor of a reflecting surface, the luminance factor of a diffusing plate for transmitted light may be measured for any specified conditions of incidence and for any angle of view. In the case of transmission the luminance factor is the ratio of the luminance of the surface to that of a perfect diffuser under the same conditions of illumination and for the same *angle* (but not direction) of view.

For measuring the transmission factor of a medium when the incident light is diffused, two spheres are used as shown in Fig. 240 [49].

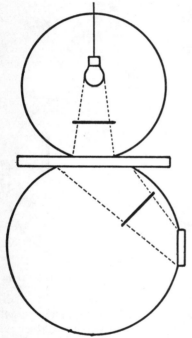

One is provided with a source of light screened from the aperture through which the medium is illuminated. Two measurements of the luminance of a window in the second sphere are made as before, one with the medium in place and the other with it removed. The effect of reflection from the medium is allowed for as in the case of direct incidence. It is to be noted that the aperture of the illuminating sphere is smaller than that of the sphere into which the light is transmitted. This is to allow for the " edge effect " caused by diffusion of light within the substance of the medium.

The light transmitted through a gas or liquid containing fine particles in suspension is sometimes used as a measure of the particle concentration. A collimated beam of light, after passing

FIG. 240. The Measurement of the Transmission Factor of a Plate (Diffused Incident Light).

through the suspension, illuminates a photocell and the value of the illumination, for a given initial beam intensity, can be related to the particle concentration by calibration of the apparatus with known concentrations [50]. This method is often used in preference to nephelometry when the amount of light scattered by the particles is large (see footnote on p. 429). In the case of the atmosphere, the measurement made is usually that of visibility (see p. 165) unless, as in the photometry of large projection apparatus, it is the loss of light due both to absorption and to scatter, that is required. The transmission factor over a short distance is then necessarily high and the measurement is made with a telephotometer, as described in a later section of this chapter (see p. 444).

Density of Photographic Images—A special problem in the measurement of transmission factors is the determination of the degree of darkening of an exposed photographic plate. This is of importance not only in general photographic sensitometry, but also in those branches of photometry where photographic methods are employed, such as stellar photometry (see p. 480), the study of line spectra, etc.

Photographic sensitometry consists, briefly, in exposing an area of a photographic plate to a known illumination for certain fixed periods of time and developing in a specified manner, the temperature and other conditions being controlled throughout [51]. The transmission of the exposed area of the plate is then measured and expressed as a density [52]. As the exposed emulsion acts to a certain extent as a diffuser, the value obtained varies somewhat according to the degree to which the incident light is diffused [53]. The measurement is therefore often made with a sheet of opal glass placed behind the plate, so as to diffuse the incident light, the density measured under these conditions being known as the " diffuse density " [54].

Instruments designed specially for measuring photographic densities are generally called " densitometers ". The best known visual densitometer is a modification of the Martens photometer (see p. 204) in which the brightness of a piece of opal glass viewed through the photographic plate is compared with that of a diffusely reflecting surface viewed directly, both opal glass and reflecting surface being illuminated by the same lamp [55].

A number of other visual densitometers have been designed [56] but in modern instruments some form of photocell is almost invariably employed [57]. The photo-electric densitometer developed by the British Photographic Research Association [58] is shown diagrammatically in Fig. 241. Two beams of light from the lamp L pass respectively through the photographic plate P and through the neutral wedge W to two windows in the photocell C which are covered with the opal plates D_1 and D_2. A cylindrical shutter S with a quadrant aperture revolves round the lamp, so that the photocell is successively exposed to the two beams and W can be adjusted to the position of equality. The instrument is calibrated by placing a series of known densities successively at P.

Sometimes it is necessary to map the lines of equal density on a photographic plate, these corresponding to lines of equal luminance

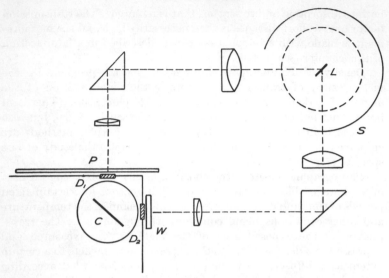

FIG. 241. The B.P.R.A. Densitometer.

in the scene photographed [59]. Special forms of densitometer, have been designed for work of this kind [60].

Microphotometry, or Microdensitometry—In such work as photographic stellar photometry, the measurement of the intensities of spectral lines by photography (see p. 365), or the examination of the sound track on kinematograph film [61], it is necessary to measure the density at any point of a photographic image [62]. Since the variation of density from point to point is frequently very rapid, the problem really reduces to that of measuring the transmision factor of an exceedingly small area of the plate and the instrument used for this purpose is called a " microphotometer " or, better, a " microdensitometer ". Microphotometry also provides a method of testing the performance of any type of photographic emulsion as regards sharpness of image [63].

The first microphotometer was that of Hartmann [64], shown diagrammatically in vertical section in Fig. 242. P is the plate under examination, supported on an ebonite table L, over the surface of which it can be moved at will so as to bring any desired portion of P into the centre of the field of the microscope ABG. This microscope has a common eyepiece A with a second horizontal microscope ABD. At B is a glass cube, constructed after the manner of a Lummer-Brodhun cube, as shown in detail at the top of the figure. The image of that part of the plate to be measured is brought to a focus at the centre of the side ab of this cube, and is viewed at A by total reflection

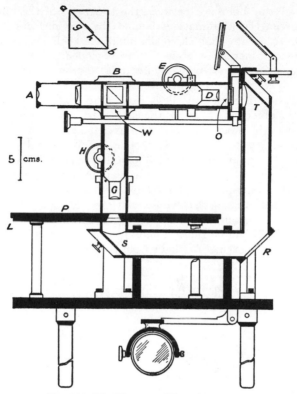

Fig. 242. The Hartmann Microphotometer.

from the silvered part *gh*. The comparison surface *O* is focused by means of *E*, at the same point, and is viewed by transmission through *ag* and *hb*. The silvered area *gh* may conveniently be elliptical in form so as to appear circular from *A*. Its apparent diameter must depend on the size of the area of *P* to be included, and on the magnification produced by *G*. The latter may conveniently be as high as 12. The plate is covered with an opaque diaphragm in which is an aperture so small that only a portion of the plate very slightly larger than that imaged on *gh* is exposed. This prevents error due to the Schwarzchild-Villiger effect, i.e. increase of brightness of the area being measured, due to light from the surrounding areas reflected by the microscope objective [65].

The comparison surface at *O* is a neutral wedge which is moved until a photometric balance is obtained. It may be calibrated by inserting filters of known transmission factor in place of *P*. The use of a substitution method such as this avoids the necessity for correcting for the difference between the two parts of the microscope and between the illuminations behind the two surfaces P and O. In order to secure that these illuminations shall bear a constant ratio to each other, the system SRT is employed. This consists of a matt translucent glass plate R, illuminated from outside the tube either by daylight or by an artificial source, and two silvered mirrors S and T, which reflect the light from R to P and O respectively. One of the objections to the Hartmann instrument is that, owing to the considerable magnification necessary, the grains of silver in the image may become separately visible. This difficulty has been overcome [66] by the insertion at W of a diaphragm with a very small aperture, upon which is focused the part of P under examination. The silvered part of the prism B is then diffusely illuminated by light from that region of P whose image covers the aperture in W.

Another instrument in which the Maxwellian view (see p. 152) is employed is the Fabry-Buisson microphotometer [67] shown diagrammatically in Fig. 243. The light from the illuminated aperture A is

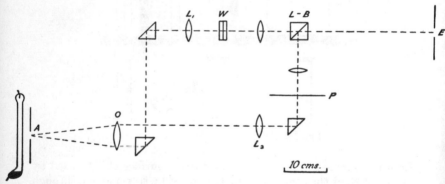

FIG. 243. The Fabry-Buisson Microphotometer.

rendered parallel by the lens O, and one-half of the resulting beam is brought to a focus by the lens L_2 at the point of the plate P which is being measured. A second image of A is similarly formed by O and L_1 at a point of the neutral wedge W. The two beams of light from these images are brought to a common focus at the eyepiece E, one by reflection, and the other by transmission in the Lummer-Brodhun cube L-B. Since the aperture in E is sufficiently small to act as a stop to both beams, the brightness of each of the two comparison surfaces in L-B appears uniform. In making a measurement the transmission of W is altered until a photometric balance is obtained in L-B. Since no microscope is used in this instrument, it is not possible to examine as small an area of plate as in the case of the Hartmann microphotometer.

In all the later types of microphotometer, the eye is replaced by a physical instrument, generally a photocell. A small area of one side of the plate under examination is strongly illuminated, e.g. by focusing on it, or on a piece of opal glass close to it, the image of a lamp filament. The light transmitted by a small portion of the illuminated area, isolated by means of a diaphragm with a tiny aperture, is measured by means of a photocell [68]. Alternatively, by the use of a microscope objective close to the plate, a magnified image of the illuminated area may be formed on a diaphragm with a small opening behind which is the photocell [69]. In either arrangement the only light reaching the photocell is that transmitted by an exceedingly small area of the plate and in fact the density of an area only a few thousandths of a millimetre across can be measured. The measurement may be made directly, the instrument being calibrated by means of a neutral wedge or a series of known densities, or a balance method may be used to eliminate the effect of small fluctuations in the intensity of the light source. In this case the cell is alternately illuminated by light transmitted through the plate and by that transmitted through a variable wedge, the same lamp being used to supply both beams. The cell is used only to indicate the position of the wedge at which equality is obtained. An instrument of this kind is shown

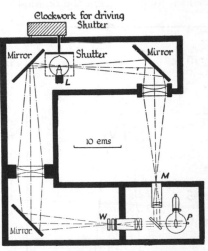

FIG. 244. The Photo-electric Densitometer.

in Fig. 244 [70]. L is a concentrated filament lamp round which a shutter revolves in such a way as to interrupt in turn the two beams of light which respectively traverse the plate M and the variable wedge W before reaching the photocell P.

In some instruments a diascope projection system is used to throw a much enlarged image of the plate, or a portion of it, on a screen with a small opening behind which is a photocell [71]. Thus the photocell receives only the light transmitted by that area on the plate which corresponds to the portion of image covering the opening in the screen. The advantage of this type of instrument is the facility with which any desired portion of the plate may be brought into position for measurement.

The Recording Microphotometer—The first photo-electric micro-photometer, that of P. P. Koch [72], was designed to give a continuous record of the density variations along any given line on a photographic plate. The plate was moved through the focused light beam in the direction required (e.g. perpendicular to the lines in a spectrum photograph or in the direction of travel of a sound track) and this movement, suitably magnified, was communicated to a photographic film, or strip of sensitive paper, on which the deflection of the instrument measuring the photocurrent was automatically recorded. In this way a graph of the density of the plate along the line of travel could be obtained with a speed depending only on the characteristics of the photocell and associated circuit [73].

Many other recording microphotometers have since been described, differing from the original instrument and from each other

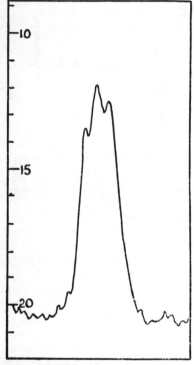

FIG. 245. Microphotometer Record of a Spectral Line.

in various respects, particularly in the type of photocell employed and the circuit used for measuring the photocurrent [74]. Although some instruments have been designed with the photo-voltaic type of photocell [75], the photo-emissive type is more commonly used since amplification of the photocurrent is then possible. In the Koch micro-photometer the measuring circuit used with the photo-cell is such that the indication obtained is independent of small variations in the luminous intensity of the light source, but in most other instruments an ordinary measuring circuit, with or without amplification, is employed and precautions must be taken to ensure the constancy of the source. In one instrument a section of the density curve can be obtained immediately as a trace on the screen of a cathode ray tube [76].

In several recording micro-photometers, notably the Moll, a thermopile is used in place of a photocell, but the general principle is otherwise the same [77]. The thermopile is of the vacuum type (described on p. 48) in order to obtain the maximum sensitivity, as no amplification of the current is possible.

Very fine detail can be resolved with a well-designed microphotometer. The example of a record shown in Fig. 245 was obtained with a magnification of 160, the breadth of the spectral line on the original photograph being about 0·14 mm. For ordinary work, however, magnifications of between 5 and 50 are generally sufficient. The micrometer screw by which the plate is moved across the light beam must be accurate and accurately geared to the recording chart. In one instrument the chart remains stationary and the galvanometer is rotated bodily by the movement of the plate [78]. The instrument may be calibrated, i.e. the density scale on the chart may be established, by the use of a series of accurately known densities [79]. Every precaution must be taken to exclude from the photocell or thermopile any light scattered by those parts of the plate which are close to the area being measured [80].

It should be noticed that in the microphotometry of very fine detail there is an inherent source of error, analogous to the error in spectrophotometry arising from the use of a finite slit width (see p. 367) [81]. This will be clear from Fig. 246. If curve A represents the true transmission curve of a line on the plate, the effective " slit width " of the microphotometer being 10 units, then the density assigned to the point A will be the mean ordinate within the region BC, so that the values obtained on a convex portion of the curve are too low, and those on

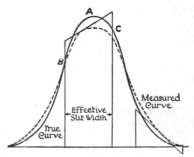

FIG. 246. The " Slit-width " Error in Microphotometry.

a concave portion are too high. The maximum density of a line, therefore, is always reduced, unless the size of the microphotometer field is very small compared with the breadth of the line.

Instruments have been devised to measure directly the density gradient at any part of a photographic record, or the difference of density between two neighbouring areas [82].

The Transmission of Optical Systems—For measuring the transmission factor of a lens or other optical system, special methods have to be used [83]. The most direct is to measure the luminance B_1 of the image formed by the system when the object is an extended diffusing surface of known luminance B_0. Since with any optical system of transmission factor unity $B_1 = B_0$ [84], it follows that in any actual system $\tau = B_1/B_0$. This method, as applied to a simple lens, is illus-

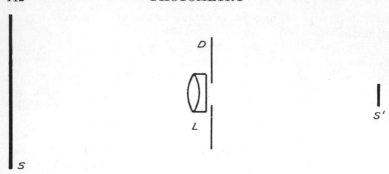

FIG. 247. The Measurement of the Transmission of an Optical System
by means of an Extended Surface.

trated in Fig. 247. S is the extended bright surface, L the lens, D an opaque diaphragm with an aperture of suitable size (i.e. the area of the exit pupil in the case of an optical system such as a telescope) and S' a photometer surface. The illumination at S' is measured with and without the lens in place and the ratio of the two values is the transmission factor required [85]. This method is open to the objection that stray light may be included in the illumination of S' when the optical system is in place [86]. Further it is important that the luminance of S, at least over the whole of the area visible from S' through D, should be quite uniform since the area which produces the illumination at S' is less when the lens is in place than when it is removed.

These difficulties are largely avoided in the method illustrated in Fig. 248 [87]. S is now a small hole in a diaphragm, on which is

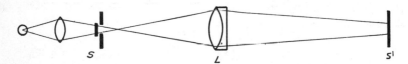

FIG. 248. The Measurement of the Transmission of an Optical System.

formed an image of a source of light of high brightness, e.g. a ribbon filament lamp or a discharge lamp of the compact source type. An enlarged image of this hole is formed on the photometer surface S' by means of the optical system under examination and the illumination of this image (E_1) is measured. The optical system is then removed and the illumination of the photometer surface (E_2) by direct light from S is measured. The ratio E_1/E_2 is equal to the product of the transmission factor of the optical system (τ) and the lens factor of that system, which is obtained by calculation from dimensions [88].

If θ' is the angle between the axis of the optical system and the most oblique ray reaching the image, the flux from S which would, in the absence of absorption, reach S' is that emitted by S within an angle θ where $\sin \theta = m \sin \theta'$, m being the linear magnification of the image at S' [89]. If θ is small, as is generally the case, this flux is equal to $aB \sin^2 \theta$ where a is the area of S and B its luminance. The transmitted flux is distributed over an area m^2a so that the illumination E_1 is $(\tau B\pi \sin^2 \theta)/m^2 = \tau B\pi \sin^2 \theta'$. E_2 is clearly equal to aB/d^2, where d is the distance between S and S', so that

$$E_1/E_2 = (\tau\pi \sin^2 \theta') \, d^2/a.$$

In the case of a lens of radius r, for example, $E_1/E_2 = \tau\pi r^2 (u + v)^2/av^2$ where u and v are respectively the distances of the lens from S and S', for in this case $\sin \theta'$ is approximately equal to r/v. When θ and θ' are not small, the lens factor has been calculated for an optical system with a circular exit pupil [90] The method illustrated in Fig. 237 has also been used for measuring the transmission factor of a lens [91].

In the case of a telescope system the transmission factor may be measured by what is, in effect, a modification of the method first described above [92]. A uniformly bright diffusing surface is placed close to the eyepiece and the luminance of the objective is measured, e.g. with a portable photometer. The ratio of this luminance to that of the diffusing surface at the eyepiece is equal to the transmission factor of the instrument. A modification of the second method has also been used for making the measurements either visually [93] or photo-electrically [94].

It is often important to determine the transmission factor of an optical system, such as a spectrometer, in which the light is dispersed into a spectrum. In this case monochromatic light must be used for the measurement. This may be obtained from a source such as a discharge lamp with a suitable filter or from a monochromator. In the latter case the general procedure is to measure with a photocell, or a thermopile, or otherwise, the flux emerging from the exit slit of the monochromator and then cause it to pass through the spectrometer being examined, both slits in this instrument being large enough not to act as stops but narrow enough to cut out stray light. The flux emerging from the exit slit of the spectrometer is then measured and the ratio of this to the flux emerging from the monochromator is the transmission factor of the spectrometer for light of the particular wave-length used [95].

The Measurement of Absorption Factor—For all practical purposes it may be said that there is no method of measuring the absorption factor of a substance directly, since there is no means of evaluating the light unless it can be caused to illuminate a photometric test surface. It follows, then, that absorption can only be measured as a difference, using the relation $\rho + \alpha + \tau = 1$. In the case of an opaque substance $\tau = 0$ and $\alpha = 1 - \rho$, so that all that is necessary is a measurement of reflection factor. Since, in general, the reflection factor of a surface depends on the direction and colour of the incident light, so also must the absorption factor similarly depend on these variables. In the case of a transparent or translucent body, both ρ and τ must be measured in order that α may be found. For a truly transparent body $\rho = 0$, except at the surface, so that $\alpha = 1 - \tau$ when surface effects have been allowed for in the measurement of τ. Although α is thus found indirectly from a measurement of τ, it is for many purposes a far more convenient constant to use, since for transparent bodies it is connected with the thickness by the simple exponential relationship given in Chapter V (p. 160).

Atmospheric Absorption—When objects have to be illuminated from considerable distances, or when a luminous object has to be viewed from afar, the absorption of light by the atmosphere, in reality a combination of true absorption and scatter, becomes very important. It has, too, to be taken into account when making photometric measurements over considerable ranges in the open (see p. 466, Chapter XIV). It is therefore necessary to have some means of measuring the transmission factor of a certain length of the atmosphere at any given time. One of the chief difficulties of the measurement lies in the fact that when the absorption is most important it is most liable to rapid and extensive fluctuations [96]. In its simplest form the apparatus used for this measurement consists of (i) an evenly illuminated surface set up at a convenient distance (of the order of half a mile) from the observing station, and large enough to fill completely the field of view of (ii) an instrument capable of measuring luminance. If the size of the surface is not to be prohibitive (e.g. more than 10 ft. square) an ordinary portable illumination photometer cannot be used for the luminance measurement at a distance of more than about 200 yards, except by the use of an undesirably small aperture. In general, therefore, a telescope is used. An image of the illuminated surface is formed in the focal plane of the eyepiece (see Fig. 249), and in this plane is an opaque white diaphragm illuminated by a comparison lamp. The aperture in this diaphragm is slightly smaller than the image of the illuminated surface, so that the eye sees a continuous field. A photometric balance is obtained by varying the illumination of the comparison surface.

If a telescope with an objective of 3 ft. focal length is used, a 10-ft. screen at a distance of half a mile gives an image which will fill an aperture of $\frac{1}{8}$ inch diameter. Such an instrument is called a " telephotometer " [97].

Other methods than that just described may be used for measuring the luminance of the image of the distant surface [98]. For example, a simple Lummer-Brodhun cube of the kind shown in Fig. 112 may be used (so long as the central area of contact is sufficiently small for the image to fill it completely) and the comparison field may be a sheet of opal glass, the luminance of which is varied by means of a neutral wedge or in any other convenient manner.

An instrument of this type is calibrated by placing it sufficiently near to the distant screen for atmospheric absorption to be neglected and then determining the relation between the telephotometer readings and the luminance of the screen, measured independently. The exit pupil of the instrument must be the same during the calibration as when measurements are being made, so that an artificial pupil, small enough to act as a stop under both conditions, must be placed at the eyepiece [99].

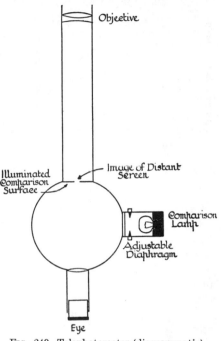

Fig. 249. Telephotometer (diagrammatic).

A disadvantage of this type of telephotometer is that the light scattered towards the photometer by the particles between it and the comparison surface causes the brightness of the latter to be increased. This defect is overcome in an instrument which measures the contrast between the comparison surface and its background [100]. The lens O (Fig. 250) forms an image of the comparison surface (which must have a sharp edge and a non-luminous background) on the translucent screen S, behind which is placed a black disc of such a size and shape that the image *exactly* fits it. The screen is illuminated from behind by the comparison lamp L. The photometric balance is obtained by moving L or (as shown) by using a variable diaphragm D over O. If B represents the luminance of the image of the comparison surface, it follows that $B\rho = B'$, where ρ is the reflection factor of the screen S and B' is its luminance due to transmitted light. It is assumed that the "haze" due to scattered light is

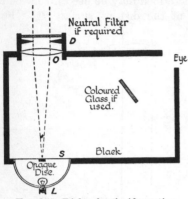

FIG. 250. Richardson's Absorption Photometer.

sufficiently uniform to produce an equal increase of luminance on both sides of the edge of the image, so that it does not affect the photometric balance. If measurements at different parts of the spectrum are required, colour filters may be placed in front of the eye.

An altogether different type of telephotometer is one which depends on measuring the light from a distant "point" source of known luminous intensity. Any of the stellar photometers described in Chapter XV could be used [101] but the instrument of this type which has been most frequently employed for making measurements of atmospheric transmission is that shown diagrammatically in Fig. 251 [102]. It depends upon the use of the Maxwellian view (see p. 152) so that no screen is required but a lamp L_1 of known

luminous intensity I_1 is placed at the distant station. O_1 is a telescope objective, which forms an image of L_1 at the position of the observer's eye E. L-B is a Lummer-Brodhun cube, which enables a comparison to be made between the luminance of O_1 and that of O_2, another objective, which forms at E an image of L_2, a local comparison lamp. The luminance of O_2 is varied by means of a pair

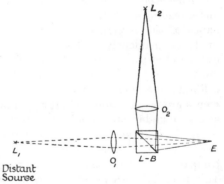

L₂

O₂

L₁

O₁

L-B

E

Distant Source

FIG. 251. The Telephotometer with Maxwellian View.

of Nicol prisms or a neutral wedge (not shown) placed between L_2 and O_2. The luminance of the lens surface as seen from E is equal to $\tau I_1 v^2/u^2$ where u and v represent respectively $O_1 L_1$ and $O_1 E$ and τ is the transmission factor of the lens (see p. 152). But $\dfrac{1}{v} = \dfrac{1}{f} - \dfrac{1}{u}$, so that this expression becomes $\tau I_1 f^2/(u-f)^2$. It is to be noted that this formula holds only so long as the image of each source is smaller than the pupil of the eye, so that the latter does not act as a stop. Further, if the image exceeds about 1 mm. in diameter a correction is necessary on account of the Stiles-Crawford effect (see p. 59) [103].

To measure the atmospheric transmission over a given range two lamps of known luminous intensities, I_1 and I_2, are required. One is placed at the far point, distant u_1 from the observing station, while the other is placed at a much shorter distance u_2 at which atmospheric absorption is negligible. The ratio of the telephotometer readings on the two lamps is $(1 - \alpha) I_1 (u_2 - f)^2 / I_2 (u_1 - f)^2$ where α is the atmospheric absorption over the distance $(u_1 - u_2)$. To avoid having to make the Stiles-Crawford correction, u_2 should be large compared with the size of the lamp. For example, the image will not exceed 0·5 mm. in diameter if u_2 is greater than $f(2D + 1)$ where D is the diameter of the lamp in mm.

Both the principles described above have been used in the design of photo-electric telephotometers. An image of a distant illuminated surface may be formed in the plane of a diaphragm by means of a telescope system ; the light passing through a small aperture completely filled by the image is then measured with a multiplier photocell [104]. Alternatively, the telescope may be used to form an image of a distant source of light within the aperture, so that an out-of-focus image is formed on a photo-emissive cell. If the source is replaced by a small projector system, the instrument becomes identical with that shown in Fig. 261 (p. 466) [105].

Instruments have been designed in which a mirror placed at the distant station reflects to a photometer a beam of light from a powerful source near the photometer. The reflected beam is then compared with a direct beam from the source [106]. The mirror should be optically worked to avoid lens effects. Sometimes it takes the form of a " corner cube ", i.e. three triangular mirrors arranged mutually at right angles so that the light reaching them is always returned on its original path.

The atmospheric absorption over a given range in the beam of a projector, such as a searchlight, may be determined by measuring the illumination produced by the projector at each end of the range (see p. 407) [107]. A somewhat similar method is to measure the total flux in a beam of very small divergence before and after it has traversed a known distance [108].

Variation of Absorption with Colour—The absorption factor of a misty atmosphere is different for light of different frequencies. The factor at any spectral region may be found by using a suitable colour screen in the eyepiece of either of the instruments described in the last section. Alternatively, a spectrophotometric method may be used over short ranges (of the order of one-half mile). The light

from a powerful source is collimated by a suitable lens and projected
to a mirror placed at the distant station. The reflected beam is then
returned to the near station and compared with the original light
from the source by means of a spectrophotometer [109]. The mirror
must be of such a size, relative to the collimating lens, that it does
not act as a stop in the optical system.

REFERENCES

1. F. A. Benford. Gen. El. Rev., 23, *1920*, p. 72.
   A. H. Taylor. Opt. Soc. Am., J., 4, *1920*, p. 9.
   E. Karrer. *Ibid.*, 5, *1921*, p. 96.
   R. Ulbricht. Z. f. Bel., 27, *1921*, p. 51.
   Z. Yamauti. · Japan Science Rev., 2, *1951*, p. 11.
   J. A. Jacquez *et al.* Opt. Soc. Am., J., 45, *1955*, pp. 460 and 971 ; 46, *1956*,
p. 428 (see also p. 343).
   See also T. Royds, Phil. Mag., 21, *1911*, p. 167 ; W. W. Coblentz, Bureau of
Standards, Bull., 9, *1913*, p. 283 ; P. G. Nutting, Illum. Eng. Soc. N.Y., Trans., 7,
1912, p. 412 ; A. Adderley and M. O. Pelton, Textile Inst., J., 20, *1929*, p. T203 ;
H. E. Beckett, Phys. Soc., Proc., 43, *1931*, p. 227 ; P. Selényi, Licht u. Lampe, 20,
1931, p. 147 ; H. J. Helwig, Licht, 7, *1937*, pp. 99, 119 and 140.
   The treatment given in the text follows that of A. H. Taylor. A more exact treat-
ment, leading to rather more complex expressions, has been given by J. S. Preston
(Opt. Soc., Trans., 31, *1930*, p. 15).

2. A. H. Taylor. Illum. Eng. Soc. N.Y., Trans., 15, *1920*, p. 811 ; Opt. Soc.
Am., J., 25, *1935*, p. 51.
   G. R. Baumgartner. Gen. El. Rev., 40, *1937*, p. 525.

3. The diffuse reflection factors of MgO and of $MgCO_3$ have been found to be 0·991
and 0·983 respectively (F. Benford, G. P. Lloyd and S. Schwarz, Opt. Soc. Am., J.,
38, *1948*, p. 145). See also J. S. Preston, Opt. Soc., Trans., 31, *1930*, p. 15.

4. A. H. Taylor. Opt. Soc. Am., J., 4, *1920*, p. 9.
   E. Karrer. *Ibid.*, 5, *1921*, p. 96.
   See also F. Benford, Opt. Soc. Am., J., 24, *1934*, p. 165 ; F. Mäder, Assn. Suisse
des Elect., Bull., 38, *1947*, p. 632.

5. H. J. McNicholas. Bureau of Standards, J. of Research, 1, *1928*, p. 29 and
13, *1934*, p. 211.
   J. M. Waldram. C.I.E., Proc., 7, *1928*, p. 1020.
   See also M. Luckiesh, Opt. Soc. Am., J., 2–3, *1919*, p. 39.

6. See, e.g., Illum. Eng. Soc. N.Y., Trans., 10, *1915*, pp. 353 *et seqq.*

7. J. W. T. Walsh. " The Making of Reflecting Surfaces," Phys. and Opt. Socs.,
1920, p. 38.
   J. H. Dowell. J. Sci. Inst., 10, *1933*, p. 153.
   See also A. Marsat, Rev. d'Opt., 7, *1928*, p. 41 ; J. Clavier, *ibid.*, 8, *1929*, p. 379;
M. Duffieux, *ibid.*, 11, *1932*, p. 212 ; F. Benford and W. A. Ruggles, Opt. Soc. Am., J.,
32, *1942*, p. 174 ; E. Kappler, Phys. Z., 44, *1943*, p. 83.

8. See also P. Lob, Z. f. techn. Phys., 11, *1930*, p. 202 ; H. C. Burger and J. B.
van Milaan, Physica, 6, *1939*, p. 435 ; J. Terrien, Rev. d'Opt., 23, *1944*, p. 105.

9. E. Hagen and H. Rubens. Ann. d. Phys., 1, *1900*, p. 352.
   W. W. Coblentz. Bureau of Standards, Bull., 16, *1920*, p. 249.

10. V. G. W. Harrison. *The Definition and Measurement of Gloss* (Patra, London,
1945).
   R. S. Hunter. Bureau of Standards, J. of Research, 18, *1937*, p. 19 (contains
an extensive bibliography of the subject of gloss, methods of measuring it and their
applications).
   H. K. Hammond and I. Nimeroff. Bureau of Standards, J. of Research, 44,
1950, p. 585.
   W. E. K. Middleton and A. G. Mungall. Canadian J. of Technol., 31, *1953*,
p. 160.
   A general treatment of the subject, with bibliography, is also given in a paper
by B. Voigt (Archiv. f. techn. Messen, *1932*. T85).

See also G. I. Pokrowski, Z. f. techn. Phys., 10, *1929*, p. 327 ; R. Kempf and J. Flügge, Z.f.I., 49, *1929*, p. 1 ; J. Flügge, Licht u. Lampe, 18, *1929*, p. 328 ; A. H. Pfund, Opt. Soc. Am., J., 20, *1930*, p. 23 ; L. Kenworthy and J. M. Waldram, Inst. of Metals, J., 55, *1934*, p. 247 ; L. Bergmann, Z. f. techn. Phys., 14, *1933*, p. 157 ; R. S. Hunter, Opt. Soc. Am., J., 26, *1936*, p. 190 ; R. F. Hanstock, Oil and Colour Chem. Assn., J., 20, *1937*, p. 91 ; Salford Elect. Insts., Ltd., J. Sci. Inst., 14, *1937*, p. 32 ; E. E. Jelpke, J. Sci. Inst., 15, *1938*, p. 181 ; R. J. Myers, Industrial and Engn. Chem. (Anal. Ed.), 12, *1940*, p. 678 ; J. Guild, J. Sci. Inst., 17, *1940*, p. 178 ; R. S. Hunter, Opt. Soc. Am., J., 36, *1946*, p. 178 ; E. A. Ollard, Electrodepositors' Techn. Soc., J., 24, *1949*, p. 1.

11. L. R. Ingersoll. Opt. Soc. Am., J., 5, *1921*, p. 213.

12. For this reason a polarisation type of photometer is unsuitable for measuring reflection factors. See, e.g., V. Návrat, Wien Ber. (IIa), 121, *1912*, p. 1289.

13. A. P. Trotter. Illum. Eng., 8, *1915*, p. 425.

14. L. A. Jones. Opt. Soc. Am., J., 6, *1922*, p. 140.
See also H. Schulz, Z. f. techn. Phys., 5, *1924*, p. 135 ; G. A. Shook, Opt. Soc. Am., J., 9, *1924*, p. 61 ; W. Ewald, Instruments, 1, *1928*, p. 111 ; G. A. Shook, Rev. Sci Inst., 3, *1932*, p. 553 ; C. W. Kendall, *ibid.*, 3, *1932*, p. 668.

15. R. Joschek. Siemens Z., 13, *1933*, p. 110.
R. E. V. Hampson and H. W. Richards. Textile Inst., J., 25, *1934*, p. T106.
J. L. Michaelson. Gen. El. Rev., 38, *1935*, p. 194.
R. S. Hunter. Bureau of Standards, J. of Research, 25, *1940*, p. 581.
A form of gauge for making approximate estimates of reflection factors has been described by O. Knoll and R. G. Weigel (Licht, 1, *1930*, pp. 60 and 85).

16. H. M. Cartwright and C. D. Hallam. J. Sci. Inst., 3, *1926*, p. 247.
G. Schwarz. Photog. Korrespondenz, 67, *1931*, p. 63.
C. W. Kendall. Rev. Sci. Inst., 3, *1932*, p. 668.
W. Bollmann. Z. wiss. Photog., 33, *1934*, p. 167.
J. W. McFarlane. Opt. Soc., Am., J., 24, *1934*, p. 19.
W. B. Ferguson and S. Read. Photog. J., 74, *1934*, p. 249.
R. E. Owen and E. R. Davies. *Ibid.*, p. 463.
E. R. Davies and R. E. Owen. *Ibid.*, 75, *1935*, p. 128.
C. A. Morrison and J. W. McFarlane. Opt. Soc. Am., J., 25, *1935*, p. 417.
N. M. Mohler and D. A. Taylor. Opt. Soc. Am., J., 26, *1936*, p. 386.
W. Falta. Z. wiss. Photog., 37, *1938*, p. 247.
A. C. Poulter. J. Sci. Inst., 18, *1941*, p. 166.
H. Nitka and D. W. Stammers. *Science and Applications of Photography* (Roy. Photog. Soc., *1955*), p. 233.
See also H. R. Hindley and E. J. Leaton, Rev. Sci. Inst., 26, *1949*, p. 396.

17. B. Lange. Sprechsaal, 65, *1932*, p. 293.
On the necessity for making allowance for inter-reflections between the sample and the microscope objective, see, e.g., L. Capdecomme, C.R., 202, *1936*, p. 1843.

18. See, e.g., P. Bouguer, *Traité d'Optique*, p. 161 ; A. Klughardt, Z. f. techn. Phys., 8, *1927*, p. 109 ; A. K. Taylor, C.I.E., Proc., 7, *1928*, p. 49 ; L. F. Richardson, Roy. Meteorolog. Soc., Quart. J., 56, *1930*, p. 31 ; J. Urbanek, Rev. d'Opt., 9, *1930*, pp. 247 and 289 ; E. R. Davies, Photog. J., 72, *1932*, pp. 57 and 118 ; M. Cohu, Rev. Gén. de l'El., 35, *1934*, p. 147 ; Illum. Eng. Soc. Lond., Trans., 1, *1936*, p. 163 ; C. L. Dows and G. R. Baumgartner, Illum. Eng. Soc. N.Y., Trans., 30, *1935*, p. 476 ; J. M. Slater, Opt. Soc. Am., J., 25, *1935*, p. 218 ; L. A. Wetlaufer and W. E. Scott, Industrial and Engng. Chem. (Anal. Ed.), 12, *1940*, p. 647 ; W. Arndt, Licht, 13, *1943*, p. 72. See also the refs. in the following note.

19. F. H. Gilpin. Illum. Eng. Soc. N.Y., Trans., 5, *1910*, p. 854.
L. A. Jones. Opt. Soc. Am., J., 6, *1922*, p. 140.
M. O. Pelton. Opt. Soc., Trans., 31, *1930*, p. 184.
H. Boffey and D. A. Derrett-Smith. J. Sci. Inst., 8, *1931*, p. 356.
D. A. Derrett-Smith. Textile Inst., J., 28, *1937*, p. T293.
P. Moon and J. Laurence. Opt. Soc. Am., J., 31, *1941*, p. 130.
V. G. W. Harrison. J. Sci. Inst., 24, *1947*, p. 27.
For a description of measurements on (Retro-reflecting materials see P. Jainski. Lichttechnik, 3, *1951*, p. 112 and 5, *1953*, pp. 40 and 68.
See also A. Blondel, Lum. El., 3, *1895*, p. 583 ; G. P. Woronkoff and G. J. Pokrowski, Z. f. Phys., 20, *1923*, p. 358 ; A. Baxter, J. Sci. Inst., 14, *1937*, p. 303 ; W. W. Barkas, J. Sci. Inst., 19, *1942*, p. 26 ; H. E. J. Neugebauer, Licht, 14, *1944*, p. 34.

20. This quantity has also been called "apparent reflectance" (H. J. McNicholas, Bureau of Standards, J. of Research, 1, *1928*, p. 33) and "brightness factor" (D. M. Finch and J. R. Cravath, Illum. Engng., 51, *1956*, p. 587). The term "facteur de brillance" or "coefficient de brillance" has been proposed for the ratio of the luminance, in candelas per unit area, to the illumination (A. Blondel, C.R., 186, *1928*, p. 1487 ; C.I.E., Proc., 9, *1935*, p. 17 and 10, *1939*, Vol. I, p. 6). This factor is thus equal to the luminance factor divided by π.

21. See, e.g., A. K. Taylor, Illum. Research Technical Paper No. 9 (H.M. Stationery Office, *1930*) ; G. Peri, Elettrot., 18, *1931*, pp. 153 and 926.

22. See, e.g. C. Wiener, Ann. d. Phys., 47, *1892*, p. 638.

23. D. B. Judd and K. S. Gibson. Bureau of Standards, J. of Research, 16, *1936*, p. 261.

24. C. H. Sharp and W. F. Little. Illum. Eng. Soc. N.Y., Trans., 15, *1920*, p. 802.
See also I. G. Priest, Bureau of Standards, J. of Research, 15, *1935*, p. 529.

25. M. Gurevič. Licht u. Lampe, 18, *1929*, p. 1427.
A. C. Hardy and O. W. Pineo. Opt. Soc. Am., J., 21, *1931*, p. 502.

26. J. W. T. Walsh. Illum. Eng. Soc. N.Y., Trans., 18, *1923*, p. 475.

27. Rayleigh. Phil. Mag., 41, *1871*, p. 107.
C. Chéneveau and R. Audubert. C.R., 168, *1919*, pp. 553 and 684 ; Ann. de Phys., 13, *1920*, p. 134.

28. See, e.g., P. V. Wells, Am. Chem. Soc., J., 44, *1922*, p. 267.

29. W. Ostwald. Kolloid Z., 13, *1913*, p. 121.

30. J. Tyndall. Roy. Soc., Proc., 17, *1869*, pp. 223 and 317.

31. See the refs. given in note (29) on p. 405 of *Photometry* (*1926*), especially W. Mecklenburg and S. Valentiner, Z.f.I., 34, *1914*, p. 209 ; P. A. Kober and S. S. Graves, J. of Industrial and Engng. Chem., 7, *1915*, p. 843. See also G. Stampe, Z.f.I., 51, *1931*, p. 400 and H. Sauer, *ibid.*, p. 408 ; E. Leitz, J. Sci. Inst., 14, *1937*, p. 252 ; J. M. W. Milatz, *ibid.*, 16, *1939*, p. 99.
Photo-electric instruments have also been described. See, e.g., F. T. Gucker, H. P. Pickard and C. T. O'Konski, Am. Chem. Soc., J., 69, *1947*, p. 429 ; Electronics, 20, *1947*, July, p. 106.
For an excellent account of the subject see J. H. Yoe and H. Kleinmann, *Photometric Chemical Analysis*, Vol. II (Nephelometry), (Wiley, N.Y.), *1929*).

32. J. M. Waldram. Illum. Eng. Soc., Lond., Trans., 10, *1945*, p. 147.
See also R. G. Beuttell and A. W. Brewer, J. Sci. Inst., 26, *1949*, p. 357.

33. F. Jicinsky. Dingler's Polytechn. J., 192, *1869*, p. 199.
See also J. Barot, Rev. d'Opt., 3, *1924*, p. 459.

34. The effect of surface reflection may be eliminated if measurements can be made on plates of identical material but of different thicknesses (F. E. Wright, Opt. Soc. Am., J., 2, *1919*, p. 65). See also A. A. Gershun, Z. f. techn. Phys., 10, *1929*, p. 18 ; T. Smith, Phys. Soc., Proc., 44, *1932*, p. 314 ; A. Maréchal, C.R., 219, *1944*, p. 451 and Rev. d'Opt., 28, *1949*, p. 487.

35. See, e.g. H. Buckley, Opt. Soc., Trans., 32, *1930*, p. 66.

36. D. B. McRae. Opt. Soc. Am., J., 33, *1943*, p. 229.
See also J. Terrien, C.R., 218, *1944*, p. 43 ; Rev. d'Opt., 23, *1944*, p. 105.

37. L. Bloch. Licht u. Lampe, 16, *1927*, p. 734 and 17, *1928*, pp. 207 and 244.
H. Korte. Article "Visuelle Photometer" in *Handbuch d. Lichttechnik* (Springer, *1938*), p. 327.
L. R. Baker. J. Sci. Inst., 32, *1955*, p. 418.

38. W. D. Haigh. Opt. Convention, *1926*, Proc., Vol. I, p. 327.

39. B. Kurrelmeyer, Nature, 117, *1926*, p. 657.
E. Glückauf. J. Sci. Inst., 22, *1945*, p. 34.

40. See, e.g. R. H. Müller, Industrial and Engng. Chem. (Anal. Ed.), 11, *1939*, p. 1 (contains an extensive bibliography) ; P. A. Clifford and B. A. Brice, *ibid.*, 12, *1940*, p. 218.

41. J. Guild. Article "Colorimeters and Colour Comparators" in Thorpe's *Dict. of Applied Chem.* (Fourth edit., Longmans, *1939*), Vol. III, p. 295.
Opt. Soc. Am., J., 35, *1945*, p. 1.

42. Adam Hilger, Ltd. J. Sci. Inst., 13, *1936*, p. 268.
See also G. A. Shook and B. J. Scrivener, Rev. Sci. Inst., 3, *1932*, p. 553 ; E. W. H. Selwyn, J. Sci. Inst., 10, *1933*, p. 116 ; L. V. Wilcox, Industrial and Engng. Chem. (Anal. Ed.), 6, *1934*, p. 167 ; F. Anselm and F. Würstlin, Z. f. techn. Phys., 16, *1935*, p. 157 ; T. W. Schmidt, Z.f.I., 55, *1935*, pp. 336 and 357 ; P. Meunier, C.R., 201, *1935*, p. 1371 ; D. C. Broome and A. R. Thomas, El. Times, 89, *1936*, p. 417 ; L. E. Howlett, Canadian J. of Research, 14 (A), *1936*, p. 38 ; R. B. Withrow, C. L. Shrewsbury and H. R. Craybill, Industrial and Engng. Chem. (Anal. Ed.), 8, *1936*, p. 214 ; F. H. Shepard, R.C.A. Rev., 2, *1937*, p. 149 ; W. L. Carson, Gen. El. Rev., 43, *1940*, p. 91 ; L. Harris, J. A. Kyger and C. N. Sjogren, Opt. Soc. Am., J., 31, *1941*, p. 263 , P. W. Cunliffe, Textile Inst., J., 34, *1943*, p. T55 ; P. Meunier, Rev. d'Opt., 22; *1943*, p. 238 ; R. H. Hamilton, Industrial and Engng. Chem. (Anal. Ed.), 16, *1944*, p. 123.

For descriptions of " flicker " instruments in which only one photocell is used, see G. Timoshenko and W. J. Glasson, Illum. Eng. Soc. N.Y., Trans., 35, *1940*, p. 162 and J. H. Humphrey and E. J. Harris, J. Sci. Inst., 25, *1948*, p. 314.

43. See also T. D. Gheorghiu, C.R., 188, *1929*, p. 1609.

44. On precautions necessary when using filters, see M. N. States and J. C. Anderson, Opt. Soc. Am., J., 32, *1942*, p. 659.

45. Much of the literature dealing with the determination of reflection factors refers also to transmission measurements.
See also M. Luckiesh and L. L. Mellor, Frank. Inst., J., 186, *1918*, p. 529 ; A. Dognon, Rev. d'Opt., 19, *1940*, p. 205.

46. See also R. Hiecke, E.u.M., 48, *1930*, p. 289.

47. L. Bloch. C.I.E., Proc., 7, *1928*, p. 990.

48. M. Luckiesh. El. World, 60, *1912*, p. 1040 and 61, *1913*, p. 883.
W. Dziobek. Z. f. Phys., 46, *1928*, p. 307.
R. G. Weigel and W. Ott. Z.f.I., 51, *1931*, pp. 1 and 61.
M. Cohu. Int. Illum. Congress, *1931*, Vol. I, p. 430.
R. Kurosawa. *Ibid.*, p. 361 ; Congrès Int. d'Electricité, Paris, *1932*, C.r., Vol. VIII, p. 133.
R. F. Hanstock. Opt. Soc., Trans., 33, *1932*, p. 137.
R. Sewig. Licht, 3, *1933*, p. 85.
E. F. M. van der Held and M. Minnaert. Physica, 2, *1935*, p. 769.
See also J. S. Preston, Inst. Illum. Congress, *1931*, Vol. I, p. 373 ; J. McG. Sowerby, J. Sci. Inst., 21, *1944*, p. 42 ; H. J. Helwig, Licht, 13, *1943*, p. 142 ; G. Hansen, Optik, 1, *1946*, pp. 227 and 269 and 2, *1947*, p. 155.

49. E. Karrer. Bureau of Standards, Bull., 17, *1921*, p. 203.
J. M. Waldram. C.I.E., Proc., 7, *1928*, p. 1020.
M. M. Gurevič. State Opt. Inst. Leningrad, 6, *1931*, No. 59, p. 27 (In Russian) ; E.u.M., 50, *1932*, Lichttech., p. 22.
G. R. Baumgartner. Illum. Eng. Soc. N.Y., Trans., 33, *1938*, p. 203.
See also H. Buckley, Illum. Eng. Soc. Lond., Trans., 7, *1942*, p. 39.

50. See, e.g., P. Jakuschoff, Z. Verein deut. Ing., 75, *1931*, p. 426 ; R. D. Bean, J. Sci. Inst., 9, *1932*, p. 391 ; J. S. Wilson, J. Sci. Inst., 10, *1933*, p. 96 ; A. S. G. Hill, J. Sci. Inst., 14, *1937*, p. 296 ; K. Nentwig, Licht u. Lampe, 28, *1939*, p. 514 ; J. G. Baier, Industrial and Engng. Chem. (Anal. Ed.), 15, *1943*, p. 144.

51. C. E. K. Mees. *Theory of the Photographic Process* (Macmillan Coy., New York, *1942*), Chap. XVI.
Photog. J., 65, *1925*, p. 290.
IX Congrès Int. de Photog., *1935*, Proc., pp. 453 *et seqq*.

52. The reciprocal of the transmission, termed the " opacity " (Ω) is sometimes used. The density $D = \log \Omega$.

53. A. Callier. Photog. J., 49, *1909*, p. 200 ; Z. wiss. Photog., 7, *1909*, p. 257.
The ratio of the density for direct light, incident normally, to that for diffused light is usually known as the Callier coefficient or Callier's Q factor. It varies from about 1·2 to 1·7 for most ordinary emulsions.
See also F. C. Toy, Photog. J., 65, *1925*, p. 164 (see also pp. 293 and 294) ; W. B. Ferguson, *ibid.*, 66, *1926*, p. 294 ; C. Tuttle, Opt. Soc. Am., J., 12, *1926*, p. 559 and 24, *1934*, p. 272 ; L. Silberstein and C. Tuttle, *ibid.*, 14, *1927*, p. 365 ; C. Tuttle and J. W. McFarlane, Soc. Motion Pict. Engrs., J., 15, *1930*, p. 345 ; G. A. Boutry, C.R., 197, *1933*, p. 642 ; C. Tuttle, Soc. Motion Pict. Engrs., J., 26, *1936*, p. 195 ; A. M. Koerner and C. Tuttle, Opt. Soc. Am., J., 27, *1937*, p. 241 ; E. W. H. Selwyn and

F. H. G. Pitt, Photog. J., 77, *1937*, p. 397 ; C. Tuttle and A. M. Koerner, Photog. J., 78, *1938*, p. 739.

54. This has been recommended as the standard procedure in sensitometry (S. O. Rawling, VIII Int. Kongress d. Photographie, Dresden, *1931*, Ber., p. 96). For a method of measuring " specular density ", i.e. $\log_{10} (1/\tau)$ where τ is that fraction of a beam of normally incident light which is transmitted without diffusion, see F. H. G. Pitt, Photog. J., 78, *1938*, p. 486.

In measuring " British standard density ", the incident light is diffused by means of an integrating sphere (" Measurement of Photographic Transmission Density," British Standard Spec. No. 1384). See also K. S. Weaver, Opt. Soc. Am., J., 40, *1950*, p. 524 ; A. S. Cross, J. Sci. Inst., 32, *1955*, p. 59 ; E. H. Belcher, B. E. Keane and M. D. Rousseau, *Science and Applications of Photography* (Roy. Photog. Soc., *1955*), p. 240.

55. F. F. Martens. Photog. Correspondenz, 38, *1901*, p. 528.

See also *Handbuch d. wiss. u. angewandten Photographie* (ed. A. Hay), Vol. IV (Springer, Berlin, *1930*).

56. D. E. Benson, W. B. Ferguson and F. F. Renwick. Photog. J., 58, *1918*. p. 155.

A. J. Bull and H. M. Cartwright. J. Sci. Inst., 1, *1923*, p. 74.

L. A. Jones. Opt. Soc. Am., J., 7, *1923*, p. 231.

W. B. Ferguson. Photog. J., 64, *1924*, p. 30.

J. G. Capstaff and N. B. Green. *Ibid*., p. 97.

" Filmograph." Rev. d'Opt., 5, *1926*, p. 470 and 9, *1930*, p. 376.

W. B. Ferguson. Photog. J., 67, *1927*, pp. 136 and 278.

J. G. Capstaff and R. A. Purdy. Soc. Motion Pict. Engrs., J., 11, *1927*, p. 607 ; J. Sci. Inst., 14, *1937*, p. 30.

L. Lobel and J. Lefèvre. Rev. d'Opt., 6, *1927*, p. 377.

W. Seifert. Photog. Industrie, 28, *1930*, p. 1364 (Goldberg densograph).

E. R. Davis and R. E. Owen. Photog. J., 75, *1935*, p. 128.

P. C. Smethurst. British J. Photog., 85, *1938*, p. 406.

57. F. C. Toy and S. O. Rawling. J. Sci. Inst., 1, *1924*, p. 362.

J. M. Blair, M. C. Hylan and G. T. Meredith. Photog. J., 73, *1933*, p. 409.

G. A. Boutry, C.R., 196, *1933*, p. 1101 (see also p. 1013) ; Réunions de l'Inst. d'Opt., 4, *1933*, p. 95.

E. B. Moss. Phys. Soc., Proc., 46, *1934*, p. 205.

Photog. Industrie, 32, *1934*, p. 487.

G. C. Henny. Am. J. Roentgenology, 31, *1934*, p. 550.

C. W. Miller. Rev. Sci. Inst., 6, *1935*, p. 125.

C. Tuttle. Opt. Soc. Am., J., 26, *1936*, p. 282.

O. H. Ingber and K. Schwerin. Soc. Franç. de Photog., Bull., 25, *1938*, p. 3.

R. Herz. Z. wiss. Photog., 37, *1938*, p. 107.

L. P. Tabor. Opt. Soc. Am., J., 29, *1939*, p. 32.

L. Lobel. Soc. Franç. de Photog., Bull., 1, *1939*, p. 154.

J. G. Frayne and G. R. Crane. Soc. Motion Pict. Engrs., J., 35, *1940*, p. 184.

J. M. Ledeboer. Philips Techn. Rev., 5, *1940*, p. 331.

M. H. Sweet. Soc. Motion Pict. Engrs., J., 38, *1942*, p. 148.

T. T. Baker. El. Rev., 132, *1943*, p. 343.

M. H. Sweet. Opt. Soc. Am., J., 37, *1947*, p. 432 ; Electronics, 18, *1945*, Mar., p. 102 and 19, *1946*, Nov., p. 105.

R. L. Huber and A. B. Rakus. Opt. Soc. Am., J., 39, *1949*, p. 873.

W. G. Kirchgessner. Rev. Sci. Inst., 22, *1951*, p. 289.

O. L. Goble. J. Sci. Inst., 30, *1953*, p. 110.

See also P. Lob, Kinotechnik, 14, *1932*, p. 330.

58. F. C. Toy. J. Sci. Inst., 4, *1927*, p. 369 and 7, *1930*, p. 253.

J. O. C. Vick. Photog. J., 67, *1927*, p. 324.

59. A. Bloch. J. Sci. Inst., 13, *1936*, p. 358.

60. J. M. Waldram. J. Sci. Inst., 13, *1936*, p. 352.

R. C. Williams and W. A. Hiltner. Publ. Observatory Univ. Michigan, 8, *1940*, p. 103 ; Astrophys. J., 98, *1943*, p. 43.

See also E. A. Harvey, Photog. J., 81, *1941*, p. 231.

61. W. R. Goehner. Soc. Motion Pict. Engrs., J., 23, *1934*, p. 318.

62. See also J. Roig, Rev. d'Opt., 17, *1938*, pp. 177 and 217.

63. O. Tugman. Astrophys. J., 42, *1915*, pp. 321 and 331.

64. J. Hartmann. Z.f.I., 19, *1899*, p. 97.
P. Lob. Kinotechnik, 12, *1930*, p. 435.
S. Jacobsohn and W. H. Kliever. Opt. Soc. Am., J., 25, *1935*, p. 244.
M. Slavin. *Ibid.*, 29, *1939*, p. 220.
H. Lorenz. Z.f.I., 56, *1936*, p. 294.

65. K. Schwarzchild and W. Villiger. Astrophys. J., 23, *1906*, p. 284.

66. P. P. Koch. Ann. d. Phys., 38, *1912*, p. 507.

67. C. Fabry and H. Buisson. J. de Phys., 9, *1919*, p. 37.
L. C. Martin. Opt. Soc., Trans., 26, *1925*, p. 109.
See also " Filmograph," Rev. d'Opt., 12, *1933*, p. 270.

68. J. O. Perrine. Opt. Soc. Am., J., 8, *1924*, p. 381.
H. Rosenberg. Z.f.I., 45, *1925*, p. 313 (see also pp. 494 and 540).
E. A. Baker. Roy. Soc. Edin., Proc., 45, *1925*, p. 166.
G. R. Harrison. Opt. Soc. Am., J., 10, *1925*, p. 157 and 16, *1928*, p. 63.
(In this instrument a thermopile is used instead of a photocell.)
C. S. Beals. Roy. Astron. Soc., M.N., 92, *1932*, p. 196.
E. Dershem. Rev. Sci. Inst., 3, *1932*, p. 43.
R. Sewig. Archiv f. techn. Messen, *1935*, T133.
P. S. Williams and G. H. Scott. Opt. Soc. Am., J., 25, *1935*, p. 347.
H. B. Vincent and R. A. Sawyer. *Ibid.*, 27, *1937*, p. 193.
A. Narath and K. Schwarz. Z. f. techn. Phys., 19, *1938*, p. 465.
M. H. Sweet. Opt. Soc. Am., J., 28, *1938*, p. 349.
D. R. White. Soc. Motion Pict. Engrs., J., 33, *1939*, p. 403.
A. H. Jay. J. Sci. Inst., 18, *1941*, p. 128.
H. W. Dietert and J. Schuch. Opt. Soc. Am., J., 31, *1941*, p. 54.
A. Taylor. J. Sci. Inst., 28, *1951*, p. 200.
See also G. O. Langstroth and D. R. McRae, Opt. Soc. Am., J., 28, *1938*, p. 440.

69. H. v. Oehmcke. Z. f. techn. Phys., 15, *1934*, p. 72.
G. Hansen. *Ibid.*, 19, *1938*, p. 330.
T. G. Mehlin. Rev. Sci. Inst., 9, *1938*, p. 374.
E. M. Thorndike. Industrial and Engng. Chem. (Anal. Ed.), 13, *1941*, p. 66.

70. G. M. B. Dobson. Roy. Soc., Proc., 104, *1923*, p. 248 ; Engineering, 122 *1926*, p. 403.
See also A. Lallemand, Rev. d'Opt., 15, *1936*, p. 109.

71. E. G. Jones and H. L. Brose. J. Sci. Inst., 8, *1931*, p. 145.
W. Duana. Nat. Acad. Sci., Proc., 18, *1932*, p. 322.
G. R. Harrison. Rev. Sci. Inst., 3, *1932*, p. 572.
R. Breckpot. Soc. Sci. Bruxelles, Ann. (Sér. B), 54, *1934*, p. 299.
L. A. Woodward and R. G. Horner. J. Sci. Inst., 12, *1935*, p. 17.
D. H. Follett. Phys. Soc., Proc., 47, *1935*, p. 125.
Adam Hilger, Ltd. J. Sci. Inst., 12, *1935*, p. 27.
J. T. M. Malpica and W. R. Fanter. Gen. El. Rev., 43, *1940*, p. 384.
S. Bodforss. Z. wiss. Photog., 40, *1941*, p. 154.
H. B. Vincent and R. A. Sawyer. Opt. Soc. Am., J., 31, *1941*, p. 639.
W. S. Baird. *Ibid.*, p. 179.
R. O'B. Carpenter. Opt. Soc. Am., J., 36, *1946*, p. 676.
H. H. Grossmann et al. *Ibid.*, 39, *1949*, p. 261.

72. P. P. Koch. Ann. d. Phys., 39, *1912*, p. 705.
F. Goos and P. P. Koch. Z. f. Phys., 44, *1927*, p. 855.
F. Goos. Z.f.I., 41, *1931*, p. 313.
See also F. Goos and P. P. Koch, Phys. Z., 27, *1926*, p. 41 ; P. P. Koch, " Photoelectric Cells and their Applications," Phys. and Opt. Socs., *1930*, p. 150.

73. E. A. Baker. " Photo-electric Cells and their Applications," Phys. and Opt. Socs., *1930*, p. 153.

74. P. Lambert and D. Chalonge. C.R., 180, *1925*, p. 924 ; Rev. d'Opt., 5, *1926*, p. 404 and 10, *1931*, p. 405.
C. Jausseran. Rev. d'Opt., 11, *1932*, p. 337.
O. Sandvik. Soc. Motion Pict. Engrs., J., 15, *1930*, p. 201.
J. A. Carroll and E. B. Moss. Roy. Astron. Soc., M.N., 91, *1930*, p. 191.
P. Lob. Kinotechnik, 12, *1930*, p. 161.
J. H. Lees. J. Sci. Inst., 8, *1931*, p. 273.

G. Todesco. N. Cimento, 9, *1932*, p. 138.

W. Schütz. Phys. Z., 34, *1933*, p. 566.

J. F. Thovert. Réunions de l'Inst. d'Opt., 4, *1933*, p. 95.

H. Kulenkampff. Phys. Z., 36, *1935*, p. 56.

N. B. Bhatt and S. K. K. Jatkar. J. Sci. Inst., 12, *1935*, p. 185.

C. S. Beals. Roy. Astron. Soc., M.N., 96, *1936*, p. 730.

H. V. Kuorr and V. M. Albers. Rev. Sci. Inst., 8, *1937*, p. 183.

R. C. Williams and W. A. Hiltner. Publ. Observatory Univ. Michigan, 8, *1940*, p. 45 ; Astrophys. J., 98, *1943*, p. 43.

Rev. Sci. Inst., 13, *1942*, p. 38.

H. R. Ronnebeck. J. Sci. Inst., 20, *1943*, p. 154.

M. Laffineur. C.R., 227, *1948*, p. 900.

A. E. Vassy and R. Chezlemas. Sci. et Indust. Photog., 16, *1945*, p. 1 and 19, *1948*, p. 56.

W. A. Wooster. J. Sci. Inst., 32, *1955*, p. 457.

J. Bor. *Ibid.*, 34, *1957*, p. 140.

See also N. Thompson, Phys. Soc., Proc., 45, *1933*, p. 441 ; O. Blüh, Z. f. Phys., 88, *1934*, p. 403 ; G. O. Langstroth, Rev. Sci. Inst., 5, *1934*, p. 255 ; F. E. Carlson and W. M. Potter, Illum. Eng. Soc. N.Y., Trans., 39, *1944*, p. 754 ; J. Schoen, Arch. techn. Messen, No. 170, Mar. *1950*, T 25.

75. B. Lange. Z. f. techn. Phys., 13, *1932*, p. 600.

W. O. Milligan. Rev. Sci. Inst., 4, *1933*, p. 496.

C. Sannié. C.R., 198, *1934*, p. 1149 ; Rev. d'Opt., 14, *1935*, p. 107.

Philips Industrial, Ltd. J. Sci. Inst., 15, *1938*, p. 348.

H. Lloyd and E. M. Guénault. J. Sci. Inst., 17, *1940*, p. 103.

G. O. Langstroth, K. B. Newbound and W. W. Brown. Canadian J. of Research, (A), 19, *1941*, p. 103.

G. Spiegler. J. Sci. Inst., 22, *1945*, p. 116.

See also W. H. J. Childs, Phys. Soc., Proc., 40, *1928*, p. 132 ; R. Freymann and R. Zouckermann, Rev. d'Opt., 11, *1932*, p. 279 ; B. C. Hiatt and C. Tuttle, Soc. Motion Pict. Engrs., J., 26, *1936*, p. 195.

76. R. Fürth. Phys. Soc., Proc., 55, *1943*, p. 34.

R. W. Pringle. Electron. Engng., 16, *1944*, p. 512.

R. Fürth and W. D. Oliphant. J. Sci. Inst., 25, *1948*, p. 289.

A " contouring microphotometer " for tracing out lines of equal density has been described by H. W. Babcock (Astron. Soc. of the Pacific, Publ., 62, *1950*, p. 18).

77. W. J. H. Moll. Phys. Soc., Proc., 33, *1921*, p. 207 ; J. Sci. Inst., 6, *1929*, p. 392 and 13, *1936*, p. 183.

E. Pettit and S. B. Nicholson. Opt. Soc. Am., J., 7, *1923*, p. 187.

M. Siegbahn. Phil. Mag., 48, *1924*, p. 217.

E. Bäcklin. Z.f.I., 47, *1927*, p. 373.

E. Albrecht and M. Dorneich. Phys. Z., 26, *1925*, p. 514.

E. Spiller. Z.f.I., 47, *1927*, p. 493.

E. A. Harrington. Opt. Soc. Am., J., 16, *1928*, p. 211.

H. H. Plaskett. Roy. Astron. Soc., M.N., 95, *1934*, p. 160.

K. B. Thomson. Rev. Sci. Inst., 6, *1935*, p. 286.

J. Sci. Inst., 12, *1935*, p. 128.

M. Minnaert and J. Houtgast. Z. f. Astrophys., 15, *1938*, p. 354.

H. Mohler. Helv. Chimica Acta, 25, *1942*, p. 978.

See also G. Bolla, N. Cimento, 9, *1932*, p. 224 ; F. K. Richtmyer and F. R. Hirsh, Rev. Sci. Inst., 4, *1933*, p. 353 ; S. Harris, *ibid.*, p. 598.

An instrument in which a radiometer is used instead of a thermopile has also been described. See S. Smith and O. C. Wilson, Astrophys. J., 76, *1932*, p. 117 ; P. A. Leighton, S. Smith and F. C. Henson, Rev. Sci. Inst., 5, *1934*, p. 431.

78. J. Weiglé. Arch. des Sci., 15, *1933*, p. 484 ; Rev. Sci. Inst., 4, *1933*, p. 595.

L. Séletsky. Rev. d'Opt., 12, *1933*, p. 363.

79. See also K. Haberl, Phys. Z., 36, *1935*, p. 59 ; E. J. Perepelkin, Acad. Sci. U.R.S.S., C.r. (Doklady), 15, *1937*, p. 25 ; H. Hemmendinger, Rev. Sci. Inst., 9, *1938*, p. 178.

80. A. Narath. Photog. Korrespondenz, 72, *1936*, pp. 71 and 89.

81. P. Jacquinot and M. Meunier. J. de Phys., 4, *1933*, p. 570.
See also A. Langseth and E. Walles, Nature, 133, *1934*, p. 210.

82. A. Jobin and G. Yvon. Rev. d'Opt., 13, *1934*, p. 179.

F. W. Sears. Opt. Soc. Am., J., 25, *1935*, p. 162.

L. A. Jones and M. E. Russell. *Ibid.*, p. 396.

A. Danten. C.R., 224, *1947*, p. 1215.

R. M. Fisher and D. S. Miller. Rev. Sci. Inst., 21, *1950*, p. 938.

83. S. O. Maisel, State Opt. Inst., Leningrad, Trans. (Trudui), 3, *1923*, No.16 p. 1 (In Russian).

D. B. McRae. Opt. Soc. Am., J., 33, *1943*, p. 229.

L. C. Martin. *Technical Optics* (Vol. II) (Pitman, *1950*), Chap. VI.

84. This may be simply demonstrated in the case of a single lens as follows : The flux reaching the lens (area L) from an elementary area S of the object is $B_0 SL/u^2$. Similarly, by the reciprocal relation connecting the flux emitted with that received (see p. 141), the flux reaching the corresponding area of the image is $B_1 S'L/v^2$. But $S/S' = u^2/v^2$ (see p. 25) so that $B_0 = B_1$.

For a rigid formal proof, see E. Abbe, Jenasche Z. f. Medicin u. Naturwiss., 6, *1871*, p. 263 ; J. D. Everett, Phil. Mag., 25, *1888*, p. 216 ; W. T. A. Emtage, *ibid.*, 41, *1896*, p. 504 ; P. Drude, *Lehrbuch d. Optik*, part I, chap IV ; A. Dargenton, Rev. d'Opt., 8, *1929*, p. 4. See also J. Dourgnon and P. Waguet, C.R., 191, *1930* p. 1314, and 192, *1931*, p. 68 ; Int. Illum. Congress, *1931*, Proc., Vol. I, p. 357.

85. Rev. d'Opt., 11, *1932*, p. 222.

86. See also B. Cuny, Rev. d'Opt., 12, *1933*, p. 201.

87. Nat. Phys. Lab. *Photometry of Telescopes and Binoculars*. H.M.S.O., *1955*.

88. See, e.g., A. C. Hardy, Frank. Inst., J., 208, *1929*, p. 773 ; R. Kingslake, J. Sci. Inst., 14, *1937*, p. 289.

89. On calculations of this kind, see, e.g., A. C. Hardy, Opt. Soc. Am., J., 33, *1943*, p. 71.

90. P. G. Nutting. Astrophys. J., 40, *1914*, p. 33.

91. D. B. McRae. Opt. Soc. Am., J., 33, *1943*, p. 229.

92. J. Guild. Opt. Soc., Trans., 23, *1922*, p. 205.

A. Blondol. C.R., 181, *1925*, p. 449.

J. Hrdlička. Rev. d'Opt., 9, *1930*, p. 149. (The measurements are made photographically instead of visually.)

See also A. Blondel, C.R., 182, *1926*, p. 739 ; V. Ronchi, N. Cimento, 7, *1930*, p. 374.

93. G. W. Moffitt and P. B. Taylor. Opt. Soc. Am., J., 8, *1924*, p. 511.

94. D. B. McRae. Opt. Soc. Am., J., 35, *1945*, p. 510.

See also H. Schober, Licht, 14, *1944*, p. 27.

95. See, e.g., W. E. Forsythe and B. T. Barnes, Rev. Sci. Inst., 1, *1930*, p. 569.

96. C. C. Paterson, J. W. T. Walsh, A. K. Taylor and W. Barnett. Inst. El. Eng., J., 58, *1920*, p. 83.

97. This name has also been applied to instruments used for measuring atmospheric diffusion by comparing the luminance of a distant object of known reflection factor with the simultaneous luminance of a portion of the sky. See W. E. K. Middleton, *Vision through the Atmosphere* (Univ. of Toronto Press, *1952*), Chap. IX.

98. A slightly modified form is described by C. H. S. Evans and E. W. Chivers (Illum. Eng., 26, *1933*, p. 80). See also F. A. Benford, Gen. El. Rev., 22, *1919*, p. 668 ; J. M. Waldram, Illum. Eng., 27, *1934*, p. 311 and Illum. Eng. Soc. Lond., Trans., 10, *1945*, p. 147.

99. L. J. Collier. Illum. Eng. Soc. Lond., Trans., 3, *1938*, p. 141.

100. L. F. Richardson. Roy. Soc., Proc., 96, *1919–20*, p. 19 ; Roy. Meterolog. Soc., J., 51, *1925*, p. 7.

See also W. E. K. Middleton, Opt. Soc. Am., J., 39, *1949*, p. 570.

101. See also W. E. K. Middleton, Roy. Soc. Canada, Proc. (Section III), 25, *1931*, p. 39 and 26, *1932*, p. 25.

102. G. Gehlhoff and H. Schering. Z. f. techn. Phys., 1, *1920*, p. 247 ; Phys. Z., 22, *1921*, p. 71.

H. Buisson and C. Fabry. J. de Phys., 1, *1920*, p. 25 ; Rev. d'Opt., 1, *1922*, p. 1.

A. Blondel. Illum. Eng., 18, *1925*, p. 237.

C. Perucca. Z.f.I., 46, *1926*, p. 74.

J. Hrdlička and J. Krombholz. Rev. d'Opt., 17, *1938*, p. 28.

L. J. Collier and W. G. A. Taylor. J. Sci. Inst., 15, *1938*, p. 5.

See also E. Karrer and A. Poritsky, Opt. Soc. Am., J., 8, *1924*, p. 355 ; A. Blondel, Int. Illum. Congress, *1931*, Proc., Vol. I, p. 240 ; F. Link and M. Hugon, Rev. d'Opt. 9, *1930*, p. 156.

103. W. Dziobek. Licht, 4, *1934*, p. 150.

104. H. S. Coleman *et al.* Opt. Soc. Am., J., 39, *1949*, p. 515.

105. C. A. Douglas. Electronics, 20, *1947*, Aug., p. 106.

F. J. Scrase, J. Sci. Inst., 25, *1948*, p. 185.

See also P. Guillery and G. Kapp, Licht, 10, *1940*, p. 100.

106. A. Blondel. C.R., 170, *1920*, p. 93.

L. Foitzik. Meteorolog. Z., 50, *1933*, p. 473.

L. Bergmann. Phys. Z., 35, *1934*, p. 177.

B. Schönwald and T. Müller. Z. f. techn. Phys., 23, *1942*, p. 30.

O. I. Popov. Svetotechnika, 3, *1957*, No. 1, p. 20 (In Russian).

107. See also Illum. Eng. Soc. N.Y., Trans., 38, *1943*, p. 515.

108. A. Rey and C. Févrot. Rev. d'Opt., 27, *1948*, p. 35.

109. E. Karrer and E. P. T. Tyndall. Bureau of Standards, Bull., 16, *1920*, p. 377.

L. Foitzik. Naturwissenschaften, 22, *1934*, p. 384.

See also F. Benford, Gen. El. Rev., 29, *1926*, p. 873 ; H. Buisson *et al.*, C.R., 190, *1930*, pp. 808 and 810 ; F. C. Breckenridge, Illum. Eng. Soc. N.Y., Trans., 27, *1932*, p. 215 ; A. Arnulf and A. Bayle, Rev. d'Opt., 28, *1949*, p. 691.

CHAPTER XIV

PHOTOMETRY OF PROJECTION APPARATUS

Of all the problems of practical photometry, the one which, it is probably true to say, presents the most difficulty, and is not infrequently carried out under conditions which render the results liable to considerable error, is the photometry of projectors. All measurements of luminous intensity depend on determining the illumination produced at a standard surface by a source placed at a measured distance from it (see Chapter VII). In order to find the luminous intensity of the source it is necessary to assume that all the light illuminating the surface proceeds from a restricted area which, to the degree of accuracy aimed at in the measurements, may be regarded as a mathematical point. In other words, the source must, for the purpose of the measurement, be such that it can legitimately be regarded as a point source situated at a definite distance from the photometer.

It is frequently impossible to make this assumption in the case of light emitted from an optical device, for in many cases this device redistributes the light in such a way that it appears to proceed from a source at infinity, while in other cases different parts of the optical system produce separate images of the primary light source, so that the resulting beam is in reality composed of a number of primary beams, each of which appears to proceed from a different point in space. The simplest problem in projector photometry is that in which the optical device produces a single image of the source at some definite position. The image produced by a lens or spherical mirror is of this kind, provided (a) the aperture of the optical device is small compared with its distance from the source, and (b) the source is not at the focus of the lens or mirror.

In a problem of this kind the only departure from ordinary photometric procedure is that the measurements involved in the application of the inverse square law must be made from the position of the image, and not from the source or the optical device. This is only true so long as the whole of the image is visible from every point of the photometer screen. It is clear that the inverse square law cannot be applied at all when the optical device is delimiting the image, so that the fraction of the whole which is visible in any particular direction depends upon the distance of the photometer from the device. When the image is so much larger than the device that the surface of the latter appears bright all over, the device itself may be regarded as the source, if the image is of uniform luminance, for the edge of the optical device then acts in the same manner as a diaphragm placed in front of a bright surface (see p. 151) * [1].

It must be remembered that in the case of a magnified image, even if the optical device is not acting as a stop, it may be necessary to use the photometer at a greater distance than would be necessary in the case of the original source. For example, in the case of a line source of length $2l$, placed along the axis of a lens of focal length f, with its centre at a distance u from the lens, by means of the formula given on p. 23 it is easy to show that the length of the image formed by the lens is $2f^2l/(f+u-l)(f+u+l)$. If, then, $f= -6$ inches, $l = 0\cdot5$ inch, and $u = 3\cdot5$ inches, the length of the image is 6 inches, and the minimum permissible distance of the photometer from the image has to be six times that which would be allowable in measuring the original source.

Parallel Beam Projectors—Probably the most important case of projector photometry is that in which the source is at the focus of the optical device, so that the image is at infinity. This is the problem presented in the photometry of searchlight projectors, where the source is placed at the focus of a parabolic mirror, or of lighthouse lanterns, where the source is at the focus of a plano-convex lens. These two cases will be considered separately. The parabolic mirror has been very fully dealt with by F. A. Benford [2]. In the case of a uniform point source the rays proceeding from the mirror are all parallel, so that the illumination is constant at all distances from the mirror, and the calculated, or apparent luminous intensity is therefore entirely dependent on the distance of the photometer. The illumination at any point in the beam is easily obtained, for (Fig. 252) if the luminous intensity of the source is I,

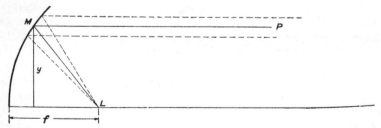

FIG. 252. Projector with a Point Source.

the flux density at M is I/LM^2, since the flux per unit solid angle from L is I lumens. If the focal length of the parabola is f, then LM

---

* The above conclusion applies equally if the image is real, and lies between the device and the photometer.

is given by $LM^2 = y^2 + \left(f - \dfrac{y^2}{4f}\right)^2$, where y is the distance of M from the axis. Hence the illumination at a point in the beam P, distant y from the axis of the mirror, is $\rho I / \left(f + \dfrac{y^2}{4f}\right)^2$, where ρ is the reflection factor of the mirror. The distribution of illumination across the beam is shown in Fig. 253.

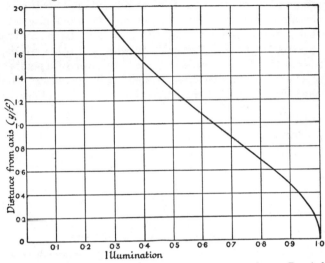

FIG. 253. Distribution of Illumination across the Beam from a Parabolic
Reflector with a Point Source.
(For absolute values multiply by $\rho I/f^2$.)

The case of a source of finite size is somewhat different. If this source has a definite luminance B, which is the same in all directions, then from a distant point P on the axis of the beam the whole surface of the mirror appears to have the luminance $B\rho$, for, (Fig. 254),

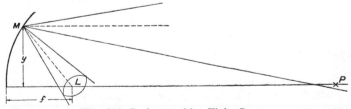

FIG. 254. Projector with a Finite Source.

considering an element M of the mirror surface, since the angles of the incident and reflected beams are equal, the angular density of the flux reflected from this element in the direction P is equal to the angular density of the flux reaching M, i.e. to that of the flux emitted by L, reduced in the ratio $\rho : 1$, so that the luminance of M, as viewed from P, is ρB. It follows that at P the apparent luminous intensity of the whole mirror is $\pi\rho R^2 B$, where R is the radius of the mirror. This holds whatever be the shape of the source, provided its luminance is uniform in all directions. In the case of a disc source, it must be remembered that the luminous intensity is zero at angles of emission greater than $90°$, so that a mirror embracing a total angle of more than $180°$ is of no advantage in this case.

In the above discussion of the apparent luminous intensity of a mirror it is assumed that P is situated so far from the mirror that the latter appears bright or "flashes" all over. In other words, it is assumed that the elementary beams due to two opposite points at the extreme edge of the mirror cross at some point between P and the mirror (see Fig. 255), so that P receives light from every part of

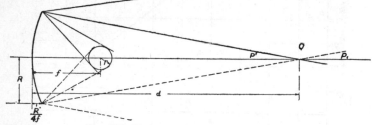

Fig. 255. Projector with a Spherical Source.

the mirror surface. No point, such as P' or Q, for which this is not the case can be assumed to have an illumination based on the formula for the apparent luminous intensity given above, and within the crossing point on the axis the inverse square law must not be assumed to hold.

For a spherical source of radius r (Fig. 255) [3] the limiting distance d for the application of the inverse square law along the axis of the mirror is given by

$$R \Big/ \left\{ d - \frac{R^2}{4f} \right\} = r \Big/ \left(f + \frac{R^2}{4f} \right),$$

so that

$$d = \frac{R^2}{4f} + \frac{R}{r} \left\{ f + \frac{R^2}{4f} \right\}.$$

For example, in the case of a mirror of 60 cm. aperture and 30 cm. focus, with a source of 1 cm. radius, d is 11·3 metres.

For a disc source (see Fig. 256), instead of r in the above expression, it is necessary to write

$$r (f - R^2/4f)/(f + R^2/4f),$$

so that [4]

$$d = R^2/4f + R \left(f + \frac{R^2}{4f} \right)^2 \Big/ r \left(f - \frac{R^2}{4f} \right).$$

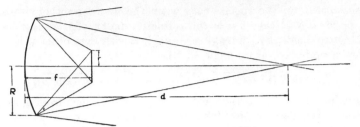

FIG. 256. Projector with a Disc Source.

It is to be noted that this expression becomes infinite when $R = 2f$, i.e. when the mirror embraces a total angle of 180° with a disc source. In the case of the dimensions used in the above example, with a spherical source, d is now equal to 18·8 metres.

The case of prism reflection may be treated similarly, for in this case, too (see Fig. 257), the angular density of the incident flux is equal to that of the reflected flux, provided the prism is isosceles.

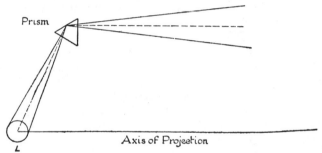

FIG. 257. Prismatic Reflection.

This is the case of the outer catadioptric elements of a lighthouse lens. The inner elements, however, depend on refraction. If in Fig. 258

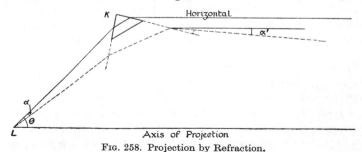

FIG. 258. Projection by Refraction.

the light from a source situated at L is refracted by the prism K so as to emerge in an approximately horizontal direction, it is easy

to show that, in the special case when the first refracting face of
the prism is vertical, if n is the refractive index of the glass (see
p. 21), two incident rays making an angle α with each other will, on
emergence, diverge at an angle α', where

$$\alpha'/\alpha = \cos\theta \; (n^2 - \sqrt{n^2 - \sin^2\theta})/\{n^2 - \sin^2\theta - \sqrt{n^2 - \sin^2\theta}\}.$$

The value of this expression will be found to *increase* from 1 as θ
increases from zero, so that for a constant value of α the elementary
beams given by the more extreme elements of the lens will be more
divergent than elementary beams from the intermediate elements.
If f is the focal length of the system and the source a sphere of radius
r, an element at an angular distance θ from the axis will give a beam
having a semi-angular depth of α', found by putting $\alpha = (r/f)\cos\theta$
in the above expression. Since the distance d at which this beam
meets the axis is equal to $y \cot\alpha'$ or y/α', i.e. to $(f/\alpha')\tan\theta$, it follows
that the minimum distance at which the inverse square law can be
applied may be found as in the case of the parabolic reflector. The
problem of the disc source may be treated similarly [5]. In all the
above cases it will be noticed that, to a first approximation, d varies
as R/r, as might, indeed, be expected *a priori* [6].

In the above discussion of the minimum distance at which it is
safe to apply the inverse square law for the calculation of apparent
luminous intensity there are three important considerations which
have not so far been mentioned. These are as follows :

(i) It has been tacitly assumed that the size of the optical
device is so small compared with d that no appreciable error would
be introduced in applying the inverse square law to a uniformly
bright disc of the same radius (R) (see p. 142).

(ii) Throughout the work d has been measured from the centre
of the optical device itself ; it must not be assumed that this point
is the effective source from which distances are to be measured.
This is not so, for in the case of the parabolic reflector, since the
whole mirror surface appears to have a uniform luminance, viz. ρB,
it may be replaced by a disc of this luminance and of the same
area as the aperture of the mirror placed in the plane of the front
edge of the mirror [7]. In the case of the lens projector the luminance
is not quite uniform, but the error introduced by assuming the
effective source to be in the plane of the lens is quite small.

(iii) All the above work has referred to luminous intensity
measured in the direction of the axis of the beam. While this is the
most important direction in the majority of problems, it is frequently
necessary to determine the distribution of luminous intensity across
the beam, and the method of finding the value of d for various
directions inclined to the axis will therefore be described in the case

of the parabola. The dioptric lens may be treated similarly, but the calculations are more lengthy [8].

Variation of Apparent Luminous Intensity across the Beam— From Fig. 259, if L is a disc, and d the distance from the mirror at

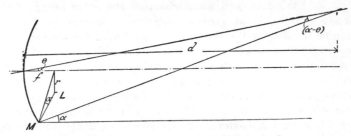

FIG. 259. Beam Measurements at Oblique Angles.

which the extreme ray of the elementary beam proceeding from M crosses the line passing through the centre of the mirror and inclined to the axis at an angle θ, then, to a first approximation, since α and θ are both small, $R/d = \alpha - \theta$, and $\alpha = r(f - R^2/4f)/(f + R^2/4f)^2$, so that

$$d = \frac{R}{r(f - R^2/4f)/(f + R^2/4f)^2 - \theta}.$$

d becomes infinite when $\theta = r(f - R^2/4f)/(f + R^2/4f)^2$. With the dimensions given in the example used above this value of θ is 0·016, or about 0·9°. When θ is 0·015, however, $d = 300$ metres. It follows that in this case, where the maximum beam divergence is 0·033 (semi-angle), the inverse square law may be applied to measurements of illumination made at distances of 300 metres or more over an angular breadth from the axis of the beam of only 0·45 times the total breadth. While this is theoretically the case, in practice the variation of the illumination with distance departs but little from this law for wider angles, since the elementary beams which cross the observation line between the 300-metre point and infinity contribute but little to the total illumination. For example, with the projector system already calculated, when $\theta = 0.03$, i.e. only 10 minutes of arc from the extreme edge of the beam, the percentage error introduced by measurements at 300 metres instead of infinity is less than 1·6 per cent. It thus appears that measurements of such a projector system may be made at a range equal to about 1,000 times the radius of the projector when the semi-divergence of the beam is not less than 2°. For approximate work one-half or even one-quarter, of this range may be sufficient, but in practice it has to be remembered that the above discussion is based on the assumption of a perfect mirror. The imperfections and irregularities of form met with in practical apparatus make it desirable to use an even longer range than that indicated above if really accurate results are required [9].

Photometry of Large Projectors: Searchlights—For large projectors there is a very serious practical difficulty in the use of long ranges, and this may well counterbalance the extra accuracy theoretically obtainable at greater distances. Searchlight projectors of double the size used in the above examples, or even more, are now common, so that ranges up to at least half a mile are necessary, with the result that measurements have to be made in the open, or at least the beam from the projector has to traverse half a mile or more of atmosphere at a distance, generally, of a few feet above the ground. The result is that absorption of light by a very slight amount of mist or other suspended matter in the air causes a reduction in the beam intensity at the end of the range, which may be as much as 20 to 30 per cent before the presence of the mist, etc. becomes noticeable to the eye [10]. If atmospheric absorption is present to any marked extent it is impossible to obtain any satisfactory photometric measurements, for the rapidity with which the transmission factor varies, both from time to time and from place to place, makes it a very uncertain method to attempt to allow for the variations by subsidiary measurements such as those to be described later. The interference due to ground mist may generally be much reduced if the beam is projected across a valley, the projector and the photometer being on the opposite slopes of the hills on either side.

In determinations of the apparent luminous intensity in various parts of the beam it is desirable to move the projector in altitude and azimuth, since at a range of half a mile a beam of 4° total divergence has a linear diameter of over 60 yards, and an angular movement of the projector is usually much easier to arrange than a lateral movement of the photometer over such a long distance [11]. In the case of vertical distribution, tilting the projector is clearly the only course practically possible. Angles may be conveniently determined by means of large scales attached to the projector or, more accurately, by means of a small telescope rigidly fixed to the projector and reading on bold horizontal and vertical scales placed at a distance of 50 to 100 feet in front of it. The projector and photometer stations should be in constant communication, preferably by telephone.

The actual photometric apparatus may take many different forms. A very convenient arrangement consists simply of a standard surface supported vertically, or so as to be normal to the light from the projector. The illumination at this surface is then measured by means of a portable illumination photometer, and the luminous intensity is calculated by means of the inverse square law [12].

Alternatively, a Lummer-Brodhun or other photometer head may be mounted on a small photometer bench whose axis is in the direction of the beam. A small comparison lamp on the side of the photometer remote from the projector enables measurements of luminous intensity to be made in the ordinary way. A difficulty in this method is the very wide range to be covered, the apparent luminous intensity in the centre of the beam being often 100 times that near the edge. It is, however, common practice to regard as the edge of the beam that line along which the luminous intensity is equal to one-tenth of the maximum [13].

The outdoor photometry of projectors is usually carried out at night, but if the smallest value of illumination to be measured is not too low, e.g. one lux or over, measurements may be made in the daytime if suitable screening is provided, such as that shown in Fig. 260. The area of the aperture in the front screen should be the

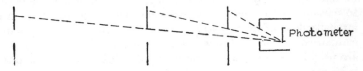

FIG. 260. Screening for Daylight Photometry of Projectors.

minimum permissible, i.e. the same as that of the photometer standard surface, so that if the distance between this screen and the photometer is, say, forty times the diameter of the aperture (e.g. 2 metres for a 5 cm. photometer disc), the " daylight factor " of the card is about 0·02 per cent (see p. 406). It follows that on a day in which the general illumination is 10,000 lux, if the background of the projector has a reflection factor of about 10 per cent, the illumination of the photometer surface due to stray light will be $1,000 \times 0·0002$, i.e. 0·2 lux. This illumination can be determined to the necessary accuracy by means of blank measurements before and after the experiment, and the amount found can then be subtracted from the measured illumination in the beam.

A different method of screening can be used if the measurements are made with a telephotometer. A diaphragm is placed in the focal plane of the telescope objective and the aperture in this is only slightly larger than the image of the projector so that nearly all stray light is excluded and what remains is allowed for as described in the last paragraph. An instrument of this kind in which the measurements are made photo-electrically [14] is shown in Fig. 261. The telescope is directed at the projector so that the image of the latter falls entirely within the aperture in the diaphragm D. The light then passes to a photocell P through a sensitivity correction

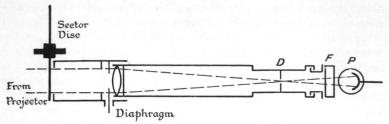

FIG. 261. Photo-electric Telephotometer for the Measurement of Projectors.

filter F. In front of the objective is a diaphragm of variable aperture for altering the scale of the instrument.

In order to allow for the effect of atmospheric absorption, readings are taken at intervals with a source of known luminous intensity substituted for the projector being measured. If the luminous intensity of this projector is very high it may be necessary to measure it by comparison with another projector of much lower intensity and of even distribution, this in turn being measured by comparison with the known source. Sector discs or neutral filters are used as required when the range of values of luminous intensity is larger.

In all photometry of projection apparatus it is essential that the source should be maintained accurately at the focus of the optical device [15]. This is not always easy to arrange when the source is an electric arc in which the carbons are gradually being consumed. The provision of a lens and scale device, termed a " focus-scope ", at the side of the barrel is a great help in this adjustment. Since the arc is frequently difficult to control for long periods, the value of telephonic communication between the projector station and the photometer station can hardly be over-estimated.

Arc-light photometry with ordinary comparison sources has the great disadvantage of introducing a large colour difference into the photometer field. Since the accuracy aimed at (or, indeed, attainable) is generally not higher than 2 to 5 per cent, the use of coloured glasses to produce an approximate colour match is almost universal in the visual photometry of searchlights.

Atmospheric Absorption—Various methods have been used for measuring and allowing for atmospheric absorption when this is not more than 10 to 20 per cent. These methods may be referred to as (i) direct measurement, (ii) the standard-beam method, and (iii) the double-range method.

The first of these methods consists in a subsidiary determination of the absorption factor of the atmosphere by means of a telephotometer or other special apparatus (see p. 444).

The second method is that described in the last section in connection with the use of the photo-electric telephotometer.

The third method consists in having two photometer stations instead of one and making measurements of the illumination at a given part of the beam at both stations. If these are nearly in a straight line with the projector, only a slight movement of the beam is necessary, and the two measurements can be made very quickly one after the other. If the distances of the stations are d_1 and d_2, then when the transmission factor of the atmosphere is τ per unit distance the illuminations are respectively

$$E_1 = I\tau^{d1}/d_1{}^2 \quad \text{and} \quad E_2 = I\tau^{d2}/d_2{}^2,$$

or, eliminating τ,

$$d_2 \log (d_1{}^2 E_1/I) = d_1 \log (d_2{}^2 E_2/I).$$

The calculations are much simplified if $d_2 = 2d_1$, so that

$$I = d_1{}^2 E_1{}^2/4E_2.$$

This method depends on the assumption that τ is constant over the whole range d_2, and consequently very contradictory results are sometimes obtained, especially over land, where slight ground mists, which are the chief source of trouble, are very variable in density from place to place [16].

Lighthouse Projectors—The lens system used for lighthouses consists of two parts, viz. a central convex lens, divided into a number of steps known as " Fresnel " or " dioptric " elements, and an outer zone of total reflection prisms or " catadioptric " elements. Both of these systems are so arranged as to give a horizontal beam of light of the smallest divergence possible with the size of source used.

The source is usually a large incandescent mantle or a tungsten lamp with the filament arranged so as to occupy a small volume at the focus of the optical system. It may usually be treated as spherical, at least to a first approximation. In many lights the optical system rotates about a vertical axis through the source, so that the effect at a distant point is that of a series of flashes at regular intervals [17].

From the theoretical treatment given on p. 461 it will be seen that the measurement of apparent luminous intensity of a projector of this kind may be made in exactly the same way as for a parabolic mirror of equal size [18], for the total reflection prisms act in exactly the same way as a mirror, giving elementary beams whose divergence is equal to that of the beams they receive while the outer parts of the central lens give beams of greater divergence. It follows that errors calculated on the same basis as for a mirror cannot be exceeded by the lens so long as the source is uniform in luminance. In practice, however, especially in the case of a tungsten filament lamp this assumption cannot be made [19] and much greater distances are necessary for making the measurements.

Sometimes the method is adopted of measuring the apparent luminous intensity of separate portions of the whole optical system by blocking out the remainder with opaque screens. The luminous intensity of the whole system is then obtained by addition [20]. In this way it is possible to make the measurements at shorter ranges, since the range may be reduced more than in proportion to the aperture of the system exposed. The position of the photometer must be arranged separately for each element measured, so that the line joining that element with the photometer makes the same angle in every case with the axis of the main beam. Thus if a projector is being measured in a direction making an angle α with the axis, the photometer must be placed on the line L_1P_1 (Fig. 262) when the element L_1 is being measured, and on the line L_2P_2 when L_2 is being measured, otherwise the luminous intensities for the two elements measured are in directions inclined to each other at the angle L_1L_2/L_1P_1.

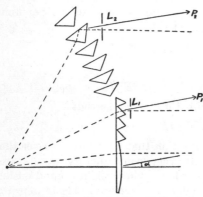

FIG. 262. The Step-by-Step Method of Projector Photometry.

Photometry of Small Projection Apparatus—The same principles as regards the range at which measurements may be made apply in the case of such apparatus as automobile or locomotive headlights as for searchlights, if all the dimensions are reduced in the same proportion. For example, if a headlight of 20 cm. diameter used with a source of 3·3 mm. radius is measured at a range of 100 metres, the measurements are subject to the same errors as those discussed on p. 463 above. Matters are greatly simplified, however, by the fact that in a photometric laboratory provided with a suitable long photometer room it is possible to make the measurements indoors [21].

The projector may conveniently be mounted on a turn-table provided with a degree scale, while the turn-table itself is carried on a kind of cradle such as that shown in Fig. 263 [22]. A movement of ± 15° to 20° in altitude is generally sufficient.

The distance used in calculating the apparent luminous intensities should be that from the photometer surface to the front face of the projector (see p. 462). This distance should always be quoted with the measured values so that an estimate may be formed of the magnitude of the errors to which the measurements are liable.

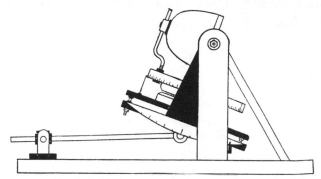

FIG. 263. Tilting Frame for Small Projectors.

Curves of light distribution for projection apparatus should always be drawn with rectangular rather than polar co-ordinates.

Sometimes the distribution of illumination on a surface perpendicular to the axis of the projector and at a given distance from it, e.g. 25 metres or 100 ft., provides more information than a curve or series of curves of distribution of luminous intensity. This is particularly the case when the distribution is asymmetrical or shows rapid changes with angle, as in the case of an automobile headlight designed to reduce dazzle [23]. For certain apparatus, such as a floodlight projector, it is often convenient to express the light distribution by means of a diagram showing, for different directions, not the luminous intensity but the flux emitted within a specified small solid angle. The flux measurements may be made as described later.

Heterogeneous Beams—In some classes of projection apparatus, as, for example, ships' navigation light lenses, the application of the inverse square law to illumination measurements is complicated by the fact that different parts of the optical system form different effective images of the source, and these images may be separated so widely from one another that it is extremely difficulty to locate their photometric centre of gravity or to determine the minimum distance at which this centre of gravity may be assumed to remain sufficiently constant for the application of the inverse square law.

In this connection it will be useful to obtain an expression for the centre of gravity of two sources of luminous intensities I_1 and I_2 placed on the axis of a photometer bench at a distance apart equal to a.

The illumination produced at the photometer screen, distant x, will be the same as that given by a source of luminous intensity $(I_1 + I_2)$ placed between the original sources and at a distance z from I_2, if $(I_1 + I_2)/x^2 = I_1/(x - z + a)^2 + I_2/(x - z)^2$. Neglecting powers of $\left(\dfrac{1}{x}\right)$ above the first, this becomes

$$(I^1 + I_2) = I_1\left(1 + \frac{2(z - a)}{x}\right) + I_2\left(1 + \frac{2z}{x}\right),$$

i.e. $(a - z)I_1 = zI_2$ or $z = aI_1/(I_1 + I_2)$, and the inverse square law may be assumed to hold if applied from the position of the centre of gravity so long as the second order terms may be neglected. The error in the illumination at distance x, owing to the omission of these terms, is $\left\{3I_1\dfrac{(z - a)^2}{x^4} + 3I_2\dfrac{z^2}{x^4}\right\}$, which, expressed as a fraction of the true illumination $(I_1 + I_2)/x^2$, is $3\{I_1(z - a)^2 + I_2z^2\}/(I_1 + I_2)x^2$. Putting $z = aI_1/(I_1 + I_2)$, this becomes $3a^2I_1I_2/x^2(I_1 + I_2)^2$, so that the error involved in assuming the inverse square law to hold from the centre of gravity is less than 1 per cent so long as x exceeds $10a\sqrt{3I_1I_2}/(I_1 + I_2)$. If $I_1 = I_2$ this becomes $5a\sqrt{3}$. As the ratio I_2/I_1 departs from unity the accuracy is improved. For instance, if $I_2 = 9I_1$, x may be reduced to $3a\sqrt{3}$.

In projection apparatus where different parts of the optical system produce separate images, the position of the centre of gravity of the images is obtained by measuring the light from each image separately, calculating its position, and then finding the centre of gravity as a result of these measurements, using the ordinary formula $\bar{x} = \Sigma I_1x_1/\Sigma I_1$. In each set of measurements the whole of the optical system, except that being measured, is covered with an opaque screen, so that the light reaching the photometer is derived only from the particular part of the optical system under investigation. It sometimes happens that the position of the centre of gravity of the images, or the " effective light centre " as it is called, is immaterial under the conditions of use. In that case the sum of the separate apparent luminous intensities of the images produced by the different parts of the optical system is the required apparent luminous intensity of the whole system, but in basing calculations of illumination on the figure of luminous intensity thus obtained, it must be remembered that the distance at which the inverse square law may be assumed to hold must be large in comparison with the maximum separation of the various images contributing to the total illumination.

Total Flux Measurements—For many purposes a measurement of the total luminous flux in the beam given by a projector may be of value quite apart from the details of distribution contained in a curve of apparent luminous intensity. This measurement can often be made quickly and conveniently by means of some form of photometric integrator (see Chapter VIII). A small projector may be placed inside a sphere or cube so long as the beam is directed towards a suitable part of the sphere wall (see p. 282) and the projection apparatus is whitened outside (see p. 268). Alternatively, the projector may be placed outside an opening in the sphere so that the beam is projected on to the opposite wall. In this case allowance must be made for the effect of the opening, as explained on p. 275. If the projector is large it may be convenient to move the source of light away from the focus in such a way as to produce a real image of suitable dimensions, as shown in Fig. 264. Allowance must then be made for the alteration in the amount of flux from the source

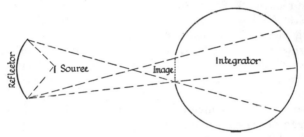

FIG. 264. The Measurement of Total Flux from a Projector.

which reaches the effective aperture of the projector. For example, a searchlight projector consisting of a mirror of radius R and focal length f, with an arc crater of radius r, receives an amount of flux which may be calculated from the formula given in Chapter V (p. 143), putting d equal to $f - (R^2/4f)$. If the crater is moved a distance $0.1f$ away from the mirror, a real image of radius $10r$ is formed at a distance $11f$ from the mirror, while the flux reaching the mirror from the crater is now less by a calculable amount, so that the readings obtained must be increased correspondingly.

An alternative method depends on the use of the integrating hemisphere mentioned on p. 280. The projector may be placed at one end of a long blackened room and the beam projected on to the open hemisphere placed at the other end. The total flux contained in different zones of the beam may be measured by providing a series of diaphragms to fit over the face of the integrating hemisphere [24].

Instead of a diffusing hemisphere, a paraboloidal mirror may be used to concentrate the flux on to a small whitened disc placed at or near the focus of the mirror, and the luminous intensity of this disc may then be measured by means of a photometer. This luminous intensity is proportional to the total flux received by the mirror. Apparatus of this kind must be calibrated by means of a steady beam, the total flux in which can be measured by a step-by-step method [25].

Lighting Fittings—Many lighting fittings, especially those used for such purposes as street lighting, include reflector or refractor elements or both. The form of the light distribution curve is therefore subject to some uncertainty if the measurements are made at too short a distance from the apparatus [26]. In most cases, however, the source is comparatively large so that any errors caused by the action of these elements are likely to be no greater than the errors introduced by other considerations, particularly the relation between the light-giving area of the fitting and the distance at which it is measured.

Measurement of Point Sources—It is sometimes necessary to measure the luminous intensity of a projector or other source of light when it is viewed from such a distance that it may be regarded as a " point source " (see p. 121). The measurement may conveniently be made with a photometer such as that described on p. 446 in which the Maxwellian view is employed, due allowance being made for atmospheric absorption.

Alternatively the source to be measured may be compared visually with another source of known luminous intensity situated at some convenient known distance, arrangements beng made to bring the two close together in the field of view [27].

In the case of a source of small dimensions, such as a reflector stud, the measurement may be made at a moderate distance, using either of the two methods mentioned above [28], or it may even be possible, with a very sensitive photo-electric photometer, to measure the illumination produced by such a source at the point of observation [29].

When a source subtends an angle of less than about 5 to 10 minutes of arc at the observer's eye its appearance is independent of its size or its luminance alone and is determined solely by the illumination it produces at the point of observation (see p. 78). This quantity measures what is frequently termed the " brightness " of a point source, but should strictly be called its " point brilliance " [30]. Point brilliance is measured, therefore, in illumination units of appropriate magnitude, e.g. microlumens per sq. ft., or microlux, or occasionally in terms of the equivalent luminous intensity at a mile or at a kilometre. It will be clear that one microlux is equal to one " candela at a kilometre ". Point brilliance is the same quantity as that measured by " magnitudes " in astronomy (see the next chapter). The scale of magnitudes, however, is logarithmic and it has the disadvantage that increasing numbers represent decreasing values of point brilliance ; it is therefore unsuitable for use in the photometry of terrestrial point sources.

GENERAL REFERENCE

F. A. Benford. Gen. El. Rev., 26, *1923*, pp. 75, 160, 230, 280, 575, 624, 780, 818 and 27, *1924*, pp. 199, 252, 504, 625, 698, 749, 830 and 28, *1925*, pp. 193 and 526.
J. M. Waldram, Illum. Eng. Soc. Lond., Trans., 16, *1951*, p. 187.

REFERENCESS

1. A. Blondel. *Théorie des Projecteurs Electriques* (Lahure, Paris, *1894*), p. 17 ; L'Industrie El., 2, *1893*, pp. 517 and 541.

2. Illum. Eng. Soc. N.Y., Trans., 10, *1915*, p. 905 and papers in Gen. El. Rev. referred to above.
See also A. Blondel and C. Lavanchy, Ann. de Phys., 7, *1917*, p. 249 ; J. Dourgnon and P. Waguet, Soc. Franç. des Elect., Bull., 9, *1929*, p. 599 ; J. W. Ryde and D. E. Yates, C.I.E., Proc., 7, *1928*, p. 359 ; L. Dunoyer, C.R., 226, *1948*, p. 1129 and Rev. d'Opt., 27, *1948*, p. 399.
On the distribution of light from optical systems in general, see A. C. Hardy, Frank. Inst., J., 208, *1929*, p. 773.

3. F. A. Benford. Gen. El. Rev., 26, *1923*, p. 230.
O. Reeb. Optik, 9, *1952*, p. 254.

4. G. Gehlhoff and H. Schering. Z. f. Bel., 25, *1919*, pp. 35 and 83.
H. Erfle. *Ibid.*, 26, *1920*, pp. 4 and 11 (see also pp. 103 and 111).
F. A. Benford. Gen. El. Rev., 26, *1923*, p. 624.
See also V. V. Novikov, State Opt. Inst. Leningrad, Trans. (Trudui), 6, *1931*, No. 59, p. 57 (In Russian) ; W. Kleinschmidt, Licht, 6, *1936*, p. 37 ; H. Slevogt, *ibid.*, 8, *1938*, p. 85 ; G. Kapp, *ibid.*, 10, *1940*, p. 101.

5. A. Blondel and C. Lavanchy. Ann. de Phys., 8, *1917*, p. 51.
J. W. T. Walsh. Opt. Convention, *1926*, Proc., Vol. I, p. 378.
W. M. Hampton. Opt. Soc., Trans., 30, *1929*, p. 185.

6. C. Féry. Lum. El., 50, *1893*, p. 551.

7. F. A. Benford. Illum. Eng. Soc. N.Y., Trans., 10, *1915*, p. 905.
G. Gehlhoff. Z. f. Bel., 25, *1919*, p. 35.

8. J. W. T. Walsh. Opt. Convention, *1926*, Proc. Vol. I, p. 378.

9. On the distribution of illumination in the beam when the source is a disc of non-uniform luminance see A. M. Godfert, Soc. Franç. des Elect., Bull., 4, *1944*, p. 125 ; A. Rey and C. Févrot, Rev. d'Opt., 28, *1949*, p. 79.

10. C. C. Paterson, J. W. T. Walsh, A. K. Taylor and W. Barnett. Inst. El. Eng., J., 58, *1920*, p. 83.

11. F. A. Benford. Gen. El. Rev., 22, *1919*, p. 668.
W. M. Hampton. Illum. Eng. Soc. Lond., Trans., 3, *1938*, p. 52.

12. See also F. Born and H. Knauer, Licht, 3, *1933*, p. 245.

13. F. A. Benford. Gen El. Rev., 26, *1923*, p. 280.
See also E.T.Z., 45, *1924*, p. 1318 ; J. Bergmans and H. A. E. Keitz, Illum. Eng., 24, *1931*, p. 284.

14. H. K. Cameron, E. H. Rayner, E. R. Thomas and G. T. Winch. " Symposium on Searchlights " (Illum. Eng. Soc., London, *1947*), p. 50.

15. E. W. Chivers and D. E. H. Jones. " Symposium on Searchlights " (Illum Eng. Soc., London, *1947*), p. 7.

16. S. Harcombe. Opt. Convention, *1926*, Proc., Vol. I, p. 388.
See also A. Marsat, Soc. Franç des Elect., Bull., 10, *1940*, p. 53.
For a table of the frequency with which different values of atmospheric absorption have been found to occur, see E. Allard, Ann. des Ponts et Chaussées, 12, *1876*, p. 5 ; A. Blondel, Illum. Eng., 8, *1915*, p. 86 ; J. Rey, *De la Portée de Projecteurs de Lumière Electrique* (Berger-Levrault, Paris, *1915*), p. 77 ; Eng. trans. by J. H. Johnson (Constable, *1917*), p. 77.

17. On the determination of the illumination-time curve of a flashing lighthouse projector, see A. Blondel, Rev. Gén. de l'El., 33, *1933*, pp. 747, 788 and 811.

18. H. N. Green. Illum. Eng., 20, *1927*, pp. 101 and 133.
See also A. Blondel, Int. Illum. Congress, *1931*, Proc., Vol. I, p. 528.

19. W. M. Hampton. Opt. Soc., Trans., 29, *1928*, p. 101.

20. A. Blondel. Rev. d'Opt., 12, *1933*, p. 97.
W. M. Hampton. Opt. Soc., Trans., 29, *1928*, p. 101.
See also British Standard No. 942.

21. Photo-electric apparatus for tracing out the light distribution curve automatically has been described by R. Sewig and W. Vaillant (see note (22) on p. 285).
See also A. Blondel, C.R., 188, *1929*, p. 1464 ; A. Marsat and P. Cibié, Soc. Franç. des Elect., Bull., 8, *1938*, p. 869.

22. J. Bergmans and H. A. E. Keitz. Illum. Eng., 24, *1931*, p. 284 ; Philips Techn. Rev., 9, *1947*, p. 114.
See also E. Perucca, Elettrot., 13, *1926*, p. 45.

23. See, e.g., P. Bossu, C.I.E., Proc., 6, *1924*, p. 423 ; F. Born, E.T.Z., 51, *1930*, p. 1239 ; Illum. Eng. Soc. N.Y., Trans., 17, *1922*, p. 105 and 25, *1930*, p. 835 ; O. Höpcke, Licht, 6, *1936*, pp. 150 and 213.

24. F. A. Benford. Opt. Soc. Am., J., 6, *1922*, p. 1040.
G. A. Horton. Illum. Engng., 44, *1949*, p. 475.

25. C. H. S. Evans and H. C. Gibson. Opt. Convention, *1926*, Proc., Vol. I, 407.

26. See, e.g., A. R. Myhill, Gas J., 160, *1922*, pp. 494, 570 and 628 ; Light and g .,29, *1936*, p. 87.

27. H. Beck. Licht, 11, *1941*, p. 160.
See also A. Blondel, Int. Illum. Congress, *1931*, Proc., Vol. I, p. 240.

28. National Phys. Laboratory Ann. Report, *1928*, p. 159.
W. Dziobek. Z. f. techn. Phys., 14, *1933*, p. 557.
G. A. Van Lear. Opt. Soc. Am., J., 30, *1940*, p. 462.
British Standard No. 2515 or 2516.
See also G. Peri, Elettrot., 19, *1932*, p. 815 ; W. S. Stiles, British J. Ophthalmology, 28, *1944*, p. 629.

29. W. F. Little and A. E. Parker. Illum. Eng. Soc. N.Y., Trans., 37, *1942*, p. 789.
See also L. T. Minchin, Illum. Eng., 23, *1930*, p. 280 ; R. Kingslake, Opt. Soc. Am., J., 28, *1938*, p. 323 ; P. Jainski, Lichttechnik, 3, *1951*, p. 112 and 5, *1953*, pp. 40 and 68.

30 C.I.E., Proc., 10, *1939*, Vol. III, p. 1.

CHAPTER XV

STELLAR PHOTOMETRY

One of the earliest applications of photometric measurement was to the determination of the relative " magnitudes " of the heavenly bodies [1]. It is therefore appropriate to give a brief outline of the principal methods and instruments now used for stellar photometry, although the subject is a very specialised one with an extensive literature and for detailed information the works mentioned in the Bibliography at the end of this chapter should be consulted.

The light-giving power of stars has, since the time of Ptolemy [2], been expressed in terms of an arbitrary scale, the magnitude of any particular star being obtained by comparing it with one or more reference stars in its immediate vicinity. The scale of magnitudes has always been approximately, and is now strictly logarithmic, being of the form $\log_{10} E = 0.4 (1 - m)$, where m is the magnitude of a star and E the ratio of its apparent intensity to that of a first magnitude star [3]. The ratio of the apparent intensities of successive magnitudes is thus $\sqrt[5]{100} = 2.512$. The term " apparent intensity " used here must be distinguished from luminous intensity. For any source of light which can be regarded as a point source as far as its visual appearance is concerned (see p. 78), the quantity which corresponds to " magnitude " in the case of a star is proportional to the illumination which the source produces at the observer's eye and it is therefore expressible in illumination units. For a terrestrial source the term " point brilliance " is used (see p. 472). It will be clear that the magnitude of a star can only be expressed on an absolute scale if the illumination produced by a first magnitude star at the earth's surface is known. A number of determinations of this quantity have been made [4] and the value is approximately 0·88 micro-lux (2·3 mile-candles).

The estimation of magnitude was at first made purely by eye [5], and later by bringing telescopic images of the two stars to be compared into as close juxtaposition as possible, generally by placing inclined mirrors or reflecting prisms in front of the objective [6]. Various methods of altering the brightness of one image to equality with the other were used by different workers [7]. A favourite method was the reduction of the effective aperture of one objective by means of a variable diaphragm [8], or by a wire gauze screen or a rotating sector [9]. In some cases a terrestrial source was used as an artificial " star " and the various real stars were compared with this in turn instead of with each other.

The Zöllner Photometer—The visual photometers now employed may be divided into two classes, viz. those in which a local source of light is used to give a comparison " star " of controllable intensity and those in which the images of two neighbouring stars are compared, the intensity of one, or both, being varied in a known manner until apparent equality is obtained. A third class, of which Pritchard's wedge photometer was typical, were the so-called " absolute " photometers in which the image of a star was reduced to extinction [10], but these are now no longer used (see p. 3).

Typical of the first class is the Zöllner photometer illustrated, in its simplest form, in Fig. 265. This instrument has undergone a

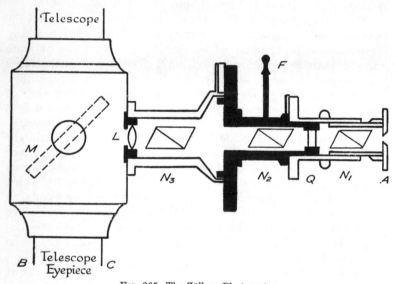

FIG. 265. The Zöllner Photometer.

number of modifications of form at various times, but the general principle has remained the same [11]. An artificial star is formed by a small aperture in the diaphragm A, behind which is placed a source of light of constant intensity, generally with a colour correction filter. The light from A passes through the Nicol prisms N_1, N_2 and N_3, the quartz plate Q, and the lens L, and is then reflected from the front and back surfaces of the glass plate M. The intensity and colour of the reflected images are varied by rotating the different parts of the optical train, the colour by rotating N_1 relative to N_2 and Q (see p. 300) [12], and the intensity by rotating the whole system

N_1QN_2, relative to N_3, by means of the handle F. N_3 is fixed in relation to the tube BC, which forms part of the eyepiece of a telescope through which the star is viewed. The telescope is so directed that the image of the star under observation is seen between the reflected images of A, so that these may be accurately adjusted to equality with it. By an obvious change of design the real star may be seen by reflection, and the artificial star by transmitted light [13]. Apparatus has been designed for automatically registering the readings made at night with this instrument [14].

Photometers in which a neutral wedge is used in front of an artificial star to reduce its brightness to equality with that of the image of a real star have been extensively used [15].

The instrument described on p. 446, for measuring the absorption of the atmosphere, may clearly be used for stellar photometry [16]. It has the great advantage that by the employment of the Maxwellian view the photometric comparison is made between extended surfaces instead of point images.

The Meridian Photometer—The most important instrument of the second class is the meridian photometer of E. C. Pickering, shown in Fig. 266 [17]. This consists essentially of a telescope with a

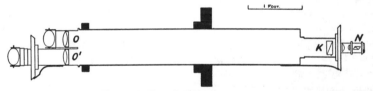

FIG. 266. The Meridian Photometer.

double objective and a single eyepiece. The telescope is placed horizontally in the east-west direction, and each objective is furnished with a mirror or 45° reflecting prism which can be rotated about the instrument axis so that the images of any two stars on or near the meridian can be compared. In practice the scale of magnitude is based on the mean values assigned to a large number of circumpolar stars, so that periodic variations are eliminated [18]. In the first form of the instrument the beams of light from the two objectives O, O' both pass through the same double-image prism K, which, consisting of a wedge of quartz or of Iceland spar cemented to a glass wedge, is approximately achromatic for a mean value of separation of the images. The position of this prism in the telescope is adjusted for each experiment, and is such that the " extraordinary " image of one of the stars to be compared is brought close to the " ordinary " image of the other, the two remaining images being stopped off. In a later form of the instrument [19] each beam of light passes through a separate achromatic prism, and the positions of these two prisms are so adjusted for each experiment that the two required images in the double-image prism are side by side when the latter is kept fixed at a point just within the common focus of the objectives. In both instruments a rotatable Nicol N in front of the eyepiece gives, by the angle of rotation necessary to produce equality, the relative intensities of the images (see p. 32). Each observation must be repeated with the position of the star images reversed in the field. This is necessary, owing to the fact that the retina is not equally sensitive all over, so that there is generally a tendency to over-estimate the magnitude of the lower stars in any field. This error may amount to several tenths of a magnitude [20], but when it has been eliminated by reversal the visual method, using a good instrument, is capable of an accuracy of at least 0·1 magnitude for neighbouring stars. Varying atmospheric conditions prevent a similar accuracy when the stars to be compared are widely separated and an artificial star has been used for making the comparison in this case [21].

Photographic Methods—Although a vast amount of useful work in stellar photometry has been done by visual methods, it will be clear from the brief account given above that there are special features in this particular problem of photometry which make physical methods more promising for accurate work, especially in the determination of the magnitudes of the fainter stars. For instance, the photographic plate possesses the great advantage of being able to integrate with respect to time the light reaching it. Unfortunately, length of exposure and increase of intensity are not exactly equivalent in producing blackening, and the connection is found to be different for different types of plates (see p. 365). The relation may, however, be determined for any given plate by subsidiary experiment.

It will be clear that, since the sensitivity of the photographic plate differs from that of the eye, the results obtained with it when comparing stars of different colours are not the same as those found visually ; magnitudes determined by means of an uncorrected photographic plate are known as " photographic magnitudes ". If, however, a panchromatic plate is used with a colour filter which makes the sensitivity curve of the combination resemble that of the photopic eye, the " photo-visual magnitudes " so obtained agree well with those found visually.

The photographic methods used for stellar photometry may be divided into two classes. In the first, an image of the star to be measured is focused on the plate. The magnitude may then be determined from a measurement of either the density or the diameter of the photographic image, for the optical image of a star is not a mathematical point, but a disc which decreases in intensity from the centre outwards. It follows that increase in either the brightness of the star image or the time of exposure will cause an enlargement of the area over which perceptible darkening takes place. From what has been said concerning the effect of exposure on photographic density, it naturally follows that the relation connecting diameter with exposure must be dependent on the particular plate used. Various empirical formulae have been proposed, e.g. the Greenwich formula $m = a - b\sqrt{d}$, where d is the diameter of the image of a star of magnitude m and a and b are constants for a particular plate [22]. Such a formula is generally used purely for interpolation, the image of the undetermined star being compared either with those of reference stars of known magnitude photographed on the same plate, or with a series of images of a single star successively reduced in intensity by mechanical means such as a sector diaphragm or a series of wire gauze screens placed over the objective [23].

The Objective Grating Method—A scale of magnitudes may be formed from one star at a single exposure by placing over the objective of the telescope a coarse diffraction grating (see p. 26) formed of wires spaced at equal intervals. The effect of such a grating is to convert each star image into a series of separate images of gradually diminishing intensity. If the thickness of the wires is t and the breadth of the spaces between them s, the distance apart of the images is $f\lambda/(t+s)$ where f is the focal length of the telescope objective and λ the wave-length of the light [24]. If the relation between the light intensities of the successive images is known, either by calculation or by subsidiary photometric measurement, these images can be used to establish a calibration curve for a photographic plate. If, then, two stars are photographed side by side, the undiffracted image of the lesser star can be located on the scale established by the diffracted images of the greater star, and so the relative magnitudes can be determined.

There are several considerations which limit the application of this method in any particular case. It is clearly necessary that the diffraction images should be distinct from one another, and, as the formula for their separation shows, an upper limit is thus set to $(t+s)$ for any given value of f and λ. On the other hand, it is seen from the same formula that, since the light forming the image is not monochromatic, each diffraction image will be spread out into a spectrum to an extent depending on (i) the wave-length range of the light, and (ii) the value of $f/(t+s)$. Hence it is desirable that $(t+s)$ should approach as closely as possible to the permissible maximum. The value of $(t+s)$ may therefore be regarded as fixed within a very narrow range. The respective values of s and t must be determined by a compromise, for, on the one hand, the absolute brightness of the images naturally increases with s, so that t must not be too great if the loss of light is not to be excessive, while, on the other hand, since the ratio of the intensity of the nth diffraction image to that of the central undiffracted image is, theoretically [25],

$$\{n\pi s/(s+t)\}^{-2}\sin^2\{n\pi s/(s+t)\},$$

too large a value of $s/(s+t)$ causes the scale to become too coarse and the number of images too small [26]. The actual relative intensities of the images may be measured directly by the method illustrated in Fig. 267 [27]. Light from the slit of a monochromator L is collimated by the parabolic mirror M_1 and after traversing the grating, G, is focused by the second parabolic mirror M_2 on the slit S after reflection from the plane mirror M_3 so that, in effect, an image of the monochromator slit is formed at S and its intensity can be measured with the photocell P. The wires of G and the two slits are parallel and M_2 can be rotated slowly about an axis parallel to them so that the relative intensities of the various images formed by diffraction at G can be determined.

Comparison of Densities—The relative magnitudes of two stars may be estimated by comparing the densities instead of the diameters of their photographic images, using for this purpose some form of microphotometer (see Chapter XIII) [28]. In this case, too, the image of one star is compared with a graded series of images of another star. When sufficient light is available it is possible to use images which are considerably out of focus so that they no longer vary appreciably in size, but only in density [29]. The density measurement

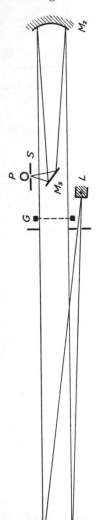

Fig. 267. The Measurement of the Intensities of Grating Images.

is as before made with some form of microphotometer [30]. An enlarged area of blackening on the plate may be obtained with a focused image by giving the plate a small regulated movement during the exposure [31]. One of the chief sources of error in this method is sky fog, the effect of which is naturally greatest for the lesser magnitude stars [32]. A visual method depending on the use of an out-of-focus image has also been described [33].

Images of uniform density can be obtained by the Fabry method [34] in which the principle of the Maxwellian view is used (see p. 152). A diaphragm with a small aperture is placed in the focal plane of the telescope objective, while a lens of very short focal length (about 3 cm.), close behind the aperture, forms an image of the objective on a photographic plate. This image is uniform and its density is a measure of the light reaching the objective from that portion of the sky whose image just fills the aperture in the diaphragm. Clearly this method is very suitable for measuring the integrated magnitude of irregular objects such as small nebulae or star clusters.

The Photo-electric Method—The most recent development in stellar photometry is the increasing use of the photocell. Since this measures the total flux incident on it, and not the illumination, an out-of-focus image is used and in fact this should not be too small or errors may be introduced by small inequalities in the sensitivity of the photocell surface (see p. 97) [35]. A convenient arrangement for the apparatus is shown diagrammatically in Fig. 268 [36]. AA is the ocular end of the telescope, the image of the star under observation being formed within a small aperture in the diaphragm BB, so that the energy from this star alone reaches the cell. The reflecting prism C and auxiliary telescope D are provided for the purpose of positioning the image at B. C is swung out to the side when a measurement is made, and the light passes on to the photocell M, which is enclosed in a light-tight box KK open only at H, where a glass filter may be placed. The electrometer W, which is used

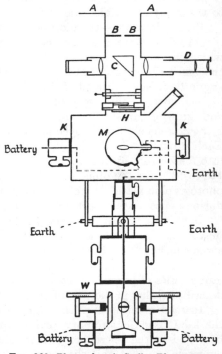

FIG. 268. Photo-electric Stellar Photometer.

for the measurements, is attached to K by a Cardan suspension, which allows it always to remain vertical as the telescope is moved. Alternatively if a Lindemann electrometer is used [37], this can be rigidly attached to the remainder of the apparatus [38]. For the measurement of very faint stars the photocurrent may be amplified. In this case the amplifier is usually attached rigidly to the telescope, the current being measured with a galvanometer which is separately mounted and connected to the amplifier by suitably shielded leads [39]. Alternatively, a photo-multiplier cell (see p. 98) may be used [40]. In order to measure magnitudes on the visual scale a colour filter must be used to correct the sensitivity curve of the cell to the photopic curve of relative luminous efficiency. This is usually placed above the window H in Fig. 268. With due precautions it is possible, except in the case of very faint stars, to attain an accuracy approaching 0·003 mag. [41], as compared with 0·02 to 0·04 mag. with a visual photometer [42], or 0·02 to 0·1 mag. by the photographic method [43]. A particularly valuable application of the photo-electric method is to the study of variable stars [44].

Other Problems—In addition to the determination of stellar magnitudes, there are various problems of celestial photometry which can only be mentioned here. Such are the measurement of the general brightness of the night sky [45] and the brightness of the sky in the neighbourhood of the sun [46].

The spectrophotometry of celestial bodies is a subject of great and growing importance in astrophysics, photographic methods being now generally employed in preference to visual observation [47]. Each star image in the focal plane of a telescope may be elongated into a spectrum by placing a prism with a refracting angle of some 12° to 16° over the objective. These spectra may be recorded on a photographic plate [48] and if the plate is given a slight movement during exposure the spectra are correspondingly widened.

In order to obtain an intensity scale at each wave-length a grating may be used as well as the prism, in the " prism-crossed-by-grating " arrangement [49]. The directions of dispersion of the prism and grating are at right angles so that each spectral image is converted into a series of parallel spectra of regularly diminishing intensity, as described earlier in the case of ordinary non-spectral measurements.

Instead of using a prism over the objective, a spectrograph of the kind used for ordinary photographic spectrophotometry may be fitted to the telescope, with its slit in the image plane of the objective, so that this slit may be illuminated by any particular star image. One of the methods described in Chapter XI may then be used to determine the spectral distribution [50]. Whichever arrangement is adopted, the standard of spectral distribution is provided by an artificial star of accurately known colour temperature [51].

Various methods have been used for estimating the colours of the stars. Since the ordinary photographic plate has a much higher sensitivity in the blue than in the red, as compared with the eye, photographic magnitudes will be numerically lower than visual or photo-visual magnitudes (see p. 478) for blue stars and higher for red stars. The difference between the two magnitudes for any given star is known as its "colour index" on a scale whose zero is defined by white stars of spectral type A_0 [52]. Blue stars have positive and red stars negative colour indexes. A much more satisfactory method of estimating the colour of a star is to measure its relative magnitude for two regions of the spectrum. The temperature may then be deduced on the assumption that the radiation from the star approximates to full radiation (see p. 40). The sensitivity of the method is increased if the measurements are made with a photocell which is sensitive over a wide range of wave-lengths, e.g. a caesium oxide cell (see p. 98), so that the wave-length bands used are widely separated [53].

BIBLIOGRAPHY

Handbuch der Astrophysik, Vol. II (Springer, Berlin, *1931*) and Vol. VII (*1936*).

Astrophysik. Vol. 26 of Wien-Harms *Handbuch der Experimentalphysik*. (Akademische Verlagsgesellschaft m.b.H., Leipzig, *1937*.)

F. W. Wood (ed.). *Astronomical Photoelectric Photometry*. (American Assn. for the Advancement of Science, *1953*.)

H. F. Weaver. Popular Astronomy, 54, *1946*, pp. 211, 287, 339, 389, 451 and 504.

H. S. Jones. Illum. Eng. Soc. Lond., Trans., 20, *1955*, p. 213.

REFERENCES

1. P. Bouguer. *Essai d'Optique*, pp. 22 *et seqq.* (Sect. I, § vi).

2. *Almagest*. See F. Baily, Roy. Astron. Soc., Memoirs, 13, *1843*, p. 1.

3. N. Pogson. Roy. Astron. Soc., M.N., 17, *1856*, p. 13. (See also Astron. and Meteor. Observations, Radcliffe Observatory, 15, *1854*, p. 297.)

4. H. N. Russell. Astrophys. J., 43, *1916*, p. 103. See also C. Fabry, C.R., 137, *1903*, p. 1242.

5. Ch. Huygens. Opera Varia, *1724*, vol. 2, p. 713 ; Cosmotheoros, Lib. II. F. W. Argelander. Astron. Nachr., 42, *1856*, col. 177 ; Roy. Astron. Soc., M.N., 16, *1856*, p. 206.

6. J. Chacornac. C.R., 58, *1864*, p. 657.

7. See, e.g., Sir W. Herschel, Phil. Trans., 107, *1817*, p. 302 ; K. A. von Steinheil, Ann. d. Phys., 34, *1835*, p. 644 and the other refs. quoted in note (7) on p. 431 of *Photometry* (*1926*).

8. The use of an iris diaphragm is open to the objection that, as the aberrations at the centre and edge of the lens are not the same, the image changes character as the aperture is altered.

9. A. Secchi. Acad. Pontificia dei nuovi Lincei, Atti, 4, *1850–1*, p. 10. S. P. Langley. Am. J. Sci., 30, *1885*, p. 210.

10. See, e.g. the refs. in notes (23) to (29) on p. 432 of *Photometry* (*1926*) and A. Markov, Acad. Sci. U.R.S.S., C.r. (Doklady), 1, *1935*, p. 449.

11. *Grundzüge einer allgemeinen Photometrie des Himmels* (Berlin, *1861*), p. 13 ; *Photometrische Untersuchungen* (Leipzig, *1865*), p. 81.

12. J. C. F. Zöllner. Ann. d. Phys., 135, *1868*, p. 59.
See also W. H. M. Christie, Roy. Astron. Soc., M.N., 34, *1874*, p. 111.

13. G. Müller (J. Wanschaff). Potsdam Astrophys. Obs., Publ., 8, *1893*, p. 1.

14. H. Clemens. Z.f.I., 24, *1904*, p. 129.
K. Schiller. *Ibid.*, 41, *1921*, p. 187.

15. See, e.g., K. Graff, Z.f.I., 35, *1915*, p. 1.

16. H. Schering. Phys. Z., 22, *1921*, p. 71.
J. Dufay. Rev. d'Opt., 8, *1929*, pp. 321 and 460 ; C.R., 190, *1930*, p. 166.
J. Hopmann. Veröffentlichungen d. Univ. Sternwarte, Leipzig, Heft III, *1932*.

17. Harvard Obs., Annals, 11, *1879*, pp. 1 and 195 and 14, *1884*, p. 1 ; Nature, 21, *1879*, p. 23.
See also A. Danjon, C.R., 186, *1928*, p. 1524.

18. E. C. Pickering. Harvard Obs., Annals, 64, *1912*, p. 201.
H. S. Leavitt. *Ibid.*, 71, *1917*, p. 47.
S. Chapman and P. J. Melotte. Roy. Astron. Soc., M.N., 74, *1913*, p. 40.
H. S. Jones. *Ibid.*, 82, *1921*, p. 21.

19. E. C. Pickering. Harvard Obs., Annals, 23, *1890*, p. 1 ; Astrophys. J., 2, *1895*, p. 89.
O. C. Wendell. Harvard Obs., Annals, 69, *1909*, p. 1.

20. A. W. Roberts. Roy. Astron. Soc., M.N., 57, *1897*, p. 483 and 59, *1899*, p. 524.
P. Lasareff. Acad. Imp. des Sci., Petrograd, Bull., 9, *1915*, p. 883.
W. Hassenstein . Astrophys. Obs. Potsdam, Publ., 25, *1926*, No. 83.

21. E. C. Pickering. Harvard Obs., Annals, 70, *1909*, p. 1.

22. G. P. Bond. Astron. Nachr., 49, *1859*, col. 81.
H. H. Turner. Roy. Astron. Soc., M.N., 65, *1905*, p. 755.
J. A. Parkhurst. Astrophys. J., 31, *1910*, p. 15.
C. E. K. Mees. *Ibid.*, 33, *1911*, p. 81.
F. E. Ross. *Ibid.*, 56, *1922*, p. 345.
J. Halm. Roy. Astron. Soc., M.N., 82, *1922*, p. 472.

23. C. W. Wirtz. Astron. Nachr., 154, *1901*, col. 317.
F. H. Seares. Astrophys. J., 39, *1914*, p. 307.

24. E. Hertzsprung. Astron. Nachr., 186, *1910*, col. 177.

25. A. Schuster and J. W. Nicholson. *Theory of Optics*, § 66.

26. S. Chapman and P. J. Melotte. Roy. Astron. Soc., M.N., 74, *1913*, p. 50.
See also H. Bucerius, Astron. Nachr., 246, *1932*, col. 33 ; 247, *1933*, col. 361 and 248, *1933*, col. 201.

27. J. Wempe. Z. f. Astrophys., 5, *1932*, p. 154.

28. A. L. Bennett. Astrophys. J., 78, *1933*, p. 305.
H. Siedentopf and H. Klauder. Astron. Nachr., 254, *1935*, col. 33 and 256, *1935*, col. 173.
H. Kienle. Naturwissenschaften, 23, *1935*, p. 759.
S. P. Liau. Rev. d'Opt., 14, *1935*, p. 305.

29. See, e.g., J. A. Parkhurst and F. C. Jordan, Astrophys. J., 26, *1907*, p. 244 and 36, *1912*, p. 169 ; E. S. King, Harvard Obs., Annals, 59, *1912*, pp. 33 and 95.
See also C. Fabry, Astrophys. J., 31, *1910*, p. 394.

30. See, e.g., A. L. Bennett, Astrophys. J., 78, *1933*, p. 305 ; W. K. Green, Opt. Soc. Am.. J., 25, *1935*, p. 190.

31. B. Meyermann and K. Swarzchild. Astron. Nachr., 170, *1906*, col. 277 and 174, *1907*, col. 137.
W. H. Christie. Astrophys. J., 78, *1933*, p. 313.

32. K. Popoff. C.R., 153, *1911*, p. 1210 and 154, *1912*, p. 925.
R. H. Baker and E. E. Cummings. Laws Obs. Bull. No. 24, *1916*, p. 111.

33. M. Maggini. C.R., 166, *1918*, p. 284.

34. C. Fabry. C.R.; 150, *1910*, p. 272.

35. E. J. Meyer. Z. f. Astrophys., 15, *1938*, p. 163.

36. P. Guthnick. Deut. Phys. Gesell., Verh., 16, *1914*, p. 1021 ; Z.f.I., 44, *1924*, p. 303.

E. E. Cummings. Lick Obs. Bull., 11, *1923*, p. 99.

E. Bouty. Rev. d'Opt., 5, *1926*, p. 31.

E. J. Meyer. Z.f.I., 55, *1935*, p. 111.

37. F. A. and A. F. Lindemann and T. C. Keeley. Phil. Mag., 47, *1924*, p. 577.

38. A. F. and F. A. Lindemann. Roy. Astron. Soc., M.N., 79, *1919*, p. 343.

J. Stebbins. Astrophys. J., 74, *1931*, p. 289.

39. A. E. Whitford. Astrophys. J., 76, *1932*, p. 213.

G. E. Kron. Lick Obs. Bull., 19, *1939*, p. 53.

See also W. A. Calder, Harvard Obs. Circular No. 405, *1935* ; Q. S. Heidelberg and W. A. Rense, Rev. Sci. Inst., 11, *1940*, p. 386.

40. G. E. Kron. Astrophys. J., 103, *1946*, p. 326. (See also Astronom. Soc. of Pacific, Publ., 59, *1947*, p. 190.)

A. Behr. Z.f. Astrophys., 28, *1951*, p. 254.

41. A. E. Whitford. Astrophys. J., 76, *1932*, p. 213.

G. E. Kron. Lick Obs. Bull., 19, *1939*, p. 59.

42. R. S. Dugan. Astrophys. J., 52, *1920*, p. 154.

J. Dufay. Rev. d'Opt., 8, *1929*, p. 321.

43. F. E. Ross. Astrophys. J., 56, *1922*, p. 345.

44. See, e.g., P. Guthnick and R. Prager, Naturwissenschaften, 3, *1915*, p. 53 ; G. E. Kron, Lick Obs. Bull., 19, *1939*, p. 59 and Astrophys. J., 96, *1942*, p. 173.

45. L. Yntema. Astron. Obs. Gröningen, Publ. No. 22, *1909*.

C. T. Elvey and F. E. Roach. Astrophys. J., 85, *1937*, p. 213.

C. T. Elvey. Astrophys. J., 97, *1943*, p. 65.

46. H. Diercks. Phys. Z., 13, *1912*, p. 562.

J. W. Evans. Opt. Soc. Am., J., 38, *1948*, p. 1083.

47. J. Baillaud. Bull. Astronomique (I), 4, *1924*, p. 275.

48. See, e.g., R. A. Sampson, Roy. Astron. Soc., M.N., 83, *1923*, p. 174 and 85, *1925*, p. 212.

49. E. Hertzsprung. Astron. Nachr., 207, *1918*, col. 75.

W. M. H. Greaves and C. R. Davidson. Roy. Astron. Soc., M.N., 86, *1925*, p. 33.

W. M. H. Greaves, C. R. Davidson and E. Martin. *Ibid.*, 87, *1927*, p. 352 and 94, *1934*, p. 488.

50. E.g., the wedge method. See H. H. Plaskett, Dominion Astrophys. Obs., Victoria, Publ., 2, *1923*, p. 211.

51. W. M. H. Greaves *et al. Loc. cit. supra.*, note (49).

52. K. Schwarzchild. Wien Ber. (IIa), 109, *1900*, p. 1127.

J. A. Parkhurst and F. C. Jordan. Astrophys. J., 27, *1908*, p. 169.

53. J. Stebbins and A. E. Whitford. Astrophys. J., 98, *1943*, p. 20.

See also Y. Öhman, Arkiv f. Mat., Astron. och Fysik, 29B, *1943*, No. 12.

CHAPTER XVI

THE PHOTOMETRIC LABORATORY

The object of the present chapter is to give a brief description of the accommodation required for a small photometric laboratory, and of the more important auxiliary apparatus needed for use in the different branches of photometric measurement dealt with in the foregoing chapters. It will be assumed that the laboratory is to be equipped for the following work : (i) the measurement of luminous intensity in a single direction, and of the total flux given by a source of light of any kind ordinarily met with in practice ; (ii) the determination of light distribution in the horizontal and vertical planes for any source or for any lighting fitting, shade, reflector, etc. ; (iii) the measurement of illumination and the calibration of illumination photometers ; (iv) the spectrophotometry of light sources and the measurement of spectral transmission or reflection curves of coloured media ; (v) colorimetry ; (vi) the life-testing of tungsten filament and discharge lamps ; (vii) the determination of light distribution curves for projection apparatus. In many laboratories, no doubt, one or more of the branches of work enumerated above need not be considered, and it will frequently be found impossible to provide the full accommodation for the whole of the apparatus mentioned below. The following description is intended mainly to serve as a guide by which the actual requirements in any particular laboratory can be approximately estimated with due regard to the special circumstances of each individual case [1].

In considering the general design of the building it should be remembered that it is generally undesirable, if not impossible, to carry on two sets of photometric measurements simultaneously in one room owing to the general necessity in photometric work for avoiding the presence of any lights in the room other than those actually being compared. It follows, therefore, that a number of small rooms must be provided if much time is not to be lost. A very convenient size for a small photometer room is about 20 by 24 feet, as such a room will comfortably accommodate a 5-metre bench in addition to the necessary tables, desk, etc. At the same time it is very desirable to have one room *at least* 100 feet long for the measurement of sources of high luminous intensity and for measurements on projection apparatus.

Power Supply—Before the different rooms are described in further detail, the general electrical supply for the laboratory must be considered, since this affects with almost equal importance every branch of photometric work.

For work of precision, such as measurement of luminous intensity to an accuracy within 1 per cent, the supply voltage must be absolutely steady, and nothing but a storage battery or batteries should be used. Other things being equal, two batteries of 100 amp.-hrs. capacity each are more convenient than one of 200 amp.-hrs., unless lamps taking over 5 amps. are likely to be worked with frequently. The highest potential available should be at least 300 volts, since 240-volt lamps are common and it may be necessary to measure these at an excess voltage of 10 to 15 per cent. The method of splitting up the battery into sections is very important. Since two workers using the same battery must necessarily tend to affect each other, the voltage in one room rising, perhaps, 0·1 per cent when the circuit in another room is switched off, it is a convenience to have the battery so split that, if only 100 to 120 volts are required in each of two rooms, the circuits in these rooms can be run off two separate portions of the battery. In addition to this, it is very convenient in measuring low-voltage lamps taking a large current to be able to use a few cells from the battery instead of having to absorb a large amount of energy in resistances. For these reasons it is generally found

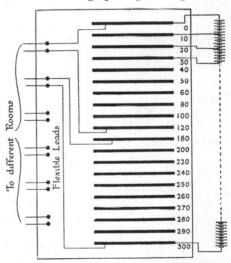

FIG. 269. The Battery Distribution Board.

convenient to divide a 300-volt battery into, say, five sections of thirty cells each, and then to subdivide the two end sections still further. If a 100-volt supply is used for charging the battery, the 60-volt sections can be connected in parallel for charging purposes. A convenient scheme of sub-division is that indicated in Fig. 269, which also shows the method of distribution to different rooms in the laboratory. It will be seen that, by means of the flexible connectors joining the battery bus-bars to the plugs connected with the terminal boards in the different rooms, any desired potential may be obtained in any room in the building [2].

A special room, isolated as completely as possible from the rest of the laboratory, should be provided for the storage batteries, while generators should be located as far as possible from rooms in which it may be necessary to use sensitive galvanometers.

It may be mentioned in passing that, in order to avoid interference between two circuits run off the same battery, when either or both have to be switched on and off frequently (as in measuring a number of lamps in succession), it is customary to use a " dummy " or " balance " circuit method, that is to say, when a lamp is switched off, an artificial load, consisting of one or more electric lamps in parallel, is put on the battery at the same instant by means of a two-way switch [3]. If the current taken by the balance circuit is nearly equal to that taken in the test circuit, no disturbance of the battery voltage is caused.

An A.C. supply is needed for operating electric discharge lamps. This should have a frequency of 50 cycles per second and the waveform should be as nearly sinusoidal as possible. Voltage regulation is most important and it is frequently convenient to use the equipment provided for life-testing electric lamps (see p. 505). Voltage regulation to a precision of about 0·1 per cent is possible with good equipment and this is usually sufficient for the photometry of discharge lamps.

The Bench Photometer Room—As all photometric work must depend ultimately on the measurement of luminous intensity by means of comparison with sub-standards on the photometer bench, the room or rooms in which this work is carried out may be regarded as the basis of the photometric laboratory. The bench room, as it may be called, is conveniently of the size mentioned above. It contains a bench mounted on rigid supports, so that the eyepiece of the photometer head is at a convenient height for an observer when seated. It also contains (i) a table, upon which may be placed the lamps and fittings to be tested, small pieces of apparatus in current use, etc., (ii) a desk for the use of the observers, (iii) special cupboards for storing the sub-standards, working standards and comparison lamps, (iv) an ordinary cupboard for storing small apparatus, (v) a table or bench to accommodate the potentiometer and other apparatus for the precise control of the electric lamps, and (vi) a table for the auxiliary apparatus required in the photometry of gas lamps, or for the indicating instruments required in the control of discharge lamps when these are being measured. The bench room should be provided with a set of fixed sector discs accurately calibrated as described in Chapter VII (see p. 226).

The main lighting of the room should be controlled from a point near the bench as well as from the door. The electrical measuring instruments and the scale on the bench (Fig. 108, p. 192) should have

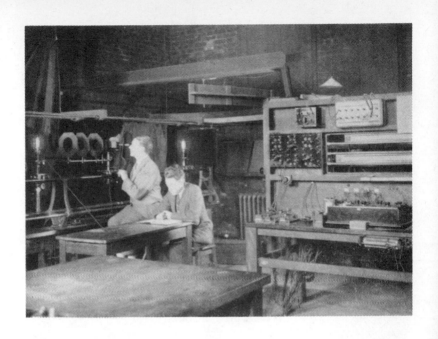

Fig 270.   Photometer Rooms.
Above : The Visual Measurement of Luminous Intensity.
Below : The Photo-electric Measurement of Luminous Flux.

separate individual lighting by low power lamps completely shaded from the observer's eyes. When the general lighting is not in use no surface in the room should have a greater brightness than the photometer field. It has been said already that the larger part of the errors made in photometry are due to stray light reaching the photometer head. Although the screening system described on p. 216 should be sufficient to avoid any possible error from this cause, the custom of painting the walls and ceiling of a bench room a dead black is one to be recommended [4]. The room should, for hygienic reasons, have an adequate number of windows, and these should be provided with internal shutters blackened on the inside so that the daylight can be completely excluded when measurements are in progress. It is convenient to have a vestibule to all doors leading to rooms in which much photometric work is carried out or to provide these rooms with light-trap entrances similar to those frequently used for photographic dark rooms.

The Sphere Photometer Room—It is convenient to have a separate room for measurements of luminous flux. This may be known as the sphere room. It contains the integrating sphere, with its accompanying bench, and electrical equipment as described in the case of the bench room. The structural features, such as rails, overhead tackle, or the like, necessary for enabling the sphere to be moved or to be opened for periodical repainting, must be designed to suit the special circumstances of the case. The sphere should be so arranged that (a) the height of the translucent window, which governs the height of the photometer head when visual methods are used, is convenient for an observer when seated at the bench, and (b) the lamp in the sphere can be easily and quickly changed without any necessity for disturbing the observer at the photometer head. Devices to achieve this have been described already in Chapter VIII, p. 273.

If it is impossible to have separate rooms for the measurement of luminous intensity and luminous flux, so that the sphere must be accommodated in the bench room, it is not infrequently placed close to one end of the bench, or else arrangements are made to enable it to be brought into this position quite easily when measurements of luminous flux are to be made visually. Otherwise the sphere is equipped permanently with its photo-electric apparatus. Generally a single set of electrical equipment is sufficient for both sphere and bench since, as stated earlier, it is practically impossible for two series of photometric measurements to be carried out in one room at the same time.

The Electrical Equipment—Most of the work in a photometric laboratory is concerned with electric lamps and as already stated in

Chapter VI, the most convenient sub-standards and comparison lamps used in modern photometry are electrical. It follows that two very important parts of the installation in the bench-room are the means provided for the ready connection of lamps on the bench to a source of electric supply, and the apparatus used for the adjustment and accurate measurement of potential and current.

Since for a tungsten lamp the luminous intensity varies at about 3·7 times the rate of the potential, while the potential varies nearly

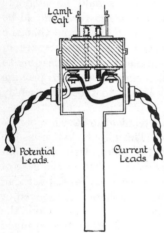

FIG. 271. The Standard Lamp Socket.

twice as much as the current owing to the high positive temperature coefficient of resistance of tungsten, it follows that the electrical measurements should be to an accuracy of at least 0·1 per cent in ordinary work, and 0·02 per cent in standardisation. The best form of indicating instrument is sufficient in the former case, but in the latter a potentiometer method of measurement must be used. Either potential or current may be used as the basis for photometric work. The latter possesses the advantage that the current measured must necessarily be that actually passing through the lamp filament, so that potential drop at the lamp terminals or in the leads may be ignored. On the other hand, potential measurement is, as stated above, nearly twice as sensitive, and if care is taken to avoid bad contacts and, by means of a separate pair of leads, to measure as close

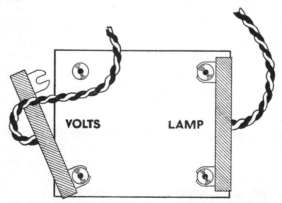

FIG. 272. The Terminal Board on the Photometer Bench.

as possible to the lamp terminals, the errors due to voltage drop can be eliminated.

A convenient form of bayonet lamp holder, in which provision is made for measuring potential at the lamp contacts, is that shown in section in Fig. 271, which is self-explanatory. Similar holders for screw-capped lamps are also required [5]. If the two pairs of leads are each terminated in a small ebonite holder such as that shown in

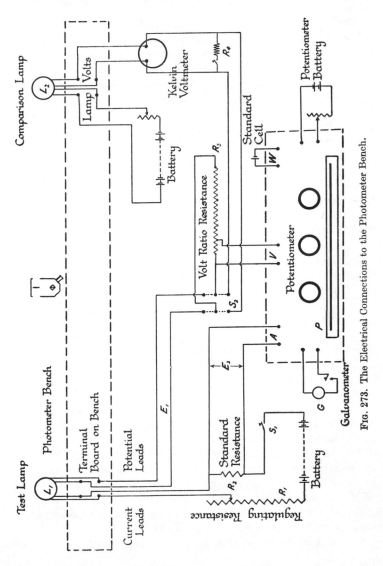

Fig. 273. The Electrical Connections to the Photometer Bench.

Fig. 272, connection to the terminal board fixed on the photometer bench (T in Fig. 107) is quick and easy. In the case of sub-standards mounted specially as described on p. 179, the potential is measured across the ends of permanent leads which are soldered to the lamp contacts. The leads are then connected to either pair of terminals on the terminal board, and the corresponding members of each pair on the board are connected by means of short horizontal copper strips.

The method of control by potential will be described here, but it will be seen that the same circuit, with the omission of the auxiliary pair of potential measuring leads, is equally suitable when current control is employed. The system of electrical connections is shown in Fig. 273. Two or more pairs of leads are brought from the battery distribution board to a terminal board in the bench room. One of these circuits is connected through a regulating resistance R_1 and a switch S_1 to the pair of terminals marked " LAMP " on the small ebonite terminal board fixed to the left-hand end of the bench (see Fig. 107). From this pair of terminals the lamp on the left of the photometer is fed directly. The potential across its contacts is measured by means of the auxiliary leads, which, by way of the other pair of terminals, marked " VOLTS ", are connected through a change-over switch S_2 to the ends of a constant high resistance R_3, generally 10,000 ohms. This resistance has tapping-off points at 100 and 1,000 ohms, so that either one-hundredth or one-tenth of the potential across the lamp contacts may be measured by means of the potentiometer P, using a Weston cell W as the standard of potential, and a galvanometer G. For the purpose of current measurement the small resistance R_2 is included in the circuit supplying the lamp. The value of this resistance is 1 or 0·1 ohm, according to the magnitude of the current to be measured, and its value should be accurate to at least 1 part in 10,000 for precision work. By measuring the potential E_2 across this resistance the current in the lamp circuit is known, being E_2/R_2. Allowance must, however, be made for the small current which is flowing in the potential circuit, for this circuit contains the resistance R_3, so that from the measured current must be subtracted the current through R_3, viz. E_1/R_3, where E_1 is the measured potential across the lamp terminals.

The electrical connections to the lamp L_2 on the right of the photometer may be made in an exactly similar way, but it is generally more convenient to use the same potentiometer for both lamps, and this is achieved by using a double-pole change-over switch at S_2. A separate battery or other source of supply is preferable, but the same source as that supplying L_1 may be used.

In the substitution method of photometry, which is the one most frequently employed in accurate work (see p. 205) the lamp L_2 has to be maintained at a constant luminous intensity, and therefore at a constant potential, throughout a series of photometric measurements. Its potential is adjusted at the beginning of the series and checked at intervals during the course of the work. If, however, the source of supply is at all liable to variation owing to either the fall of potential of a freshly-charged battery, variation in external load, or even the variation of current due to change of the lamp L_1 when the same battery is being used for L_1 and L_2, then it is unsafe to assume constancy of potential on L_2, even over short periods of time, and an electrostatic voltmeter is used for keeping a watch on the potential in the intervals between the check measurements with the potentiometer. It is unsafe to rely on this instrument for very long periods, however, owing to creep in the suspension, so that check measurements should be made at intervals of not more than twenty minutes to half an hour.

The voltmeter should be shunted with a high balancing resistance R_4, which is equal to R_3, and which can be open-circuited when the check measurements are being made. By this means the current in the potential circuit of L_2 is maintained at the same value whether the potentiometer is connected to it or not. The Kelvin electrostatic voltmeter may conveniently have a circular scale of about 10 feet radius, on which 1 volt is represented by about 2 inches in the 100-volt region [6].

It will be clear that the difficulties met with in making the electrical measurements necessary in photometry are, in the main, those met with in all kinds of precision electrical work. Faulty insulation, often due to surface leakage over exposed ebonite parts, or over wood, may be a source of considerable trouble and can only be cured by thorough cleaning, although such expedients as immersion in paraffin wax may prove efficacious. Loose contacts manifest themselves by unsteadiness of indication on the measuring instruments. It may, perhaps, be mentioned here that some electric lamps develop an inherent unsteadiness due to uncertainty of contact between the filament and the leading-in wires (see p. 179). This may be detected by gently tapping the lamp while alight, the galvanometer key on the potentiometer being held down continuously. If the lamp is unsteady the spot will be jerked to one side or the other at every tap.

In laboratories where the accuracy aimed at is not so high, or where it is impossible for some reason or another to adopt the methods of electrical supply and measurement described above, considerable simplifications may be made in the arrangements of the photometer room. Indicating instruments of the laboratory standard type with large scales may, with suitable precautions, be used in place of the potentiometer and Kelvin voltmeter [7], but even in the most approximate photometry the electricity supply from the public service mains is too unsteady for use in the ordinary way. If, however, two electric lamps *of the same type* are being compared, so that the intensity/voltage characteristics are the same on both sides of the photometer, the two lamps may be put in parallel on the outside supply, and if the voltages are adjusted so that both are correct at any instant, the photometric comparison will remain valid to a reasonable degree of accuracy in spite of fluctuations of voltage during the course of the observations [8]. Tungsten filament vacuum lamps or gas-filled lamps may be compared in this way quite satisfactorily, and vacuum lamps may be compared with gas-filled lamps if the voltage changes do not exceed 1 or 2 per cent.

When sources other than filament lamps are being measured, the above procedure cannot be followed and some automatic device

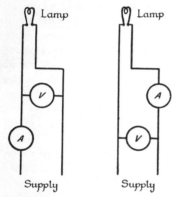

for regulating the voltage on the comparison lamp must be employed [9]. If alternating current is used, a constant voltage transformer provides an easy means of securing quite a good degree of regulation if the supply variations are not too great. The transformer should be used at between about one-quarter and two-thirds of its rated maximum load. Unless the frequency is very constant, a transformer which gives the necessary voltage regulation and is at the

Fig. 274. Alternative Arrangements of Measuring Instruments.

same time insensitive to small changes of frequency should be used. In gas photometry a mantle lamp has been used as a comparison lamp [10].

If indicating instruments are used in place of the potentiometer, they may be connected in either of the two ways shown in Fig. 274. In the first arrangement the voltmeter V is placed in parallel with the lamp, and the current taken by it must therefore be deducted from the current indicated by the ammeter A in order to obtain the true lamp current. In the second arrangement the voltmeter measures the potential drop across both ammeter and lamp, so that the potential drop in the ammeter must be subtracted from the indication of V in order to obtain the true voltage applied at the lamp terminals. If the switch changing from the test lamp to the balance lamps (see p. 488) is on the lamp side of the indicating instruments, the latter are always used with the coils heated to the same temperature.

Alternatively the instruments may be connected as shown in Fig. 275, where G is a galvanometer and R_1 and R_2 are variable resistances. These are adjusted until both the desired indication is obtained on either V or A and the reading on G is zero, indicating that the bridge is balanced. Under these conditions, no corrections are required to the readings of V and A. These may be respectively the pressure and current coils of a watt-meter, which then gives directly the power consumed by the lamp [11].

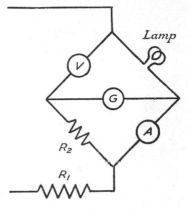

FIG. 275. Bridge for Power Measurement.

It should be noted that all electrical indicating instruments require checking at frequent intervals by means of a potentiometer. Further, unless the instruments used are well shielded, they should not be placed close together or the readings may be affected by mutual interference of the magnetic fields.

Measurements on Discharge Lamps [12]—The electrical measurements needed for the control of discharge lamps are much less straightforward than those described above. These lamps are usually operated on alternating current and need a stabilizer which usually takes the form of an inductive ballast. The wave-form of the lamp current differs considerably from that of the supply and the presence of measuring instruments in the lamp circuit may affect the light output of the lamp unless suitable precautions are taken.

The wave-form of the supply voltage should be as nearly sinusoidal as possible ; it has been specified that the total harmonic content should not exceed 3 per cent., harmonic content being defined as the r.m.s. summation of the individual harmonic components, taking the fundamental as 100 per cent. [13] The ballast used should have accurately known characteristics representative of those of the ballasts generally employed with the particular type of lamp being measured.

A suitable circuit for making the measurements is shown in Fig. 276 [14]. V_1 is a voltmeter connected across the supply ; A is an ammeter which measures the lamp current, together with the currents taken by the voltmeter V_2 and the pressure coil of the watt-meter W when these are in circuit ; its impedance and that of the current coil of the wattmeter should be as low as possible. V_2 is a second voltmeter which measures the voltage across the lamp ; its impedance and that of the pressure coil of the wattmeter should be as high as possible. All the instruments except V_1 can be switched out of circuit when necessary.

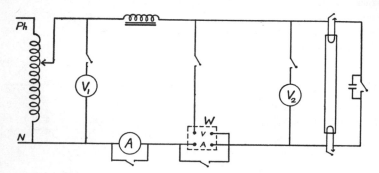

Fig. 276. Electrical Control Circuit for a Discharge Lamp.

Discharge lamps are commonly regulated for photometric measurement by wattage and in adjusting this to the specified value allowance must be made for the watts lost in W unless these are very small, as in an instrument in which the coils are supplied from electronic amplifiers taking only negligible power from the circuit [15]. The correction necessary on account of the presence of W in the circuit may be found by the " light restoration " method. After the lamp has become stabilized, with no instruments in circuit, the light output is carefully determined, although an absolute value is not required at this stage. W is then put into circuit and its reading is noted. The light output of the lamp is now brought back to its former value by increasing the supply voltage and W is read again. The difference between the two readings is the correction to be applied on account of watt losses in the instrument. During the photometric measurements V_2 is switched out of circuit.

The lamp is usually started by means of a manually operated switch. This should be shunted with a condenser of the same capacity as that incorporated in the starter switch normally used with the lamp. After the discharge has been started, the two electrode filaments should be short-circuited by means of the auxiliary switches shown ; otherwise the results obtained may differ slightly according to the way in which the lamp is connected in the circuit [16].

It is to be noted that the performance of a discharge lamp may be considerably affected by the temperature of its surroundings and it is therefore usual to carry out the measurements at some specified ambient temperature or alternatively to state the temperature prevailing at the time of measurement.

When a tubular discharge lamp of considerable length, such as a tubular fluorescent lamp, is placed in an integrating sphere for the measurement of luminous flux, some consideration has to be given to its position relative to the sphere window. The light distribution is symmetrical about the axis of the tube and the polar curve in any plane passing through this axis is very roughly represented by two circles as shown by B in Fig. 90 (p. 150). The spherical reduction factor is therefore approximately $\pi/4$. On the general principle that the luminous intensity of the source in the directions of (a) the window and (b) the area of the sphere opposite to it, should be as far as possible equal to the average luminous intensity, it follows that the axis of the tube should make an angle θ with the diameter passing

through the window of the sphere, where $\cos \theta = \pi/4$. In practice θ may have any value between 30° and 45°. Fluorescent lamps are usually measured with the axis horizontal and Fig. 277 shows in plan the arrangement of the tube and the opaque strip, slightly deeper than the diameter of the tube, required to screen the window.

Stabilization Period—Certain types of lamps, in particular discharge lamps, take some considerable time, up to 30 minutes, to reach a steady state after being switched on [17].

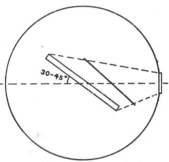

FIG. 277. Position of a Tubular Fluorescent Lamp in an Integrating Sphere.

When a number of such lamps have to be measured, arrangements are sometimes made for several to be run simultaneously in a special pre-heating circuit until the time comes for them to be transferred to the test circuit [18]. If this transfer is made without extinguishing the lamp it may be measured at once. If, however, the lamp is extinguished for a few seconds a further, but much reduced, period of stabilization is required.

Certain types of filament lamps, particularly low voltage lamps taking a comparatively heavy current, require a certain time for the light output to reach its final value, although the delay is usually not so long as with a discharge lamp. This matter has already been mentioned in connection with the battery lamps used in visual illumination photometers (see p. 389). When lamps of this kind, or others such as the bulbs used in miners' lamps, have to be measured in considerable numbers, special arrangements are usually made for each to be in circuit for the period necessary for stabilization before the measurements on it are begun [19].

The Gas Equipment—The measuring apparatus required in the photometry of gas lamps includes (*a*) a consumption meter, (*b*) a pressure regulator, (*c*) a pressure gauge, (*d*) a calorimeter and (*e*) apparatus for determining the atmospheric conditions, viz. pressure temperature and humidity.

The consumption meter used may be of any standard form. The pressure of the gas should be regulated both before and after it passes through the meter. Any ordinary form of regulator may be used for this purpose. The pressure gauge may consist of a simple U-tube containing water or, if high-pressure gas is being used, mercury. It should be placed between the second pressure regulator and the burner, so that the pressure measured is that actually provided at the burner inlet. This is important, since the light output of a mantle is approximately proportional to the rate of consumption of gas (of a given calorific value and specific gravity) and this rate is, in turn, approximately proportional to the square root of the gas pressure [20].

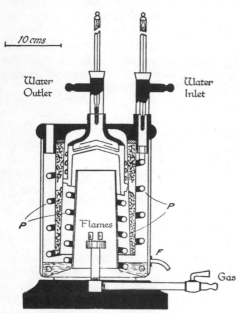

FIG. 278. The Boys' Calorimeter.

A very important factor in the photometry of incandescent gas burners is the calorific value of the gas used and it is therefore necessary to measure the gas with a calorimeter every time photometric measurements are made, since the calorific value may vary by several per cent from time to time. The type of calorimeter generally used is that designed by C. V. Boys [21] and shown in section in Fig. 278. It consists of a base holding a double burner, at which the gas to be measured is burnt at the rate of 4 to 5 cubic feet per hour. A steady flow of water passes through the coiled copper pipe P, P, and the inlet and outlet temperatures T_1 and T_2 are measured when a steady state has been reached. If the quantities of water and gas entering the calorimeter in a given time are respectively W litres and G cubic feet, the gross calorific value of the gas [22] is $1,000(T_2 - T_1)\ W/G$ calories per cubic foot, T_1 and T_2 being measured in degrees Centigrade. This figure is converted to British Thermal Units per cubic foot by multiplying by the constant 0·003968. Small correction factors are applied for (a) difference between the room temperature and the temperature of the air and products of combustion leaving the calorimeter, and (b) the barometric pressure and room temperature.

The general arrangement of the auxiliary apparatus may be as shown diagrammatically in Fig. 279. O is the gas outlet from the

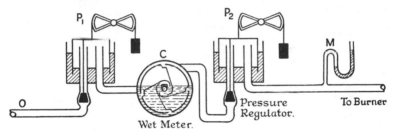

FIG. 279. The Control Apparatus for Gas Testing.

feed pipes, C is the consumption meter, P_1 and P_2 the pressure regulators, and M the manometer or pressure gauge.

A barometer and thermometer for recording the air pressure and temperature are needed, as well as a hygrometer for measuring the humidity. In addition, some form of test burner may be required, so that the combustion characteristics of the gas used for a test may be described in terms of a test-burner number [23].

Sub-standards—The sub-standards of luminous intensity used in the bench room and elsewhere in the laboratory should be lamps of special construction, as described on p. 179, whose luminous intensities have been determined at a standardising laboratory. They should be handled with great care and should be stored in the bench-room in a cupboard specially fitted with shelves as shown in Fig. 280. The upper surface of the shelf at A, where the cap of the lamp rests, should have a washer of rubber or felt to prevent jarring when the lamp is put away. The lamps should always be stored in their normal burning position, i.e. upright in the case of the type of sub-standard described in Chapter VI. The value of luminous intensity assigned to each lamp is generally accurate to about one-quarter of 1 per cent. It should be marked on a small label tied to the flexible lead attached to the lamp. This label should also show (i) the correct voltage of the lamp, (ii) the distance from the photometer screen in millimetres at which the lamp gives an illumination of exactly 10 lux, (iii) the current taken by the lamp, and (iv) the date at which the

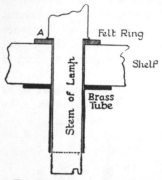

Fig. 280. Section of Shelf for Storing Standard Lamps.

lamp was last standardised. Needless to say, the lamp itself should be indelibly marked with a reference number, and the four items of information above enumerated should be entered in a book under this number, in case the label should be lost.

It may be assumed that a tungsten filament vacuum standard lamp will fall in luminous intensity at a rate not exceeding 5 per cent per 100 hours of actual burning, i.e. if used regularly for five minutes per day, its luminous intensity will decrease at a rate of about 1 per cent per annum. The frequency with which it is sent back to the standardising laboratory for re-standardisation must depend on the number of times it is used and the period of use on each occasion ; five minutes is probably an under-estimate of the time taken for a standardisation by two observers (see p. 210). Where much photometric work has to be done it is frequently found convenient to have several sub-standards and to reserve one or more of these for checking the others at intervals of two or three months. Further, other lamps for use as working standards may be measured by comparison with the sub-standards issued by the standardising laboratory, and these lamps may be used for all photometric work in which the highest accuracy is not required[24]. These lamps may be re-checked at frequent intervals so that changes in their luminous intensity values may at once be detected. In some laboratories the working standards are adjusted, in use, to a definite value of watts instead of a definite voltage. This reduces the effective rate of deterioration of luminous intensity.

The current taken by a sub-standard should be measured on every occasion on which it is used for standardisation, and any difference greater than about 1 part in 2,000 from the value marked on the label should be regarded as an indication of some variation in the lamp itself, or else of some defect in the measuring apparatus involving, possibly, a slight error in the voltage applied to the lamp. The following table shows the results actually obtained over a period of ten years in the re-standardisation of a satisfactory tungsten filament sub-standard lamp :

TYPICAL PERFORMANCE OF STANDARD LAMP AT 100 VOLTS

Date.	Candelas.	Amps.
February, 1913 - -	$14 \cdot 2_1$	0·2337
July, 1916 - - -	$14 \cdot 1_9$	0·2338
May, 1919 - - -	$14 \cdot 1_0$	0·2338
September, 1920 - -	$14 \cdot 0_2$	0·2337
July, 1922 - - -	$14 \cdot 0_0$	0·2336

It is hardly necessary to repeat that the luminous intensity value of a lamp may be altered seriously by even a momentary excess voltage of more than about 5 per cent [25]. Most standards are somewhat under-run, so that a very slight excess voltage applied for a brief period generally produces no change of luminous intensity. It is always necessary, however, after any such over-run to measure carefully the current taken by the lamp. If this is unchanged, the lamp may safely be assumed to have received no harm. If a change of current is found, or if the over-running has been at all severe, the lamp should be re-standardised before being used again.

Sub-standards and working standards of luminous flux may conveniently be kept in a special cupboard not far from the integrating sphere. They should be treated in exactly the same way as other sub-standards, but if normally used in the pendent position when in the sphere, they should be stored in this position.

Heterochromatic Photometry, Spectrophotometry and Colorimetry—In order to cover the range of colour temperatures commonly met with in filament lamps it is convenient to arrange that all the sub-standards and working standards should operate at two definite colour temperatures, e.g. about 2360° and 2800° K and to have sets of colour filters by means of which lamps of colour temperatures within this range and beyond it may be measured without the introduction of too large a colour difference in the photometric comparison. The range from 2360° to 2800° K may conveniently be divided into four by the use of two colour filters giving respectively colour steps of about 330 and 165 mireds (see p. 299). If blue filters are used, their transmission factors, separately and in combination, should be determined precisely for the colour temperatures of the two sets of standards. They can then be used, not only for measuring lamps of colour temperatures between 2360° and 2800° K with a difference of colour never greater than 90 mireds, but also for extending the range upwards as far as is necessary for any filament lamp.

Blue filters have the disadvantage that they are necessarily used with a standard which is of a lower colour temperature than the test lamp and therefore frequently also of lower luminous intensity. For this reason the provision of two yellow colour filters in addition to the blue filters and producing about the same amount of colour difference is to be recommended for use within the range 2360° to 2800° K.

Glass filters should be used in preference to gelatine filters and their transmission factors should be re-determined at intervals of not more than five years. Each should be indelibly marked so that there is no risk of confusing it with a similar filter which may have a slightly different transmission factor. The box containing a filter should show (i) the distinguishing mark of the filter, (ii) its colour and the colour difference, e.g. " 163 mireds blue ", (iii) its transmission factors and the colour temperatures for which these have been determined, e.g. " 0·41 at 2360°, 0·48 at 2800° K ", (iv) the date at which these transmission factors were last determined.

The colour differences met with when measuring discharge lamps are much more troublesome [26]. Special colour filters are sometimes used for measurements on lamps of a particular type giving a fairly well-determined spectral distribution, while for routine measurements of luminous flux, discharge lamps of the same type as those to be measured have sometimes been used as working standards [27]. These are checked at frequent intervals by making a measurement of the luminous intensity in a defined direction, using a tungsten filament lamp with a suitable colour filter. For measurements on light sources unrestricted as to colour, equipment such as that described in Chapter IX (especially pp. 312–13) must be provided.

For measuring the colour of light sources, some form of trichromatic colorimeter is required (see Chapter X), while for determining the spectral distribution of the light given by a source some form of spectrophotometer must be provided (see Chapter XI, especially pp. 356 to 363) and a sub-standard of spectral distribution is necessary. This may be either a full radiator (see pp. 35 and 174) or, more frequently, a filament lamp of which the spectral energy distribution curve at some known voltage and current has been determined by comparison with a full radiator at the standardising laboratory.

For the wave-length calibration of a spectrometer or spectrophotometer it is necessary to have certain suitable discharge lamps and colour filters.

Illumination Photometers—The bench room may conveniently serve as the permanent home of the illumination photometers used in the laboratory. Each photometer should be kept in a separate case with its own test plate, the latter being clearly marked with a reference to the particular instrument with which it is used. The containing case should bear a sheet giving (i) the name and distinguishing mark of the photometer, (ii) the correct voltage or current for the lamp, (iii) a list of correction factors or a reference to the instrument calibration curve, (iv) the transmission factors of any neutral or coloured filters with which the instrument is fitted, (v) the date on which the lamp in the instrument was first taken into use, (vi) the date on which the instrument was last checked on the photometer bench.

In order that an illumination photometer may be used for measuring luminance it is necessary to know the reflection factor of its test surface. This should be checked from time to time by comparison with a standard surface, such as a sheet of pot opal glass permanently mounted with either a black or a white opaque backing. The reflection factor of this surface should be carefully determined at a standardising laboratory or by a fundamental method such as that described in Chapter XIII (p. 426).

Projection Photometry—For the photometry of projectors a long room is necessary. Many pieces of projection apparatus, such as automobile headlights, should be tested at distances of 50 feet or more, so that 100 feet by 20 feet is the minimum size for the projector room. This should be provided with a white screen at one end, so that the distribution of light in the beam of a projector may be examined visually. It is most important that the walls, ceiling and floor of this room should be kept as dark as possible. Further, large portable screens should be set up at intervals along the room so that the surface of the photometer cannot receive light from anywhere but a small region surrounding the source of light under test. These screens should be dimensioned and placed so that they act in the same way as the screens used on a photometer bench (see p. 216).

Measurement of Light Distribution.—In many laboratories the projector room may conveniently be used also for the measurement of the light distribution curves of large sources and fittings by means of the mirror apparatus described on p. 247. The luminous intensities to be measured often cover a very wide range of magnitude, even with a single source, so that either a very long bench must be employed or, preferably, a shorter (e.g. 3-metre) bench may be mounted on a table provided with rollers, so that it can be moved bodily along rails laid in the floor for the whole length of the room. The table is provided with a pointer which can be set at any one of a number of fixed marks on the rails. These marks are generally at intervals of a metre, so that the bench can be placed in such a position that the photometer head, when clamped at the zero end, is at such a distance from the source that the comparison lamp takes up a convenient position on the bench, e.g. between 1,500 and 2,000 millimetres.

In this work, again, careful attention must be given to the arrangement of screens to give adequate protection from stray light. Portable screens are required, too, for (a) covering the mirrors and (b) cutting off the direct light from the lamp during the test (see p. 249). The electrical measurements, both in the case of projection photometry and in the determination of light distribution curves, may be made with precision indicating instruments, since in neither case can an accuracy better than about 1 per cent be obtained without very elaborate precautions.

Life Tests—Most specifications for electric lamps include, among other matters, requirements as regards the life of the lamps and the maintenance of their light output during life. The life testing of lamps under the conditions laid down in the appropriate specification is frequently an important part of the work of a photometric laboratory. The test conditions must be very carefully controlled. Particularly, in the case of filament lamps, since the life varies inversely as a high power of the voltage [28], the mean voltage of the life-test circuit is regulated to an accuracy of about 0·1 per cent, momentary fluctuations not exceeding 1 per cent [29].

The lamps are usually run at rated voltage, although since the test is necessarily by sample, usually a small sample [30], a life test at a specified value of efficiency, viz. the mean efficiency at rated voltage of the whole batch of lamps represented, gives more reliable results [31]. Such a test is, however, rather more troublesome to make since it is necessary (a) to measure each lamp at two or more voltages and then to deduce the voltage at which the required efficiency is obtained [32]; (b) to adjust the voltage on each individual lamp to the value thus found, placing in series with it a small local resistance of suitable value [33]. The reliability of a test at rated voltage is improved by specifying that the mean efficiency at this voltage for the lamps in the life-test sample must not differ by more than a specified small amount from the mean efficiency at rated voltage for the whole batch of lamps represented. Further, the possibility of quite fortuitous variations in individual lamps make it undesirable to base any conclusions on a life test of less than a stated number of lamps of any one type and rating, and the larger the number tested the more reliable are the results obtained [34].

The lamps undergoing a life test are accommodated in sockets fixed to horizontal iron racks arranged in a skeleton framework. These racks can be rotated so that the lamps may be run either pendent or upright. The sockets in each rack are wired in parallel and the supply is arranged so that any potential, to the nearest 5 volts, can be supplied to any rack. The potential applied to the lamps on a rack is adjusted by means of a small series resistance, the value of which must be kept as low as possible for, since it is in series with a number of lamps which are themselves in parallel, the failure of any one of these lamps reduces the current through this resistance and so raises the potential on the remaining lamps. It is for this reason that the supply must be available in steps of not more than 5 volts.

The supply must be from a storage battery if a test on direct current is required [35]. For a test on alternating current [36] the most convenient arrangement is that in which a generator, governed by some form of automatic voltage regulator [37], supplies an auto-transformer with a number of tappings in convenient voltage steps. A continuous record of the voltage on the supply should be kept by means of a recording voltmeter. The racks are inspected at convenient time intervals, and lamp failures are noted [38]. It is generally sufficient if the period of burning of each lamp is known to the nearest ten or twelve hours. Alternatively, some automatic device may be used for recording the lamp failures [39].

A measurement of luminous flux is made on each lamp at stated intervals during the life test. These measurements are usually made at rated voltage even in the case of a life test carried out at specified efficiency [40]. If the filament of a lamp fractures during actual burning it is removed from the test and noted as broken, even though the loose limb of the filament may fall across another portion and so cause the lamp to continue burning. If a filament fractures during handling, the lamp is considered to be accidentally broken, and the results on it are not included in the life-test figures [41]. The lamps are usually switched off at stated intervals during the test.

In order to avoid the long delay caused by a full 1,000-hour test and the cost of the power consumed in such a test, especially in the case of high wattage lamps, a " forced " life test is sometimes made. This is a test in which the lamps are run at a voltage which is some definite small percentage higher than the rated voltage, or at the voltage at which their efficiency is a definite percentage above the normal efficiency. A correction factor is applied to the results of such a test in order to arrive at the result which would probably have been obtained by means of a normal life test on the same lamps [42]. The intervals at which photometric measurements are made are generally shorter in the case of a forced life test than in a normal test, and the number of lamps chosen to represent a given batch is usually larger.

Discharge lamps, particularly tubular fluorescent lamps, may be tested for life in the same way as filament lamps [43], but each lamp must be connected to the regulated supply through a separate ballast of appropriate rating. Although photometric measurements are made with the lamps taking their rated wattage (see p. 495), the life test is usually carried out with the rated voltage applied to the lamp circuit, including the ballast. Since a discharge lamp is much less sensitive to voltage changes than a filament lamp, the limits laid down for fluctuations from the rated voltage can be much less severe, e.g. 6 per cent. The frequency of the supply is important ; this is usually specified in this country as 50 cycles per second.

Fluorescent lamps may be run in any position ; horizontal is often the most convenient. Other discharge lamps must be run in the normal operating position. Since the effect of the frequency with which a lamp is switched on and off is much greater in the case of a discharge lamp than it is for a filament lamp, provision is usually made for discharge lamps to be automatically switched off for a period at intervals of a few hours throughout the duration of the life test.

The life of a fluorescent lamp is usually very long and to continue the test until the lamps failed, or the light output reached, say, 70 per cent. of its initial value, would make the test prohibitively protracted and costly. It is therefore usual to run the lamps for 2000 hours, although occasionally the test is continued for 70 per cent of the rated life, which may be 5000 hours or longer. It is to be noted here that, since the light from a fluorescent lamp shows a rapid initial fall, all lamps are run for a period of 100 hours before a test is begun. So far, no form of accelerated life test comparable with that described above for filament lamps has been developed for use with fluorescent lamps.

Mechanical and Other Tests —Most lamp specifications provide for certain mechanical and other tests in addition to those for light output and for life. Although these tests have nothing to do with photometry, it is usual for them to be applied in the photometric laboratory. It is therefore necessary for this laboratory to be provided with (a) templates for checking the mechanical dimensions of lamps, (b) apparatus for measuring the light-centre-length in the case of filament lamps, i.e. the distance from the geometrical centre of the filament to the contact plates in the cap [44], (c) apparatus for applying a specified torque to a lamp to test the strength of attachment of the cap. Means must be available, too, for measuring the insulation resistance between the filament and the shell of the cap in the case of a lamp with a bayonet cap.

Tests of mechanical strength and tests of ability to withstand shock or vibration are sometimes included in a lamp specification but the apparatus used for such tests is not in any way standardised [45].

A specification for fluorescent lamps may call for a test of the starting characteristics of the lamps. The circuit shown in Fig. 281 is convenient for making this test. The voltage applied to the lamp circuit is lower than the rated voltage by a specified amount and the

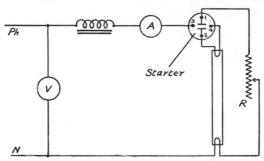

FIG. 281. Starting Test for Fluorescent Lamps.

pre-heating current through the electrodes is limited to a stated value by means of the resistance R. Under these conditions the lamp should start fully within a short time (e.g. one minute) of switching on.

REFERENCES

1. For a description of some photometric laboratories, see, e.g.
   J. Teichmüller, Z. f. techn. Phys., 5, *1924*, p. 321 ; Licht, 1, *1930*, pp. 29 and 55 ;
   Illum. Eng., 20, *1927*, p. 107 ;
   H. Buckley, Illum. Eng., 20, *1927*, pp. 174 and 197 ;
   J. W. T. Walsh, World Power, 15, *1931*, p. 34 ;
   W. Lulofs and J. C. van Staveren, Conférence Int. des Grands Réseaux Electriques, C.r., 6, *1931*, Vol. III, p. 547 ;
   E. Meyer, Licht u. Lampe, 23, *1934*, pp. 329 and 366 ;
   J. W. T. Walsh, Illum. Eng. Soc. Lond., Trans., 1, *1936*, p. 148 ;
   R. Deaglio, Reale Accad. d'Italia, Viaggi di Studio, 4, *1938*, p. 23.
   H. F. Stephenson. Illum. Eng. Soc. Lond., Trans., 17, *1952*, p. 2.

2. For a description of a distribution system in which flexible connectors are avoided, see J. W. T. Walsh, Illum. Eng. Soc. Lond., Trans., 1, *1936*, p. 148.

3. C. H. Sharp. *Lectures on Illuminating Engineering* (Johns Hopkins Univ. Press, *1911*), Vol. I, p. 451.

4. See, however, E. P. Hyde, Bureau of Standards, Bull., 1, *1904–5*, p. 417 ; G. T. Winch, Light and Ltg., 30, *1937*, p. 97.

5. See, e.g. G. Lebaupin, C.I.E., Proc., 6, *1924*, p. 132 ; W. Leo, H. Schleicher and K. Stübenrath, Lichttechnik, 4, *1952*, p. 190.

6. E. H. Rayner. Phys. Soc., Proc., 24, *1912*, p. 449 ; Inst. El. Eng., J., 59. *1921*, p. 138.

7. See, in this connection, E. J. Edwards, Am. I.E.E., Trans., 31, *1912*, p. 1517.

8. J. S. Dow. Electrician, 57, *1906*, p. 855.
   C. H. Sharp. Illum. Eng. Soc. N.Y., Trans., 23, *1928*, p. 383.
   A slightly different procedure is described by C. H. Sharp in *Lectures on Illuminating Engineering* (Johns Hopkins Univ. Press, *1911*), Vol. I, p. 453.

9. See, e.g., F. G. H. Lewis, Phys. Soc., Proc., 34, *1921*, p. 17 ; P. Vernotte, C.R., 183, *1926*, p. 347 ; P. J. Higgs, J. Sci. Inst., 13, *1936*, p. 114 ; F. V. Hunt and R. W. Hickman, Rev. Sci. Inst., 10, *1939*, p. 6 ; A. Glynne, Inst. El. Eng., J. (Part II), 90,

1943, p. 101 ; S. L. Parsons, Opt. Soc. Am., J., 32, *1942*, p. 153 ; H. W. Dietert and M. F. Hasler, *ibid.*, 33, *1943*, p. 45 ; R. J. Hercock, J. Sci. Inst., 25, *1948*, p. 320.

10. C. Carpenter and J. W. Helps. C.I.E., Proc., 1, *1903*, p. 143.

11. K. Sauermann. E.T.Z., 57, *1936*, p. 1317.

12. W. Trojok. Licht, 14, *1944*, p. 13.
W. F. Little and E. H. Salter. Illum. Engng., 42, *1947*, p. 217.
H. G. Frühling and J. Marterstock. Lichttechnik, 5, *1953*, p. 186.
D. F. Chapman. Light and Ltg., 50, *1957*, p. 181.

13. British Standard No. 1853.

14. M. H. Gabriel, C. F. Koenig and E. S. Steeb. Gen. El. Rev., 54, *1951*, Sept., p. 30 and Oct., p. 23.
M. S. Kapnik. Elektrichestvo, *1953*, No. 9, p. 61 (In Russian).
E. H. Salter, R. G. Slauer and A. W. Weeks. C.I.E., Proc., 13, *1955*, Section 2.1.2.
W. R. Blevin. Illum. Eng. Soc. Lond., Trans., 22, *1957*, p. 164.
See also Illum. Engng., 49, *1954*, p. 267 and 52, *1957*, p. 538.

15. K. A. Macfadyen and N. D. Hill. G.E.C. Journ., 11, *1941*, p. 182.
A. H. M. Arnold and J. J. Hill. Inst. El. Eng., Proc., 103, *1956*, Part C, p. 325.

16. See, e.g., C. W. Jerome, Illum. Engng., 49, *1954*, p. 237.

17. G. R. Baumgartner. Illum. Eng. Soc. N.Y., Trans., 36, *1941*, p. 1340.

18. P. D. Oakley. Illum. Eng., 28, *1935*, p. 181.
See also P. J. Oranje, Philips Techn. Rev., 5, *1940*, p. 166.

19. C. B. Platt and H. C. Lister. Light and Ltg., 29, *1936*, p. 239.

20. See also L. T. Minchin, British Junior Gas Assns., Proc., 24, *1934*, p. 305.

21. C. V. Boys. Roy. Soc. Proc., 77, *1905*, p. 122 ; Article " Gas Calorimeter " in *Dict. Appl. Phys.*, vol. I, p. 411. See also Inst. Gas Eng., Trans., *1921–2*, p. 348 ; General Notification of the Gas Referees for *1933*, p. 38.

22. This value includes the heat evolved by the condensation of the steam formed to water at room temperature.

23. See, e.g., Inst. Gas Eng., Trans., 87, *1937*, p. 75 and 88, *1938*, p. 39.

24. R. W. Shenton. El. Rev. and Western Elect., 62, *1913*, p. 154.

25. On the effect of over-running in carbon filament lamps, see J. S. Dow, Electrician, 57, *1906*, p. 855.

26. See, e.g. J. Urbanek, C.I.E., Proc., 9, *1935*, p. 205.

27. E. Rulla and W. Trojok. Licht, 12, *1942*, pp. 13 and 33.
W. Trojok. *Ibid.*, 14, *1944*, p. 13.

28. It may be assumed that for ordinary tungsten filament lamps the life and voltage are connected by the relation $l \propto v^{-n}$ where n is about 13 for vacuum lamps and 14 for gas-filled lamps.
See W. E. Forsythe, Gen. El. Rev., 37, *1934*, p. 191.

29. British Standard No. 161 for Tungsten Filament General Service Electric Lamps.
El World, 66, *1915*, p. 12.

30. The method adopted in the selection of lamps for life tests, and the interpretation of the results obtained are matters which fall outside the scope of this book. For details see the Brit. Std. No. 161.

31. J. W. T. Walsh. World Power, 11, *1929*, p. 142.

32. Apparatus has been devised for obtaining, by means of a single observation the voltage at which a lamp has a certain specified efficiency.
See H. W. B. Gardiner, J. Sci. Inst., 1, *1923*, p. 90 ; B. S. Willis, Illum. Eng. Soc. N.Y., Trans., 18, *1923*, p. 62.

33. C. C. Paterson and E. H. Rayner. Illum. Eng., 1, *1908*, p. 845.
Other methods of voltage adjustment have been used. See, e.g. G. W. Middlekauff, B. Mulligan and J. F. Skogland, Bureau of Standards, Bull., 12, *1916*, p. 605 and C. H. Sharp, El. World, 72, *1918*, p. 206.

34. This is a matter which has been carefully studied in connection with the application of statistics to quality control. See, e.g., E. S. Pearson, *The Application*

of Statistical Methods to Industrial Standardisation and Quality Control (British Standards Institution, *1935*).

35. See also G. T. Winch and A. Bone, J. Sci. Inst., 6, *1929*, p. 247.

36. It appears that, for tungsten lamps, whether vacuum or gas-filled, the fall of candle-power when the lamps are run on direct current is slightly more rapid than when they are run on alternating current. See Am. I.E.E., J., 42, *1923*, p. 544 ; J. W. Lieb, Illum. Eng. Soc. N.Y., Trans., 18, *1923*, p. 5.

37. See, e.g. H. P. Young, *Electric Power System Control* (Chapman and Hall, *1942*), Chapters II and III ; F. L. Kilpatrick and C. P. Bernhardt, Electronics, 7, *1934*, p. 352 ; A. L. Whiteley, Inst. El. Eng., J., 78, *1936*, p. 516 ; K. Sauermann, E.T.Z., 58, *1937*, p. 1003 ; N. A. J. Voorhoeve and F. H. de Jong, Philips Techn. Rev., 3. *1938*, p. 97.

38. W. M. Skiff. Illum. Eng. Soc. N.Y., Trans., 7, *1912*, p. 212.

39. See, e.g., E.T.Z., 22, *1901*, p. 67.

An automatic arrangement might very easily be devised to take a photograph of each life-test rack every hour.

40. See, however, J. F. Skogland and R. P. Teele, Bureau of Standards, Technol. Papers, 20, *1926*, p. 681.

41. British Standard No. 161.

42. For a limited range of the variables, the life and efficiency of a filament lamp are connected by the relation $l \propto (W/lm)^n$ where $n = 5 \cdot 83$ for carbon filament lamps and in the case of tungsten filament vacuum lamps varies from about 6 for smaller sizes to about $7 \cdot 4$ for large lamps. (See, e.g. G. W. Middlekauff, B. Mulligan and J. F. Skogland, Bureau of Standards Bull., 12, *1916*, p. 605 ; L. J. Lewinson, Illum. Eng. Soc. N.Y., Trans., 11, *1916*, p. 815 ; Article " Incandescence Lamps " in *Dict. Appl. Phys.*, vol. II, p. 379 ; R. Becker, Z. f. techn. Phys., 6, *1925*, p. 309. See also J. F. Skogland and J. F. Meyer, El. World, 84, *1924*, p. 1302.) For gas-filled lamps n has been found to vary from about $6 \cdot 8$ to $7 \cdot 6$, again according to size. (See W. E. Forsythe, Gen. El. Rev., 37, *1934*, p. 191.)

43. British Standard No. 1853.

44. F. J. C. Brookes. J. Sci. Inst., 13, *1936*, p. 415.

45. For a description of a shock test for gas mantles see the British Standard for Low Pressure Gas Mantles (No. 884). A shock test for filament lamps has been described by Vincent (Electrician, 67, *1911*, p. 941) and by C. F. Wood (South African Inst. El. Eng., Trans., 19, *1928* p. 162).

APPENDIX I

List of Books Published on Photometry

The books in the first section deal exclusively with photometry ; those in the second section are on illuminating engineering but the subject of photometry is treated at considerable length. No attempt has been made to list the numerous and often lengthy articles which have appeared in collective works such as encyclopaedias or the extensive *Handbücher* published in Germany.

Section I

1729. P. Bouguer. *Essai d'Optique sur la gradation de la Lumière*. (Paris.) Reprinted, Paris, *1921*, in *Les Maîtres de la Pensée Scientifique*. (Gauthier-Villars.)

1760. P. Bouguer. *Traite d'Optique sur la gradation de la Lumière*. (Paris.) Latin trans., Vienna, *1762*. Russian Translation, *1950*.

1760. J. H. Lambert. *Photometria, sive de mensura et gradibus luminis colorum et umbrae*. (Augsburg.) German trans. by E. Anding, published *1892*, in Ostwald's *Klassiker d. Exacten Wissenschaften*. (Engelmann, Leipzig.)

1886. H. Krüss. *Elektrotechnische Photometrie*. (Hartleben, Vienna.)

1889. W. J. Dibdin. *Practical Photometry*. (King, London.)

1892. A. Palaz. *Photométrie Industrielle*. (Carré, Paris.) English trans. by G. W. and M. R. Patterson, first published *1894*. (Van Nostrand, New York.)

1900. W. M. Stine. *Photometrical Measurements*. (Macmillan, New York.)

1907. E. Liebenthal. *Praktische Photometrie*. (Vieweg, Brunswick.)

1909. G. Schuchardt. *Praktische Anleitung zum Photometrieren*. (Krayn, Berlin.)

1912. F. Uppenborn-B. Monasch. *Lehrbuch der Photometrie*. (Oldenbourg, Munich and Berlin.)

1927. C. Fabry. *Introduction Générale à la Photometrie*. (Revue d'Optique Press, Paris.)

Section II

1910. C. P. Steinmetz. *Radiation, Light and Illumination*. (McGraw-Hill, New York.)

1910. W. E. Wickenden. *Photometry and Illumination*. (McGraw-Hill, New York.)

1911. C. H. Sharp. " The Measurement of Light," in *Lectures on Illuminating Engineering*, p. 411. (Johns Hopkins Univ. Press.)

1911. A. P. Trotter. *Illumination, Its Distribution and Measurement*. (Macmillan, London.)

1917. C. H. Sharp. Article " Modern Photometry " in *Illuminating Engineering Practice*, p. 99. (McGraw-Hill, New York.)

1919. L. Gaster and J. S. Dow. *Modern Illuminants and Illuminating Engineering*. (Pitman, London.) 2nd ed.

1920. G. Peri. Scienza e Tecnica dell' Illuminazione : Fotometria. (S. Lattes, Turin.)

1921. W. Wedding. Section " Photometrie " in *Lichttechnik*, p. 50. (Oldenbourg, Munich and Berlin.)

1921. A. P. Trotter. *Elements of Illuminating Engineering*. (Pitman, London.)

1923. J. W. T. Walsh. *Elementary Principles of Lighting and Photometry*. (Methuen, London.)

1925. F. E. CADY, H. B. DATES *et al.* *Illuminating Engineering.* (Wiley, New York.)

1925. H. BOHLE. *Electrical Photometry and Illumination.* (Griffin, London.) 2nd. ed.

1929. W. KUNERTH. *Text-book of Illumination.* (Wiley, New York.)

1935. *A Symposium on Illumination,* edited by C. J. W. GRIEVESON. (Chapman and Hall, London.)

1936. P. MOON. *The Scientific Basis of Illuminating Engineering.* (McGraw-Hill, New York.)

1938. *Handbuch der Lichttechnik,* edited by R. SEWIG. (Springer, Berlin.) 2 vols.

1949. M. COHU. *Rayonnement, Photométrie et Eclairage.* (Gauthier-Villars, Paris.)

1951. W. E. BARROWS. *Light, Photometry and Illuminating Engineering.* (McGraw-Hill, New York.) This supersedes earlier books by the same author published in 1908 and 1912.

1952. *I.E.S. Lighting Handbook.* (Illum. Eng. Soc., New York.)

1952. W. R. STEVENS. *Principles of Lighting.* (Constable, London.)

1954. J. W. T. WALSH. *Textbook of Illuminating Engineering,* 2nd ed. (Pitman, London.)

1955. H. A. E. KEITZ. *Light Calculations and Measurements.* (Philips Technical Library, Cleaver Hume Press, London.)

Summaries of current developments in photometry (with extensive bibliographies) will be found in the *Comptes rendus* of the Commission Internationale de l'Eclairage, especially the volumes for 1939 (Vol. I, pp. 64-135) and for 1948 (pp. 178-237) and in *Reports on Progress in Physics* published by the Physical Society (see articles by H. Buckley in Vol. 1, 1934, pp. 150-160 and Vol. 8, *1941*, pp. 318-337). An extensive treatment of the fundamental principles underlying photometric and colorimetric measurement will be found in *Der Begriff der Helligkeit* by H. König (Editions du Griffon, Neuchatel. *1947*).

APPENDIX II

Symbols and Abbreviations

The symbols used in this book for the various photometric quantities are those now agreed internationally or, where there is no international agreement, those most commonly employed in the literature. This applies also to the abbreviations used for the names of the units. Both symbols and abbreviations are listed in the table overleaf which includes as well the defining equations showing the relations between the various quantities.

Certain other terms have been used for units of illumination and luminance, particularly when the values are low. These are :

$$1 \text{ nox } = 10^{-3} \text{ lx}.$$
$$1 \text{ skot } = 10^{-3} \text{ asb}.$$

The lux was at one time called the metro-candle (m.c.).

A unit of luminance, the lambert equal to $1/\pi$ candles per sq. cm., was at one time widely used in the U.S.A., generally in the form of its sub-multiple the millilambert. One millilambert is roughly equal to one foot-lambert.

The names of the various units of luminous intensity used before the introduction of the candela are mentioned in the text, particularly in Chapters I and VI.

The unit of retinal illumination, the troland (previously the photon), is described on p. 59.

Definitions

Many sets of definitions of the principal photometric quantities have been proposed at different times but most, if not all, fail in the difficult task of combining clarity with formal correctness and logical approach. The most authoritative definitions are those of the Commission Internationale de l'Eclairage which are to be found in the volumes of the *Comptes rendus* of the Commission for 1921 and onwards and which have been collected and supplemented in the *Vocabulaire International de l'Eclairage* published by the Commission in 1958. This vocabulary, which is in French, English and German, contains over 500 definitions covering not only fundamental concepts, photometry, colorimetry and vision, but also the production of light, light sources and illuminating engineering.

There are two authoritative sets of definitions published in Great Britain, viz. the *British Standard Glossary of Terms used in Illumination and Photometry* (B.S. No. 232) and the *British Standard Glossary of Colour Terms used in Science and Industry* (B.S. No. 1611).

An entirely new system of nomenclature for photometry has been devised by P. Moon and D. E. Spencer (see bibliography).

The definitions given below follow closely those in the international vocabulary referred to above, though the wording is not always precisely the same. Other sets of definitions will be found in papers listed in the Bibliography at the end of this Appendix and in papers published before 1926 and listed in *Photometry* (1926), pp. 467-9.

1. *Light.* (*Visible Radiation.*) Radiant energy capable of stimulating the eye so as to produce the sensation of vision.

2. *Luminous flux.* That quantity which is characteristic of a flow of radiant energy and which expresses its capacity to produce visual sensation,

TABLE OF SYMBOLS, UNITS (WITH ABBREVIATIONS) AND DEFINING EQUATIONS FOR THE PRINCIPAL PHOTOMETRIC QUANTITIES

Name	Symbol	Unit	Abbreviation	Defining Equation *
Luminous flux - - -	F	lumen	lm.	—
Luminous intensity - -	I	candela	cd.	$\mathrm{Lim}_{\omega=0} F/\omega$
Illumination - - -	E	lux	lx.	$\mathrm{Lim}_{s=0} F/s$
		† lumen per sq. ft., or foot-candle	† lm/ft.² (or f.c.)	
Luminance - - -	L or B	candela per sq. metre	cd/m²	$\mathrm{Lim}_{s=0}(I/s) \sec \theta$
		stilb (=cd/cm.²)	sb.	
		† apostilb (=1/π cd/m.²)	† asb.	
		† candela per sq. in., sq. ft., etc.	† cd/in.², cd/ft.², etc.	
		† foot-lambert (=1/π cd/ft.²)	† ft.-L.	
Luminance factor - -	β	—	—	ratio
Reflection factor - -	ρ	—	—	,,
Absorption factor - -	α	—	—	,,
Transmission factor - -	τ	—	—	,,
Luminous efficiency - -	‡ K	lumen per watt	lm/W	$F'/$(radiant energy flux)
Relative luminous efficiency	‡ V	—	—	ratio

* s =surface area ; ω =solid angle in steradians ; θ =angle from normal to surface ; W =watt.
† Not international.
‡ Value at a particular wave-length indicated by subscript, e.g. K_λ, V_λ.

evaluated in accordance with the standard values of relative luminous efficiency.

3. *Luminous intensity* (in any direction). The quotient of the luminous flux emitted from a source (or from an element of a source) in an infinitesimal cone containing this direction, by the solid angle of the cone.

4. *Luminous emittance* (from a point of a surface). The quotient of the luminous flux emitted from an infinitesimal element of surface containing the point under consideration, by the area of that surface.

5. *Illumination* (at a point of a surface). The quotient of the luminous flux incident on an infinitesimal element of surface containing the point by the area of this element.

6. *Luminance* (at a point of a surface and in any direction). The quotient of the luminous intensity in this direction of an infinitesimal element of the surface containing the point, by the orthogonally projected area of this element on a plane perpendicular to the direction considered.

7. *Point brilliance.* A quantity which occurs in the visual observation of a source of light when it is looked at directly from a distance so great that the source has no appreciable dimensions. The point brilliance is measured by the illumination produced by the source on a plane normal to the light and situated at the pupil of the observer's eye.

8. *Luminosity.* (*Subjective brightness.*) The attribute of a visual perception in accordance with which a part of the visual field appears to emit more or less light.

9. *Candela.* The unit of luminous intensity : it is of such a magnitude that the luminance of a full radiator (black body) at the temperature of solidification of platinum is 60 candelas per sq. cm.

10. *Mean spherical intensity.* The average value of the luminous intensity of a source in all directions.

11. *Mean horizontal intensity.* The average value of the luminous intensity of a source in all directions in a horizontal plane passing through the centre of the source.

12. *Lumen.* The unit of luminous flux. The flux emitted in a solid angle of one steradian by a uniform point source with a luminous intensity of one candela.

13. *Lux.* A unit of illumination : one lumen per square metre.

14. *Quantity of light.* The product of luminous flux and the time during which it is maintained.

15. *Quantity of illumination.* The product of an illumination and the time during which it is maintained.

16. *Full radiator.* (*Planckian radiator.*) A light source emitting radiation, the spectral distribution of which is dependent on the temperature only and not on the material and nature of the source.

17. *Colour temperature* (of a light source). The temperature of a full radiator which would emit radiation of substantially the same distribution in the visible region as the radiation from the light source and which would have the same colour.

18. *Luminance temperature.* The temperature of a full radiator which has, at a specified wave-length, the same luminance as the radiator concerned at the same wave-length. This wave-length must be stated.

19. *Equivalent luminance* (of a coloured light at low luminance). The luminance of light with colour temperature equal to the temperature of solidification of platinum which, under specified conditions, is of the same luminosity as the light considered.

Note—The use of this conception is usually required when dealing with lights of various spectral compositions at low luminance levels since, owing to the Purkinje effect, luminosity matches between lights of different spectral compositions vary with the luminance levels at which the matches are made.

20. *Foot-candle.* A unit of illumination : one lumen per square foot.

21. *Apostilb*. A unit of luminance : that of a uniform diffuser emitting one lumen per square metre.

22. *Foot-lambert*. A unit of luminance : that of a uniform diffuser emitting one lumen per square foot.

23. *Luminous efficiency* (of radiation). The quotient of the luminous flux by the corresponding radiant energy flux.

24. *Relative luminous efficiency* (of a monochromatic radiation). The ratio of the luminous efficiency K_λ of that radiation to the maximum luminous efficiency K_m.

Note—The values of this quantity have been internationally agreed and form the basis of heterochromatic photometry.

25. *Luminous efficiency* (of a light source). The luminous flux emitted by a source divided by the power consumed. In the case of an electric lamp it is expressed in lumens per watt ; in the case of a source depending on combustion it may be expressed in lumens per thermal unit per unit of time.

26. *Direct reflection*. (*Specular reflection*.) Reflection in accordance with the laws of optical reflection, as in a mirror.

27. *Diffuse reflection*. Reflection such that the light incident upon a surface is reflected from every part of the surface in many directions.

28. *Preferential diffuse reflection*. Diffuse reflection in which the spatial distribution of reflected flux is such that the luminance exhibits one or more maxima.

29. *Uniform diffuse reflection*. Diffuse reflection in which the spatial distribution of reflected flux is such that the luminance is the same in all directions.

30. *Mixed reflection*. Direct and preferential diffuse reflection occurring simultaneously.

31. *Uniform diffuser*. A surface having a reflection factor independent of the angle of illumination, and luminance independent of the angle of view.

32. *Perfect diffuser*. A uniform diffuser having a total reflection factor of unity (necessarily white).

33. *Reflection factor*. The ratio of the reflected luminous flux to the incident luminous flux. Where mixed reflection occurs, the total reflection factor can be divided into two parts, *direct reflection factor* and *diffuse reflection factor* corresponding respectively to the two modes of reflection referred to in 26 and 27. In general the values of the various reflection factors depend upon the angle of incidence, the mode of illumination and the spectral composition of the incident light.

34. *Luminance factor*. The ratio of the luminance of a reflecting or transmitting surface viewed from a given direction to that of a perfect diffuser receiving the same illumination. In general the value depends upon the angle of incidence, the mode of illumination and the spectral composition of the incident light.

35. *Absorption factor*. The ratio of the absorbed luminous flux to the incident luminous flux.

36. *Direct transmission*. Transmission of light without scatter.

37. *Diffuse transmission*. Transmission such that the light passing through a body is scattered in many directions.

38. *Preferential diffuse transmission*. Diffuse transmission in which the spatial distribution of transmitted flux is such that the luminance exhibits one or more maxima.

39. *Uniform diffuse transmission*. Diffuse transmission in which the spatial distribution of transmitted flux is such that the luminance is the same in all forward directions.

40. *Mixed transmission*. Direct and preferential diffuse transmission occurring simultaneously.

41. *Transmission factor*. The ratio of the transmitted luminous flux to the incident luminous flux. Where mixed transmission occurs, the total transmission factor can be divided into two parts, *direct transmission factor* and

diffuse transmission factor corresponding respectively to the two modes of transmission referred to in 36 and 37. In general, the values of the various transmission factors depend upon the angle of incidence, the modes of illumination and the spectral composition of the incident light.

42. *Internal transmission factor*. The ratio of the luminous flux reaching the second surface of a body to the flux leaving the first surface. (Generally definite only for a plane parallel plate.)

43. *Internal absorption factor*. The ratio of the directed luminous flux absorbed by a transparent body during a single passage from the first surface to the second surface (difference between the flux leaving the first surface and that reaching the second surface) to the flux leaving the first surface.

44. *Reflectivity*. The total reflection factor of a layer of material of such a thickness that there is no change of reflection factor with further increase in thickness.

45. *Transmissivity*. The internal transmission factor of unit thickness of the transmitting material.

46. *Absorptivity*. The internal absorption factor of unit thickness of the absorbing material.

47. *Transmittancy*. The ratio of the transmission factor of a liquid or solid solution to that of the solvent of the same form and thickness.

48. *Opacity*. The reciprocal of the transmission factor.

49. *Density*. The logarithm, to the base 10, of the opacity.

50. *Internal density*. The logarithm, to the base 10, of the reciprocal of the internal direct transmission factor.

51. *Absorption (or Extinction) coefficient*. The internal absorption factor of an infinitesimally thin layer of a medium divided by the thickness of the layer.

52. *Scattering coefficient*. The fraction of the light scattered in passing through unit thickness of a material.

53. *Attenuation coefficient*. The sum of the scattering coefficient and the absorptivity.

54. *Isophot curve*. The locus of points on a surface where the illumination has the same value.

55. *Isocandela diagram* (for a source). An array of isocandela curves, i.e. curves traced on an imaginary sphere with the source at its centre, each joining all the points corresponding to those directions in which the luminous intensity is the same.

56. *Daylight factor*. The ratio of the illumination measured at a point inside a building to that on a horizontal plane in the open, both under an unobstructed hemisphere of sky of uniform luminance.

57. *Sky factor*. At a given point inside a building. The ratio of the illumination received directly from the sky to the illumination on a horizontal plane due to an unobstructed hemisphere of sky of uniform luminance equal to that of the visible sky. This ratio may be calculated geometrically, ignoring the effect of glass and glazing bars.

58. *Uniformity ratio*. Of illumination over a given area. The ratio of the minimum illumination to the average illumination over that area.

59. *Diversity ratio*. The ratio of the maximum illumination to the minimum.

The following terms have particular application in colorimetry :

60. *Equal energy source*. A light source for which the amount of energy radiated is constant for the same wave-length interval throughout the visible spectrum.

61. *Matching stimuli* * (instrumental stimuli). The three defined stimuli of a trichromatic colorimeter.

62. *Standard illuminant*. An agreed light source specified in such a way that its energy distribution is reproducible.

* The word " stimulus " is here used to denote the physical cause of a visual sensation. Compare the definition of " light ".

63. *Trichromatic system.* Any system of colour specification based on the possibility of matching all colours by the additive mixture (positive or negative) of three suitably chosen standard stimuli.

64. *Reference stimuli.* The three standard stimuli of a trichromatic system of colour specification. They might, but do not generally, correspond to the matching stimuli of a colorimeter.

65. *Basic stimulus.* The standard visual stimulus (usually achromatic) used to determine the units of the reference stimuli of any trichromatic system.

66. *Cardinal stimuli.* Four standard visual stimuli by means of which the three reference stimuli and the basic stimulus of any trichromatic system may be defined. Light of wave-lengths 700, 546·1 and 435·8$m\mu$ and Illuminant B have been adopted by the C.I.E.

67. *Tristimulus values* (of a light). The amounts of the three reference stimuli required to give a match with the light considered in a given trichromatic system. In the standard C.I.E. (1931) colorimetric system the symbols X, Y, Z are recommended for the tristimulus values.

68. *Chromaticity co-ordinates.* The ratio of each of the tristimulus values of a light to their sum. In the standard C.I.E. (1931) colorimetric system the symbols x, y, z are recommened for the chromaticity co-ordinates.

69. *Distribution coefficients.* The relative tristimulus values of the spectral components of an equal energy spectrum. In the standard C.I.E. (1931) colorimetric system they are denoted by $\bar{x}$, $\bar{y}$ and $\bar{z}$.

70. *Trichromatic units.* Relative units of stimulus quantity applicable to stimuli of any colour and such that the quantity of any stimulus, when expressed in these units, is equal to the sum of the tristimulus values.

71. *Chromaticity* (of a stimulus). The colour quality definable by the chromaticity co-ordinates, or by the dominant (or complementary) wave-length and purity.

72. *Dominant wave-length* (of a coloured light, not purple). The wave-length of the spectral radiation which, when combined in suitable proportions with the specified achromatic light, yields a match for the standard eye with the light considered.

73. *Complementary wave-length* (of a light). The wave-length of the spectral radiation which, when combined in suitable proportions with the light considered, yields a match (for the standard eye) with the specified achromatic light.

74. *Excitation purity.* The ratio of the distances, on a two-dimensional chromaticity diagram, from the adopted achromatic stimulus (i) to the sample stimulus and (ii) to that stimulus lying on the spectral locus (or the straight line joining its extremes) which, by additive mixture with the adopted achromatic stimulus, can form a match with the sample stimulus. (Symbol p_e.)

75. *Colorimetric purity.* The ratio B_d/B, where B is the luminance of the sample stimulus and B_d is the luminance of a spectral stimulus (or of a suitable combination of extreme spectral red and extreme spectral violet) which, by additive mixture with the adopted achromatic stimulus, forms a match with the sample stimulus in both luminance and chromaticity. (Symbol p_c.)

76. *Hue.* That attribute of certain visual sensations by which we distinguish red, green, blue, yellow, purple, etc., from one another and by which the eye distinguishes different parts of the spectrum.*

77. *Saturation.* That attribute of visual sensations which permits a judgment to be made of the proportion of colourfulness in the total sensation. Sensations of the same hue and luminosity can be arranged in a series of increasing saturation ranging from grey to that member of the series in which the hue appears most marked.*

* These two terms are the subjective analogues of dominant wave-length (except for purples) and purity.

A number of other terms used in photometry are explained at the appropriate places in the text. Such are :

Point source (p. 122).
Candle-power (p. 122).
Mean spherical (horizontal) candle-power (p. 123).
Spherical reduction factor (p. 124).
(Polar) Curve of light distribution (p. 124).
Mechanical equivalent of light (p. 138).
Light-watt (p. 140).
Diffusing power (p. 163).
Chromaticity diagram (pp. 322 and 327).
Utilization factor (p. 397).
Shadow factor (p. 398).
Magnitude (astronomical) (p. 475).

BIBLIOGRAPHY FROM 1926

Illum. Eng. Soc. N.Y., Trans., 20, *1925*, p. 629.
C. Fabry. Rev. d'Opt., 6, *1927*, p. 21.
A Blondel. Rev. Gén. de l'El., 22, *1927*, p. 537.
R. Hiecke. E.u.M., 45, *1927*, Lichttech., p. 30.
U. Bordoni. Elettrot., 15, *1928*, p. 243.
C.I.E., Proc., 7, *1928*, pp. 10, 15, 605 and 754.
A. Blondel. C.I.E., Proc., 7, *1928*, p. 768.
J. Teichmüller. Licht u. Lampe, 18, *1929*, pp. 1295 and 1364.
Illum. Eng. Soc. N.Y., Trans., 25, *1930*, p. 725.
C.I.E., Proc., 8, *1931*, pp. 244 and 314.
O. Reeb. C.I.E., Proc., 8, *1931*, p. 603.
H. Lux. Licht u. Lampe, 21, *1932*, p. 295.
Illum. Eng. Soc. N.Y., Trans., 28, *1933*, p. 263.
W. Dziobek. Licht, 5, *1935*, p. 9.
O. Reeb. Licht, 5, *1935*, p. 11 ; Licht u. Lampe, 24, *1935*, p. 50.
A. Dresler. Licht, 5, *1935*, p. 59 (see also p. 62).
E. Elvegård. Licht, 6, *1936*, pp. 145 and 230.
A. Dresler. Licht, 6, *1936*, p. 149.
G. H. Stickney and E. C. Crittenden. Illum. Eng. Soc. N.Y., 33, *1938*, p. 193.
E. C. Crittenden. Opt. Soc. Am., J., 29, *1939*, p. 103.
Illum. Eng. Soc. N.Y., Trans., 36, *1941*, p. 813.
P. Moon and D. E. Spencer. Opt. Soc. Am., J., 32, *1942*, p. 348 and 36, *1946*, p. 666 ; Illum. Engng., 42, *1947*, p. 611 (see also 39, *1944*, p. 507) ; Am. J. of Phys., 10, *1942*, p. 134 and 14, *1946*, p. 431 and 15, *1947*, p. 84 (see also 11, *1943*, p. 200 and 14, *1946*, p. 285).
O. Reeb. Lichttechnik, 4, *1952*, p. 67 ; Arch. techn. Messen, *1953*, p. 123.
D. E. Spencer. Illum. Engng., 49, *1954*, p. 394.
Y. Le Grand. Rev. d'Opt., 34, *1955*, p. 525.

The following deal primarily, but not exclusively, with the definitions of terms used in colorimetry :

L. A. Jones. Opt. Soc. Am., J., 27, *1937*, p. 207.
Physical Society Colour Group. *Report on Colour Terminology, 1948.*
H. D. Murray. Oil and Colour Chem. Assn., J., 24, *1941*, p. 205.
P. Moon and D. E. Spencer. Opt. Soc. Am., J., 35, *1945*, p. 399 and 36, *1946*, pp. 120, 306 and 427 (see also D. B. Judd *ibid.*, p. 120).

APPENDIX III

Conversion Factors

I

Illumination Units

	lux (lx.)	phots (ph.)	foot-candles (ft.-c.)
Lux (metre-candles) (lm/m.²) - -	1	0·0001	0·0929
Phots (lm/cm.²) - -	10,000	1	929
Foot-candles (lm/ft.²) - -	10·764	0·001076	1

II

Luminance Units

	cd/m²	stilbs (sb.)	cd/in.²	cd/ft.²	millilamberts (mL.)	foot-lamberts (ft.-L.)	apostilbs (asb.)
Candelas per sq. m. -	1	0·0001	0·000645	0·0929	0·3142	0·2919	3·1416
Stilbs (cd/cm.²) -	10,000	1	6·452	929	3141·6	2919	31,416
Candelas per sq. in. -	1550	0·155	1	144	486·9	452·4	4869
Candelas per sq. ft. -	10·764	0·001076	0·00694	1	3·382	3·1416	33·82
Millilamberts -	3·183	0·0003183	0·002054	0·2957	1	0·929	10
Foot-lamberts -	3·426	0·0003426	0·002211	0·3183	1·0764	1	10·764
Apostilbs -	0·3183	0·00003183	0·0002054	0·02957	0·1	0·0929	1

(Value in unit in left-hand column) × (conversion factor) = (value in unit shown at top of column)

APPENDIX IV

THE RELATIVE LUMINOUS EFFICIENCY OF RADIATION (V_λ)

(THE LUMINOSITY (VISIBILITY) FACTOR)

$m\mu$	0	1	2	3	4	5	6	7	8	9
400	0004	0005	0006	0006	0007	0008	0009	0009	0010	0011
10	0012	0013	0015	0017	0019	0022	0025	0028	0031	0035
20	0040	0046	0052	0058	0065	0073	0081	0089	0098	0107
30	0116	0126	0136	0146	0157	0168	0180	0192	0204	0217
40	023	024	026	027	028	029	031	032	034	036
450	038	040	042	044	046	048	050	053	055	058
60	060	063	065	068	071	074	077	080	084	087
70	091	095	099	103	108	112	117	122	128	133
80	139	144	150	156	163	169	176	183	191	199
90	208	217	227	237	247	258	270	282	295	309
500	323	339	355	372	389	407	426	445	464	483
10	503	524	545	566	587	608	629	650	670	690
20	710	728	745	762	778	793	808	822	836	849
30	862	874	885	896	906	915	924	932	940	947
40	954	960	966	971	975	980	984	987	990	993
550	995	997	998	999	1	1	1	999	998	997
60	995	993	990	987	983	979	974	969	964	958
70	952	945	938	931	923	915	907	898	889	880
80	870	860	849	839	828	817	805	793	781	769
90	757	745	732	720	707	695	682	670	657	644
600	631	618	605	593	580	567	554	541	528	515
10	503	490	478	465	453	441	429	417	405	393
20	381	369	357	345	333	321	309	298	287	276
30	265	255	245	235	226	217	208	199	191	183
40	175	167	160	152	145	138	132	125	119	113
650	107	101	096	091	086	081	077	073	069	065
60	061	057	054	051	048	045	042	039	037	034
70	032	030	028	026	025	023	022	020	019	018
80	017	0159	0148	0138	0128	0119	0111	0103	0095	0088
90	0082	0076	0071	0066	0061	0057	0053	0050	0047	0044
700	0041	0038	0036	0033	0031	0029	0028	0026	0024	0022
10	0021	00196	00183	00171	00159	00148	00138	00129	00120	00112
20	00105	00098	00091	00085	00079	00074	00069	00064	00060	00056
30	00052	00048	00045	00042	00039	00036	00033	00031	00029	00027
40	00025	00023	00022	00020	00019	00017	00016	00015	00014	00013
750	00012	00011	00010	00009	00009	00008	00008	00007	00007	00006
60	00006									

Note—The above table has been constructed by interpolation between the internation-ally adopted values given in the second column.

See also D. B. Judd, Opt. Soc. Am., J., 21, *1931*, p. 267.   Z. Yamauti and M. Okamatu, Electrotechn. Lab. Tokyo, Researches No. 388, *1935*.

APPENDIX V

THE SPECTRAL ENERGY DISTRIBUTION FOR A FULL RADIATOR
(PLANCKIAN DISTRIBUTION)

Tables for the spectral energy distribution for a full radiator at different temperatures have been published at various times, using different values of c_2 (see p. 40). The now accepted value of this constant is 1·438 cm. degs. and the spectral distribution shown for a temperature T in any given set of tables applies to a temperature, on the international scale, of $T(1·438/c_2)$ where c_2 has the value used in calculating the tables. The principal tables are as follows :

(I) J. F. Skogland. "Tables of Spectral Energy Distribution and Luminosity for Use in Computing Light Transmission and Relative Brightnesses from Spectrophotometric Data" (Bureau of Standards, Miscellaneous Publ. No. 86, *1929*). $T = 2000 - 20 - 3120°$ K, $c_2 = 1·433$. This publication contains also (i) tables at 80° intervals of relative spectral luminance (energy $\times V_\lambda$) adjusted to a maximum of unity and (ii) similar tables adjusted to make the area under each curve ($\lambda = 0·40$ to $0·76\mu$) equal to unity. These last tables are convenient for computing reflection (or transmission) factors for light of known colour temperature when the spectral reflection (or transmission) curve is known.

(IIa) P. Moon. "A Table of Planck's Function from 3500° to 8000° K." (J. of Maths. and Phys., 16, *1937*, p. 133). $T = 3500 - 10 - 8000°$ K., $c_2 = 1·432$, $c_1 = 3·697 \times 10^{-12}$.

(IIb) P. Moon. "A Table of Planck's Function." (Massachusetts Inst. of Technology, U.S.A., *1947*.) $T = 2000 - 10 - 3500°$ K. c_2 and c_1 as above. Published also in abbreviated form (temp. intervals 100°) in Opt. Soc. Am., J., 38, *1948*, p. 291.

It is to be noted that since, at any given wave-length, the rate of change of emission with temperature is very rapid, interpolation is only possible with very extensive tables in which the intervals of T are very small.

For most practical purposes Wien's formula (see p. 40) may be used instead of Planck's throughout the visible spectrum up to a temperature of at least 3000° K. This formula is suitable for computation by means of logarithms since $J_\lambda = c_1 \lambda^{-5} e^{c_2/\lambda T} \delta\lambda$. If J_λ is expressed in watts per sq. cm., λ and $\delta\lambda$ in cm. and T in degrees K, the best values for the constants are

$$c_1 = 3·74 \times 10^{-12} \text{ watt cm.}^2$$
$$c_2 = 1·438 \text{ cm. degs.}$$

If λ and $\delta\lambda$ are expressed in microns

$$c_1 = 37400 \ \mu^4 \text{ watt cm.}^{-2}$$
$$c_2 = 14380\mu \text{ degs.}$$

and, using logarithms to base 10,

$$\log J_\lambda = 4·57287 - 5 \log \lambda - 6245/\lambda T.$$

If desired, the true value of J_λ derived from Planck's formula can be obtained by multiplying by a factor varying with λT as shown in the following table :

λT (μ degs.)	J_P/J_W
2000	1·0008
2500	1·003
3000	1·008
3500	1·017
4000	1·028
4500	1·043
5000	1·060

APPENDIX VI

TABLES FOR COLORIMETRIC COMPUTATION

The fundamental tables on which the Standard (C.I.E.) System of Colorimetry is based are those published in the C.I.E. Proceedings, 8, *1931*, pp. 19 et seqq. They give (a) the colour co-ordinates in the R,G,B triangle, and the corresponding distribution coefficients (r, g, b), for spectral radiation at $5m\mu$ intervals, (b) the spectral energy distributions of the Standard Illuminants at 10μ intervals and (c) the chromaticity co-ordinates on the C.I.E. system, with corresponding distribution coefficients ($\bar{x}$, $\bar{y}$, $\bar{z}$), for spectral radiation at $5m\mu$ intervals. More extended tables have been published, giving (b) at $5m\mu$ intervals and (c) at 1 $m\mu$ intervals [1].

For calculating the chromaticity co-ordinates of reflected or transmitted light it is convenient to have tables giving $E\bar{x}$, $E\bar{y}$, and $E\bar{z}$ at equal intervals throughout the spectrum, E being the spectral energy of the illuminant (see p. 330). Such tables have been published for Standard Illuminants A, B and C at $5m\mu$ intervals [1] and for these illuminants, and the equi-energy stimulus, at intervals of $10m\mu$ [2]. These latter (condensed) tables are given on the left-hand sides of the following pages. It is to be noted that the values in these tables are approximately double those in the full tables so that the sums of the corresponding columns may remain unchanged. Similar tables for an illuminant of any colour temperature from 1500 to 3500° K by 250° intervals have also been published [3].

An alternative method of computation is the " selected ordinate " method described on p. 331. The necessary tables of 100 ordinates and of 30 (or 10) ordinates have been published [4]; it is on the latter that the tables on the right-hand sides of the following pages have been based.

Many of the tables referred to above have been reproduced in other publications than those quoted, especially in the Journal of the Optical Society of America, Vol. 34, *1944*, p. 633. This publication also gives tables for a number of important illuminants, including a full radiator at any temperature from 2000° to 4000° K by 100° intervals ($c_2 = 1·435$) and a number of different phases of daylight.

REFERENCES

1. T. Smith and J. Guild. Opt. Soc., Trans., 33, *1932*, p. 73.
   D. B. Judd. Opt. Soc. Am., J., 23, *1933*, p. 359.

2. T. Smith. Phys. Soc., Proc., 46, *1934*, p. 372.

3. H. G. W. Harding and R. B. Sisson. Phys. Soc., Proc., 59, *1947*, p. 814 ($c_2 = 1·435$).

4. A. C. Hardy. *Handbook of Colorimetry* (Massachusetts Inst. of Technol., *1936*).
   F. T. Bowditch and M. R. Null. Opt. Soc. Am., J., 28, *1938*, p. 500 (equi-energy stimulus).

Distribution Coefficients for an equal energy stimulus			
Wave length (mμ)	$\bar{x}$	$\bar{y}$	$\bar{z}$
380	0·0023	0·0000	0·0106
390	0·0082	0·0002	0·0391
400	0·0283	0·0007	0·1343
410	0·0840	0·0023	0·4005
420	0·2740	0·0082	1·3164
430	0·5667	0·0232	2·7663
440	0·6965	0·0458	3·4939
450	0·6730	0·0761	3·5470
460	0·5824	0·1197	3·3426
470	0·3935	0·1824	2·5895
480	0·1897	0·2772	1·6193
490	0·0642	0·4162	0·9313
500	0·0097	0·6473	0·5455
510	0·0187	1·0077	0·3160
520	0·1264	1·4172	0·1569
530	0·3304	1·7243	0·0841
540	0·5810	1·9077	0·0408
550	0·8670	1·9906	0·0174
560	1·1887	1·9896	0·0077
570	1·5243	1·9041	0·0042
580	1·8320	1·7396	0·0032
590	2·0535	1·5144	0·0023
600	2·1255	1·2619	0·0016
610	2·0064	1·0066	0·0007
620	1·7065	0·7610	0·0003
630	1·2876	0·5311	0·0000
640	0·8945	0·3495	
650	0·5681	0·2143	
660	0·3292	0·1218	
670	0·1755	0·0643	
680	0·0927	0·0337	
690	0·0457	0·0165	
700	0·0225	0·0081	
710	0·0117	0·0042	
720	0·0057	0·0020	
730	0·0028	0·0010	
740	0·0014	0·0006	
750	0·0006	0·0002	
760	0·0003	0·0001	
770	0·0001	0·0000	

Selected Ordinates for computing chromaticity co-ordinates for a light source		
$\lambda(x)$	$\lambda(y)$	$\lambda(z)$
(millimicrons)		
424	470	410
× 437	493	420
447	505	424
458	512	427
× 472	518	430
532	523	433
545	527	435
× 553	532	437
560	536	439
566	539	441
× 570	543	443
575	547	445
579	550	447
× 583	554	449
586	557	451
590	561	453
× 593	565	455
597	568	457
600	572	459
× 604	576	462
607	580	464
610	584	466
× 614	589	469
618	593	471
622	599	474
× 627	604	478
632	611	482
639	619	488
× 648	630	497
665	650	514

When 10 ordinates are used instead of 30, they should be those at the wave-lengths marked ×.

If the ordinate of the spectral energy distribution curve at wave-length λ is J_λ, the x chromaticity co-ordinate is (left-hand table):

$$\Sigma J_\lambda \bar{x}_\lambda / \{\Sigma J_\lambda \bar{x}_\lambda + \Sigma J_\lambda \bar{y}_\lambda + \Sigma J_\lambda \bar{z}_\lambda\}$$

or (right-hand table):

$$\Sigma J_{\lambda(x)} / \{\Sigma J_{\lambda(x)} + \Sigma J_{\lambda(y)} + \Sigma J_{\lambda(z)}\}.$$

Distribution Coefficients for Standard Illuminant A				*Selected Ordinates for computing chromaticity under Standard Illuminant A*		
Wave length $(m\mu)$	$E_A\bar{x}$	$E_A\bar{y}$	$E_A\bar{z}$	$\lambda(x)$	$\lambda(y)$	$\lambda(z)$
				(millimicrons)		
380	0·0010	0·0000	0·0048			
390	0·0046	0·0001	0·0219			
				444	488	416
400	0·0193	0·0005	0·0916	×517	508	425
410	0·0688	0·0019	0·3281	544	517	429
420	0·2666	0·0080	1·2811	554	524	433
430	0·6479	0·0265	3·1626	×561	530	436
440	0·9263	0·0609	4·6469			
				567	535	439
450	1·0320	0·1167	5·4391	572	539	441
460	1·0207	0·2098	5·8584	×576	544	444
470	0·7817	0·3624	5·1445	580	548	446
480	0·4242	0·6198	3·6207	584	552	448
490	0·1604	1·0398	2·3266			
				×587	555	450
500	0·0269	1·7956	1·5132	590	559	453
510	0·0572	3·0849	0·9674	594	563	455
520	0·4247	4·7614	0·5271	×597	566	457
530	1·2116	6·3230	0·3084	599	570	459
540	2·3142	7·5985	0·1625			
				602	573	461
550	3·7329	8·5707	0·0749	×605	577	463
560	5·5086	9·2201	0·0357	608	580	465
570	7·5710	9·4574	0·0209	611	584	467
580	9·7157	9·2257	0·0170	×614	588	469
590	11·5841	8·5430	0·0130			
				617	592	472
600	12·7103	7·5460	0·0096	620	596	474
610	12·6768	6·3599	0·0044	×623	600	477
620	11·3577	5·0649	0·0020	627	605	480
630	8·9999	3·7122	0·0000	631	610	483
640	6·5487	2·5587				
				×635	615	488
650	4·3447	1·6389		640	622	493
660	2·6234	0·9706		647	629	499
670	1·4539	0·5327		×656	640	508
680	0·7966	0·2896		673	659	527
690	0·4065	0·1467				
				$F(x)$	$F(y)$	$F(z)$
700	0·2067	0·0744		0·03661	0·03333	0·01186
710	0·1108	0·0398				
720	0·0556	0·0195				
730	0·0280	0·0100				
740	0·0144	0·0062		When 10 ordinates are used instead of 30, they should be those at the wave-lengths marked × and the multiplying factors are then $3F(x)$, $3F(y)$, $3F(z)$.		
750	0·0063	0·0021				
760	0·0032	0·0011				
770	0·0011	0·0000				

If the ordinate of the spectral reflection (or transmission) curve at wave-length λ is ρ_λ, the x chromaticity co-ordinate of the reflected light under standard illuminant A is (left-hand table) :

$$\Sigma\rho_\lambda(E_A\bar{x})_\lambda/\{\Sigma\rho_\lambda(E_A\bar{x})_\lambda + \Sigma\rho_\lambda(E_A\bar{y})_\lambda + \Sigma\rho_\lambda(E_A\bar{z})_\lambda\}$$

or (right-hand table) :

$$F(x)\Sigma\rho_{\lambda(x)}/\{F(x)\Sigma\rho_{\lambda(x)} + F(y)\Sigma\rho_{\lambda(y)} + F(z)\Sigma\rho_{\lambda(z)}\}.$$

The reflection factor (per cent) is $\Sigma\rho_\lambda(E_A\bar{y})_\lambda$ or $(100/n)\,\Sigma\rho_{\lambda(y)}$, where n is the number of ordinates used.

Distribution Coefficients for Standard Illuminant B			
Wave length (mμ)	$E_B\bar{x}$	$E_B\bar{y}$	$E_B\bar{z}$
380	0·0025	0·0000	0·0113
390	0·0123	0·0003	0·0585
400	0·0558	0·0014	0·2650
410	0·2091	0·0057	0·9970
420	0·8274	0·0248	3·9750
430	1·9793	0·0810	9·6617
440	2·6889	0·1768	13·4883
450	2·7460	0·3105	14·4729
460	2·4571	0·5050	14·1020
470	1·7297	0·8018	11·3825
480	0·8629	1·2609	7·3655
490	0·2960	1·9190	4·2939
500	0·0437	2·9133	2·4552
510	0·0810	4·3669	1·3694
520	0·5405	6·0602	0·6709
530	1·4555	7·5959	0·3705
540	2·6899	8·8322	0·1889
550	4·1838	9·6060	0·0840
560	5·8385	9·7722	0·0378
570	7·4723	9·3341	0·0206
580	8·8406	8·3947	0·0154
590	9·7329	7·1777	0·0109
600	9·9523	5·9086	0·0075
610	9·4425	4·7373	0·0033
620	8·1290	3·6251	0·0014
630	6·2135	2·5629	0·0000
640	4·3678	1·7066	
650	2·8202	1·0638	
660	1·6515	0·6110	
670	0·8796	0·3223	
680	0·4602	0·1673	
690	0·2218	0·0801	
700	0·1065	0·0384	
710	0·0538	0·0193	
720	0·0253	0·0089	
730	0·0120	0·0043	
740	0·0058	0·0025	
750	0·0024	0·0008	
760	0·0012	0·0004	
770	0·0004	0·0000	

Selected Ordinates for computing chromaticity under Standard Illuminant B		
$\lambda(x)$	$\lambda(y)$	$\lambda(z)$
(millimicrons)		
428	472	415
× 442	494	423
454	506	427
468	513	430
× 528	520	433
543	525	435
552	529	438
× 558	534	440
564	538	442
569	541	444
× 573	545	446
577	549	448
581	552	450
× 585	556	452
588	559	454
591	562	456
× 595	566	458
598	569	460
601	573	462
× 605	577	464
608	581	466
612	585	468
× 615	589	471
619	594	474
623	599	477
× 628	605	480
633	612	484
640	620	490
× 649	631	499
666	651	515
$F(x)$ 0·03303	$F(y)$ 0·03333	$F(z)$ 0·02844

When 10 ordinates are used instead of 30, they should be those at the wave-lengths marked × and the multiplying factors are then $3F(x)$, $3F(y)$ and $3F(z)$.

For the method of use of these tables see the bottom of page 525.

The tables on the left-hand sides of pp. 524 to 527 are reproduced from a paper by H. G. W. Harding and R. B. Sisson published in the *Proceedings* of the Physical Society (Vol. 59, p. 814, 1947) by kind permission of the authors and the Society.

Distribution Coefficients for Standard Illuminant C				Selected Ordinates for computing chromaticity under Standard Illuminant C		
Wave length (mμ)	$E_C\bar{x}$	$E_C\bar{y}$	$E_C\bar{z}$	$\lambda(x)$	$\lambda(y)$	$\lambda(z)$
					(millimicrons)	
380	0·0036	0·0000	0·0164			
390	0·0183	0·0004	0·0870	424	466	414
				× 436	489	422
400	0·0841	0·0021	0·3992	444	500	426
410	0·3180	0·0087	1·5159	452	509	429
420	1·2623	0·0378	6·0646	× 461	515	432
430	2·9913	0·1225	14·6019			
440	3·9741	0·2613	19·9357	474	521	434
				531	525	437
450	3·9191	0·4432	20·6551	× 544	530	439
460	3·3668	0·6920	19·3235	552	534	441
470	2·2878	1·0605	15·0550	558	538	443
480	1·1038	1·6129	9·4220			
490	0·3639	2·3591	5·2789	× 564	541	444
				569	545	446
500	0·0511	3·4077	2·8717	573	548	448
510	0·0898	4·8412	1·5181	× 577	552	450
520	0·5752	6·4491	0·7140	581	555	452
530	1·5206	7·9357	0·3871			
540	2·7858	9·1470	0·1956	585	558	454
				× 589	562	456
550	4·2833	9·8343	0·0860	592	565	458
560	5·8782	9·8387	0·0381	596	569	460
570	7·3230	9·1476	0·0202	× 600	573	462
580	8·4141	7·9897	0·0147			
590	8·0678	6·6283	0·0101	603	570	464
				607	580	466
600	8·9536	5·3157	0·0067	× 611	585	469
610	8·3294	4·1788	0·0029	615	590	471
620	7·0604	3·1485	0·0012	619	595	474
630	5·3212	2·1948	0·0000			
640	3·6882	1·4411		× 624	601	478
				630	608	482
650	2·3531	0·8876		636	616	487
660	1·3589	0·5028		× 646	627	495
670	0·7113	0·2606		662	647	512
680	0·3657	0·1329				
690	0·1721	0·0621				
				$F(x)$	$F(y)$	$F(z)$
700	0·0806	0·0290		0·03269	0·03333	0·03941
710	0·0398	0·0143				
720	0·0183	0·0064				
730	0·0085	0·0030		When 10 ordinates are used instead of 30, they should be those at the wave-lengths marked × and the multiplying factors are then $3F(x)$, $3F(y)$ and $3F(z)$.		
740	0·0040	0·0017				
750	0·0017	0·0006				
760	0·0008	0·0003				
770	0·0003	0·0000				

For the method of use of these tables see the bottom of page 525.

The table on the right-hand side of p. 524 is based on that given in the paper by F. T. Bowditch and M. R. Null and is included by kind permission of the authors and of the Optical Society of America. The tables on the right-hand sides of pp. 525 to 527 are based, by kind permission, on tables in the *Handbook of Colorimetry*, by Arthur C. Hardy, published by the Technology Press of the Massachusetts Institute of Technology.

REFLECTION FACTORS OF CERTAIN SUBSTANCES

Material	Reflection Factor	
	Diffuse	Direct *
Magnesium oxide - - -	0·975 [1][2]	1·005 [2]
($\lambda = 0·45\mu$) -	0·970 [1]	1·007 [2]
($\lambda = 0·55\mu$) -	0·975 [1]	1·005 [2]
($\lambda = 0·65\mu$) -	0·975 [1]	1·007 [2]
Magnesium carbonate - -	0·98 [1]	0·95 [3]
Matt white celluloid, or thick white blotting paper - -	0·80–0·85 [4]	0·75–0·80 [4]
Depolished opal glass - -	0·75–0·85 [5]	0·75–0·85 [5]
Polished silver ($\lambda = 0·45\mu$) - -	—	0·90 [6]
($\lambda = 0·55\mu$) - -	—	0·92 [6]
($\lambda = 0·65\mu$) - -	—	0·935 [6]
Back-silvered glass ($\lambda = 0·45\mu$) -	—	0·79–0·85 [7]
($\lambda = 0·55\mu$) -	—	0·82–0·88 [7]
($\lambda = 0·65\mu$) -	—	0·84–0·90 [7]

* Normal incidence. In the case of a diffusing surface the angle of view is 30° and the figure given is relative to a perfect diffuser, i.e. it is the luminance factor (see p. 169).

REFERENCES

1. G. W. Gordon-Smith. Phys. Soc., Proc., (B), 65, *1952*, p. 275.
    See also F. Benford, G. P. Lloyd and S. Schwarz, Opt. Soc. Am., 38, *1948*, p. 445 and W. E. K. Middleton and C. L. Sanders, *ibid.*, 41, *1951*, p. 419 ; P. A. Tellex and J. R. Waldron, Opt. Soc. Am., J., 45, *1955*, p. 19.

2. J. S. Preston. Opt. Soc., Trans., 31, *1930*, p. 15 (Angle of view, 45°).
    J. S. Preston and G. W. Gordon-Smith. Phys. Soc., Proc., (B), 65, *1952*, p. 76.

3. Most probable value deduced from various published papers.

4. Measurements made at the National Physical Laboratory.

5. C. H. Sharp and W. F. Little. Illum. Eng. Soc. N.Y., Trans., 15, *1920*, p. 808.

6. E. Hagen and H. Rubens. Ann. d. Phys., 8, *1902*, p. 16.
    W. W. Coblentz. Bureau of Standards, Bull., 7, *1911*, p. 201.

7. E. Hagen and H. Rubens. Ann. d. Phys., 1, *1900*, p. 373.
    J. T. Tate. Phys. Rev., 34, *1912*, p. 327.

Values for other substances are given in the International Critical Tables, Vol. V, pp. 253–263. The reflection factors of various surfaces met with out-of-doors have been determined by W. W. Coblentz (Bureau of Standards, Bull., 9, *1913*, p. 283) and by H. H. Kimball (Illum. Eng. Soc. N.Y., Trans., 19, *1924*, p. 225).

APPENDIX VIII

LUMINANCE, LUMINANCE TEMPERATURE AND COLOUR TEMPERATURE OF COMMON LIGHT SOURCES

Source	Luminance cd/cm^2	Lum. Temp. (degs. K) ($\lambda = 0·665\mu$)	Colour Temp. (degs. K)
Candle - - - - -	0·6 [1]	—	1925 [2]
Hefner (whole flame) - - -	—	—	1875 [2]
Pentane (10 c.p.) - - -	—	—	1915 [2]
Paraffin (flat wick) - - -	1·25 [2]	1500 [2]	2050 [2]
(round wick) - -	1·5 [2]	1530 [2]	1915 [2]
Acetylene (Kodak burner) -	10·8 [2]	1725 [2]	2350 [2]
Welsbach mantle (inverted) -	7 [1]	—	—
(high pressure)	25 [1]	—	—
Tungsten filament lamp			
vacuum, 10 lm./watt - -	260 [3]	2270 [3]	2540 [3]
gas-filled, 13 lm./watt - -	710 [3]	2450 [3]	2780 [3]
16 lm./watt - -	890 [3]	2500 [3]	2850 [3]
20 lm./watt - -	1070 [3]	2570 [3]	2940 [3]
Sodium vapour lamp	70 [3]		
Mercury vapour lamp (h.p.) -	150 [3]	—	—
Arc crater (plain carbon) - -	16,000 [4]	3650 [5] ($\lambda = 0·653\mu$)	3820 [5]
Clear blue sky - - - -	0·2–0·6 [6]	—	12,000–24,000 [7]
Overcast sky - - - -	0·3–0·7 [6]	—	6400 [8]
Zenith sun (obs. from earth's surface) - - - -	165,000 [2]	—	5300 [8]

REFERENCES

N.B. It is to be noted that the values given in the above table are expressed on the International Temperature Scale of 1948. They have been derived from values given in the following papers by making the necessary corrections.

1. L. Bloch. Licht u. Lampe, 13, *1924*, p. 523.

2. E. P. Hyde and W. E. Forsythe. Illum. Eng. Soc. N.Y., Trans., 16, *1921*, p. 426.

3. W. E. Forsythe and E. M. Watson. Gen. El. Rev., 44, *1941*, p. 489 and 45, *1942*, p. 402.
    W. E. Forsythe and E. Q. Adams. *Ibid.*, 47, *1944*, Sept., p. 26 and Oct., p. 59.
    See also W. E. Forsythe and A. G. Worthing, Astrophys. J., 61, *1925*, p. 146 ; H. A. Jones and I. Langmuir, Gen. El. Rev., 30, *1927*, pp. 310, 354 and 408 ; C. Zwikker, Amsterdam Acad., Proc., 28, *1925*, p. 499 ; G. Wels, Licht, 11, *1941*, pp. 146 and 162 ; G. A. W. Rutgers and J. C. de Vos, Physica, 20, *1954*, p. 715.

4. J. T. MacGregor-Morris. Illum. Eng. Soc. Lond., Trans., 5, *1940*, p. 123. Inst. El. Eng., J., 91 (Part I), *1944*, p. 183.

5. H. G. MacPherson. Opt. Soc. Am., J., 30, *1940*, p. 189.
    For values obtained with a graphite anode see also N. K. Chaney, V. C. Hamister and S. W. Glass, Electrochem. Soc., Trans., 67, *1935*, p. 107.

6. H. H. Kimball. Illum. Eng. Soc. N.Y., Trans., 16, *1921*, p. 255 (luminance at zenith).

7. I. G. Priest. Opt. Soc. Am., J., 7, *1923*, p. 1184 (see also p. 78).
    A. H. Taylor. Illum. Eng. Soc. N.Y., Trans., 25, *1930*, p. 154.

8. G. H. Taylor and G. P. Kerr. Opt. Soc. Am., J., 31, *1941*, p. 3.
    P. Moon. Frank. Inst., J., 244, *1947*, p. 441.

APPENDIX IX

THE COLOUR AND SPECTRAL DISTRIBUTION OF LIGHT SOURCES

Colour

The chromaticity co-ordinates of a light source to which a colour temperature is assigned in Appendix VIII may be obtained, to a close approximation, from the " black-body locus " on the chromaticity diagram (see Fig. 188 on p. 341) [1]. The values for a sodium lamp are almost exactly those for monochromatic light of wave-length 0.589μ, viz. $x = 0.5693$ and $y = 0.4300$. For other sources the values are as follows :

Source	x	y
Welsbach mantle [2] - -	0·450	0·435
Mercury vapour lamp [3] -	0·290	0·360
	to 0·330	0·410
Sunlight [4] - - - -	0·343	0·357
Overcast sky [4] - - -	0·313	0·328
Blue sky [4] - - -	0·263	0·279

On the colour of various types of fluorescent lamps see P. Moon (Illum. Eng. Soc. N.Y., Trans., 36, *1941*, p. 334 and Frank. Inst., J., 244, *1947*, p. 441). Colorimetric data for a large number of Wratten colour filters have been given by D. L. MacAdam (Opt. Soc. Am., J., 35, *1945*, p. 670).

Spectral Distribution

The spectral distribution of the flame sources listed in Appendix VIII is the Planckian distribution corresponding to the colour temperature shown. This is also true, to a close approximation, for a tungsten filament lamp, but the spectral distributions measured for a large number of types of such lamps have been given by B. T. Barnes and W. E. Forsythe (Opt. Soc. Am., J., 26, *1936*, p. 313).

A representative spectral distribution curve for sunlight has been proposed by P. Moon [5] and experimental curves for sunlight and for different phases of daylight have been determined by A. H. Taylor and G. P. Kerr [4] and others [6].

The spectral distribution of the plain carbon arc is, for most of the spectrum, that of a full radiator at a temperature slightly below the colour temperature shown in Appendix VIII, viz. about 3805° K. The radiation is increased irregularly in the region 0.35 to 0.42μ by the presence of the cyanogen bands [7]. Curves for various types of fluorescent lamps have been collected by P. Moon and D. E. Spencer (Frank. Inst. J., 244, *1947*, p. 441). On the spectral distribution of sources giving a prominent line spectrum see p. 373.

REFERENCES

1. See also W. E. Forsythe and E. Q. Adams, Opt. Soc. Am., J., 35, *1945*, pp. 108 and 306.

2. Computed from a spectral distribution curve given by H. E. Ives, Illum. Eng. Soc. N.Y., Trans., 5, *1910*, p. 189.

3. Various published figures. See especially P. Moon, Illum. Eng. Soc. N.Y., Trans., 36, *1941*, p. 334.

4. A. H. Taylor and G. P. Kerr. Opt. Soc. Am., J., 31, *1941*, p. 3.
 P. Moon. Frank. Inst., J., 230, *1940*, p. 583 and 244, *1947*, p. 441.

5. P. Moon. Frank. Inst., J., 230, *1940*, p. 583.

6. H. H. Kimball and I. F. Hand. Illum. Eng. Soc. N.Y., Trans., 16, *1921*, p. 255.
 F. W. Cunliffe. Textile Inst., J., 20, *1929*, p. T34.
See also Opt. Soc. Am., J., 34, *1944*, p. 637.

7. H. G. MacPherson. Opt. Soc. Am., J., 30, *1940*, p. 189.
See also Opt. Soc. Am., J., 34, *1944*, p. 639.
On the spectral distribution from high-intensity arcs (cored carbons) see, e.g., F. T. Bowditch and A. C. Downes, Soc. Motion Picture Engrs., J., 30, *1938*, p. 400.

APPENDIX X

CHARACTERISTIC EQUATIONS FOR TUNGSTEN FILAMENT LAMPS

The relations between luminous flux (or intensity), potential and current for electric lamps are often expressed by empirical equations of the general form $A = mB^n$ or $\dfrac{B}{A} \dfrac{dA}{dB} = n$ [1]. The values of n for modern lamps are as follows :

Type of Lamp	$\dfrac{E}{F} \cdot \dfrac{dF}{dE}$	$\dfrac{I}{F} \cdot \dfrac{dF}{dI}$	$\dfrac{E}{I} \cdot \dfrac{dI}{dE}$
Vacuum (8 lm./watt) - -	3·59	6·16	0·58
Gas-filled, small (10 lm./w.) -	3·80	7·28	0·52
large (16 lm./w.) -	3·38	6·24	0·54

The above values refer to lamps operating at about the normal working efficiency for each type. It has been found that, although n is constant for small variations of the quantities concerned, it alters gradually with the efficiency of the lamp. A more complicated expression than that given above is, therefore, required for interpolation over wide ranges and an equation of the form $y = Ax^2 + Bx + C$ has been found to represent the observed values satisfactorily [2]. In this equation x represents the logarithm of any given voltage ratio and y the logarithm of the corresponding ratio of luminous flux, current, etc. Different values of the constants are required for lamps of different types with different normal operating efficiencies.

The relationship between the colour temperature of a tungsten lamp and the logarithm of the luminous flux (or intensity) is very nearly represented by the equation $\log F = A - 11{,}350/T$ where T is the colour temperature and A is a constant [3].

REFERENCES

1. See the refs. in note (1) on pp. 483–4 of *Photometry (1926)*.

2. L. E. Barbrow and J. F. Meyer. Bureau of Standards, J. of Research, 9, *1932*, p. 721.

See also G. W. Middlekauff and J. F. Skogland, Bureau of Standards, Bull., 11, *1915*, p. 483 and Illum. Eng. Soc. N.Y., Trans., 9, *1914*, p. 734 ; W. E. Forsythe and A. G. Worthing, C.I.E. Proc., 6, *1924*, p. 100 ; H. Pécheux, Rev. Gén. de l'El., 25, *1929*, p. 165 and 32, *1932*, p. 867 ; Y. Isida, World Engineering Congress, Tokyo, *1929*, Proc., Vol. 24, p. 167 ; W. E. Forsythe and E. Q. Adams, Gen. El. Rev., 39, *1936*, p. 497.

3. K. S. Weaver and H. E. Hussong. Opt. Soc. Am., J., 29, *1939*, p. 16.

INDEX

The numbers refer to pages. Numbers in brackets indicate reference notes.

CATALOGUE OF DOVER BOOKS

BOOKS EXPLAINING SCIENCE AND MATHEMATICS

General

WHAT IS SCIENCE?, Norman Campbell. This excellent introduction explains scientific method, role of mathematics, types of scientific laws. Contents: 2 aspects of science, science & nature, laws of science, discovery of laws, explanation of laws, measurement & numerical laws, applications of science. 192pp. 5⅜ x 8.   S43 Paperbound **$1.25**

THE COMMON SENSE OF THE EXACT SCIENCES, W. K. Clifford. Introduction by James Newman, edited by Karl Pearson. For 70 years this has been a guide to classical scientific and mathematical thought. Explains with unusual clarity basic concepts, such as extension of meaning of symbols, characteristics of surface boundaries, properties of plane figures, vectors, Cartesian method of determining position, etc. Long preface by Bertrand Russell. Bibliography of Clifford. Corrected, 130 diagrams redrawn. 249pp. 5⅜ x 8.
T61 Paperbound **$1.60**

SCIENCE THEORY AND MAN, Erwin Schrödinger. This is a complete and unabridged reissue of SCIENCE AND THE HUMAN TEMPERAMENT plus an additional essay: "What is an Elementary Particle?" Nobel laureate Schrödinger discusses such topics as nature of scientific method, the nature of science, chance and determinism, science and society, conceptual models for physical entities, elementary particles and wave mechanics. Presentation is popular and may be followed by most people with little or no scientific training. "Fine practical preparation for a time when laws of nature, human institutions . . . are undergoing a critical examination without parallel," Waldemar Kaempffert, N. Y. TIMES. 192pp. 5⅜ x 8.
T428 Paperbound **$1.35**

FADS AND FALLACIES IN THE NAME OF SCIENCE, Martin Gardner. Examines various cults, quack systems, frauds, delusions which at various times have masqueraded as science. Accounts of hollow-earth fanatics like Symmes; Velikovsky and wandering planets; Hoerbiger; Bellamy and the theory of multiple moons; Charles Fort; dowsing, pseudoscientific methods for finding water, ores, oil. Sections on naturopathy, iridiagnosis, zone therapy, food fads, etc. Analytical accounts of Wilhelm Reich and orgone sex energy; L. Ron Hubbard and Dianetics; A. Korzybski and General Semantics; many others. Brought up to date to include Bridey Murphy, others. Not just a collection of anecdotes, but a fair, reasoned appraisal of eccentric theory. Formerly titled IN THE NAME OF SCIENCE. Preface. Index. x + 384pp. 5⅜ x 8.   T394 Paperbound **$1.50**

A DOVER SCIENCE SAMPLER, edited by George Barkin. 64-page book, sturdily bound, containing excerpts from over 20 Dover books, explaining science. Edwin Hubble, George Sarton, Ernst Mach, A. d'Abro, Galileo, Newton, others, discussing island universes, scientific truth, biological phenomena, stability in bridges, etc. Copies limited; no more than 1 to a customer,
FREE

POPULAR SCIENTIFIC LECTURES, Hermann von Helmholtz. Helmholtz was a superb expositor as well as a scientist of genius in many areas. The seven essays in this volume are models of clarity, and even today they rank among the best general descriptions of their subjects ever written. "The Physiological Causes of Harmony in Music" was the first significant physiological explanation of musical consonance and dissonance. Two essays, "On the Interaction of Natural Forces" and "On the Conservation of Force," were of great importance in the history of science, for they firmly established the principle of the conservation of energy. Other lectures include "On the Relation of Optics to Painting," "On Recent Progress in the Theory of Vision," "On Goethe's Scientific Researches," and "On the Origin and Significance of Geometrical Axioms." Selected and edited with an introduction by Professor Morris Kline. xii + 286pp. 5⅜ x 8½.   T799 Paperbound **$1.45**

BOOKS EXPLAINING SCIENCE AND MATHEMATICS

Physics

CONCERNING THE NATURE OF THINGS, Sir William Bragg. Christmas lectures delivered at the Royal Society by Nobel laureate. Why a spinning ball travels in a curved track; how uranium is transmuted to lead, etc. Partial contents: atoms, gases, liquids, crystals, metals, etc. No scientific background needed; wonderful for intelligent child. 32pp. of photos, 57 figures. xii + 232pp. 5⅜ x 8.   T31 Paperbound **$1.35**

THE RESTLESS UNIVERSE, Max Born. New enlarged version of this remarkably readable account by a Nobel laureate. Moving from sub-atomic particles to universe, the author explains in very simple terms the latest theories of wave mechanics. Partial contents: air and its relatives, electrons & ions, waves & particles, electronic structure of the atom, nuclear physics. Nearly 1000 illustrations, including 7 animated sequences. 325pp. 6 x 9.
T412 Paperbound **$2.00**

FROM EUCLID TO EDDINGTON: A STUDY OF THE CONCEPTIONS OF THE EXTERNAL WORLD, Sir Edmund Whittaker. A foremost British scientist traces the development of theories of natural philosophy from the western rediscovery of Euclid to Eddington, Einstein, Dirac, etc. The inadequacy of classical physics is contrasted with present day attempts to understand the physical world through relativity, non-Euclidean geometry, space curvature, wave mechanics, etc. 5 major divisions of examination: Space; Time and Movement; the Concepts of Classical Physics; the Concepts of Quantum Mechanics; the Eddington Universe. 212pp. 5⅜ x 8. T491 Paperbound $1.35

PHYSICS, THE PIONEER SCIENCE, L. W. Taylor. First thorough text to place all important physical phenomena in cultural-historical framework; remains best work of its kind. Exposition of physical laws, theories developed chronologically, with great historical, illustrative experiments diagrammed, described, worked out mathematically. Excellent physics text for self-study as well as class work. Vol. 1: Heat, Sound: motion, acceleration, gravitation, conservation of energy, heat engines, rotation, heat, mechanical energy, etc. 211 illus. 407pp. 5⅜ x 8. Vol. 2: Light, Electricity: images, lenses, prisms, magnetism, Ohm's law, dynamos, telegraph, quantum theory, decline of mechanical view of nature, etc. Bibliography. 13 table appendix. Index. 551 illus. 2 color plates. 508pp. 5⅜ x 8.
Vol. 1 S565 Paperbound **$2.00**
Vol. 2 S566 Paperbound **$2.00**
The set **$4.00**

A SURVEY OF PHYSICAL THEORY, Max Planck. One of the greatest scientists of all time, creator of the quantum revolution in physics, writes in non-technical terms of his own discoveries and those of other outstanding creators of modern physics. Planck wrote this book when science had just crossed the threshold of the new physics, and he communicates the excitement felt then as he discusses electromagnetic theories, statistical methods, evolution of the concept of light, a step-by-step description of how he developed his own momentous theory, and many more of the basic ideas behind modern physics. Formerly "A Survey of Physics." Bibliography. Index. 128pp. 5⅜ x 8. S650 Paperbound **$1.15**

THE ATOMIC NUCLEUS, M. Korsunsky. The only non-technical comprehensive account of the atomic nucleus in English. For college physics students, etc. Chapters cover: Radioactivity, the Nuclear Model of the Atom, the Mass of Atomic Nuclei, the Disintegration of Atomic Nuclei, the Discovery of the Positron, the Artificial Transformation of Atomic Nuclei, Artificial Radioactivity, Mesons, the Neutrino, the Structure of Atomic Nuclei and Forces Acting Between Nuclear Particles, Nuclear Fission, Chain Reaction, Peaceful Uses, Thermonuclear Reactions. Slightly abridged edition. Translated by G. Yankovsky. 65 figures. Appendix includes 45 photographic illustrations. 413 pp. 5⅜ x 8. S1052 Paperbound **$2.00**

PRINCIPLES OF MECHANICS SIMPLY EXPLAINED, Morton Mott-Smith. Excellent, highly readable introduction to the theories and discoveries of classical physics. Ideal for the layman who desires a foundation which will enable him to understand and appreciate contemporary developments in the physical sciences. Discusses: Density, The Law of Gravitation, Mass and Weight, Action and Reaction, Kinetic and Potential Energy, The Law of Inertia, Effects of Acceleration, The Independence of Motions, Galileo and the New Science of Dynamics, Newton and the New Cosmos, The Conservation of Momentum, and other topics. Revised edition of "This Mechanical World." Illustrated by E. Kosa, Jr. Bibliography and Chronology. Index. xiv + 171pp. 5⅜ x 8½. T1067 Paperbound **$1.00**

THE CONCEPT OF ENERGY SIMPLY EXPLAINED, Morton Mott-Smith. Elementary, non-technical exposition which traces the story of man's conquest of energy, with particular emphasis on the developments during the nineteenth century and the first three decades of our own century. Discusses man's earlier efforts to harness energy, more recent experiments and discoveries relating to the steam engine, the engine indicator, the motive power of heat, the principle of excluded perpetual motion, the bases of the conservation of energy, the concept of entropy, the internal combustion engine, mechanical refrigeration, and many other related topics. Also much biographical material. Index. Bibliography. 33 illustrations. ix + 215pp. 5⅜ x 8½. T1071 Paperbound **$1.25**

HEAT AND ITS WORKINGS, Morton Mott-Smith. One of the best elementary introductions to the theory and attributes of heat, covering such matters as the laws governing the effect of heat on solids, liquids and gases, the methods by which heat is measured, the conversion of a substance from one form to another through heating and cooling, evaporation, the effects of pressure on boiling and freezing points, and the three ways in which heat is transmitted (conduction, convection, radiation). Also brief notes on major experiments and discoveries. Concise, but complete, it presents all the essential facts about the subject in readable style. Will give the layman and beginning student a first-rate background in this major topic in physics. Index. Bibliography. 50 illustrations. x + 165pp. 5⅜ x 8½. T978 Paperbound **$1.00**

THE STORY OF ATOMIC THEORY AND ATOMIC ENERGY, J. G. Feinberg. Wider range of facts on physical theory, cultural implications, than any other similar source. Completely non-technical. Begins with first atomic theory, 600 B.C., goes through A-bomb, developments to 1959. Avogadro, Rutherford, Bohr, Einstein, radioactive decay, binding energy, radiation danger, future benefits of nuclear power, dozens of other topics, told in lively, related, informal manner. Particular stress on European atomic research. "Deserves special mention . . . authoritative," Saturday Review. Formerly "The Atom Story." New chapter to 1959. Index. 34 illustrations. 251pp. 5⅜ x 8. T625 Paperbound **$1.45**

THE STRANGE STORY OF THE QUANTUM, AN ACCOUNT FOR THE GENERAL READER OF THE GROWTH OF IDEAS UNDERLYING OUR PRESENT ATOMIC KNOWLEDGE, B. Hoffmann. Presents lucidly and expertly, with barest amount of mathematics, the problems and theories which led to modern quantum physics. Dr. Hoffmann begins with the closing years of the 19th century, when certain trifling discrepancies were noticed, and with illuminating analogies and examples takes you through the brilliant concepts of Planck, Einstein, Pauli, de Broglie, Bohr, Schroedinger, Heisenberg, Dirac, Sommerfeld, Feynman, etc. This edition includes a new, long postscript carrying the story through 1958. "Of the books attempting an account of the history and contents of our modern atomic physics which have come to my attention, this is the best," H. Margenau, Yale University, in "American Journal of Physics." 32 tables and line illustrations. Index. 275pp. 5⅜ x 8.   T518 Paperbound **$1.50**

THE EVOLUTION OF SCIENTIFIC THOUGHT FROM NEWTON TO EINSTEIN, A. d'Abro. Einstein's special and general theories of relativity, with their historical implications, are analyzed in non-technical terms. Excellent accounts of the contributions of Newton, Riemann, Weyl, Planck, Eddington, Maxwell, Lorentz and others are treated in terms of space and time, equations of electromagnetics, finiteness of the universe, methodology of science. 21 diagrams. 482pp. 5⅜ x 8.   T2 Paperound **$2.00**

THE RISE OF THE NEW PHYSICS, A. d'Abro. A half-million word exposition, formerly titled THE DECLINE OF MECHANISM, for readers not versed in higher mathematics. The only thorough explanation, in everyday language, of the central core of modern mathematical physical theory, treating both classical and modern theoretical physics, and presenting in terms almost anyone can understand the equivalent of 5 years of study of mathematical physics. Scientifically impeccable coverage of mathematical-physical thought from the Newtonian system up through the electronic theories of Dirac and Heisenberg and Fermi's statistics. Combines both history and exposition; provides a broad yet unified and detailed view, with constant comparison of classical and modern views on phenomena and theories. "A must for anyone doing serious study in the physical sciences," JOURNAL OF THE FRANKLIN INSTITUTE. "Extraordinary faculty . . . to explain ideas and theories of theoretical physics in the language of daily life," ISIS. First part of set covers philosophy of science, drawing upon the practice of Newton, Maxwell, Poincaré, Einstein, others, discussing modes of thought, experiment, interpretations of causality, etc. In the second part, 100 pages explain grammar and vocabulary of mathematics, with discussions of functions, groups, series, Fourier series, etc. The remainder is devoted to concrete, detailed coverage of both classical and quantum physics, explaining such topics as analytic mechanics, Hamilton's principle, wave theory of light, electromagnetic waves, groups of transformations, thermodynamics, phase rule, Brownian movement, kinetics, special relativity, Planck's original quantum theory, Bohr's atom, Zeeman effect, Broglie's wave mechanics, Heisenberg's uncertainty, Eigen-values, matrices, scores of other important topics. Discoveries and theories are covered for such men as Alembert, Born, Cantor, Debye, Euler, Foucault, Galois, Gauss, Hadamard, Kelvin, Kepler, Laplace, Maxwell, Pauli, Rayleigh, Volterra, Weyl, Young, more than 180 others. Indexed. 97 illustrations. ix + 982pp. 5⅜ x 8.   T3 Volume 1, Paperbound **$2.00**
          T4 Volume 2, Paperbound **$2.00**

SPINNING TOPS AND GYROSCOPIC MOTION, John Perry. Well-known classic of science still unsurpassed for lucid, accurate, delightful exposition. How quasi-rigidity is induced in flexible and fluid bodies by rapid motions; why gyrostat falls, top rises; nature and effect on climatic conditions of earth's precessional movement; effect of internal fluidity on rotating bodies, etc. Appendixes describe practical uses to which gyroscopes have been put in ships, compasses, monorail transportation. 62 figures. 128pp. 5⅜ x 8.   T416 Paperbound **$1.00**

THE UNIVERSE OF LIGHT, Sir William Bragg. No scientific training needed to read Nobel Prize winner's expansion of his Royal Institute Christmas Lectures. Insight into nature of light, methods and philosophy of science. Explains lenses, reflection, color, resonance, polarization, x-rays, the spectrum, Newton's work with prisms, Huygens' with polarization, Crookes' with cathode ray, etc. Leads into clear statement of 2 major historical theories of light, corpuscle and wave. Dozens of experiments you can do. 199 illus., including 2 full-page color plates. 293pp. 5⅜ x 8.   S538 Paperbound **$1.85**

THE STORY OF X-RAYS FROM RÖNTGEN TO ISOTOPES, A. R. Bleich. Non-technical history of x-rays, their scientific explanation, their applications in medicine, industry, research, and art, and their effect on the individual and his descendants. Includes amusing early reactions to Röntgen's discovery, cancer therapy, detections of art and stamp forgeries, potential risks to patient and operator, etc. Illustrations show x-rays of flower structure, the gall bladder, gears with hidden defects, etc. Original Dover publication. Glossary. Bibliography. Index. 55 photos and figures. xiv + 186pp. 5⅜ x 8.   T662 Paperbound **$1.35**

ELECTRONS, ATOMS, METALS AND ALLOYS, Wm. Hume-Rothery. An introductory-level explanation of the application of the electronic theory to the structure and properties of metals and alloys, taking into account the new theoretical work done by mathematical physicists. Material presented in dialogue-form between an "Old Metallurgist" and a "Young Scientist." Their discussion falls into 4 main parts: the nature of an atom, the nature of a metal, the nature of an alloy, and the structure of the nucleus. They cover such topics as the hydrogen atom, electron waves, wave mechanics, Brillouin zones, co-valent bonds, radioactivity and natural disintegration, fundamental particles, structure and fission of the nucleus, etc. Revised, enlarged edition. 177 illustrations. Subject and name indexes. 407pp. 5⅜ x 8½.   S1046 Paperbound **$2.25**

OUT OF THE SKY, H. H. Nininger. A non-technical but comprehensive introduction to "meteoritics", the young science concerned with all aspects of the arrival of matter from outer space. Written by one of the world's experts on meteorites, this work shows how, despite difficulties of observation and sparseness of data, a considerable body of knowledge has arisen. It defines meteors and meteorites; studies fireball clusters and processions, meteorite composition, size, distribution, showers, explosions, origins, craters, and much more. A true connecting link between astronomy and geology. More than 175 photos, 22 other illustrations. References. Bibliography of author's publications on meteorites. Index. viii + 336pp. 5⅜ x 8.   T519 Paperbound **$1.85**

SATELLITES AND SCIENTIFIC RESEARCH, D. King-Hele. Non-technical account of the manmade satellites and the discoveries they have yielded up to the autumn of 1961. Brings together information hitherto published only in hard-to-get scientific journals. Includes the life history of a typical satellite, methods of tracking, new information on the shape of the earth, zones of radiation, etc. Over 60 diagrams and 6 photographs. Mathematical appendix. Bibliography of over 100 items. Index. xii + 180pp. 5⅜ x 8½.   T703 Paperbound **$2.00**

BOOKS EXPLAINING SCIENCE AND MATHEMATICS

Mathematics

CHANCE, LUCK AND STATISTICS: THE SCIENCE OF CHANCE, Horace C. Levinson. Theory of probability and science of statistics in simple, non-technical language. Part I deals with theory of probability, covering odd superstitions in regard to "luck," the meaning of betting odds, the law of mathematical expectation, gambling, and applications in poker, roulette, lotteries, dice, bridge, and other games of chance. Part II discusses the misuse of statistics, the concept of statistical probabilities, normal and skew frequency distributions, and statistics applied to various fields—birth rates, stock speculation, insurance rates, advertising, etc. "Presented in an easy humorous style which I consider the best kind of expository writing," Prof. A. C. Cohen, Industry Quality Control. Enlarged revised edition. Formerly titled "The Science of Chance." Preface and two new appendices by the author. Index. xiv + 365pp. 5⅜ x 8.   T1007 Paperbound **$1.85**

PROBABILITIES AND LIFE, Emile Borel. Translated by M. Baudin. Non-technical, highly readable introduction to the results of probability as applied to everyday situations. Partial contents: Fallacies About Probabilities Concerning Life After Death; Negligible Probabilities and the Probabilities of Everyday Life; Events of Small Probability; Application of Probabilities to Certain Problems of Heredity; Probabilities of Deaths, Diseases, and Accidents; On Poisson's Formula. Index. 3 Appendices of statistical studies and tables. vi + 87pp. 5⅜ x 8½.   T121 Paperbound **$1.00**

GREAT IDEAS OF MODERN MATHEMATICS: THEIR NATURE AND USE, Jagjit Singh. Reader with only high school math will understand main mathematical ideas of modern physics, astronomy, genetics, psychology, evolution, etc., better than many who use them as tools, but comprehend little of their basic structure. Author uses his wide knowledge of non-mathematical fields in brilliant exposition of differential equations, matrices, group theory, logic, statistics, problems of mathematical foundations, imaginary numbers, vectors, etc. Original publication. 2 appendices. 2 indexes. 65 illustr. 322pp. 5⅜ x 8.   S587 Paperbound **$1.75**

MATHEMATICS IN ACTION, O. G. Sutton. Everyone with a command of high school algebra will find this book one of the finest possible introductions to the application of mathematics to physical theory. Ballistics, numerical analysis, waves and wavelike phenomena, Fourier series, group concepts, fluid flow and aerodynamics, statistical measures, and meteorology are discussed with unusual clarity. Some calculus and differential equations theory is developed by the author for the reader's help in the more difficult sections. 88 figures. Index. viii + 236pp. 5⅜ x 8.   T440 Clothbound **$3.50**

THE FOURTH DIMENSION SIMPLY EXPLAINED, edited by H. P. Manning. 22 essays, originally Scientific American contest entries, that use a minimum of mathematics to explain aspects of 4-dimensional geometry: analogues to 3-dimensional space, 4-dimensional absurdities and curiosities (such as removing the contents of an egg without puncturing its shell), possible measurements and forms, etc. Introduction by the editor. Only book of its sort on a truly elementary level, excellent introduction to advanced works. 82 figures. 251pp. 5⅜ x 8.
                                                                             T711 Paperbound **$1.35**

MATHEMATICS—INTERMEDIATE TO ADVANCED

General

INTRODUCTION TO APPLIED MATHEMATICS, Francis D. Murnaghan. A practical and thoroughly sound introduction to a number of advanced branches of higher mathematics. Among the selected topics covered in detail are: vector and matrix analysis, partial and differential equations, integral equations, calculus of variations, Laplace transform theory, the vector triple product, linear vector functions, quadratic and bilinear forms, Fourier series, spherical harmonics, Bessel functions, the Heaviside expansion formula, and many others. Extremely useful book for graduate students in physics, engineering, chemistry, and mathematics. Index. 111 study exercises with answers. 41 illustrations. ix + 389pp. 5⅜ x 8½.
S1042 Paperbound **$2.00**

OPERATIONAL METHODS IN APPLIED MATHEMATICS, H. S. Carslaw and J. C. Jaeger. Explanation of the application of the Laplace Transformation to differential equations, a simple and effective substitute for more difficult and obscure operational methods. Of great practical value to engineers and to all workers in applied mathematics. Chapters on: Ordinary Linear Differential Equations with Constant Coefficients;; Electric Circuit Theory; Dynamical Applications; The Inversion Theorem for the Laplace Transformation; Conduction of Heat; Vibrations of Continuous Mechanical Systems; Hydrodynamics; Impulsive Functions; Chains of Differential Equations; and other related matters. 3 appendices. 153 problems, many with answers. 22 figures. xvi + 359pp. 5⅜ x 8½.
S1011 Paperbound **$2.25**

APPLIED MATHEMATICS FOR RADIO AND COMMUNICATIONS ENGINEERS, C. E. Smith. No extraneous material here!—only the theories, equations, and operations essential and immediately useful for radio work. Can be used as refresher, as handbook of applications and tables, or as full home-study course. Ranges from simplest arithmetic through calculus, series, and wave forms, hyperbolic trigonometry, simultaneous equations in mesh circuits, etc. Supplies applications right along with each math topic discussed. 22 useful tables of functions, formulas, logs, etc. Index. 166 exercises, 140 examples, all with answers. 95 diagrams. Bibliography. x + 336pp. 5⅜ x 8.
S141 Paperbound **$1.75**

Algebra, group theory, determinants, sets, matrix theory

ALGEBRAS AND THEIR ARITHMETICS, L. E. Dickson. Provides the foundation and background necessary to any advanced undergraduate or graduate student studying abstract algebra. Begins with elementary introduction to linear transformations, matrices, field of complex numbers; proceeds to order, basal units, modulus, quaternions, etc.; develops calculus of linears sets, describes various examples of algebras including invariant, difference, nilpotent, semi-simple. "Makes the reader marvel at his genius for clear and profound analysis," Amer. Mathematical Monthly. Index. xii + 241pp. 5⅜ x 8.
S616 Paperbound **$1.50**

THE THEORY OF EQUATIONS WITH AN INTRODUCTION TO THE THEORY OF BINARY ALGEBRAIC FORMS, W. S. Burnside and A. W. Panton. Extremely thorough and concrete discussion of the theory of equations, with extensive detailed treatment of many topics curtailed in later texts. Covers theory of algebraic equations, properties of polynomials, symmetric functions, derived functions, Horner's process, complex numbers and the complex variable, determinants and methods of elimination, invariant theory (nearly 100 pages), transformations, introduction to Galois theory, Abelian equations, and much more. Invaluable supplementary work for modern students and teachers. 759 examples and exercises. Index in each volume. Two volume set. Total of xxiv + 604pp. 5⅜ x 8.
S714 Vol I Paperbound **$1.85**
S715 Vol II Paperbound **$1.85**
The set **$3.70**

COMPUTATIONAL METHODS OF LINEAR ALGEBRA, V. N. Faddeeva, translated by **C. D. Benster.** First English translation of a unique and valuable work, the only work in English presenting a systematic exposition of the most important methods of linear algebra—classical and contemporary. Shows in detail how to derive numerical solutions of problems in mathematical physics which are frequently connected with those of linear algebra. Theory as well as individual practice. Part I surveys the mathematical background that is indispensable to what follows. Parts II and III, the conclusion, set forth the most important methods of solution, for both exact and iterative groups. One of the most outstanding and valuable features of this work is the 23 tables, double and triple checked for accuracy. These tables will not be found elsewhere. Author's preface. Translator's note. New bibliography and index. x + 252pp. 5⅜ x 8.
S424 Paperbound **$1.95**

ALGEBRAIC EQUATIONS, E. Dehn. Careful and complete presentation of Galois' theory of algebraic equations; theories of Lagrange and Galois developed in logical rather than historical form, with a more thorough exposition than in most modern books. Many concrete applications and fully-worked-out examples. Discusses basic theory (very clear exposition of the symmetric group); isomorphic, transitive, and Abelian groups; applications of Lagrange's and Galois' theories; and much more. Newly revised by the author. Index. List of Theorems. xi + 208pp. 5⅜ x 8.
S697 Paperbound **$1.45**

Differential equations, ordinary and partial; integral equations

INTRODUCTION TO THE DIFFERENTIAL EQUATIONS OF PHYSICS, L. Hopf. Especially valuable to the engineer with no math beyond elementary calculus. Emphasizing intuitive rather than formal aspects of concepts, the author covers an extensive territory. Partial contents: Law of causality, energy theorem, damped oscillations, coupling by friction, cylindrical and spherical coordinates, heat source, etc. Index. 48 figures. 160pp. 5⅜ x 8.
S120 Paperbound **$1.25**

INTRODUCTION TO THE THEORY OF LINEAR DIFFERENTIAL EQUATIONS, E. G. Poole. Authoritative discussions of important topics, with methods of solution more detailed than usual, for students with background of elementary course in differential equations. Studies existence theorems, linearly independent solutions; equations with constant coefficients; with uniform analytic coefficients; regular singularities; the hypergeometric equation; conformal representation; etc. Exercises. Index. 210pp. 5⅜ x 8. S629 Paperbound **$1.65**

DIFFERENTIAL EQUATIONS FOR ENGINEERS, P. Franklin. Outgrowth of a course given 10 years at M. I. T. Makes most useful branch of pure math accessible for practical work. Theoretical basis of D.E.'s; solution of ordinary D.E.'s and partial derivatives arising from heat flow, steady-state temperature of a plate, wave equations; analytic functions; convergence of Fourier Series. 400 problems on electricity, vibratory systems, other topics. Formerly "Differential Equations for Electrical Engineers." Index 41 illus. 307pp. 5⅜ x 8.
S601 Paperbound **$1.65**

DIFFERENTIAL EQUATIONS, F. R. Moulton. A detailed, rigorous exposition of all the non-elementary processes of solving ordinary differential equations. Several chapters devoted to the treatment of practical problems, especially those of a physical nature, which are far more advanced than problems usually given as illustrations. Includes analytic differential equations; variations of a parameter; integrals of differential equations; analytic implicit functions; problems of elliptic motion; sine-amplitude functions; deviation of formal bodies; Cauchy-Lipschitz process; linear differential equations with periodic coefficients; differential equations in infinitely many variations; much more. Historical notes. 10 figures. 222 problems. Index. xv + 395pp. 5⅜ x 8. S451 Paperbound **$2.00**

DIFFERENTIAL AND INTEGRAL EQUATIONS OF MECHANICS AND PHYSICS (DIE DIFFERENTIAL-UND INTEGRALGLEICHUNGEN DER MECHANIK UND PHYSIK), edited by P. Frank and R. von Mises. Most comprehensive and authoritative work on the mathematics of mathematical physics available today in the United States: the standard, definitive reference for teachers, physicists, engineers, and mathematicians—now published (in the original German) at a relatively inexpensive price for the first time! Every chapter in this 2,000-page set is by an expert in his field: Carathéodory, Courant, Frank, Mises, and a dozen others. Vol I, on mathematics, gives concise but complete coverages of advanced calculus, differential equations, integral equations, and potential, and partial differential equations. Index. xxiii + 916pp. Vol. II (physics): classical mechanics, optics, continuous mechanics, heat conduction and diffusion, the stationary and quasi-stationary electromagnetic field, electromagnetic oscillations, and wave mechanics. Index. xxiv + 1106pp. Two volume set. Each volume available separately. 5⅝ x 8⅜.
S787 Vol I Clothbound **$7.50**
S788 Vol II Clothbound **$7.50**
The set **$15.00**

LECTURES ON CAUCHY'S PROBLEM, J. Hadamard. Based on lectures given at Columbia, Rome, this discusses work of Riemann, Kirchhoff, Volterra, and the author's own research on the hyperbolic case in linear partial differential equations. It extends spherical and cylindrical waves to apply to all (normal) hyperbolic equations. Partial contents: Cauchy's problem, fundamental formula, equations with odd number, with even number of independent variables; method of descent. 32 figures. Index. iii + 316pp. 5⅜ x 8. S105 Paperbound **$1.75**

THEORY OF DIFFERENTIAL EQUATIONS, A. R. Forsyth. Out of print for over a decade, the complete 6 volumes (now bound as 3) of this monumental work represent the most comprehensive treatment of differential equations ever written. Historical presentation includes in 2500 pages every substantial development. Vol. 1, 2: EXACT EQUATIONS, PFAFF'S PROBLEM; ORDINARY EQUATIONS, NOT LINEAR: methods of Grassmann, Clebsch, Lie, Darboux; Cauchy's theorem; branch points; etc. Vol. 3, 4: ORDINARY EQUATIONS, NOT LINEAR; ORDINARY LINEAR EQUATIONS: Zeta Fuchsian functions, general theorems on algebraic integrals, Brun's theorem, equations with uniform periodic cofficients, etc. Vol. 4, 5: PARTIAL DIFFERENTIAL EQUATIONS: 2 existence-theorems, equations of theoretical dynamics, Laplace transformations, general transformation of equations of the 2nd order, much more. Indexes. Total of 2766pp. 5⅜ x 8. S576-7-8 Clothbound: the set **$15.00**

PARTIAL DIFFERENTIAL EQUATIONS OF MATHEMATICAL PHYSICS, A. G. Webster. A keystone work in the library of every mature physicist, engineer, researcher. Valuable sections on elasticity, compression theory, potential theory, theory of sound, heat conduction, wave propagation, vibration theory. Contents include: deduction of differential equations, vibrations, normal functions, Fourier's series, Cauchy's method, boundary problems, method of Riemann-Volterra. Spherical, cylindrical, ellipsoidal harmonics, applications, etc. 97 figures. vii + 440pp. 5⅜ x 8. S263 Paperbound **$2.00**

ELEMENTARY CONCEPTS OF TOPOLOGY, P. Alexandroff. First English translation of the famous brief introduction to topology for the beginner or for the mathematician not undertaking extensive study. This unusually useful intuitive approach deals primarily with the concepts of complex, cycle, and homology, and is wholly consistent with current investigations. Ranges from basic concepts of set-theoretic topology to the concept of Betti groups. "Glowing example of harmony between intuition and thought," David Hilbert. Translated by A. E. Farley. Introduction by D. Hilbert. Index. 25 figures. 73pp. 5⅜ x 8. S747 Paperbound **$1.00**

Number theory

INTRODUCTION TO THE THEORY OF NUMBERS, L. E. Dickson. Thorough, comprehensive approach with adequate coverage of classical literature, an introductory volume beginners can follow. Chapters on divisibility, congruences, quadratic residues & reciprocity, Diophantine equations, etc. Full treatment of binary quadratic forms without usual restriction to integral coefficients. Covers infinitude of primes, least residues, Fermat's theorem, Euler's phi function, Legendre's symbol, Gauss's lemma, automorphs, reduced forms, recent theorems of Thue & Siegel, many more. Much material not readily available elsewhere. 239 problems. Index. I figure. viii + 183pp. 5⅜ x 8. S342 Paperbound **$1.65**

ELEMENTS OF NUMBER THEORY, I. M. Vinogradov. Detailed 1st course for persons without advanced mathematics; 95% of this book can be understood by readers who have gone no farther than high school algebra. Partial contents: divisibility theory, important number theoretical functions, congruences, primitive roots and indices, etc. Solutions to both problems and exercises. Tables of primes, indices, etc. Covers almost every essential formula in elementary number theory! Translated from Russian. 233 problems, 104 exercises. viii + 227pp. 5⅜ x 8. S259 Paperbound **$1.60**

THEORY OF NUMBERS and DIOPHANTINE ANALYSIS, R. D. Carmichael. These two complete works in one volume form one of the most lucid introductions to number theory, requiring only a firm foundation in high school mathematics. "Theory of Numbers," partial contents: Eratosthenes' sieve, Euclid's fundamental theorem, G.C.F. and L.C.M. of two or more integers, linear congruences, etc "Diophantine Analysis": rational triangles, Pythagorean triangles, equations of third, fourth, higher degrees, method of functional equations, much more. "Theory of Numbers": 76 problems. Index. 94pp. "Diophantine Analysis": 222 problems. Index. 118pp. 5⅜ x 8. S529 Paperbound **$1.35**

Numerical analysis, tables

MATHEMATICAL TABLES AND FORMULAS, Compiled by Robert D. Carmichael and Edwin R. Smith. Valuable collection for students, etc. Contains all tables necessary in college algebra and trigonometry, such as five-place common logarithms, logarithmic sines and tangents of small angles, logarithmic trigonometric functions, natural trigonometric functions, four-place antilogarithms, tables for changing from sexagesimal to circular and from circular to sexagesimal measure of angles, etc. Also many tables and formulas not ordinarily accessible, including powers, roots, and reciprocals, exponential and hyperbolic functions, ten-place logarithms of prime numbers, and formulas and theorems from analytical and elementary geometry and from calculus. Explanatory introduction. viii + 269pp. 5⅜ x 8½. S111 Paperbound **$1.00**

MATHEMATICAL TABLES, H. B. Dwight. Unique for its coverage in one volume of almost every function of importance in applied mathematics, engineering, and the physical sciences. Three extremely fine tables of the three trig functions and their inverse functions to thousandths of radians; natural and common logarithms; squares, cubes; hyperbolic functions and the inverse hyperbolic functions; $(a^2 + b^2)$ exp. ½a; complete elliptic integrals of the 1st and 2nd kind; sine and cosine integrals; exponential integrals $Ei(x)$ and $Ei(-x)$; binomial coefficients; factorials to 250; surface zonal harmonics and first derivatives; Bernoulli and Euler numbers and their logs to base of 10; Gamma function; normal probability integral; over 60 pages of Bessel functions; the Riemann Zeta function. Each table with formulae generally used, sources of more extensive tables, interpolation data, etc. Over half have columns of differences, to facilitate interpolation. Introduction. Index. viii + 231pp. 5⅜ x 8. S445 Paperbound **$1.75**

TABLES OF FUNCTIONS WITH FORMULAE AND CURVES, E. Jahnke & F. Emde. The world's most comprehensive 1-volume English-text collection of tables, formulae, curves of transcendent functions. 4th corrected edition, new 76-page section giving tables, formulae for elementary functions—not in other English editions. Partial contents: sine, cosine, logarithmic integral; factorial function; error integral; theta functions; elliptic integrals, functions; Legendre, Bessel, Riemann, Mathieu, hypergeometric functions, etc. Supplementary books. Bibliography. Indexed. "Out of the way functions for which we know no other source," SCIENTIFIC COMPUTING SERVICE, Ltd. 212 figures. 400pp. 5⅜ x 8. S133 Paperbound **$2.00**

CHEMISTRY AND PHYSICAL CHEMISTRY

ORGANIC CHEMISTRY, F. C. Whitmore. The entire subject of organic chemistry for the practic-ing chemist and the advanced student. Storehouse of facts, theories, processes found else-where only in specialized journals. Covers aliphatic compounds (500 pages on the properties and synthetic preparation of hydrocarbons, halides, proteins, ketones, etc.), alicyclic com-pounds, aromatic compounds, heterocyclic compounds, organophosphorus and organometallic compounds. Methods of synthetic preparation analyzed critically throughout. Includes much of biochemical interest. "The scope of this volume is astonishing," INDUSTRIAL AND ENGINEER-ING CHEMISTRY. 12,000-reference index. 2387-item bibliography. Total of x + 1005pp. 5⅜ x 8.
Two volume set.
S700 Vol I Paperbound **$2.00**
S701 Vol II Paperbound **$2.00**
The set **$4.00**

THE MODERN THEORY OF MOLECULAR STRUCTURE, Bernard Pullman. A reasonably popular account of recent developments in atomic and molecular theory. Contents: The Wave Func-tion and Wave Equations (history and bases of present theories of molecular structure); The Electronic Structure of Atoms (Description and classification of atomic wave functions, etc.); Diatomic Molecules; Non-Conjugated Polyatomic Molecules; Conjugated Polyatomic Molecules; The Structure of Complexes. Minimum of mathematical background needed. New translation by David Antin of "La Structure Moleculaire." Index. Bibliography. vii + 87pp. 5⅜ x 8½.
S987 Paperbound **$1.00**

CATALYSIS AND CATALYSTS, Marcel Prettre, Director, Research Institute on Catalysis. This brief book, translated into English for the first time, is the finest summary of the principal modern concepts, methods, and results of catalysis. Ideal introduction for beginning chem-istry and physics students. Chapters: Basic Definitions of Catalysis (true catalysis and generalization of the concept of catalysis); The Scientific Bases of Catalysis (Catalysis and chemical thermodynamics, catalysis and chemical kinetics); Homogeneous Catalysis (acid-base catalysis, etc.); Chain Reactions; Contact Masses; Heterogeneous Catalysis (Mechanisms of contact catalyses, etc.); and Industrial Applications (acids and fertilizers, petroleum and petroleum chemistry, rubber, plastics, synthetic resins, and fibers). Trans-lated by David Antin. Index. vi + 88pp. 5⅜ x 8½.
S998 Paperbound **$1.00**

POLAR MOLECULES, Pieter Debye. This work by Nobel laureate Debye offers a complete guide to fundamental electrostatic field relations, polarizability, molecular structure. Partial con-tents: electric intensity, displacement and force, polarization by orientation, molar polariza-tion and molar refraction, halogen-hydrides, polar liquids, ionic saturation, dielectric con-stant, etc. Special chapter considers quantum theory. Indexed. 172pp. 5⅜ x 8.
S64 Paperbound **$1.50**

THE ELECTRONIC THEORY OF ACIDS AND BASES, W. F. Luder and Saverio Zuffanti. The first full systematic presentation of the electronic theory of acids and bases—treating the theory and its ramifications in an uncomplicated manner. Chapters: Historical Background; Atomic Orbitals and Valence; The Electronic Theory of Acids and Bases; Electrophilic and Electrodotic Reagents; Acidic and Basic Radicals; Neutralization; Titrations with Indicators; Displacement; Catalysis; Acid Catalysis; Base Catalysis; Alkoxides and Catalysts; Conclu-sion. Required reading for all chemists. Second revised (1961) eidtion, with additional examples and references. 3 figures. 9 tables. Index. Bibliography xii + 165pp. 5⅜ x 8.
S201 Paperbound **$1.50**

KINETIC THEORY OF LIQUIDS, J. Frenkel. Regarding the kinetic theory of liquids as a gen-eralization and extension of the theory of solid bodies, this volume covers all types of arrangements of solids, thermal displacements of atoms, interstitial atoms and ions, orientational and rotational motion of molecules, and transition between states of matter. Mathematical theory is developed close to the physical subject matter. 216 bibliographical footnotes. 55 figures. xi + 485pp. 5⅜ x 8.
S95 Paperbound **$2.55**

THE PRINCIPLES OF ELECTROCHEMISTRY, D. A. MacInnes. Basic equations for almost every subfield of electrochemistry from first principles, referring at all times to the soundest and most recent theories and results; unusually useful as text or as reference. Covers coulometers and Faraday's Law, electrolytic conductance, the Debye-Hueckel method for the theoretical calculation of activity coefficients, concentration cells, standard electrode potentials, thermo-dynamic ionization constants, pH, potentiometric titrations, irreversible phenomena, Planck's equation, and much more. "Excellent treatise," AMERICAN CHEMICAL SOCIETY JOURNAL. "Highly recommended," CHEMICAL AND METALLURGICAL ENGINEERING. 2 Indices. Appendix. 585-item bibliography. 137 figures. 94 tables. ii + 478pp. 5⅝ x 8⅜.
S52 Paperbound **$2.45**

THE PHASE RULE AND ITS APPLICATION, Alexander Findlay. Covering chemical phenomena of 1, 2, 3, 4, and multiple component systems, this "standard work on the subject" (NATURE, London), has been completely revised and brought up to date by A. N. Campbell and N. O. Smith. Brand new material has been added on such matters as binary, tertiary liquid equilibria, solid solutions in ternary systems, quinary systems of salts and water. Completely revised to triangular coordinates in ternary systems, clarified graphic repre-sentation, solid models, etc. 9th revised edition. Author, subject indexes. 236 figures. 505 footnotes, mostly bibliographic. xii + 494pp. 5⅜ x 8.
S91 Paperbound **$2.45**

PHYSICS

General physics

FOUNDATIONS OF PHYSICS, R. B. Lindsay & H. Margenau. Excellent bridge between semi-popular works & technical treatises. A discussion of methods of physical description, construction of theory; valuable to physicist with elementary calculus who is interested in ideas that give meaning to data, tools of modern physics. Contents include symbolism, mathematical equations; space & time foundations of mechanics; probability; physics & continua; electron theory; special & general relativity; quantum mechanics; causality. "Thorough and yet not overdetailed. Unreservedly recommended," NATURE (London). Unabridged, corrected edition. List of recommended readings. 35 illustrations. xi + 537pp. 5⅜ x 8.
S377 Paperbound **\$2.75**

FUNDAMENTAL FORMULAS OF PHYSICS, ed. by D. H. Menzel. Highly useful, fully inexpensive reference and study text, ranging from simple to highly sophisticated operations. Mathematics integrated into text—each chapter stands as short textbook of field represented. Vol. 1: Statistics, Physical Constants, Special Theory of Relativity, Hydrodynamics, Aerodynamics, Boundary Value Problems in Math. Physics; Viscosity, Electromagnetic Theory, etc. Vol. 2: Sound, Acoustics, Geometrical Optics, Electron Optics, High-Energy Phenomena, Magnetism, Biophysics, much more. Index. Total of 800pp. 5⅜ x 8.   Vol. 1 S595 Paperbound **\$2.00**
Vol. 2 S596 Paperbound **\$2.00**

MATHEMATICAL PHYSICS, D. H. Menzel. Thorough one-volume treatment of the mathematical techniques vital for classic mechanics, electromagnetic theory, quantum theory, and relativity. Written by the Harvard Professor of Astrophysics for junior, senior, and graduate courses, it gives clear explanations of all those aspects of function theory, vectors, matrices, dyadics, tensors, partial differential equations, etc., necessary for the understanding of the various physical theories. Electron theory, relativity, and other topics seldom presented appear here in considerable detail. Scores of definitions, conversion factors, dimensional constants, etc. "More detailed than normal for an advanced text . . . excellent set of sections on Dyadics, Matrices, and Tensors," JOURNAL OF THE FRANKLIN INSTITUTE. Index. 193 problems, with answers. x + 412pp. 5⅜ x 8.   S56 Paperbound **\$2.00**

THE SCIENTIFIC PAPERS OF J. WILLARD GIBBS. All the published papers of America's outstanding theoretical scientist (except for "Statistical Mechanics" and "Vector Analysis"). Vol I (thermodynamics) contains one of the most brilliant of all 19th-century scientific papers—the 300-page "On the Equilibrium of Heterogeneous Substances," which founded the science of physical chemistry, and clearly stated a number of highly important natural laws for the first time; 8 other papers complete the first volume. Vol II includes 2 papers on dynamics, 8 on vector analysis and multiple algebra, 5 on the electromagnetic theory of light, and 6 miscellaneous papers. Biographical sketch by H. A. Bumstead. Total of xxxvi + 718pp. 5⅝ x 8⅜.
S721 Vol I Paperbound **\$2.00**
S722 Vol II Paperbound **\$2.00**
The set **\$4.00**

BASIC THEORIES OF PHYSICS, Peter Gabriel Bergmann. Two-volume set which presents a critical examination of important topics in the major subdivisions of classical and modern physics. The first volume is concerned with classical mechanics and electrodynamics: mechanics of mass points, analytical mechanics, matter In bulk, electrostatics and magnetostatics, electromagnetic interaction, the field waves, special relativity, and waves. The second volume (Heat and Quanta) contains discussions of the kinetic hypothesis, physics and statistics, stationary ensembles, laws of thermodynamics, early quantum theories, atomic spectra, probability waves, quantization in wave mechanics, approximation methods, and abstract quantum theory. A valuable supplement to any thorough course or text.
Heat and Quanta: Index. 8 figures. x + 300pp. 5⅜ x 8½.   S968 Paperbound **\$1.75**
Mechanics and Electrodynamics: Index. 14 figures. vii + 280pp. 5⅜ x 8½.
S969 Paperbound **\$1.75**

THEORETICAL PHYSICS, A. S. Kompaneyets. One of the very few thorough studies of the subject in this price range. Provides advanced students with a comprehensive theoretical background. Especially strong on recent experimentation and developments in quantum theory. Contents: Mechanics (Generalized Coordinates, Lagrange's Equation, Collision of Particles, etc.), Electrodynamics (Vector Analysis, Maxwell's equations, Transmission of Signals, Theory of Relativity, etc.), Quantum Mechanics (the Inadequacy of Classical Mechanics, the Wave Equation, Motion in a Central Field, Quantum Theory of Radiation, Quantum Theories of Dispersion and Scattering, etc.), and Statistical Physics (Equilibrium Distribution of Molecules in an Ideal Gas, Boltzmann statistics, Bose and Fermi Distribution, Thermodynamic Quantities, etc.). Revised to 1961. Translated by George Yankovsky, authorized by Kompaneyets. 137 exercises. 56 figures. 529pp. 5⅜ x 8½. S972 Paperbound **\$2.50**

ANALYTICAL AND CANONICAL FORMALISM IN PHYSICS, André Mercier. A survey, in one volume, of the variational principles (the key principles—in mathematical form—from which the basic laws of any one branch of physics can be derived) of the several branches of physical theory, together with an examination of the relationships among them. Contents: the Lagrangian Formalism, Lagrangian Densities, Canonical Formalism, Canonical Form of Electrodynamics, Hamiltonian Densities, Transformations, and Canonical Form with Vanishing Jacobian Determinant. Numerous examples and exercises. For advanced students, teachers, etc. 6 figures. Index. viii + 222pp. 5⅜ x 8½.   S1077 Paperbound **\$1.75**

MATHEMATICAL PUZZLES AND RECREATIONS

AMUSEMENTS IN MATHEMATICS, Henry Ernest Dudeney. The foremost British originator of mathematical puzzles is always intriguing, witty, and paradoxical in this classic, one of the largest collections of mathematical amusements. More than 430 puzzles, problems, and paradoxes. Mazes and games, problems on number manipulation, unicursal and other route problems, puzzles on measuring, weighing, packing, age, kinship, chessboards, joining, crossing river, plane figure dissection, and many others. Solutions. More than 450 illustrations. vii + 258pp. 5⅜ x 8.　　　　　　　　　　　　　　　　T473 Paperbound **$1.25**

SYMBOLIC LOGIC and THE GAME OF LOGIC, Lewis Carroll. "Symbolic Logic" is not concerned with modern symbolic logic, but is instead a collection of over 380 problems posed with charm and imagination, using the syllogism, and a fascinating diagrammatic method of drawing conclusions. In "The Game of Logic," Carroll's whimsical imagination devises a logical game played with 2 diagrams and counters (included) to manipulate hundreds of tricky syllogisms. The final section, "Hit or Miss" is a lagniappe of 101 additional puzzles in the delightful Carroll manner. Until this reprint edition, both of these books were rarities costing up to $15 each. Symbolic Logic: Index, xxxi + 199pp. The Game of Logic: 96pp. Two vols. bound as one. 5⅜ x 8.　　　　　　　　　　　　　　　　T492 Paperbound **$1.50**

MAZES AND LABYRINTHS: A BOOK OF PUZZLES, W. Shepherd. Mazes, formerly associated with mystery and ritual, are still among the most intriguing of intellectual puzzles. This is a novel and different collection of 50 amusements that embody the principle of the maze: mazes in the classical tradition; 3-dimensional, ribbon, and Möbius-strip mazes; hidden messages; spatial arrangements; etc.—almost all built on amusing story situations. 84 illustrations. Essay on maze psychology. Solutions. xv + 122pp. 5⅜ x 8.　　T731 Paperbound **$1.00**

MATHEMATICAL RECREATIONS, M. Kraitchik. Some 250 puzzles, problems, demonstrations of recreational mathematics for beginners & advanced mathematicians. Unusual historical problems from Greek, Medieval, Arabic, Hindu sources: modern problems based on "mathematics without numbers," geometry, topology, arithmetic, etc. Pastimes derived from figurative numbers, Mersenne numbers, Fermat numbers; fairy chess, latruncles, reversi, many topics. Full solutions. Excellent for insights into special fields of math. 181 illustrations. 330pp. 5⅜ x 8.　　　　　　　　　　　　　　　　　　　　　　　T163 Paperbound **$1.75**

MATHEMATICAL PUZZLES OF SAM LOYD, Vol. I, selected and edited by M. Gardner. Puzzles by the greatest puzzle creator and innovator. Selected from his famous "Cyclopedia of Puzzles," they retain the unique style and historical flavor of the originals. There are posers based on arithmetic, algebra, probability, game theory, route tracing, topology, counter, sliding block, operations research, geometrical dissection. Includes his famous "14-15" puzzle which was a national craze, and his "Horse of a Different Color" which sold millions of copies. 117 of his most ingenious puzzles in all, 120 line drawings and diagrams. Solutions. Selected references. xx + 167pp. 5⅜ x 8.　　　　　　　T498 Paperbound **$1.00**

MY BEST PUZZLES IN MATHEMATICS, Hubert Phillips ("Caliban"). Caliban is generally considered the best of the modern problemists. Here are 100 of his best and wittiest puzzles, selected by the author himself from such publications as the London Daily Telegraph, and each puzzle is guaranteed to put even the sharpest puzzle detective through his paces. Perfect for the development of clear thinking and a logical mind. Complete solutions are provided for every puzzle. x + 107pp. 5⅜ x 8½.　　　　　　　　　T91 Paperbound **$1.00**

MY BEST PUZZLES IN LOGIC AND REASONING, H. Phillips ("Caliban"). 100 choice, hitherto unavailable puzzles by England's best-known problemist. No special knowledge needed to solve these logical or inferential problems, just an unclouded mind, nerves of steel, and fast reflexes. Data presented are both necessary and just sufficient to allow one unambiguous answer. More than 30 different types of puzzles, all ingenious and varied, many one of a kind, that will challenge the expert, please the beginner. Original publication. 100 puzzles, full solutions. x + 107pp. 5⅜ x 8½.　　　　　　　　　　　T119 Paperbound **$1.00**

MATHEMATICAL PUZZLES FOR BEGINNERS AND ENTHUSIASTS, G. Mott-Smith. 188 mathematical puzzles to test mental agility. Inference, interpretation, algebra, dissection of plane figures, geometry, properties of numbers, decimation, permutations, probability, all enter these delightful problems. Puzzles like the Odic Force, How to Draw an Ellipse, Spider's Cousin, more than 180 others. Detailed solutions. Appendix with square roots, triangular numbers, primes, etc. 135 illustrations. 2nd revised edition. 248pp. 5⅜ x 8.　　T198 Paperbound **$1.00**

MATHEMATICS, MAGIC AND MYSTERY, Martin Gardner. Card tricks, feats of mental mathematics, stage mind-reading, other "magic" explained as applications of probability, sets, theory of numbers, topology, various branches of mathematics. Creative examination of laws and their applications with scores of new tricks and insights. 115 sections discuss tricks wtih cards, dice, coins; geometrical vanishing tricks, dozens of others. No sleight of hand needed; mathematics guarantees success. 115 illustrations. xii + 174pp. 5⅜ x 8.　　　　　　　　　　　　　　　　　　　　　　　T335 Paperbound **$1.00**

RECREATIONS IN THE THEORY OF NUMBERS: THE QUEEN OF MATHEMATICS ENTERTAINS, Albert H. Beiler. The theory of numbers is often referred to as the "Queen of Mathematics." In this book Mr. Beiler has compiled the first English volume to deal exclusively with the recreational aspects of number theory, an inherently recreational branch of mathematics. The author's clear style makes for enjoyable reading as he deals with such topics as: perfect numbers, amicable numbers, Fermat's theorem, Wilson's theorem, interesting properties of digits, methods of factoring, primitive roots, Euler's function, polygonal and figurate numbers, Mersenne numbers, congruence, repeating decimals, etc. Countless puzzle problems, with full answers and explanations. For mathematicians and mathematically-inclined laymen, etc. New publication. 28 figures. 9 illustrations. 103 tables. Bibliography at chapter ends. vi + 247pp. 5⅜ x 8½. **T1096 Paperbound $1.85**

PAPER FOLDING FOR BEGINNERS, W. D. Murray and F. J. Rigney. A delightful introduction to the varied and entertaining Japanese art of origami (paper folding), with a full crystal-clear text that anticipates every difficulty; over 275 clearly labeled diagrams of all important stages in creation. You get results at each stage, since complex figures are logically developed from simpler ones. 43 different pieces are explained: place mats, drinking cups, bonbon boxes, sailboats, frogs, roosters, etc. 6 photographic plates. 279 diagrams. 95pp. 5⅝ x 8⅜. **T713 Paperbound $1.00**

1800 RIDDLES, ENIGMAS AND CONUNDRUMS, Darwin A. Hindman. Entertaining collection ranging from hilarious gags to outrageous puns to sheer nonsense—a welcome respite from sophisticated humor. Children, toastmasters, and practically anyone with a funny bone will find these zany riddles tickling and eminently repeatable. Sample: "Why does Santa Claus always go down the chimney?" "Because it soots him." Some old, some new—covering a wide variety of subjects. New publication. iii + 154pp. 5⅜ x 8½. **T1059 Paperbound $1.00**

EASY-TO-DO ENTERTAINMENTS AND DIVERSIONS WITH CARDS, STRING, COINS, PAPER AND MATCHES, R. M. Abraham. Over 300 entertaining games, tricks, puzzles, and pastimes for children and adults. Invaluable to anyone in charge of groups of youngsters, for party givers, etc. Contains sections on card tricks and games, making things by paperfolding—toys, decorations, and the like; tricks with coins, matches, and pieces of string; descriptions of games; toys that can be made from common household objects; mathematical recreations; word games; and 50 miscellaneous entertainments. Formerly "Winter Nights Entertainments." Introduction by Lord Baden Powell. 329 illustrations. v + 186pp. 5⅜ x 8. **T921 Paperbound $1.00**

DIVERSIONS AND PASTIMES WITH CARDS, STRING, PAPER AND MATCHES, R. M. Abraham. Another collection of amusements and diversion for game and puzzle fans of all ages. Many new paperfolding ideas and tricks, an extensive section on amusements with knots and splices, two chapters of easy and not-so-easy problems, coin and match tricks, and lots of other parlor pastimes from the agile mind of the late British problemist and gamester. Corrected and revised version. Illustrations. 160pp. 5⅜ x 8½. **T1127 Paperbound $1.00**

STRING FIGURES AND HOW TO MAKE THEM: A STUDY OF CAT'S-CRADLE IN MANY LANDS, Caroline Furness Jayne. In a simple and easy-to-follow manner, this book describes how to make 107 different string figures. Not only is looping and crossing string between the fingers a common youthful diversion, but it is an ancient form of amusement practiced in all parts of the globe, especially popular among primitive tribes. These games are fun for all ages and offer an excellent means for developing manual dexterity and coordination. Much insight also for the anthropological observer on games and diversions in many different cultures. Index. Bibliography. Introduction by A. C. Haddon, Cambridge University. 17 full-page plates. 950 illustrations. xxiii + 407pp. 5⅜ x 8½. **T152 Paperbound $2.00**

CRYPTANALYSIS, Helen F. Gaines. (Formerly ELEMENTARY CRYPTANALYSIS.) A standard elementary and intermediate text for serious students. It does not confine itself to old material, but contains much that is not generally known, except to experts. Concealment, Transposition, Substitution ciphers; Vigenere, Kasiski, Playfair, multafid, dozens of other techniques. Appendix with sequence charts, letter frequencies in English, 5 other languages, English word frequencies. Bibliography. 167 codes. New to this edition: solution to codes. vi + 230pp. 5⅜ x 8. **T97 Paperbound $1.95**

MAGIC SQUARES AND CUBES, W. S. Andrews. Only book-length treatment in English, a thorough non-technical description and analysis. Here are nasik, overlapping, pandiagonal, serrated squares; magic circles, cubes, spheres, rhombuses. Try your hand at 4-dimensional magical figures! Much unusual folklore and tradition included. High school algebra is sufficient. 754 diagrams and illustrations. viii + 419pp. 5⅜ x 8. **T658 Paperbound $1.85**

CALIBAN'S PROBLEM BOOK: MATHEMATICAL, INFERENTIAL, AND CRYPTOGRAPHIC PUZZLES, Phillips ("Caliban"), S. T. Shovelton, G. S. Marshall. 105 ingenious problems by the great-living creator of puzzles based on logic and inference. Rigorous, modern, piquant, and reflecting the author's unusual personality, these intermediate and advanced puzzles all require the ability to reason clearly through complex situations; some call for mathematical knowledge, ranging from algebra to number theory. Solutions. xi + 180pp. 5⅜ x 8. **T736 Paperbound $1.25**

FICTION

THE LAND THAT TIME FORGOT and THE MOON MAID, Edgar Rice Burroughs. In the opinion of many, Burroughs' best work. The first concerns a strange island where evolution is individual rather than phylogenetic. Speechless anthropoids develop into intelligent human beings within a single generation. The second projects the reader far into the future and describes the first voyage to the Moon (in the year 2025), the conquest of the Earth by the Moon, and years of violence and adventure as the enslaved Earthmen try to regain possession of their planet. "An imaginative tour de force that keeps the reader keyed up and expectant," NEW YORK TIMES. Complete, unabridged text of the original two novels (three parts in each). 5 illustrations by J. Allen St. John. vi + 552pp. 5⅜ x 8½.
T1020 Clothbound **$3.75**
T358 Paperbound **$2.00**

AT THE EARTH'S CORE, PELLUCIDAR, TANAR OF PELLUCIDAR: THREE SCIENCE FICTION NOVELS BY EDGAR RICE BURROUGHS. Complete, unabridged texts of the first three Pellucidar novels. Tales of derring-do by the famous master of science fiction. The locale for these three related stories is the inner surface of the hollow Earth where we discover the world of Pellucidar, complete with all types of bizarre, menacing creatures, strange peoples, and alluring maidens—guaranteed to delight all Burroughs fans and a wide circle of adventure lovers. Illustrated by J. Allen St. John and P. F. Berdanier. vi + 433pp. 5⅜ x 8½.
T1051 Paperbound **$2.00**

THE PIRATES OF VENUS and LOST ON VENUS: TWO VENUS NOVELS BY EDGAR RICE BURROUGHS. Two related novels, complete and unabridged. Exciting adventure on the planet Venus with Earthman Carson Napier broken-field running through one dangerous episode after another. All lovers of swashbuckling science fiction will enjoy these two stories set in a world of fascinating societies, fierce beasts, 5000-ft. trees, lush vegetation, and wide seas. Illustrations by Fortunino Matania. Total of vi + 340pp. 5⅜ x 8½. T1053 Paperbound **$1.75**

A PRINCESS OF MARS and A FIGHTING MAN OF MARS: TWO MARTIAN NOVELS BY EDGAR RICE BURROUGHS. "Princess of Mars" is the very first of the great Martian novels written by Burroughs, and it is probably the best of them all; it set the pattern for all of his later fantasy novels and contains a thrilling cast of strange peoples and creatures and the formula of Olympian heroism amidst ever-fluctuating fortunes which Burroughs carries off so successfully. "Fighting Man" returns to the same scenes and cities—many years later. A mad scientist, a degenerate dictator, and an indomitable defender of the right clash—with the fate of the Red Planet at stake! Complete, unabridged reprinting of original editions. Illustrations by F. E. Schoonover and Hugh Hutton. v + 356pp. 5⅜ x 8½.
T1140 Paperbound **$1.75**

THREE MARTIAN NOVELS, Edgar Rice Burroughs. Contains: Thuvia, Maid of Mars; The Chessmen of Mars; and The Master Mind of Mars. High adventure set in an imaginative and intricate conception of the Red Planet. Mars is peopled with an intelligent, heroic human race which lives in densely populated cities and with fierce barbarians who inhabit dead sea bottoms. Other exciting creatures abound amidst an inventive framework of Martian history and geography. Complete unabridged reprintings of the first edition. 16 illustrations by J. Allen St. John. vi + 499pp. 5⅜ x 8½. T39 Paperbound **$1.85**

THREE PROPHETIC NOVELS BY H. G. WELLS, edited by E. F. Bleiler. Complete texts of "When the Sleeper Wakes" (1st book printing in 50 years), "A Story of the Days to Come," "The Time Machine" (1st complete printing in book form). Exciting adventures in the future are as enjoyable today as 50 years ago when first printed. Predict TV, movies, intercontinental airplanes, prefabricated houses, air-conditioned cities, etc. First important author to foresee problems of mind control, technological dictatorships. "Absolute best of imaginative fiction," N. Y. Times. Introduction. 335pp. 5⅜ x 8. T605 Paperbound **$1.50**

28 SCIENCE FICTION STORIES OF H. G. WELLS. Two full unabridged novels, MEN LIKE GODS and STAR BEGOTTEN, plus 26 short stories by the master science-fiction writer of all time. Stories of space, time, invention, exploration, future adventure—an indispensable part of the library of everyone interested in science and adventure. PARTIAL CONTENTS: Men Like Gods, The Country of the Blind, In the Abyss, The Crystal Egg, The Man Who Could Work Miracles, A Story of the Days to Come, The Valley of Spiders, and 21 more! 928pp. 5⅜ x 8.
T265 Clothbound **$4.50**

THE WAR IN THE AIR, IN THE DAYS OF THE COMET, THE FOOD OF THE GODS: THREE SCIENCE FICTION NOVELS BY H. G. WELLS. Three exciting Wells offerings bearing on vital social and philosophical issues of his and our own day. Here are tales of air power, strategic bombing, East vs. West, the potential miracles of science, the potential disasters from outer space, the relationship between scientific advancement and moral progress, etc. First reprinting of "War in the Air" in almost 50 years. An excellent sampling of Wells at his storytelling best. Complete, unabridged reprintings. 16 illustrations. 645pp. 5⅜ x 8½.
T1135 Paperbound **$2.00**

SEVEN SCIENCE FICTION NOVELS, H. G. Wells. Full unabridged texts of 7 science-fiction novels of the master. Ranging from biology, physics, chemistry, astronomy to sociology and other studies, Mr. Wells extrapolates whole worlds of strange and intriguing character. "One will have to go far to match this for entertainment, excitement, and sheer pleasure . . . ," NEW YORK TIMES. Contents: The Time Machine, The Island of Dr. Moreau, First Men in the Moon, The Invisible Man, The War of the Worlds, The Food of the Gods, In the Days of the Comet. 1015pp. 5⅜ x 8. T264 Clothbound **$4.50**

BEST GHOST STORIES OF J. S. LE FANU, Selected and introduced by E. F. Bleiler. LeFanu is deemed the greatest name in Victorian supernatural fiction. Here are 16 of his best horror stories, including 2 nouvelles: "Carmilla," a classic vampire tale couched in a perverse eroticism, and "The Haunted Baronet." Also: "Sir Toby's Will," "Green Tea," "Schalken the Painter," "Ultor de Lacy," "The Familiar," etc. The first American publication of about half of this material: a long-overdue opportunity to get a choice sampling of LeFanu's work. New selection (1964). 8 illustrations. 5⅜ x 8⅜. T415 Paperbound **$1.85**

THE WONDERFUL WIZARD OF OZ, L. F. Baum. Only edition in print with all the original W. W. Denslow illustrations in full color—as much a part of "The Wizard" as Tenniel's drawings are for "Alice in Wonderland." "The Wizard" is still America's best-loved fairy tale, in which, as the author expresses it, "The wonderment and joy are retained and the heartaches and nightmares left out." Now today's young readers can enjoy every word and wonderful picture of the original book. New introduction by Martin Gardner. A Baum bibliography. 23 full-page color plates. viii + 268pp. 5⅜ x 8. T691 Paperbound **$1.45**

GHOST AND HORROR STORIES OF AMBROSE BIERCE, Selected and introduced by E. F. Bleiler. 24 morbid, eerie tales—the cream of Bierce's fiction output. Contains such memorable pieces as "The Moonlit Road," "The Damned Thing," "An Inhabitant of Carcosa," "The Eyes of the Panther," "The Famous Gilson Bequest," "The Middle Toe of the Right Foot," and other chilling stories, plus the essay, "Visions of the Night" in which Bierce gives us a kind of rationale for his aesthetic of horror. New collection (1964). xxii + 199pp. 5⅜ x 8⅜. T767 Paperbound **$1.00**

HUMOR

MR. DOOLEY ON IVRYTHING AND IVRYBODY, Finley Peter Dunne. Since the time of his appearance in 1893, "Mr. Dooley," the fictitious Chicago bartender, has been recognized as America's most humorous social and political commentator. Collected in this volume are 102 of the best Dooley pieces—all written around the turn of the century, the height of his popularity. Mr. Dooley's Irish brogue is employed wittily and penetratingly on subjects which are just as fresh and relevant today as they were then: corruption and hypocrisy of politicans, war preparations and chauvinism, automation, Latin American affairs, superbombs, etc. Other articles range from Rudyard Kipling to football. Selected with an introduction by Robert Hutchinson. xii + 244pp. 5⅜ x 8½. T626 Paperbound **$1.00**

RUTHLESS RHYMES FOR HEARTLESS HOMES and MORE RUTHLESS RHYMES FOR HEARTLESS HOMES, Harry Graham ("Col. D. Streamer"). A collection of Little Willy and 48 other poetic "disasters." Graham's funniest and most disrespectful verse, accompanied by original illustrations. Nonsensical, wry humor which employs stern parents, careless nurses, uninhibited children, practical jokers, single-minded golfers, Scottish lairds, etc. in the leading roles. A precursor of the "sick joke" school of today. This volume contains, bound together for the first time, two of the most perennially popular books of humor in England and America. Index. vi + 69pp. 5⅜ x 8. T930 Paperbound **75¢**

A WHIMSEY ANTHOLOGY, Collected by Carolyn Wells. 250 of the most amusing rhymes ever written. Acrostics, anagrams, palindromes, alphabetical jingles, tongue twisters, echo verses, alliterative verses, riddles, mnemonic rhymes, interior rhymes, over 40 limericks, etc. by Lewis Carroll, Edward Lear, Joseph Addison, W. S. Gilbert, Christina Rossetti, Chas. Lamb, James Boswell, Hood, Dickens, Swinburne, Leigh Hunt, Harry Graham, Poe, Eugene Field, and many others. xiv + 221pp. 5⅜ x 8½. T195 Paperbound **$1.25**

MY PIOUS FRIENDS AND DRUNKEN COMPANIONS and MORE PIOUS FRIENDS AND DRUNKEN COMPANIONS, Songs and ballads of Conviviality Collected by Frank Shay. Magnificently illuminated by John Held, Jr. 132 ballads, blues, vaudeville numbers, drinking songs, cowboy songs, sea chanties, comedy songs, etc. of the Naughty Nineties and early 20th century. Over a third are reprinted with music. Many perennial favorites such as: The Band Played On, Frankie and Johnnie, The Old Grey Mare, The Face on the Bar-room Floor, etc. Many others unlocatable elsewhere: The Dog-Catcher's Child, The Cannibal Maiden, Don't Go in the Lion's Cage Tonight, Mother, etc. Complete verses and introductions to songs. Unabridged republication of first editions, 2 Indexes (song titles and first lines and choruses). Introduction by Frank Shay. 2 volumes bounds as 1. Total of xvi + 235pp. 5⅜ x 8½. T946 Paperbound **$1.00**

MAX AND MORITZ, Wilhelm Busch. Edited and annotated by H. Arthur Klein. Translated by H. Arthur Klein, M. C. Klein, and others. The mischievous high jinks of Max and Moritz, Peter and Paul, Ker and Plunk, etc. are delightfully captured in sketch and rhyme. (Companion volume to "Hypocritical Helena.") In addition to the title piece, it contians: Ker and Plunk; Two Dogs and Two Boys; The Egghead and the Two Cut-ups of Corinth; Deceitful Henry; The Boys and the Pipe; Cat and Mouse; and others. (Original German text with accompanying English translations.) Afterword by H. A. Klein. vi + 216pp. 5⅜ x 8½.
T181 Paperbound **$1.00**

THROUGH THE ALIMENTARY CANAL WITH GUN AND CAMERA: A FASCINATING TRIP TO THE INTERIOR, Personally Conducted by George S. Chappell. In mock-travelogue style, the amusing account of an imaginative journey down the alimentary canal. The "explorers" enter the esophagus, round the Adam's Apple, narrowly escape from a fierce Amoeba, struggle through the impenetrable Nerve Forests of the Lumbar Region, etc. Illustrated by the famous cartoonist, Otto Soglow, the book is as much a brilliant satire of academic pomposity and professional travel literature as it is a clever use of the facts of physiology for supremely comic purposes. Preface by Robert Benchley. Author's Foreword. 1 Photograph. 17 illustrations by O. Soglow. xii + 114pp. 5⅜ x 8½.
T376 Paperbound **$1.00**

THE BAD CHILD'S BOOK OF BEASTS, MORE BEASTS FOR WORSE CHILDREN, and A MORAL ALPHABET, H. Belloc. Hardly an anthology of humorous verse has appeared in the last 50 years without at least a couple of these famous nonsense verses. But one must see the entire volumes—with all the delightful original illustrations by Sir Basil Blackwood—to appreciate fully Belloc's charming and witty verses that play so subacidly on the platitudes of life and morals that beset his day—and ours. A great humor classic. Three books in one. Total of 157pp. 5⅜ x 8.
T749 Paperbound **$1.00**

THE DEVIL'S DICTIONARY, Ambrose Bierce. Sardonic and irreverent barbs puncturing the pomposities and absurdities of American politics, business, religion, literature, and arts, by the country's greatest satirist in the classic tradition. Epigrammatic as Shaw, piercing as Swift, American as Mark Twain, Will Rogers, and Fred Allen. Bierce will always remain the favorite of a small coterie of enthusiasts, and of writers and speakers whom he supplies with "some of the most gorgeous witticisms of the English language." (H. L. Mencken) Over 1000 entries in alphabetical order. 144pp. 5⅜ x 8.
T487 Paperbound **$1.00**

THE COMPLETE NONSENSE OF EDWARD LEAR. This is the only complete edition of this master of gentle madness available at a popular price. A BOOK OF NONSENSE, NONSENSE SONGS, MORE NONSENSE SONGS AND STORIES in their entirety with all the old favorites that have delighted children and adults for years. The Dong With A Luminous Nose, The Jumblies, The Owl and the Pussycat, and hundreds of other bits of wonderful nonsense. 214 limericks, 3 sets of Nonsense Botany, 5 Nonsense Alphabets. 546 drawings by Lear himself, and much more. 320pp. 5⅜ x 8.
T167 Paperbound **$1.00**

SINGULAR TRAVELS, CAMPAIGNS, AND ADVENTURES OF BARON MUNCHAUSEN, R. E. Raspe, with 90 illustrations by Gustave Doré. The first edition in over 150 years to reestablish the deeds of the Prince of Liars exactly as Raspe first recorded them in 1785—the genuine Baron Munchausen, one of the most popular personalities in English literature. Included also are the best of the many sequels, written by other hands. Introduction on Raspe by J. Carswell. Bibliography of early editions. xliv + 192pp. 5⅜ x 8.
T698 Paperbound **$1.00**

HOW TO TELL THE BIRDS FROM THE FLOWERS, R. W. Wood. How not to confuse a carrot with a parrot, a grape with an ape, a puffin with nuffin. Delightful drawings, clever puns, absurd little poems point out farfetched resemblances in nature. The author was a leading physicist. Introduction by Margaret Wood White. 106 illus. 60pp. 5⅜ x 8.
T523 Paperbound **75¢**

JOE MILLER'S JESTS OR, THE WITS VADE-MECUM. The original Joe Miller jest book. Gives a keen and pungent impression of life in 18th-century England. Many are somewhat on the bawdy side and they are still capable of provoking amusement and good fun. This volume is a facsimile of the original "Joe Miller" first published in 1739. It remains the most popular and influential humor book of all time. New introduction by Robert Hutchinson. xxi + 70pp. 5⅜ x 8½.
T423 Paperbound **$1.00**

Prices subject to change without notice.

Dover publishes books on art, music, philosophy, literature, languages, history, social sciences, psychology, handcrafts, orientalia, puzzles and entertainments, chess, pets and gardens, books explaining science, intermediate and higher mathematics, mathematical physics, engineering, biological sciences, earth sciences, classics of science, etc. Write to:

Dept. catrr.
Dover Publications, Inc.
180 Varick Street, N.Y. 14, N.Y.